Global London

Where to find almost everything ethnic and cultural in the multilingual capital

Compiled by

Philip Baker & Jeehoon Kim

battlebridge

2003

© Battlebridge Publications
Box 421, 37 Store St, London WC1E 7QF, UK
Phone (+44) (0) 20 7278 1246; Fax (+44) (0) 20 7636 5550
e-mail <battlebridge@talk21.com>
website <www.battlebridge.com>

ISBN 1-903292-09-3

Cover design:
Jeehoon Kim
<jkim@synx.net>

Photography:
© Philip Baker
<bakerp@wmin.ac.uk> / <pb@soas.ac.uk>

Printing:
Latimer Trend & Company Ltd, Estover Rd, Plymouth PL6 7PY, UK

Introduction

Global London is for:

- People based in London who wish to extend their knowledge and experience of what the diverse range of the city's inhabitants have to offer.
- Visitors to London who want to explore the very wide range of ethnic and cultural services available in this international city.
- Business people and others currently based elsewhere in the world who are contemplating relocating to London who want to know that the city caters for their own cultural needs.

In order to meet these needs, *Global London* has set about compiling, for the first time ever, a comprehensive listing of all the facilities and services available in the capital for each of some 600 cultural, ethnic, linguistic, and national groups living in Greater London. Entries for each group are arranged under up to 22 headings - ACCOMMODATION, ARTS & CULTURE, ASSOCIATIONS, BARS & NIGHTCLUBS, BUSINESS, EDUCATION, EMPLOYMENT, FREIGHT, GOVERNMENT, HEALTH & BEAUTY, LANGUAGES, LEGAL, MEDIA & INFORMATION, MOTORING, RECREATION, RELIGION, RESTAURANTS, SHOPS, SPECIAL, TRANSLATION, TRAVEL, WELFARE. Entries under these headings are further categorized by topic or locality in some cases. Information about what is included under each of these headings is given below.

The headings used are those applied to the groups concerned rather than to the places they may come from, e.g. Dutch rather than Holland or the Netherlands, Kittitian rather than St Kitts, and Turkish rather than Turkey – as well as under hundreds of cultural, ethnic, and language names. In a few cases, two or more names may have overlapping or even identical meanings. However, we have not combined these under single headings unless we are sure that there are no significant cultural or political reasons for choosing one over the other. Thus there are separate headings for Afro-Caribbean and West Indian, as well as for Iranian and Persian. But in all such cases, alternative or overlapping names are cross-references.

Although there are a few publications and websites which list a selection of London restaurants by a dozen or so ethnic and national cuisines, and others which list shops where certain ethnic or national goods may be purchased, *Global London* is the first to attempt to list ALL ethnic, cultural, national, and language facilities and services available in the city. The total number of entries contained in this book exceeds 10,000.

Global London is more than a book; it is also a website <www.global-london.com>. Visit this site for its search engine, to use one of its message boards, to get a street map of a particular area, or to obtain the latest information.

While great care has been taken to ensure the accuracy of the information provided here, *Global London* cannot accept responsibility for any errors. But it does undertake to correct speedily all errors brought to its attention by contacting <tellus@global-london.com>. Information for future editions can also be sent to Battlebridge Publications, Box 421, 37 Store St, London WC1E 7QF, UK.

Almost every entry in this book includes a telephone number. Fixed lines in central and most of outer London have eight-digit numbers such as 7278 1246, listed here as two sequences of four digits. To call any of these numbers from elsewhere in the United Kingdom, you need to prefix them with the area code 020. All other telephone numbers are listed with the full dialling code from within the UK. To call any number listed in this book from outside the UK, replace the first 0 of the full internal UK number with 44 (the country code).

All the photographs which appear in this book or on this website were taken by members of the *Global London* team. In no case were they taken at the request of the organizations concerned nor does the inclusion of a photograph in any way imply recommendation by *Global London.*

ACCOMMODATION

This category includes organizations which:
(a) offer residential or commercial accommodation in London intended to appeal to a particular ethnic. cultural, or national group; or
(b) sell or rent property in the country of the relevant national category.

The alphabetical list of headings under which there are entries for ACCOMMODATION is as follows:

American, Arab, Australian, Austrian, Balkan, Bangladeshi, Barbadian, Bavarian, Black, British, Caribbean, Celtic, Christian, Danish, English, French, German, Greek, Grenadian, Gulf, Hong Kong Chinese, Iberian, Indian, Irish, Italian, Jamaican, Japanese, Javanese, Korean, Kurdish, Latin American, Latvian, Londoner, Malaysian, Norwegian, Oriental, Polish, Provençal, Scottish, Serbian, Spanish, Swedish, Sylheti, Taiwanese, Tamil, Taoist.

ARTS & CULTURE

This section includes art galleries, dance troupes, musical groups, etc. It also includes museums except where their specialization is such that they can more conveniently be included in another category. The alphabetical list of headings under which there are entries for ARTS & CULTURE is as follows:

African, Afro, American, Arab, Argentinian, Asian, Balinese, Basque, Bengali, Black, Brazilian, British, Buddhist, Celtic, Chinese, Commonwealth, Cuban, Eastern, English, European, Greek, Indian, Indonesian, Iranian, Irish, Islamic, Italian, Japanese, Jewish, Latin American, London(er), Polish, Portuguese, Romani, Russian, Scottish, Spanish, Sufi, Welsh.

ASSOCIATIONS

The basic intention is that this section should include all associations and similar organizations which exist primarily to enable people to meet together for social and/or cultural purposes. Where an organization whose name includes the word "association" appears to be primarily concerned with education, religion, or welfare, it is included in those categories rather than under "associations". Anyone who feels that their particular association has been wrongly categorized should e-mail to <tellus@global-london.com> so that the listing can be changed. The alphabetical list of headings under which there are entries for ASSOCIATIONS is as follows:

Afghan, African, African Caribbean, Ahmadiyya, Albanian, Algerian, American, Angolan, Arab, Arabic, Argentinian, Asian, Assyrian, Australian, Austrian, Bahamian, Bahraini, Bangladeshi, Basque, Belgian, Bengali, Black, Bosnian, Brazilian, British, Buddhist, Bulgarian, Cameroonian, Caribbean, Chilean, Chinese, Christian, Colombian, Commonwealth, Congo-Brazzaville, Congo-Kinshasa, Cuban, Cypriot, East African, Eastern, East European, Egyptian, English, Eritrean, Ethiopian, European, Falasha, Finnish, French, Gambian, German, Ghanaian, Greek, Greek Cypriot, Guatemalan, Gujarati, Hindi, Hindu, Horn of Africa, Hungarian, Indian, International, Irish, Islamic, Israeli, Italian, Ivoirien, Jain, Jamaican, Japanese, Jewish, Jordanian, Kenyan, Korean, Kosova, Kuwaiti, Latin American, Latvian, Lebanese, Libyan, Lingala, Lithuanian, Malawian, Malaysian, Maltese, Mauritian, Middle Eastern, Moroccan, Muslim, Namibian, Near Eastern, New Zealander, Nicaraguan, Nigerian, Norwegian, Palestinian, Panjabi, Peruvian, Polish, Portuguese, Rastafarian, Romani, Russian, Saudi Arabian, Serbian, Sierra Leonean, Sikh, Sindhi, Slav, Somali, Spanish, Sri Lankan, Sudanese, Swahili, Swiss, Tamil, Tanzanian, Tibetan, Tigrinya, Trinidadian, Tunisian, Turkish, Turkish Cypriot, Ukrainian, Vietnamese, Welsh, West Indian, Yemeni, Zambian.

BARS & NIGHTCLUBS

Our intention in this section is that all the bars listed should be places which exist primarily for the purpose of serving alcoholic drinks (and thus coffee bars, etc. are excluded). Unfortunately the available information has not always enabled us to distinguish between these two kinds of bars. A further complication is that there is no clear-cut distinction between bars and restaurants: most bars serve some food; many restaurants include a bar area. As far as possible, we have listed establishments better known for their drinks than their food as bars, and those better known for their food than their drinks as restaurants. Any bar and/or restaurant which is unhappy with the way it has been categorized should e-mail to <tellus@global-london.com> so that the listing can be changed. The alphabetical list of headings under which there are entries for BARS & NIGHTCLUBS is as follows:

African, American, Australasian, Australian, Brazil, Caribbean, Cockney, Cuban, Cypriot, Ecuadorian, Egyptian, French, Gascon, Greek, International, Irish, Italian, Jamaican, Japanese, Latin American, Mauritian, Mexican, Monégasque, Nordic, Oriental, Panjabi, Polish, Portuguese, Russian, South African, Spanish, Thai, Vietnamese.

BUSINESS

The alphabetical list of headings under which there are entries for BUSINESS is as follows:

Abu Dhabi, Afghan, African, Algerian, American, Andorran, Angolan, Arab, Arabian, Arabic, Argentinian, Armenian, Ashanti, Asian, Australian, Austrian, Azerbaijani, Bahraini, Bali, Baltic,

Bangladeshi, Barbadian, Bavarian, Belgian, Bengali, Bermudan, Black, Bolivian, Brazilian, British, Bulgarian, Cambodian, Canadian, Caribbean, Catalan, Celtic, Channel Islander, Chilean, Chinese, Cockney, Commonwealth, Continental, Cornish, Cuban, Cypriot, Danish, Dubaian, Dutch, East African, Egyptian, English, Eritrean, East European, Far Eastern, Filipino, Finnish, French, Galician, German, Ghanaian, Greek, Gujarati, Gulf, Hawaiian, Hungarian, Iberian, Indian, Indonesian, Iranian, Irish, Islamic, Israeli, Italian, Jamaican, Japanese, Javan, Jewish, Jordanian, Kazakh, Korean, Kuwaiti, Latin American, Lebanese, Levantine, London(er), Luxembourger, Macedonian, Malaysian, Maltese, Mauritian, Mediterranean, Mexican, Middle Eastern, Monégasque, Moroccan, Muslim, New Zealander, Nigerian, Nordic, Northern Irish, Norwegian, Omani, Oriental, Pacific, Pakistani, Panjabi, Polish, Portuguese, Qatari, Romanian, Russian, Saudi Arabian, Scandinavian, Scottish, Seychellois, Siberian, Sicilian, Singaporean, South African, South American, Southern African, Spanish, Sri Lankan, Sudanese, Swedish, Swiss, Sylheti, Taiwanese, Tanzanian, Thai, Trinidadian, Tunisian, Turkish, Turkish Cypriot, Ukrainian, United Arab Emirates, Welsh, West Indian, Zambian, Zimbabwean.

EDUCATION

This section includes not only organizations which provide courses in particular languages but also those concerned with (a) the funding of students, (b) links between educational organizations, and (c) research. The alphabetical list of headings under which there are entries for EDUCATION is as follows:

Adangme, Afghan, African, Afrikaans, Afro-Caribbean, Albanian, Algerian, American, Amharic, Arab, Arabian, Arabic, Aramaic, Armenian, Asian, Azeri, Bahraini, Balochi, Barbadian, Bari, Basque, Belarusian, Bengali, Black, Bravanese, Brazilian, British, Bulgarian, Burmese, Cambodian, Canadian, Caribbean, Catalan, Celtic, Channel Islander, Chilean, Chinese, Cockney, Commonwealth, Continental, Cornish, Cuban, Cypriot, Danish, Dubaian, Dutch, Edo, Egyptian, English, Estonian, European, Ewe, Farsi, Finnish, French, Gã, Gaelic, Georgian, German, Ghanaian, Greek, Gujarati, Gulf, Hausa, Hebrew, Hindi, Hungarian, Icelandic, Igbo, Indian, Indo-Chinese, Indonesian, International, Iraqi, Islamic, Ismaili, Israeli, Italian, Jain, Japanese, Jewish, Lao, Latin, Latin American, Latvian, Libyan, Lingala, Lithuanian, Luganda, Luo, Macedonian, Malay, Malayalam, Malinké, Mandarin, Mandingo, Mauritian Creole, Mende, Middle Eastern, Mongolian, Moroccan, Muslim, Ndebele, Near Eastern, Nepali, Nigerian, North African, Norwegian, Nuer, Oriental, Oromo, Palestinian, Panjabi, Pashto, Persian, Polish, Portuguese, Romani, Romanian, Russian, Sanskrit, "Serbo-Croat", Setswana, Shona, Sikh, Sinhala, Slavonic, Slovak, Slovene, Somali, Southern African, Spanish, Swahili, Swedish, Sylheti, Tamil, Thai, Tibetan, Tigrinya, Turkish, Turkish Cypriot, Twi, Ukrainian, Urdu, Urhobo, Uzbek, Vietnamese, Welsh, Xhosa, Yiddish, Yoruba, Zulu.

EMPLOYMENT

This section includes organizations concerned with finding either (a) employment in London for people of particular cultural, ethnic, linguistic, or national backgrounds, or (b) employment in particular countries outside the UK for people who are currently based in London.

The alphabetical list of headings under which there are entries for EMPLOYMENT is as follows:

Arabian, Australasian, Australian, Black, Chinese, European, Filipino, Italian, Japanese, Kazakh, Khmer, Korean, Kurdish, Kuwaiti, Kyrghyz, New Zealander, Oriental, Scottish, Spanish..

FREIGHT

This section lists companies specializing in the transport of goods to and from particular countries and regions. The alphabetical list of headings under which there are entries for FREIGHT is as follows:

African, American, Arab, Arabian, Asian, Australasian, Australian, Austrian, Balkan, Baltic, Brazilian, British, Caribbean, Cayman Islander, Congo-Kinshasa, Continental, Dutch, European, Far Eastern, Gaelic, German, Greek, Gulf, Indian, Iranian, Irish, Italian, Japanese, Korean, Levantine, Mediterranean, Middle Eastern, New Zealander, Nigerian, Nordic, North African, Pacific, Portuguese, Saudi Arabian, Scandinavian, Spanish, Sri Lankan, Swiss, Welsh, Yemeni.

GOVERNMENT

This section lists consulates, embassies, high commissions, and associated organizations. It also includes information about the administration of certain territories. The alphabetical list of headings under which there are entries for GOVERNMENT is as follows:

Afghan, Albanian, Algerian, American, Andorran, Angolan, Anguillan, Antiguan, Argentinian, Armenian, Australian, Austrian, Azerbaijani, Bahamian, Bahraini, Bangladeshi, Barbadian, Belarusian, Belgian, Belizean, Beninois, Bermudan, Bolivian, Bosnian, Botswana, Brazilian, British Virgin Islander, Bruneian, Bulgarian, Burmese, Burundi, Cambodian, Cameroonian, Canadian, Caribbean, Cayman Islander, Chadian, Chilean, Chinese, Colombian, Commonwealth, Comoran, Congo-Brazzaville, Congo-Kinshasa, Costa Rican, Croatian, Cuban, Cypriot, Czech, Danish, Dominican (Island of Dominica), Dominican (Dominican Republic), Dubaian, Dutch, Ecuadorian, Egyptian, Equatorial Guinea, Eritrean, Estonian, Ethiopian, European, Falklander, Fijian, Filipino, Finnish, French, Gabonese, Gambian, Georgian, German, Ghanaian, Gibraltarian, Greek, Grenadian, Guatemalan, Guinean, Guinea-Bissauan, Guyanese, Hawaiian, Honduran, Hong Kong Chinese, Hungarian, Indian, Indonesian, International, Iranian, Iraqi, Irish, Israeli, Italian, Ivorien, Jamaican, Japanese, Jordanian, Kazakh, Kenyan, Korean, Kuwaiti, Kyrghyz, Latvian, Lebanese, Lesotho, Liberian, Libyan, Lithuanian, London(er), Luxembourger, Macanese, Macedonian, Madagascan, Malawian, Malaysian, Maldivian, Maltese, Mauritanian, Mauritian, Mexican, Moldovan, Monégasque, Mongolian, Montserratian, Moroccan, Mozambican, Muslim, Namibian, Nauruan, Nepali, New Zealander, Nicaraguan, Nigerian, Northern Irish, Norwegian, Omani, Pakistani, Panamanian, Papua New Guinean, Paraguayan, Peruvian, Polish, Portuguese, Qatari, Romanian, Russian, Rwanda, Saint Helenan, Saint Lucian, Samoan, Sanmarinese, Saudi Arabian, Scottish, Senegalese, Seychellois, Sierra Leonean, Singaporean, Slovak, Slovenian, Solomon Islander, Somali, South African, Spanish, Sri Lankan, Sudanese, Swazi, Swedish, Swiss, Syrian, Taiwanese, Tajiki, Tanzanian, Thai, Tibet, Tongan, Trinidadian, Tunisian, Turkish, Turkish Cypriot, Turkmen, Turks & Caicos Islander, Ugandan, Ukrainian, United Arab Emirates, Uruguayan, Uzbek, Venezuelan, Vietnamese, Vincentian, Welsh, Yemeni, Yugoslav, Zambian, Zimbabwean.

HEALTH & BEAUTY

The alphabetical list of headings under which there are entries for HEALTH & BEAUTY is as follows:
African, Afro, Afro-Caribbean, American, Arab, Ashanti, Bengali, Black, Brazil, British, Cantonese, Chinese, Continental, Eastern, English, European, Far Eastern, Filipino, French, Gujarati, Hindi, Hungarian, Indian, Islamic, Italian, Japanese, Kashmiri, Korean, Kurdish, London(er), Oriental, Panjabi, Scandinavian, Swedish, Taiwanese, Taoist, Thai, Turkish, Urdu, Vietnamese, West Indian.

LANGUAGES

Language entries give information about the number of London schoolchildren from homes in which each of these are spoken, as published in the *Multilingual Capital* (2000) survey. Maps showing the distribution of speakers of more than 30 of these languages can be viewed at <www.global-london/gallery>. For details of the Linguasphere language classification system used in these entries, see the table on page 222 at the end of this book.

The alphabetical list of headings under which there are entries for LANGUAGE(S) is given below. These include ethnic and national names as well as the names of individual languages.

Abe, Abkhaz, Abua, Acholi, Adangme, 'Afar, Afghan, African, Afrikaans, Akan, Akpafu, Aku, Albanian, Algerian, Alur, Ambo, American, Amerindian, Amharic, Anaang, Andorran, Angolan, Antiguan, Anyi, Arabic, Aramaic, Argentinian, Armenian, Ashanti, Assamese, A-Teso, Australian, Austrian, Azeri, Baining, Bali, Balochi, Bangladeshi, Bantu, Barawan, Barbadian, Bari, Bariba, Basque, Bassa, Bata, Beja, Belarusian, Belgian, Belizean, Bemba, Bende, Bengali, Benin, Beninois, Benuic, Berber, Berri, Bihari, Bimoba, Bini, Bisayan, Bolivian, Bosnian, Botswana, Brass, Bravanese, Brazilian, Bruneian, BSL Signer, Bukusu, Bulgarian, Buli, Buma, Burmese, Burundi, Burushaski, Calabari, Cambodian, Cameroonian, Canadian, Cantonese, Carib, Catalan, Cebuano, Che, Chewa, Chiga, Chilean, Chinese, Chokwe, Colombian, Comoran, Congolese-Brazzaville, Congolese-Kinshasa, Costa Rican, Creole, Croatian, Cuban, Czech, Dagari, Dagbane, Damara, Danish, Dari, Dhivehi, Dhopadhola, Dinka, Dutch, Dyula, Ebira, Ecuadorian, Edo, Efik, Efutu, Eggon, Egyptian, Ekpeye, Eleme, Emai, English, English Creole, Equatorial Guinean, Eritrean, Esan, Estonian, Ethiopean, Ewe, Ewondo, Fang, Fante, Farsi, Fijian, Filipino, Finnish, Flemish, Fon, Frafra, French Creole, Fula, Gã, Gaelic, Galician, Galla, Gambian, Georgian, German, Ghanaian, Gikuyu, Goan, Gogo, Gokana, Gola, Gonja, Gora, Greek, Guarani, Guatemalan, Guinean, Guinea-Bissauan, Gujarati, Gurenge, Gurma, Hahon, Hainanese, Haitian, Hakka, Harari, Hausa, Hawaiian, Hebrew, Herero, Hesperonesic, Hiligaynon, Hindi, Honduran, Hunanese, Hungarian, Ibibio, Icelandic, Idoma, Idon, Igala, Igbo, Igede, Ijo, Ikwere, Ilocano, Indian, Indonesian, Iranian, Iraqi, Irish, Isoko, Israeli, Italian, Itigo, Itsekiri, Ivoirien, Japanese, Jingpho, Jonkha, Kahe, Kaje, Kakwa, Kalenjin, Kamba, Kannada, Karen, Kashmiri, Katab, Katchi, Kazakh, Kenyan, Keralite, Khana, Khasi, Khmer, Ki, Kimbundu, Kimeru, Kingwana, Kirundi, Kisi, Komi, Kongo, Konkani, Kono, Korean, Korku, Kosova, Kpelle, Kposo, Krio, Krobo, Kru, Kurdish, Kurmanji, Kusaie, Kwa, Kwangwa, Kyrghyz, Lahnda, Lam-nso, Lango, Lao, Lati, Latin, Latvian, Lebanese, Liberian, Libyan, Limba, Lingala, Lithuanian, Logba, Logoli, Losengo, Lozi, Luba, Luganda, Lugbara, Lui, Lumasaba, Lunda, Luo, Lusoga, Luvale, Luxembourger, Luziba, Macanese, Macedonian, Madagascan, Ma'di, Maghrebi, Malagasy, Malawian, Malay, Malayalam, Malaysian, Maldivian, Malinké, Maltese, Mampruli, Mandarin, Manding, Mandingo, Mandinka, Mangbetu, Maori, Marathi, Masaba, Mashriqi, Mauritanian, Mauritian (Creole), Maya, Mbum, "Memon", Mende, Mexican, Mindanao, Min-nan, Mirpuri, Moldovan, Mongolian, Moroccan, Motu, Mozambican, Mungaka, Namibian, Nauruan, Ndebele, Nembe, Nepali, Newari, New Zealander, Ngoni, Nicaraguan, Nigerian, Norwegian, Nsenga, Nubian, Nuer, Nupe, Nwa, Nyakyusa, Nyang, Nyoro, Nzema, Odual, Ogori, Okrika, Olulumo, Omani, Ora, Oring, Oriya, Oromo, Oron, Oshikwanyama, Pakistani,

Pampangan, Panamanian, Pangasinan, Panjabi, Papua New Guinean, Paraguayan, Parji, Pashto, Patwa, Persian, Peruvian, Pidgin English, Polish, Portuguese, Portuguese Creole, Putonghua, Quechua, Rajasthani, Romani, Romanian, Runyankore, Russian, Rutoro, Rwanda, Saho, Saint Lucian, Samoan, Sanmarinese, Sanskrit, Sardinian, Saudi Arabian, Senegalese, Senga, Serbian, "Serbo-Croat", Sesotho, Setswana, Seychellois, Shelta, Shilluk, Shona, Sidamo, Sierra Leonean, Sindhi, Singaporean, Sinhala, Slavonic, Slovak, Slovene, Somali, South African, South Indian, Spanish, Sri Lankan, Sudanese, Swahili, Swazi, Swedish, Swiss (German), Sylheti, Tagalog, "Taiwanese", Tajiki, Tamil, Tangale, Tanzanian, Telugu, Temne, Thai, Tibetan, Tigre, Tigrinya, Tiv, Tok Pisin, Tonga, Tongan, Trinidadian, Tumbuka, Tunisian, Turkish, Turkmen, Ugandan, Ukaan, Ukrainian, Urdu, Urhobo, Urugayan, Uzbek, Venezuelan, Vietnamese, Wa, Wali, Welsh, Wolof, Xhosa, Yemeni, Yiddish, Yoruba, Yugoslav, Zambian, Zande, Zimbabwean, Zulu

LEGAL

This section includes both individuals and organizations with experience of providing legal representation or assistance for certain ethnic, social, and national groups, as well as those with specialist knowledge of the legal system of particular countries or areas outside the UK. The alphabetical list of headings under which there are entries under LEGAL is as follows:

Abu Dhabi, African, American, Arab, Asian, Australian, Bahraini, Black, British, Caribbean, Central American, Chinese, Commonwealth, Dubaian, European, International, Irish, Islamic, Italian, Japanese, Kashmiri, Kurdish, Kuwaiti, Latin American, Middle Eastern, Monégasque, Muslim, New Zealander, Omani, Pacific, Pakistani, Panjabi, Polish, Romani, Russian, Saudi Arabian, Spanish, Turkish, Ukrainian.

MEDIA & INFORMATION

This section includes newspapers, magazines, radio, television, and video services as well as organizations providing general information services. The alphabetical list of headings under which there are entries for MEDIA & INFORMATION is as follows:

African, Afro, Ahmadiyya, American, Angolan, Arab, Arabic, Asian, Australasian, Australian, Austrian, Baha'i, Baltic, Bangladeshi, Basque, Bengali, Bermudan, Black, Brazil, British, Canadian, Caribbean, Celtic, Chinese, Christian, Commonwealth, Cornish, East African, Eastern, Eritrean, Ethiopian, European, Far Eastern, Farsi, French, German, Ghanaian, Gibraltarian, Greek, Greek Cypriot, Gujarati, Gulf, Hebrew, Hindi, Indian, International, Iranian, Irish, Islamic, Italian, Japanese, Jewish, Jordanian, Kashmiri, Kenyan, Korean, Kosova, Latin American, Lithuanian, London(er), Maghrebi, Mashriqi,

Mauritian, Middle Eastern, Moroccan, Muslim, Namibian, New Zealander, Nigerian, Nordic, North African, Oriental, Rastafarian, Russian, Saudi Arabian, Scandinavian, Scottish, Serbian, Sikh, Singaporean, Sinhala, Somali, South African, Spanish, Sudanese, Swazi, Tamil, Tanzanian, Thai, Tibetan, Tunisian, Turkish, Ugandan, Ukrainian, Urdu, Welsh, West African, Yemeni, Zimbabwean.

MOTORING

This section includes (a) suppliers and repairers of motor vehicles manufactured by particular nationalities (Swedish, Japanese, Italian, etc.) and (b) driving schools catering for people who want instruction in a language other than English or who belong to a specific religion or ethnic group. The alphabetical list of headings under which there are entries for **MOTORING** is as follows:

American, Australasian, Bavarian, British, Continental, East African, Eritrean, European, French, Galician, German, Indian, Islamic, Italian, Japanese, Korean, Latin American, Mexican, Nordic, Oriental, Russian, Somali, Spanish, Swedish, Turkish..

RECREATION

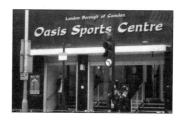

This section includes sports, pastimes, dancing, martial arts, etc. The alphabetical list of headings under which there are entries for **RECREATION** is as follows:

African, American, Argentinian, Ashanti, Asian, Australian, Basque, Brazilian, British, Celtic, Chinese, Colombian, Commonwealth, English, European, Irish, Israeli, Italian, Japanese, Korean, Latin American, Lithuanian, London(er), Nigerian, Oriental, Portuguese, Scottish, Sikh, Spanish, Thai, Turkish, Ukrainian, Welsh.

RELIGION

This category includes, primarily:

(a) for religious groups: places of worship where that religion is practised. (Where the number of places of worship is very great, as with the various Christian churches, only one or two entries for each sect is given but these may be contacted for details of others.)

(b) for ethnic, cultural, and national groups: places of worship relevant to members of particular ethnic or national groups or to speakers of particular languages.

The alphabetical list of headings under which there are entries under **RELIGION** is as follows:

Afghan, African, Ahmadiyya, Albanian, Algerian, American, Amharic, Andorran, Armenian, Asian, Assyrian, Austrian, Baha'i, Belgian, Belizean, Bengali, Bolivian, Bosnian, Brazilian, British, Buddhist, Bulgarian, Burmese, Caribbean, Central African, Chilean, Chinese, Christian, Colombian, Commonwealth, Comoran, Coptic, Croatian, Cypriot, Danish, Dutch, Egyptian, Eritrean, Estonian, Ethiopian, European, Filipino, Finnish, French, Georgian, German, Ghanaian, Greek, Gujarati, Hebrew, Hindi, Hindu, Hungarian, Indian, Indonesian, Iranian, Irish, Islamic, Ismaili, Israeli, Italian, Jain, Japanese, Jewish, Keralite, Korean, Latin, Latin American, Latvian, Lebanese, Libyan, Lithuanian, Luxembourger, Malayalam, Malaysian, Maldivian, Maltese, Maronite, Mauritanian, Mauritian, Mongolian, Moroccan,

Muslim, Nepali, Nigerian, Norwegian, Omani, Pakistani, Panjabi, Papua New Guinean, Polish, Portuguese, Romanian, Russian, Sanmarinese, Saudi Arabian, Scottish, Senegalese, Serbian, Sikh, Sinhala, Slovak, South African, Southern African, South Indian, Spanish, Sri Lankan, Sudanese, Sufi, Swahili, Swedish, Swiss, Syrian, Tamil, Thai, Tibetan, Tunisian, Turkish, Ukrainian, Vietnamese, Welsh, Zoroastrian.

RESTAURANTS

This category includes both restaurants and take-aways because it is impossible to entirely separate the two. Almost all restaurants will provide food to take away if asked, while most take-away establishments have some facilities for people who want to eat on the premises. In addition, many places describe themselves as "restaurant and take-away". In this listing the names of all establishments believed to cater primarily for the take-away market are followed by the abbreviation *T/A*. Anyone who feels that their restaurant or take-away has been wrongly categorized should e-mail to <tellus@global_london.com> so that the entry can be amended.

Under all ethnic, national, etc. headings, restaurants and take-aways are listed by location. Those in Central London with postcodes beginning EC, SE1, SW1, W1 or WC are listed first followed by the 32 London boroughs in alphabetical order from Barking & Dagenham to Westminster. (The City of London is located entirely within the EC area so is not listed separately. Details of restaurants located within those parts of Camden, Hackney, Islington, Lambeth, Southwark, and Westminster which have Central London postcodes are not repeated in the listings for these boroughs.)

The alphabetical list of all the headings under which there are entries for RESTAURANTS is as follows:

Afghan, African, African Caribbean, Afro-Caribbean, Albanian, Alsatian, American, Argentinian, Armenian, Asian, Australasian, Australian, Austrian, Azerbaijani, Balinese, Baltic, Bangladeshi, Basque, Belgian, Bengali, Bolivian, Brazilian, British, Buddhist, Burmese, Calabari, Cameroonian, Cantonese, Caribbean, Chinese, Cockney, Colombian, Congolese-Kinshasa, Continental, Cornish, Creole, Cuba, Cypriot, Czech, Danish, Dutch, Eastern, East European, Ecuadorian, Egyptian, English, Eritrean, Ethiopian, European, Far Eastern, Filipino, French, Galician, Gascon, Georgian, German, Ghanaian, Goan, Greek, Greek Cypriot, Gujarati, Gurkha, Guyanese, Hainanese, Hawaiian, Hong Kong Chinese, Horn of Africa, Hunanese, Hungarian, Indian, Indonesian, International, Iranian, Irish, Italian, Jamaican, Japanese, Javanese, Jewish, Kashmiri, Keralite, Korean, Lao, Latin American, Lebanese, Levantine, Lithuanian, Madeiran, Malaysian, Mauritian, Mediterranean, Mexican, Middle Eastern, Monégasque, Mongolian, Moroccan, Muslim, Nepali, New Zealander, Nigerian, North African, Oriental, Pacific, Pakistani, Panjabi, Pekingese, Persian, Peruvian, Polish, Portuguese, Provençal, Rajasthani, Rastafarian, Russian, Sanmarinese, Sardinian, Scandinavian, Scottish, Sicilian, Singaporean, Slavic, Slovak, Somali, South African, South Indian, South American, Spanish, Sri Lankan, Sudanese, Swedish, Sylheti, Szechuan, Taiwanese, Tamil, Thai, Tibetan, Trinidadian, Tunisian, Turkish, Turkish Cypriot, Ukrainian, Vietnamese, West Indian.

SHOPS

The alphabetical list of headings under which there are entries for SHOPS is as follows:

Afghan, African, Afro, Afro-Caribbean, Algerian, American, Arabic, Asian, Austrian, Balinese, Basque, Belgian, Bengali, Black, Bolivian, Brazilian, British, Buddhist, Caribbean, Catalan, Celtic, Chinese, Christian, Cockney, Colombian, Continental, Creole, Cuban, Cypriot, Czech, Danish, Dutch, Eastern, Egyptian, English, Ethiopian, European, Far Eastern, Filipino, French, Galician, Gascon, German, Ghanaian, Greek, Hebrew, Hungarian, Indian, International, Irish, Islamic, Italian, Jamaican, Japanese, Javan, Jewish, Kashmiri, Kenyan, Korean, Madeiran, Maghrebi, Malaysian, Mashriqi, Mauritian, Mediterranean, Mexican, Middle Eastern, Monégasque, Moroccan, Muslim, Pakistani, Panjabi, Persian, Peruvian, Polish, Portuguese, Provençal, Rastafarian, Romanian, Russian, Sardinian, Scottish, Senegalese, Sicilian, Slovak, Somali, South African, Spanish, Sri Lankan, Swedish, Sylheti, Tamil, Thai, Tibetan, Turkish, Ukrainian, Urdu, Vietnamese, West Indian, Yiddish.

SPECIAL

The main aim of this section is to list organizations which cannot conveniently be listed under one of the other 21 categories and which are important for certain minority groups. In a few cases where we had been unable to determine the most appropriate category under which organizations should be listed by the time of going to press, they have been put under SPECIAL pending further investigation. The alphabetical list of headings under which there are entries under SPECIAL is as follows:

African, African-Caribbean, Afro-Caribbean, American, Angolan, Arab, Argentinian, Asian, Australian, Balinese, Barbadian, Basque, Black, Brazilian, British, Buddhist, Canadian, Celtic, Commonwealth, Cuban, East African, Estonian, European, Far Eastern, French, German, Greek, Hawaiian, Hebrew, Hungarian, Indian, Iranian, Islamic, Ismaili, Israeli, Jain, Japanese, Jewish, Kashmiri, Korean, Latin American, Levantine, Maltese, Middle Eastern, Monégasque, Moroccan, Mozambican, Palestinian, Polish, Portuguese, Romani, Russian, Saudi Arabian, Scandinavian, Scottish, Singaporean, Somali, Spanish, Sri Lankan, Sylheti, Tibetan, Turkish, West African, Zoroastrian.

TRANSLATION

This category lists organizations (and, occasionally, individuals) which (a) specialize in translating texts into or from particular languages or (b) offer interpreting services for the languages under which they are listed. Note that *Global London* cannot in any way guarantee their quality. However, a very useful resource for those seeking translators or interpreters is the Business Language Information Service at <www.languagesnto.org.uk>. This on-line database lists translation, interpreting and cultural briefing services available in London for more than 100 languages - by locality and with details of the professional bodies to which those organisations belong.

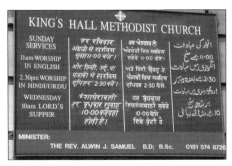

The alphabetical list of headings under which there are entries for TRANSLATION is as follows:

   Albanian, American, Arabic, Armenian, Azeri, Bengali, BSL Signer, Bulgarian, Chinese, Croatian, Czech, Dutch, East European, Eritrean, Estonian, Farsi, Finnish, French, German, Greek, Hebrew, Hungarian, Icelandic, Indian, Iranian, Italian, Japanese, Korean, Kosova, Kurdish, Latin American, Latvian, Lithuanian, Macedonian, Mandarin, Middle Eastern, Norwegian, Panjabi, Polish, Portuguese, Romanian, Russian, Slovak, Spanish, Thai, Turkish, Turkish Cypriot, Urdu,

TRAVEL

This section includes organizations specializing in travel arrangements to and from individual countries and regions associated with particular ethnic or cultural groups. It also includes those offering travel facilities in the London area which are aimed at specific groups. The alphabetical list of headings under which there are entries for TRAVEL is as follows:

   Afghan, African, Afro-Caribbean, Algerian, American, Andorran, Angolan, Anguillan, Antiguan, Arab, Argentinian, Armenian, Asian, Australian, Austrian, Azerbaijani, Bahamian, Balkan, Baltic, Bangladeshi, Barbadian, Belarusian, Belgian, Bengali, Bermudan, Bolivian, Brazilian, Brazilian, British, British Virgin Islander, Bruneian, Canadian, Caribbean, Catalan, Cayman Islander, Celtic, Channel Islander, Chilean, Chinese, Christian, Cockney, Colombian, Corsican, Croatian, Cuban, Cypriot, Czech, Danish, Dominican (Island of Dominica), Dominican (Dominican Republic), Dubaian, Dutch, Ecuadorian, Egyptian, English, Estonian, European, Falkland Islander, Far Eastern, Filipino, Finnish, French, Gambian, Gascon, German, Ghanaian, Goan, Greek, Grenadian, Gulf, Hawaiian, Hong Kong Chinese, Hungarian, Iberian, Icelandic, Indian, Indonesian, Iranian, Irish, Islamic, Israeli, Italian, Jamaican, Japanese, Jordanian, Keralite, Korean, Kuwaiti, Latin American, Libyan, Luxembourger, Macanese, Macedonian, Madeiran, Malawian, Malaysian, Maldivian, Maltese, Mauritian, Mediiterranean, Mexican, Middle Eastern, Monégasque, Moroccan, Norwegian, Namibian, Nepali, Nevisian, New Zealander, Nigerian, Northern Irish, Norwegian, Oriental, Pacific, Pakistani, Panjabi, Papua New Guinean, Peruvian, Polish, Portuguese, Puerto Rican, Qatari, Romanian, Russian, Saint Lucian, Sardinian, Saudi Arabian, Scandinavian, Scottish, Seychellois, Sicilian, Singaporean, Slovenian, Solomon Islander, South African, South American, Southern African, Spanish, Sri Lankan, Sudanese, Swazi, Swedish, Swiss, Sylheti, Syrian, Tajiki, Tanzanian, Thai, Tibetan, Trinidadian, Tunisian, Turkish, Turkish Cypriot, Turks & Caicos Islander, United Arab Emirates, Uzbek, Venezuelan, Vietnamese, Vincentian, Welsh, West Indian, Yemeni, Yugoslav, Zambian, Zimbabwean.

WELFARE

The alphabetical list of headings under which there are entries for WELFARE is as follows:

   Afghan, African, African Caribbean, Afro, Afro-Caribbean, Albanian, Algerian, Angolan, Arab, Arabic, Armenian, Asian, Bangladeshi, Basque, Bengali, Black, Bosnian, Bravanese, British, Buddhist, Burmese, Caribbean, Chinese, Christian, Commonwealth, Congolese-Kinshasa, Cypriot, Czech, English, Eritrean, European, Falklander, Filipino, Finnish, French, German, Ghanaian, Greek, Greek Cypriot, Gujarati, Gurkha, Haitian, Hindi, Horn of Africa, Igbo, Indian, International, Irish, Islamic, Israeli, Italian, Jain, Jamaican, Japanese, Jewish, Kashmiri, Kosova, Kurdish, Latin American, Lebanese, Lithuanian, Mauritian, Montserratian, Moroccan, Muslim, Nepali, Nigerian, Northern Irish, Pakistani, Palestinian, Panjabi, Polish, Portuguese, Romani, Romanian, Russian, Scottish, Serbian, Sikh, Slovak, Somali, Southern African, Spanish, Sudanese, Swahili, Sylheti, Tamil, Tanzanian, Thai, Tibetan, Tigrinya, Turkish, Turkish Cypriot, Ugandan, Urdu, Vietnamese, West African, West Indian, Zimbabwean.

Abbreviations and references

Ave = Avenue

Baker, Philip & Eversley, John (eds) 2000 *Multilingual Capital. The languages of London's schoolchildren and their relevance to economic, social, and educational policies.* London: Battlebridge.

Bdg(s) = Building(s)

Cl = Close

Ct = Court

Dalby, David 1999-2000 *The Linguasphere Register of the World's Languages and Speech Communities.* Hebron (Wales): Linguasphere Press, 2 vols.

Dr = Drive

Ethnologue, see Grimes (ed.)

Fl = Floor

Floodlight, see Miller (ed.)

Gdns = Gardens

Grimes, Barbara (ed.) 1996 *Ethnologue. Languages of the World.* Dallas: Summer Institute of Linguistics, 13th edition.

Gt = Great

Ho = House

La = Lane

Mann, Michael & Dalby, David 1987 *A thesaurus of African languages.* London: Hans Zell for the International African Institute.

Miller, Philippa (ed.) 2000-2001 *Floodlight*

Multilingual Capital (2000); *see* Baker & Eversley 2000

N = North

Pde = Parade

Pl = Place

QMW = Queen Mary Westfield College, University of London

Rd = Road

S = South

SOAS = School of Oriental and African Studies, University of London

SSEES = School of Slavonic and East European Studies, University College London, University of London.

St = Saint *and* Street

T/A = Take-away

UCL = University College London, University of London.

Whitaker's Almanack 2002; see White, Vanessa (ed.) 2001

Whitehouse, Elizabeth (ed.) 2001 *Middle East Places in London. A concise directory.* London: SOAS.

White, Vanessa (ed.) 2001 *Whitaker's Almanack 2002* London: The Stationery Office.

www.ethnologue.org A website which gives the information contained in Grimes (ed.) 1996.

www.floodlight.co.uk A website which contains up-to-date information on courses available on particular languages and on the full range of other subjects available throughout Greater London (corresponding to the current edition of *Floodlight;* following Miller (ed.) 2000-2001).

www.resourceunit.com = A website which gives details of all the places in Greater London in which mother tongue education for young children is available in languages other than English.

Acknowledgements

We are grateful to everyone who has helped by providing us with information. These include: Sylvia Broughton, James Copnall, David Dalby, Annika Hagley, Georgette Kat Kawel, Heyoung Kim, Ulrich Kratz, John Ladhams, Tanya Pascual, Paulo Peres de Pinho, Gwyn Richards, Antony Sanderson, Deborah Sutherland, Laura Wright, and Anthony Zurbrugg.

A

Abe

Abe is an Aframic language spoken in the Ivory Coast. The *Multilingual Capital* (2000) survey reported that this was the language of three pupils in Lewisham.

Abkhaz

Abkhaz is a language of the Caucasus geozone spoken in Abkhazia (Russian Federation). While not recorded in the *Multilingual Capital* (2000) survey, Abkhaz has been reported as the home language of a few pupils in London in recent years.

Abua

Abua is a Benuic language spoken in Nigeria. The *Multilingual Capital* (2000) survey reported this as the home language of three London schoolchildren.

Abu Dhabi

BUSINESS Abu Dhabi Petroleum Co Ltd, Brettenham Ho, 1 Lancaster Pl, Holborn WC2E 7EE (7379 7611); Abu Dhabi Investment Authority, 1 Knightsbridge, SW1X 7LX (7259 6655); *National Bank of Abu Dhabi,* 1 Knightbridge, SW1X 7LY (7393 3600).

GOVERNMENT See under *United Arab Emirates.*

LEGAL *Richards Butler,* 15 St Botolph St, EC3A 7EE (7247 6555) [office in Abu Dhabi]; *Trowers & Hamlins,* Sceptre Ct, 40 Tower Hill, Ec3N 4BN (7423 8000) [office in Abu Dhabi].

Abyssinian

Abyssinia is the former name of Ethiopia. For organizations and services whose names include the words *Abyssinia* and *Abyssinian*, see under **Ethiopian.**

Acholi

Acholi is a Nilotic language spoken in Uganda and Sudan. It is closely related to **Luo** (*Dhopaluo*). The *Multilingual Capital* (2000) survey reported that there were 122 pupils from **Acholi**-speaking homes in London.

Adangme

EDUCATION Mother-tongue classes for children in **Adangme** are available in Islington; see <www.resourceunit.com> for details.

LANGUAGE *Adangme* (also known as *Dangme*) is an Aframic language spoken in Ghana which is closely related to *Gā*. (In the *Multilingual Capital* (2000) survey, pupils recorded as Adangme-speakers were added the the figures for Gā.)

'Afar

> **'Afar** is a Cushitic language spoken in Ethiopia, Eritrea and Djibouti. The *Multilingual Capital* (2000) survey recorded only one pupil speaking this language, in Hammersmith & Fulham.

Afghan

ASSOCIATIONS *Afghan Association of London,* 88 Pinner Rd, Harrow HA1 4HZ (8861 6990); *Afghan Eketa Society,* 67 King St, Southall UB2 4DQ (8574 4651).

BUSINESS *Afghan Business Centre,* 502b High Rd, Wembley HA9 7BH (8900 9388); *Afghan National Credit and Finance Ltd,* New Roman House, 10 East Rd, N1 6AD (7251 4100).

EDUCATION For mother-tongue education for Afghan children, see entries for **Pashto** and **Dari**.

GOVERNMENT *Embassy of the Democratic Republic of Afghanistan,* 31 Princes Gate, SW7 1QQ (7589 8891).

LANGUAGES More than 85% of Afghans speak Iranic languages. *Pashto* (60%) is the most important of these while the other 25% speak *Dari* or other varieties closely related to *Farsi* (Persian). A further 8% of the population speak Turkic languages such as **Uzbek** and **Turkmen**. Some 40 other languages and dialects are spoken in Afghanistan, all of them by small minorities.

RELIGION Almost all Afghans are **Muslim**.

RESTAURANTS
West 1 *Caravanserai – The Afghan Restaurant,* 50 Paddington St, W1U 4HP (7935 1208).

Islington *Afghan Kitchen T/A,`* 35 Islington Green, N1 8DU (7359 8019);
Tower Hamlets *Jalalabad Tandoori,* 51 Burdett Rd, Bow E3 4TN (8980 1550).

SHOPS *Afghan Bakery,* 211 Uxbridge Rd, W7 3TH (8840 6111); *Afghan Fancy Goods and Cosmetics,* Granville Arcade, Coldharbour La, SW9 8PR (7733 4452); *Afghan Grocery,* 120 Broadway, W13 0SY (8357 6711); *Dawgems Afghan Carpets,* Unit 8, Atlas Business Centre, Oxgate La, NW2 7HJ (8800 8707).

TRAVEL *Jalalabad Travel,* 183 Cannon St, E1 (7488 1198).

WELFARE *Helping Hand for Afghan Refugees,* 98 Grimthorpe Ho, Agdon St, EC1V 0BR (7253 2785); *Society of Afghan Residents,* West Acton

Community Centre, Churchill Gdns, W3 0JN (8993 8168).

African

See also **African Caribbean, East African, Horn of Africa, North African, South African, Southern African, West African**, and names of individual African nationalities from **Algerian** to **Zimbabwean.**

ARTS *African Players Theatre Company,* 218 Lambeth Rd, SE1 7JY (7928 0341); *Sugumugu Sunday African Arts Window International,* 6 Grange Pl, Kinsgate Rd, NW6 4JU (7625 9231);

ASSOCIATIONS *African Francophone Community Association,* c/o Mr J Nzau-Matomisa, 3rd fl, The Irish Centre, Pretoria Rd, Tottenham N17 8DX (8808 0999) [languages: **French** and **Lingala**]; *African Journalist Foundation,* 100 Piccadilly, W1J 7NH (7495 7968); *African Medical and Research Foundation,* 4 Grosvenor Pl, SW1X 7YL (7201 6070); *African Studies Associattion of the UK,* SOAS, Thornhaugh St, Russell Sq, WC1H 0XG (7898 4389); *Africa Youth Organisation,* 364 Barking Rd, E13 8HL (7476 5183); *Centre For Inter-African Relations,* 19 St John's Church Rd, E9 6EJ (8985 4235); *London African Volunteers Network Unit,* 210 Camberwell Commercial Centre, SE5 7HN (7701 7422); *Mama Africa Women's Association,* 48 Artillery Pl, SE18 4AB (8317 6777); *Newham African Caribbean Resource Centre,* 627-633 Barking Rd, E13 9EZ (8471 2258); *Pan African Community Organization,* 66 Charlton Church La, SE7 7AB (8293 0440); *Royal African Society,* S O A S , Thornhaugh St, Russell Sq, WC1H 0XG (7898 4389).

BARS & NIGHT-CLUBS *Africa Bar,* Africa Centre, 38 King St, WC2E 8JT (7836 1976); *African Tavern,* 46 Grundy St, E14 (79871177); *Charlie Wright's International Bar,* 45 Pitfield St, N1 (7490 8345); *Chimes Bar,* 231 Lower Clapton Rd, E5 (8533 7994); *Dele Adelegan,* Club Afrique, 145-149 Barking Rd, Canning Town E16 (7511 8494).

BUSINESS *Africa Archipelago Ltd,* 1 Ashlone Rd, SW15 1LS (8780 5838); *Africa Development Partners Ltd,* Tudor Leaf Business Centre, Fountayne Rd, N15 4QL (8808 0055); *Africa Import Export Company.Ltd,* Afrex Ho, Beresford Ave, Wembley HA0 1FX (8903 9877); *Africa Matters Ltd,* 51 Causton St, SW1P 4AT (7976 6850); *Africa Trade & Industrial Corporation Ltd,* 6 Hardwicks Way, SW18 4AJ (8871 4810); *Anglo African Trading Agencies Ltd,* 5 Cinnamon Row SW11 3TW (7738 1800); *Arab African International Bank,* 19 Berkeley St, W1J 8DZ (7495 4881); *Conservation Corporation Africa UK Ltd,* SW1A 1JT (7493 1312); *First African Remittances Ltd,* Unit 3, Chapel Pl, N17 8DR (8880 9765); *Mart Africa Ltd,* Uneek Ho, Amberley Way, Hounslow TW4 6BH (8572 6310); *Mobil Africa & Middle East Ltd,* Mobil Court 3, Clements Inn, WC2A 2EB (7412 4000); *Oriental & African Strategic Investment Services Ltd,* 3 Park Pl, SW1A 1LP (7629 7626).

EDUCATION *Africa Educational Trust,* 38 King St, WC2B 6TP (7836 5075); *African Studies Association of the UK,* SOAS, Thornhaugh St, Russell Sq, WC1H 0XG (7898 4389); *Centre for African Language Learning,* 38 King St, WC2E 8JS (7240 0199); *Foods of Africa & the Caribbean Educational Trust (FACET),* 48 Endlesham Rd, SW12 8JL (8874 3662); *Francophone Africa, Caribbean, & the Pacific Research Group,* SSHS, University of Westminster, 309 Regent St, W1B 2UW (7911 5000 x2078); *Institute for African Alternatives,* Lyndhurst Hall, Warden Rd, NW5 4RE (7482 4660); *School of Oriental & African Studies,* Thornhaugh St, Russell Sq, WC1H 0XG (7898 4888).

FREIGHT *Africa Courier Ltd,* Unit 5, Regent Business Centre, Pump La, Hayes UB3 3NB (8848 7742); *Africa International Services Unit,* 69 Parkside Business Estate, Blackhorse Rd, SE8 5JA (8691 1314); *East African Conference Lines,* 88-90 Middlesex St, E1 7EZ (7247 6538); *OT Africa Line,* Marc Ho, 13-14 Great St Thomas Apostle, EC4V 2BB (7332 6000).

HEALTH & BEAUTY *African Beauty Cosmetics Ltd,* 381 Green St, E13 (8470 3004); *African Dreams,* 255 High Rd, Tottenham N15 5BT (8800 3100); *African Herbal Solutions,* 19a Well St, E9 7QX (8533 1953); *Faze 2 Barbers,* 529 Kingsland Rd, E8 (7503 7942).

LANGUAGES At least 2,000 languages are spoken in Africa and about half of these are located in West Africa. This *Global London* listing includes individual entries for all the more than 100 African languages, from **Abe** to **Zulu**, which were reported as being the home languages of London schoolchildren in the *Multilingual Capital* (2000) survey.

LEGAL *Africa Advocacy Foundation,* Crowndale Centre, 218 Eversholt St, Camden Town NW1 1BD (7691 0234); *African, Caribbean and Asian Lawyers Group,* 100-113 Chancery La, Holborn WC2A 1PL; *African Immigration Bureau,* 215-223 Kingsland Rd, E2 (7613 1721); *Human Rights Watch – Africa Watch* Lancaster House, Islington High St, N1 9LH (7713 1995); *Justice Africa,* 35 Islington High St, N1 9LH (7837 7888); *Newham African Organisation* [legal services], 284a Romford Rd, E7 9HD (8534 4731).

MEDIA & INFORMATION *Africa Analysis,* Suite 2f, Diamond Ho, 36-38 Hatton Garden, EC1N 8EB [publishers] (7404 4321); *Africa Confidential,* 73

Farringdon Rd, EC1M 3JQ (7831 3511); *Africa International,* Northway Ho, 1379 High Rd, N20 9LP *and* 64 Sutton Crescent, EN5 2SS [publishers] (8449 9403); *Africa Media Specialists,* 69 Bondway, SW8 1SQ (7820 9511); *Africa Research & Information Bureau,* 5 Westminster Bridge Rd, SE1 7XW (7928 8728); *African Video Centre,* 92 Peckham High St, SE15 5ED (7732 5460); *Africa Analysis,* Ludgate Ho, 107-111 Fleet St, EC4 (7353 1117); *Africa Confidential,* 73 Farringdon Rd, EC1 (7831 3511); *Africa Factsfile,* 223 Shoreditch High St, E1 6PJ (0773771120); *Africa Financing Review,* 31 Dunstan Rd, NW11 (7731 8392 and 7731 8221); *Africa Forum,* P O Box 1374, SW9 8ET; *African Dawn,* 15 Wilken St, NW5 (7267 9421 ext. 160); *African Business Connections,* Unit 417, 71 Bondway, Vauxhall, SW8 1SQ (7820 9515); *African Business,* 7 Coldbath Square, EC1 (7713 7711); *African Economic Digest,* Aare Abiola Hse, 26-32 Whistler St, N5 1NH (7359 5335); *African Expatriate,* Landmark Business Communication Ltd, 10 Cleverland Way, E1 4TR (7790 2424); *African Farming & Food Processing,* 27 Wilfred St, SW1E 6PR (7834 7676); *African News,* Centre of African Studies, SOAS, University of London, Thornhaugh St, Russell Sq, WC1; *Africa Now,* 7 Rudolph Pl, Miles St, SW8 1RP (7735 8071) and 4 Rickett St, SW6 1RU (7386 5200); *African Prince Publications,* 41 Sara La Ct, Stanway St, N1 (7613 4360); *Africans Around Town,* DBI Communications Grove Ho, 82 East Dulwich Grove, SE22 8TW; *African Soccer Magazine,* Canon Collins Ho, 64 Essex Rd, N1 8LR (7704 6300); *African Times,* Hansib Publishing Ltd, 139-149 Fouthill Rd, N4 3HF (7281 1191); *African Topics,* African Periscope Communications, Suite 106, 99-103 Lomond Grove, SE5 7HN (77084520); *African Video Centre,* 7 Balls Pond Rd, N1 (7923 4224).

Africa Today, Afromedia UK Ltd, 313 Kilburn La, W9 3EG (8968 6633); *Africa World Review,* 5 Westminster Bridge Rd, SE1 7XW (7620 1430); *Afrique Communications* (7252 5781); *Akina mama wa Afrika,* 4 Wild Ct, WC2B 4AU (7405 0678); *Business in Africa,* Goldcity Communications Ltd, Unit f11, Shakespeare Business Centre, 245A Coldharbour Lane, SW9 8RR (7737 5933); *Business in Africa Magazine,* 100 Piccadilly, W1V 9FN (7495 7969); *Calabash,* Centreprise, 136-138 Kingsland High St, E8 2NS (7254 9632); *Casablanca Magazine,* 31 Clerkenwell Close, EC1 (7608 3784); *Chic Magazine,* 15 Brittania St, WC1X 9JB (7837 7278); *DER (The African Economy),* 11 Church La, E11 1HG (8257 9593); *Echoes,* Black Echoes Ltd, 7 Charlotte St, W1 (7436 4550, 7255 2402, 7323

0178); *Focus,* 106 Cronin St, SE15 6JD (77084479); *Focus on Africa,* Bush Hse, P.O. Box 76, Strand, WC2B 4PH (7257 2906); *Horn of Africa Advice and Information Centre,* 124 Kingsland High Rd, E8 2NS (7923 2402); *Kenya Times,* 7 High St Kensington, W8 (7411 3111); *Main Issue,* 10-12 Cleverland Way, E1 4TR (7790 2424); *News Reel,* 14 Acre Lane, SW2 5SG; *Newslinks Africa Ltd,* 7-11 Kensington High St, W8 5NP (7376 1996); *New Envoy,* Liberty Publications Unit B19, Metropolitan Business Centre, Kingsland Rd, N1 5AZ (0800 2791249); *News Africa UK Ltd,* 334 Goswell Rd, EC1V 7LQ (7713 8135); *Ovation International Limited,* Suite 15, Beaufort Ct, Admirals Way, Marsh Wall, Docklands, E14 9XL (75373432); *Pan Africa,* Suite 250, Camberwell Commercial Centre, 99 Lomond Grove, SE5 7HN; *Peacock Communication Ltd* [entertainment and leisure magazine], 99-03 Lomond Grove, Suite 225, SE5 7HN; *Profile,* Minority Rights International, 379 Brixton Rd, SW9 7DE (7738 6265); *Searchlight Communications,* 75 Redchurch St, Shoreditch, E2 7DJ (fax 7613 5796); *Spectrum Radio,* International Radio Centre, 4 Ingate Pl, SW8 3NS (7627 4433) [broadcasting on African topics 12.00 - 13.00 and 15.00 - 17.00 Saturdays only]; *West Africa Magazine,* 43-45 Coldharbour La, SE5 9NR (7737 2946).

RECREATION *Africa Centre,* 38 King St, WC2E 8JS (7836 1973).

RELIGION *Africa Inland Mission,* 2 Vorley Rd, N19 5HE (7281 1184); *Mid-Africa Ministry,* 157 Waterloo Rd, SE1 8XN (7261 1370); *Missionary Sisters of Africa,* 5 Charlbury Grove, W5 2DU (8997 7912); *Society of Missionaries of Africa* (White Fathers), 42 Stormont Rd, N6 4NP (8340 5036).

RESTAURANTS (see also entries under **African Caribbean** and the names of individual African ethnic groups and nationalities.)

East Central *Akina Mama Wa Africa,* 334-336 Goswell Rd, EC1V 7LQ (7713 5166).

South East 1 *Bamboo Inn,* 266 Old Kent Rd, SE1 5HB (7708 0055, 7701 2255); *Tops Foods,* 75 Tower Bridge Rd, SE1 4TW (7771 0062).

West Central *Calabash,* 38 King St, WC2E 8JT (78361976).

Brent *Dooshima African Kitchen,* 36 Park Parade, NW10 4JE (8965 8389); *Oasis,* 108 Cricklewood Broadway, NW2 3EJ (8452 0463).

Camden *African Express*, The Stable Market, Chalk Farm Rd, NW1; *Buka African Kitchen*, 122 Kilburn High Rd, NW6 (7625 1550); *Oasis* [African & Caribbean], 108 Cricklewood Broadway, NW2 (8452 0463).

Hackney *Africa 2000*, 210 Seven Sisters Rd N4 3NX (7281 7555); *African Kitchen*, 64 Old Hill St, N16 (8806 9136, fax 8806 9137); *Fassika*, 152 Seven Sisters Rd, N4 (7272 7572); *Moonwalk*, 100-102 Hoxton St, N1 (7613 4071); *Osto*, 3A Rectory Rd, N16 7QP (7275 9789, fax 7916 3829); *Out of Africa*, 68 Chatsworth Rd E5 0LS (8533 5486); *Yum yum T/A,* 242 Graham Rd, Hackney E8 (8533 7901).

Haringey *Ahenfie*, 272 High Rd N15 (8493 9177); *Andy's*, 90 West Green Rd N15.

Islington *Afri Carib Nigerian*, 1 Stroud Green Rd, N4 (7263 7440, 7263 5464); *Oodua*, 9 Balls Pond Rd, Dalston N1 4 AX (7503 5529).

Lambeth *Adulis*, 44 Brixton Rd SW9 (7735 4126); *Destos Food*, 132 Landor Rd, SW9 (7733 2163); *Enjoy*, 53A Streatham Hill, SW2 (7671 3571); *Labalaba Butterfly*, 330A Coldharbour La, SW9 (7274 6676); *La Bamba*, 540 Streatham High Rd, SW16 3QF (8679 9641); *Roots*, 73 Venn St, SW4 0BD (7652 5653); *Smokey Bites*, Clapham Park Rd, SW4 (7720 9027).

Lewisham *Afab-star*, 4 Deptford Broadway SE8 (8691 3315); *Toni's Kitchen*, 27-28 Deptford Market St, SE8 (8694 9352); *2001 Afro Restaurant*, 201 Lewisham Way, SE4 1AU (8694 9955).

Newham *La Différence 2000*, 342 Romford Rd E7 (8536 0303).

Southwark *Africana*, 91A Camberwell Rd, SE5 (7277 4977); *Ardani*, 175 New Kent Rd SE1 4AG (7207 4754 fax 7232 2132); *BB's African and Caribbean Restaurant*, 245-249 Dartmouth Rd, SE26 4QY (8699 7777); *Cool and Cosy*, 455A New Cross Rd, SE15 (8694 9320); *Eva's*, 71 Southwark Park Rd, SE16 (7237 7150); *Helade*, 35 Peckham High St, SE15 5EB (7708 4764); *Kaliso's Afrokankankan*, Elm Grove, Peckham SE15; *La Cascade*, 8-10 Blenheim Grove, Peckham SE15 (7277 9038); *Obalende Suya Spot*, 29 Peckham High St, SE15 1YR (7252 4627).

Wandsworth *Taste of Africa*, 31 Falcon Rd, SW11 2PH (7924 7878).

SHOPS

Bookshops *Africa Book Centre*, 38 King St, WC2E 8JT (7240 6649); *Africa Books Ltd,* 3 Galena Rd, W6 0LT (8746 3646); *African Connection*, 6 Tunstall Rd, SW9 8BN (7501 9445); *Arthur Probsthain* [Oriental and African bookshop], 41 Gt Russell St, WC1 3PL (7636 1096) *and* Brunei Gallery, SOAS, Thornhaugh St, Russell Sq, WC1H 0XG (7898 4470); *Soma Books*, 38 Kennington La, SE11 4LS (7735 2101; fax 7735 3076).

Food *Africa Food Centre*, 137 Lambeth Walk, SE11 6EE (7793 8666); *African Food Shop,* 154 Rye La, SE15 4NB (7639 9505); *African Stores*, 143 Peckham High St, SE15 5SL (7277 9060); *Ali Brothers Halal Butchers*, 27 Deptford High St, SE8 (8691 3363); *Back Home Foods*, 83 Granville Arcade, SW9 (7738 5655); *Bims African Food Store,* 102 Rye La, Peckham SE15 4RZ (7732 1564); *Blessed African Food Centre*, 7 Morning La, E9 6ND (8525 0721); *B & Y African Food Store,* S59-60 New Shepherds Bush Market, Uxbridge Rd, W12 7JS (8740 1525); *Blue Mountain Peak*, 2a-8 Craven Park Rd, NW10 (8965 3859); *Calabash*, 110 Cricklewood Broadway, NW2; *D-Bess Bakery*, 58-59 Granville Arcade, SW9 (7738 7394); *First Choice Bakery*, 40 Atlantic Rd, SW9 (7501 9579); *Kenkay African Shop*, 2 Bramlands Close, SW11 2NR (7978 5052); *St Gabriel Delicatessen*, 12 Blackstock Rd, N4 (7354 5104); *Timmy's African & Continental Grocery Store,* 104 Weymouth Terrace, E2 8LR (7684 0654).

Other *African Crafts Centre*, 38 King St, WC2E 8JT (7240 6098); *African Enterprises Ltd,* Unit 3, The Arches, Villiers St, WC2N 6NG (7839 5707); *African Majesty*, 21 North End Parade, W14 0SJ (7751 1080) [crafts]; *African Music Store & Travel Services*, 417 Coldharbour La, SW9 8LH (7733 7779); *African Textile Corner*, 3 Goldhawk Rd, W12 8QQ (8740 0239); *Fowy Africa Art & Video Store,* 21 Brixton Station Rd, SW9 8PB (7738 6457); *Gee Fashions* [African designer outfits], Cricklewood Broadway, NW2 (8450 8051).

SPECIAL *Africa Astrology*, 84 Studley Rd, E7 9LY (8548 8666); *Africa Centre*, 38 King St, WC2E 8JT (7836 1973).

Not yet categorized: *Africa Foundation for Development*, 54 Camberwell Rd, SE5 0EN (7703 0653); *Africa International Services*, 69 Parkside Business Estate, Blackhorse Rd, SE8 5HZ (8691 2882); *Africa Worldwide*, St Lawrence Business Centre, Victoria Rd, Feltham TW13 7LT (8867 0004); *Africa Youth League Ltd,* Estuary Ho, Ballards Rd, Dagenham RM10 9AB (8593 3222); *Alliances for Africa*, Aberdeen Centre, Highbury Grove, N5 2EA (7359 1181); *Capital Africa*, 1 Norfolk Pl, W2 1QN (7402 3185); *Link Africa*, Kings Exchange, Tileyard Rd, N7 9AH (7691 1818); *Trans Africa UK Ltd*, GEC Estate, Magnet Rd, East La, Wembley HA9 7RG (8908 0982); *Transform Africa,*

Leroy Ho, Essex Rd, N1 3QP (7354 5455); *Vintage Africa (UK) Ltd,* 299 Rayners La, Pinner HA5 5EH (8429 9444).

TRAVEL *About Africa Ltd,* 1st fl, 10 Barley Mow Passage, W4 4PH (8747 0177); *Absolute Africa,* 41 Swanscombe Rd, W4 2HL (8742 0226); *Africa,* 27 Central Chambers, The Broadway Ealing, W5 2NR (8840 8881); *Africa Explorer Ltd,* 5 Strand on the Green, W4 3PQ (8987 8742); *Africa International & Middle East Travel (AIMET),* 71 Bondway, Suite 405, SW8 1SQ (7820 3660); *African Air Planners,* 69 Wigmore St, W1U 2SQ (7486 8886); *African Music Store & Travel Services,* 417 Coldharbour La, SW9 8LH (7733 7779); *African Travel Centre,* 21 Leigh St, WC1 (7387 1211); *African Travel Specialists,* 229 Old Kent Rd, SE1 5LU (0870 3455454); *African World Travel Services,* Radnor Ho. suite 501, 93 Regent St, W1B 4ER (7734 7181); *Caribbean Holidays & African Safaris,* 79 Sefton Ave, Harrow Weald HA3 5JP (8424 0917); *Drive Africa Safaris,* Nightingale Centre, 8 Balham Hill, SW12 9EA (8675 3974); *Hayes & Jarvis Travel Ltd* [African reservations], W6 0QU (0870 898 9890); *Pulse Africa (UK) Ltd,* Nightingale Centre, 8 Balham Hill, SW12 9EA (8995 5909); *Rainbow Tours (African Travel),* 64 Essex Rd, N1 8LR (7226 1004); *Routes of Africa,* 9 Bridge Rd, East Molesey KT8 9EU (8873 3589); *Skyway To Africa,* 4 Medway Ct, WC1H 9QX (7387 1211); *Travelbag plc,* Africa Department, 52 Regent St, W1A 3BJ (7287 5535); *Wine Tours to South Africa,* 5 Moreton Ho, Holly Walk, NW3 6RA (7433 3713).

WELFARE *Action for Southern Africa,* 28 Penton St, N1 9SA (7833 3133); *Africa Archipelago Ltd,* 55 Fulham High St, Fulham SW6 3JJ (8780 5838); *Africa Now,* 4 Rickett St, SW6 1RU (7386 5200); *Farm Africa,* 9-10 Southampton Pl, WC1A 2EA (7430 0440); *Greenwich African Welfare Organisation,* 3-4, Beresford St, SE18 6BE (8855 1100); *African Women's Welfare Association - Ayoka Project,* 15a Old Ford Rd, E2 9PJ (8981 9603); *African Women's Welfare Group,* 301 White Hart La, N17 7BT (8885 5822); *Central African Refugee Project Unit,* 103 1st floor, Tudor Leaf Business Centre, N15 4QL (8885 6582); *Help Africa Trust,* 12 Winchester Ho, 9 Cranmer Rd, SW9 6EJ (7582 5222); *Mid-Africa Ministry,* 157 Waterloo Rd, SE1 8UU (7261 1370); *Southwark African Family Support Services,* 54 Camberwell Rd, SE5 0EW (7701 0486); *Street Child Africa Ltd,* The Priory Home of Compassion, High St, Thames Ditton KT7 0II (8972 9820); *Umoja* [drop-in facility for African communities and their carers living with HIV], Edmonton Family Centre, 5, Lacey Close, Edmonton N9 (8379 8013) [1st and 3rd Wed of each month,

16.30 - 19.30]; *Unity African Caribbean Project,* Prah Rd, N4 2RA (7359 8111); *West Nile Welfare Association,* 10 New River Ct, Petherton Rd, N5 2RH (7704 2931).

Plaque in Riding House St, W1.

African Caribbean

Modelled on *African American,* **African Caribbean** has made some limited progress towards replacing **Afro-Caribbean** (see below) in some contexts. Note that **Caribbean** alone, **Carib,** and the older term **West Indian** continue to be used in very similar senses and that entries for these alternative names should also be consulted.

ASSOCIATIONS *African Caribbean Disablement Association,* Unit 14, Alpha Business Centre, South Grove, E17 7NX (8521 6429); *Barnet African Caribbean Association,* Marsh Drive, Colindale NW9 7QQ (8202 0095); *Brent African & Caribbean Disabled Peoples Association,* Disability Alliance Centre, The Old Refectory, Acton La, Willesden NW10 7NS (8963 1731); *African Caribbean Medical Society,* 52 Carson Rd, Dulwich SE21 8HU (8690 7353).

RELIGION *African Caribbean Evangelical Alliance,* Whitefield Ho, 186 Kennington Park Rd, Lambeth SE11 4BT (7735 7373); *African-Caribbean Funeral Services,* Mable Carter Ho, 99 Stoke Newington Church St, Stoke Newington N16 0UD (7275 0175).

RESTAURANTS *African Caribbean,* 12 St Loy's Rd, Tottenham N17 (8880 3203).

SPECIAL *African Caribbean Leadership Council,* 9 Clarendon Rd, Hornsey N8 0DJ (8881 5881);

WELFARE *African and Caribbean Elders* [day centre], 86 Abbey Rd, NW8 0QA (7372 0862); *African Caribbean Centre,* Ive Farm Sports Ground, Ive Farm La, Leyton E10 5HL (8558 0838); *African Caribbean Day Nursery,* 30 Hornsey Park Rd, Hornsey N8 0JP (8889 6896); *African Caribbean Disablement Association,* Unit 14, Alpha Business Centre, South Grove, E17 7NX (8521 6429); *African Caribbean Family Mediation Service,* 2-4 St. Johns Crescent, Brixton SW9 7LZ (7737 2366); *African Caribbean Marriage Support Services,* Drop In Centre, Suite 6, 49 Effra Rd, Brixton SW2 1BZ (7737 2474); *African-Caribbean Youth Achievement Scheme,* Palingswick Ho, 241 King St, Hammersmith W6 9LP (8741 5715); *Barnet African Caribbean Day Centre* within Barnet Multi-Culture Centre, Algernon Rd, NW4 3TA (8202 0095); *Brent African & Caribbean Disabled Peoples Association,*

Disability Alliance Centre, The Old Refectory, Acton La, Willesden NW10 7NS (8963 1731); *Croydon African Caribbean Family Organisation*, 40 Northwood Rd, Thornton Heath, Surrey CR7 8HQ (8771 9700); *East London African & Caribbean Counselling Service*, Stratford Advice Arc, 107-109 The Grove, Stratford E15 1HP (8221 1233); *Hackney African Caribbean People With Disabilities*, Alfred Heath Centre, Homerton High St, E9 6AG (8525 1195*); Harrow African Caribbean Association*, 27 Northolt Rd, Harrow HA2 0LH (8930 9420); *Lambo African-Caribbean Centre* [day centre], 48 Despard Rd, Archway N19 5NW (7263 3046); *Newham African Caribbean and Asian Advocacy Project Office*, 8 Stratford Advice Arcade, 107-109 The Grove, Stratford E15 1EN (8519 8311); *Newham African Caribbean Resource Centre*, 627-633 Barking Rd, Plaistow E13 9EZ (8471 2258); *Organisation of Blind African Caribbean*, 1 Gloucester Ho, Camberwell New Rd, SE5 0TA (7735 3400).

Afrikaans

EDUCATION Courses in **Afrikaans** are available at the *SOAS Language Centre* (7898 4888).

LANGUAGE **Afrikaans** derives mainly from **Dutch**, with which it remains largely mutually intelligible. It is spoken by several million people in South Africa. In London **Afrikaans** was reported as the first language of 64 London schoolchildren in the *Multilingual Capital* (2000) survey, of whom 22 lived in Enfield.

Afro

ARTS *Afro International Theatre Productions*, Unit 10, Tottenham Green Co-operative Workshop, N17 9EJ (8808 9619).

HEALTH & BEAUTY *A & A Afro Cosmetics*, 345 Lea Bridge Rd, E10 7LA (8558 7467); *Afro Beauty Salon*, 3 Choumert Rd, The Market, SE15 4SG (7277 5335); *Afro Centric Unisex Salon*, 364 Lea Bridge Rd, E10 7LD (8556 9198); *Afro Cosmetics* 213a Rye La, Peckham SE15 4TP (7732 0641); *Afro Cosmetics*, 110 Mitcham Rd, SW17 9NG (8672 8882); *Afro Cosmetics*, 491a High Rd, Tottenham N17 6QA (8365 0674); *Afro Cosmetics*, 237 High St, E17 7BH (8520 1341); *Afro Dreams Cosmetics*, 8 Lee High Rd, SE13 5LQ (8852 5877); *Afro Hair UK Ltd*, 198 High St, E17 7JH (8521 8804); *Afro International*, 8 Westbury Ave, N22 6BN (8881 8840); *Afro International*, 297 Mare St, E8 1EJ (8533 0020); *Afro World*, 7 Kingsland High St, E8 2JS [hair] (7275 8848); *Afro World International*, 57 Craven Park, NW10 8SR (8963 1730); *Amarsons Afro Products*, 70 Queen's Market, E13 9BA (8470 4845); *Babson Afro Hair Salon*, 6 Spray St, SE18 6AD (8855 5779); *Carlton Afro European Barbers*, 156 Mare St, E8 3RD (8985 9418); *Classy Design Afro Hair Salon*, 39a Burnt Ash Hill, SE12 0AE (8851 4793); *Ebony Afro Cosmetics*, 13 Northwold Rd, Stoke Newington N16 7HL (7923 2676); *Fenbico Afro Cosmetics*, 117 Fore St, N18 2XF (8807 4490);

Ginger Group Afro Hair Innovations, 211 Uxbridge Rd, W13 9AA (8567 2760); *Jay & Jay Afro Cosmetics*, 29 Bedford Hill, SW12 9EX (8675 1428); *Juliet's Afro World Superstore*, 120 Rye La, SE15 4RZ [hairdressing] (7358 1688); *Juliette's Afro Cosmetics*, 5 High St, NW10 4NA (8838 4700); *Kiaz Afro Cosmetics*, 219 Kilburn High Rd, NW6 7JG (7328 9343); *Klass Afro European Cosmetics*, 832 High Rd, Tottenham N12 9RA (8493 0540); *Le Circle Afro Hair Salon*, 28 Westow Hill, SE19 1RX (8670 3221); *Mirage Afro European Hair Salon*, 76 Upton La, Forest Gate E7 9LW (8548 0480); *Sophie's Unisex Afro Hair Salon*, 1156 London Rd, SW16 4DS (8679 1381); *Super Afro Cosmetics*, 80 High St, NW10 4SJ (8838 5565).

MEDIA & INFORMATION *Afro Hair & Beauty* [magazine], Trident Public Relations, 155 Fawe Park Rd, SW15 2EG; *Afro Hollywood*, 7 Holles Ho, Myatts Field South, SW9 7JN [film and video production] (7274 3933); *Afro Times Ltd*, 69 Sunny Gardens Rd, NW4 (8203 7063, 8203 7356); *Afro Wisdom Films*, 138-140 Old St, EC1V 9BJ (7490 8386); *UK Afro & Caribbean News Magazine*, 313 Romford Rd, Forest Gate E7 9HA (8257 5672);

SHOPS *Afro Asian Foods*, 3 Arndale Walk, Arndale Centre, Wandsworth, SW18 4BX (8870 5060); *Afro Design and Textile Centre*, 311 East St, SE17 2SX (7703 4057); *Afro-Euro Drugstore*, 2 East St, Walworth, SE17 2DN (7703 6973); *Afro Food Centre*, 94 Rye La, SE15 4RZ (7635 7588); *Afro Muslim Butchers*, 16 Deptford High St, SE8 4AF (8692 8490); *Divine Choice Afro Foods*, 70 Herbert Rd, SE18 3SH (8316 5508); *J K Afro World International*, 127 High St W3 6LY [groceries] (8993 7355); *Joesaabs Bus Afro Caribbean*, 38 Lee High Rd, SE13 5PT [women's clothing] (8318 4700).

WELFARE *Afro - Care Umbrella*, c/o Andy Hammond, 45 North Sq, Edmonton Green N9 0HY (8372 5528) [languages: French, Igbo, Swahili, English].

Afro-Caribbean

See also **African Caribbean**, **Carib**, **Caribbean**, and **West Indian** for related entries.

EDUCATION *Foods of Africa & the Caribbean Educational Trust (FACET)*, 48 Endlesham Rd, SW12 8JL (8874 3662);

HEALTH & BEAUTY *Afro Caribbean Barbers*, 1 Marischal Rd, SE13 5LE (8318 4262); *Mo Betta Cutz*, 316a Ladbroke Grove, W10 (8968 3434).

RESTAURANTS *Afri Carib Nigerian*, 1 Stroud Green Rd, N4 (7263 7440, 7263 5464); *Afrodish*, 93 West Green Rd, N15.

SHOPS

Food *Afro-Caribbean Foods*, 5 Holcombe Rd, N17 9AE (8808 0010); *Afro-Caribbean Food Units*, 27-28 The Inn Shops, 37-43 South Mall, N9 0TT (8803 7086); *Afro Caribbean Store*, 306a Ruislip Road East, Greenford UB6 9BH (8578 6414); *Delamy Afro Caribbean Groceries*, 8 Granville Arcade, Coldharbour La, SW9 8PR (7738 3753); *Emmanuel's Afro-Caribbean Foods*, 2 Jonathan St, Kennington SE11 5NH (7787 6383); *EYD Foods (Afro-Caribbean Foods)*, 18 Deptford High St, SE8 4AF (8692 7218); *Joesaabs Bus Afro Caribbean* [greengrocery], 38 Lee High Rd, Lewisham SE13 5PT (8318 4700); *KM Butchers*, 29 Stroud Green Rd, N4 (7263 6625); *L'An Kompressor 2000* [African food], 29 Cricklewood Broadway, NW2 (8450 6316); *Laurie's*, 86 Deptford High St, SE8 (8691 0514); *M M Cash & Carry* [Afro Food Centre], 31 Electric Ave, Brixton; *Stroud Green Food Store*, 65 Stroud Green Rd, N4 (7272 0348); *Tropic Melody Afro Latin Records & Travel Centre*, 409-17 Coldharbour La, SW9 8LH (7738 7278).

SPECIAL *Afro Caribbean Introductions*, P O Box 16573, NW6 7ZF (7625 1534).

TRAVEL *Tropic Melody Afro Latin Records & Travel Centre*, 409-17 Coldharbour La, SW9 8LH (7738 7278).

WELFARE *Afro Caribbean Elders Association*, William Morris Community Centre, Greenleaf Rd, E17 6QQ (8509 0067); *Afro Caribbean Senior Citizens Club*, 6 Colworth Rd, Waltham Forest E11 1HY (8558 7256).

Afro-Caribbean Patwa

See under **Patwa**.

Ahmadiyya

ASSOCIATIONS *Ahmadiyya Muslim Association*, Erskine Rd, E17 (8520 1247); *Ahmadiyya Muslim Association*, 16 Gressenhall Rd, Wandsworth SW18 5QL (8870 1999); *Ahmadiyya Muslim Association*, 10 Hardwicks Way, SW18 4AJ (8870 0919);

Ahmadiyya Muslim Association, 53 Melrose Rd, SW18 (8870 1999); *Ahmadiyya Muslim Youth Association*, 10 Hardwicks Way, SW18 4AJ (8870 9955).

MEDIA & INFORMATION *Muslim Television Ahmadiyya*, 16 Gressenhall Rd, Wandsworth SW18 5QL (8870 0922).

RELIGION *Ahmadiyya Fazal Mosque* and *Ahmadiyya Movement in Islam*, 16 Gressenhall Rd, Wandsworth SW18 5QL (8870 8517); *Ahmadiyya Muslim Association*, 16 Gressenhall Rd, Wandsworth SW18 5QL (8870 6134).

Akan

EDUCATION See under **Twi**.

LANGUAGES The **Akan** people of southern Ghana speak a number of closely related Aframic languages, including **Fante** and **Twi**, which are known collectively as **Akan**. There are several million speakers in all, accounting for about 40% of the population of Ghana.

The *Multilingual Capital* (2000) survey reported that there were 6,094 London pupils from homes in which **Akan** languages are spoken (including **Ashanti**, a dialect of **Twi**). Haringey is the borough in which the greatest number of speakers of **Akan** languages (1,145) was found. The distribution of pupils speaking **Akan** languages across London and within the borough of Haringey can be seen on Maps 1 and 2 at <www.global-london.com/gallery>.

Akpafu

Akpafu is an Aframic language of northern Ghana. The *Multilingual Capital* (2000) survey reported this as the first language of four pupils in Lewisham.

Aku

Aku is an **English Creole** spoken in the Gambia. A very few speakers of this were found in the *Multilingual Capital* (2000) survey but these were added to the figures for **Krio** (of Sierra Leone) of which **Aku** is generally considered to be a dialect.

Albanian

ASSOCIATIONS *Albanian Association Clubhouse*, Summers La, N12 0PD (8445 9589); *Anglo-Albanian Association*, 1 Rossdale Rd, SW15 1AD (8789 0320).

EDUCATION Mother-tongue classes for children in **Albanian** are available in several places in London. For further information, see <www.resourceunit.com>. University courses in **Albanian** are among the subjects taught at *SSEES* (7636 8000).

GOVERNMENT *Embassy of the Republic of Albania*, 2nd fl, 24 Buckingham Gate, SW1E 6LB (7828 8897).

LANGUAGE **Albanian** (*Shqipe*) is an Indo-European language but is not closely related to any other language of that family. The *Multilingual Capital* (2000) survey identified 934 London pupils from Albanian-speaking homes. The main areas where they are located can be seen on Map 3 at <www.global-london.com/gallery>.

RELIGION About 70% of Albanians are Muslims. The remainder are Christians (20% Greek Orthodox, 10% Roman Catholics). No Albanian religious services in London were identified.

RESTAURANTS
Brent *Lisi,* 5 Malvern Rd, NW6 5PS (7625 8932).

TRANSLATION *Albanian & Kosovan Interpreting,* 29 Castle Ave, West Drayton UB7 8LG (07956 322095); *Tramont Translation Management,* 57 Upper Park Rd, NW3 2UL (7692 6319; fax 7504 8638).

WELFARE *Albanian Youth Action,* Westminster Business Square, Durham St, SE11 5JH (7582 6082).

Algerian

ASSOCIATIONS *Algerian Community Association,* c/o The Vestry, Union Chapel, Compton Ave, N1 2XD, (7289 4970).

BUSINESS *Anadarko Algeria Corporation,* 1 Harefield Rd, Uxbridge UB8 1PH (01895 209400).

EDUCATION *Society for Algerian Studies,* c/o CNMES, SOAS, Thornhaugh St, Russell Sq, WC1H 0XG (7898 4330).

GOVERNMENT *Algerian Consulate,* 6 Hyde Park Gate, SW7 5EW (7589 6885). *Algerian Embassy,* 54 Holland Park, W11 3RS (7221 7800).

LANGUAGES The principal languages of Algeria are (**Maghrebi**) **Arabic** (first language of about 80% of the population) and various **Berber** languages (19%). **French** is the mother tongue of a small minority but is an important language of the media and tertiary education.

RELIGION Algerians are overwhelmingly Muslims (Sunni Islam).

SHOPS *Algerian Coffee Stores,* 52 Old Compton St, Soho W1D 4PB (7437 2480); *L'Algéroise* [halal meat; Mediterranean groceries], 130 Cricklewood Broadway, NW2 (8452 3638).

TRAVEL *Air Algérie,* 10 Baker St, W1M 1DA (7487 5709).

WELFARE *Algerian Community Association,* c/o The Vestry, Union Chapel, Compton Ave, N1 2XD, (7289 4970); *Algeria Refugee Council* (7354 8088).

Alsatian

RESTAURANTS *Schnecke,* 58-59 Poland St, Soho, W1 (7287 6666).

Alur

A l u r is a Nilotic language spoken in Congo (Kinshasa) and Uganda. The presence of a few Alur-speaking schoolchildren was recorded in some London boroughs in the 1990s but none were reported in the *Multilingual Capital* (2000) survey.

Ambo

Ambo is a Bantuic language of Zambia, spoken by two pupils in Islington according to the *Multilingual Capital (*2000) survey.

American

In this section, as in general British usage, the word *American* is applied to people and things of the United States of America only (rather than to the Americas in general).

ACCOMMODATION *American Accommodation Agency,* 21 Grafton St, London, W1X 3LD (7493 2117); *American Agency,* 103a Old Brompton Rd, SW7 3LE (7581 5353); *Anglo American Estates Ltd ,* 88 Kingsway, Holborn, WC2B 6AA (7831 5885).

ARTS *British American Arts Association,* 118 Commercial St, E1 6NF (7247 5385).

ASSOCIATIONS *America-European Community Association Ltd,* Northumberland House, 11 The Pavement, Popes Lane, Ealing, W5 4NG; *American Club Inc,* Latham Ho, 16 Minories, EC3N 1AX; *American Forest & Paper Association Inc,* Shirley Ho, 10 Throgmorton Ave, EC2N 2DL; *American Institute of Architects,* Benjamin Franklin Ho, 36 Craven St, Holborn, WC2N 5NG (7930 9124); *American Press Association* [Trade Union], 102 Belsize Road, Kilburn, NW6 4BG (7372 4981); *American Womens Club Ltd,* 68 Old Brompton Rd, South Kensington, SW7 3LQ (7589 8292); *British North American Research Association,* 35-37 Grosvenor Gdns, Westminster, SW1W 0BS (7828 6644); *British American Arts Association,* 118 Commercial St, Whitechapel, E1 6NF (7247 5385); *Radiological Society Of North America,* 15 Roehampton La, Putney, SW15 5LS (8876 2340).

BARS & NIGHT-CLUBS *Arbuckles,* Mast Leisure Centre, Surrey Quays Rd, SE16 2XU (7232 1901); *Herman's,* 142 Hermon Hill, E18 1QH (8532 2526); *Newt and Cucumber,* 34 King St, WC2E 8JD (7240 4008).

BUSINESS
General *America Web Ltd* [Computer Systems & Software], 54 Runnymede Gardens, Western Avenue, Greenford, UB6 8SU; *Captain America Consultancy Ltd* [Business Consultants], 30 Northampton Square, Clerkenwell, EC1V 0ES; *Anglo American Business Consultants,* 28 Nottingham Pl, W1M 3FD (7486 4217); *Argus Vickers American Equity Research* [Financial Consultants], 7 Tower House, Chapel Place, Rivington St, Moorgate, EC2A 3DQ (7739 9949); *British-American Chamber of Commerce,* 8 Staple Inn, Bloomsbury, WC1V 7QH (7404 6400).

Insurance *American Re-Insurance Co*, 77 Gracechurch St, Monument, EC3V 0DL (7337 2100); *Odyssey America Reinsurance*, 5/4/3 Minster Court, Mincing Lane, Monument, EC3R 7DD (7617 4567).

Banks *American Express*, 60 Buckingham Palace Rd, Westminster, SW1W 0RR (7824 6000); *Bank of America National Trust & Savings Association*, 1 Alie St, Whitechapel, E1 8DE (7634 4000); *Bank of America*, New Broad St House, 35 New Broad St, Moorgate, EC2M 1NH (7282 2200); *Bank of New York*, 46 Berkeley St, W1X 6AA (7499 1234); *First National Bank of Chicago*, 1 Triton Sq, NW1 3FN (7388 3456); *Republic National Bank of New York*, 30 Monument St, EC3R 8NB (7860 3000); *Saudi-American Bank*, 65 Curzon St, Mayfair, W1Y 8NB (7355 4411).

Other Financial Services *American Equities Overseas (UK) Ltd* [stockbrokers], 16 Old Bond St, W1S 4PS (7495 7999); *American European Equities & Real Estate*, Northway House, 1379 High Rd, Totteridge, N20 9LP (8445 6600); *American Financial Corp Ltd* [Consultants], 9 Whitehall, Westminster, SW1A 2DD (7976 2266); *American Securities Ltd Partnership* [Financial Consultants], 1 Appold St, Moorgate, EC2A 2AA; *American World Finance Corp Ltd* [Financial Consultants], 37 Praed St, Bayswater, W2 1NR; *English Association of American Bond & Share-holdings* [Financial Consultants], 100 City Rd, Clerkenwell, EC1Y 2BP (7490 4946); *Euro American Management Consultancy*, 10-11 Lower John St, W1R 3PE (7437 5339); *Euro American Investment Ltd* [Financial Consultants], 6 Alfoxton Avenue, Seven Sisters, N15 3DD; *European American Research Ltd* [Financial Consultants], 43 Eagle St, Bloomsbury, WC1R 4AP (7404 2923); *European American Securities Inc*, [Stockbrokers], British Columbia House, 1 Regent St, Westminster, SW1Y 4NS (7468 7600); *European American Securities Inc*, 1 Regent St, SW1Y 4NS (7468 7600); *Second London American Trust plc* [Financial Consultants], 10 Park Place, Westminster, SW1A 1LP; *North American Financial Markets Ltd* [Investment Companies], 28 Wimpole St, W1M 7AD (7636 5238); *Anglo American Financial Corp Ltd*, [Consultants], Malcolm House, Empire Way, Wembley, HA9 0LW; *Anglo American Plc*, [FTSE 100], Head Office, 20 Carlton House Terrace, Westminster, SW1Y 5AP (7698 8500); *Phoenix Investments Ltd*, 99 Charterhouse St, Clerkenwell, EC1M 6AB (7287 3974).

EDUCATION *American College*, 110 Marylebone High St, W1M 3DB (7486 1772); *American Community School*, Hillingdon Court, 108 Vine La, Uxbridge UB10 0BE (01895 259771); *American School in London*, 2-8 Loudoun Rd, NW8 0NP (7449 1200); *American Institute For Foreign Study Ltd* [Tour Operators], 37 Queens Gate, South Kensington, SW7 5HR (7590 7474); *American University*, 97-101 Seven Sisters Rd, Holloway, N7 7QP (7263 2986); *British American College London*, Regents College, Inner Circle, Camden, NW1 4NS

(7487 7507); *British American Drama Academy*, Cecil Sharp House, 2 Regents Park Rd, Camden, NW1 7AY (7267 4428); *City University Of America (London Academic Centre)*, The Egyptian Ho, 170-173 Piccadilly, W1V 0JL (7491 9457); *Higher Education In Europe Ltd*, Education Agencies & Authorities, 10 York Terrace East, Camden, NW1 4PT (7935 5516); *International University Of America*, Temple Chambers, 3-7 Temple Ave, St Paul's, EC4Y 0HA (7627 8446); *Richmond, The American International University in London*, 16 Young St, Kensington W8 5EH (8332 9000, 7368 8488).

FREIGHT *North-American Van Lines*, [shipping & overseas removals], 15-16 Chestnut Way, Feltham, TW13 7DP (8844 2000); *Goynia America Shipping Lines*, 28-42 Banner St, Clerkenwell, EC1A 9HA (7600 4978).

GOVERNMENT *American Embassy*, 24 Grosvenor Sq, W1A 1AE (7499 9000).

HEALTH & BEAUTY *American Beauty Bar Ltd*, 41 Lowndes St, Westminster, SW1X 9HX (7245 6242); *American Counselling Centre*, 85 Wimpole St, W1M 8AJ (7935 1606); *American Cosmetic Surgery*, 111 Harley St, W1G 6AW (7487 4654); *American Nail Fashions*, 419 Coldharbour La, SW9 8LH (7738 6588); *American Nail Fashions*, 80 Peckham High St, SE15 5ED (7635 5967); *Anglo American Dental Group, The*, Salisbury Ho, Suite 1, 29 Finsbury Circus, Moorgate, EC2M 5QQ (7638 6600); *Black American Hair Centre*, 11 Salisbury Pavement, Dawes Rd, Fulham, SW6 7RE (7386 8932); *Diamond Nails*, 7 Chapel Market, N1 9EZ (7278 1012); *Star Nails*, 121 Mitcham Rd, SW17 9PE (8767 9888); *Top Nails*, 246 North End Rd, SW6 1NL (7381 4666); *Top Nails*, 51 Streatham Hill, SW2 4TS (8671 7006).

LANGUAGE English is the dominant language of the USA but many other languages are also spoken, of which Spanish is by far the most important.

LEGAL *Anglo-American Court Reporters Tennyson & Co*, 150 Minories, EC3N 1LS (7264 2088).

MEDIA & INFORMATION

General *Americas* [information services], 1a Salcott Rd, Battersea, SW11 6DQ (7223 4330); *British American Security Information Council*, The Leather Market, Weston St, Southwark, SE1 3ER (7407 2977).

Audiovisual *American Broadcasting Co*, 8 Carburton St, W1P 7DT (7637 9222); *American*

21

Telemedia Ltd, 2 Harbour Exchange Sq, Poplar, E14 9GE (7519 3000); *American Video Equipment Ltd*, [CCTV & Video Equipment], Millmarsh Ln, Enfield, EN3 7QG (8805 9323); *Anglo-American Recording Transfer Service*, 192 Castelnau, Barnes, SW13 9DH (8748 3479); *Anglo American Audio-Visual Services*, 22b Prince of Wales Mansions, Battersea, SW11 4BQ (7498 8645); *Voice of America*, 76 Shoe La, St Paul's, EC4A 3JB (7410 0960).

Music *American Recordings* [Record Company], 86 Turnham Green Terr, Chiswick, W4 1QN (8987 9123).

Telecom *America First*, Exchange Tower, 1 Harbour Exchange Square, Poplar, E14 9GB (7577 7575); *Anglo-American Communications Ltd*, 72 New Bond St, W1Y 9DD; *North American Gateway Ltd*, [Telecommunication Services], Devonshire House, 1 Devonshire St, W1N 2DR; *North American Gateway Ltd*, [Answering Services], 140 Kings Cross Rd, Bloomsbury, WC1X 9DS (7575 7500); *Pan American Crossing UK Ltd*, 200 Aldersgate St, Clerkenwell, EC1A 4HD.

Print *American Library Association* [Distribution], 3 Henrietta St, Holborn, WC2E 8LU (7240 0856); *American Trading Co Ltd* [Journalists], 16 Pall Mall, Westminster, SW1Y 5LU (7930 3088); *Chicago Tribune*, 169 Piccadilly, W1V 9DD (7499 8769); *Intercomtex Publishing Of America* [Books], 96A Old St, Clerkenwell, EC1V 9AY (7253 4674); *Essentially America* [Newspapers & Magazines], 18-20 Scrutton St, Moorgate, EC2A 4TG (7247 0537); *New York Times London Bureau*, 66 Buckingham Gate, SW1E 6AU (7799 5050); *Scientific American Newspapers & Magazines*, Thavies Inn House, 3-4 Holborn Circus, Clerkenwell, EC1N 2HB (7842 4343).

MOTORING *American Auto Services*, Station Rd, Hayes, UB3 4DD (8561 8387); *American Car Care Centre*, 57/65 Randells Rd, N1 0DJ (7278 9786); *American Car Care Services*, 57-65 Randells Rd, Kings Cross, Islington, N1 0DH (7278 9786); *American Car Spares*, Bigley, The Common, West Drayton, UB7 7HQ (01895 445196); *American Car Repairs*, 68 East Rd, Wimbledon, SW19 1AH (8544 9941); *American Car Imports*, 57 - 63 Coburg Rd, Wood Green, N22 6UB (8889 4545); *American Carwash Co, The*, 35 Great Eastern St, Moorgate, EC2A 3ER (7739 6345); *American Carwash Co, The*, 78-80 Pancras Rd, Camden, NW1 1UJ (7387 2832); *Heathrow Car Centre*, Sipson House, 611 Sipson Road, West Drayton, UB7 0JD (8897 3331); *Heathrow Car Centre*, Copse Hill Farm, Denham Rd, Uxbridge, UB9 5ER (01895 831351).

RECREATION

Dancing *Boots N Blisters American Line Dance Club*, PO Box 23880, London SE15 3WG (7732 7008); *Boots N Blisters American Line Dance Club*, St.Thomas Mores Social Club, 116a Lordship Lane, East Dulwich, SE22 8HD (8516 4844);

Golf *American Golf At Sunbury*, Charlton La, Shepperton, TW17 8QA (01932 771414); *American Golf Discount Centre*, 12-14 Ashbourne Parade,

Finchley Rd, Golders Green, NW11 0AD (8458 0297).

Pool *Riley's Snooker & American Pool Club*, 35-43 High St, Harrow, HA3 5DE (8863 3705); *Rileys Snooker & American Pool Club*, 236a High St, Hounslow, TW3 1HB (8814 1399); *Rileys Snooker & American Pool Club*, 4 Walworth Rd, Southwark, SE1 6SP (7703 0983); *Riley's American Pool & Snooker Club*, 638-640 Wandsworth Rd, South Lambeth, SW8 3JW (7498 0432); *Riley American Pool & Snooker Club*, 237 Lewisham High St, Lewisham, SE13 6NQ (8690 0726); *Rushey Green Snooker & American Pool Centre*, 96-102 Rushey Green, Catford, SE6 4HW (8314 1090); *Upton Park Snooker & American Pool Centre*, 358-362 Green St, Plaistow E13 9AP (8471 3638).

RELIGION *The American Church in London*, 79a Tottenham Court Rd, W1P 9HB (7580 2791).

RESTAURANTS
East Central *American Pie* [TA], 44 Clerkenwell Green, Clerkenwell, EC1R 0EB (7251 4111); *Fatboy's Diner*, 296 Bishopgate, EC2 (7375 2763); *Fatboy's Diner*, 23 Horner Square, Moorgate, EC2M 4QX (7375 2763).

South West 1 *American Steak House*, 170 Victoria St, Westminster, SW1E 5LB (7834 5860);*Biguns Ribs*, 1 Warwick Way, Westminster, SW1V 1RU (7834 7350); *T.G.I. Fridays*, 25-29 Coventry St, Haymarket, Westminster, SW1Y 7FG (7839 6262).

West 1 *American Burger* [TA], 455 Oxford St, W1R 1DB (7629 1603); *American Cafe Bistro* [TA], 455 Oxford St, W1R 1DB (7629 1602); *American Coffee Traders Ltd*, 86-88 Wardour St, W1V 3LF (7494 3225); *Classic Diners Of America Ltd* [TA], 7 Kenrick Place, W1H 3FF; *Ed's Easy Diner*, 12 Moor St, W1V 5LH (7439 1955); *Ed's Easy Diner*, Old Compton St, Soho W1 (7434 4439); *Ed's Easy Diner*, 38 Shaftesbury Avenue, W1V 7DD (7287 1951); *Great American Bagel Factory* [TA], 20 Charlotte St, W1P 1HJ (7631 0790); *Greigs*, 25, Bruton Pl, Mayfair W1X 7AB (7629-5613); *Hard Rock Café*, 150 Old Park Lane, W1Y 3LN (7629 0382); *Smollensky's on the Strand*, 105 Strand, WC2R 0AA (7497 2101); *Smollenskys Balloon*, 1 Dover St, W1X 3PJ (7491 1199); *Sports Café*, Head Office, Victory House, 99-101 Regent St, W1R 7HB (7494 1444); *Sports Café*, New Zealand Ho, 80 Haymarket, SW1Y 4TQ (7839 8300); *Sugar Reef*, 42-44 Great Windmill St, Soho W1 (7851 0800);

Zazoom, 3 New Burlington St, W1X 1FD (7287 1991).

West Central *All American Fried Chicken* [TA], 21 Charing Cross Rd, Holborn, WC2H 0ES (7839 5424); *Christopher's American Grill,* 18 Wellington St, Holborn, WC2E 7DD (7240 4222); *Detroit,* 35 Earlham St, Covent Garden, WC2 (7240 2662); *Great American Bagel Co,* 19a Odhams Walk, WC2H 9SA (7836 8191); *Great American Bagel Factory,* 18 Endell St, Holborn, WC2H 9BD (7836 7676); *Joe Allen,*13 Exeter St, Covent Garden WC2 (7836 0651); *Manhattan Exchange,* 450 Strand, Holborn, WC2R 0RG (7839 7980); *Maxwells Restaurants Ltd,* 9 King St, Holborn, WC2E 8HN (7379 6132); *Old Orleans,* 31 Wellington St, Holborn, WC2E 7DA (7497 2433); *Palmares T/A,* Jubilee Hall Market, Tavistock St, Holborn, WC2E 7PA (7379 0225); *Prospect Grill,* 4-6 Garrick St, Covent Garden WC2 (7379 0412); *T G I Fridays,* 6 Bedford St, Holborn, WC2E 9HZ (7379 0585).

Barnet *Ed's Easy Diner,* Unit 5 The Food Gallery, Brent Cross Shopping Centre, Hendon, NW4 3NB (8202 0999); *Exchange Bar Diner,* Finchley Leisure Complex, High Rd, North Finchley, N12 0AP (8343 9272); *Express Diner,* 54 Ballanerds Lane, Finchley Central, N3 2BU (8346 5592); *T.G.I Fridays*, Watford Way, Mill Hill, NW7 3JA (8203 9779).

Camden *Ed's Easy Diner,* 16 Hampstead High St, Hampstead, NW3 1PX (7431 4314); *Fat Sam's American Diner,* 156-158 Fortress Rd, Kentish Town, NW5 2HP (7419 9482); *Gaucho Grill* 64 Heath St, Hampstead, NW3 1DN (7431 8222); *Maxwells,* 76 Heath St, Hampstead, NW3 1DN (7794 5450); *Smollensky's,* 02 Centre, 255 Finchley Rd, NW3 (7431 5007); *Tootsies,* 196 Haverstock Hill, Hampstead, NW3 2AG. (8940 3349).

Croydon *American Fried Chicken T/A,* 75 Portland Rd, South Norwood, SE25 4UN (86541909).

Ealing *American Burger & Kebab Bar* [TA], 4 Crown St, Acton, W3 8SB (8896 3807); *Old Orleans,* 26-42 Bond St, Ealing, W5 5AA (8579 7413); *Starvin Marvins American Diner,* Western Avenue, Greenford, UB6 8XQ (8998 5132).

Enfield *American Kitchen T/A,* 63 Southbury Rd, Enfield, EN1 1PJ (8363 0895); *T.G.I. Fridays,* Great Cambridge Rd, Enfield, EN1 3RZ (8363 5200).

Hackney *Eastside Bar & Diner,* 578 Kingsland Rd, Hackney, E8 4AH (7923 7654); *Sweet Georgia Brown,* 155a Stoke Newington Church St, Hackney, N16 0UH (7241 3555).

Hammersmith & Fulham *Montana,* 125-129 Dawes Rd, Fulham SW6 (7385 9500).

Haringey *American Steakhouse Plc* [TA], 23 Turnpike Lane, Hornsey, N8 0EP; *Barbella American & Mexican Bar,* 1 Park Rd, Hornsey, N8 8TD (8348 5609); *Idaho,*13 North Hill, Highgate N6 (8341 6633).

Harrow *American Burger & Kebab House* [TA], 249 Preston Rd, Harrow, HA3 0PS (8908 5984);

American Burger & Kebab House [TA], 131a Wembley Park Dr, Wembley, HA9 8HQ (8903 3787); *Fatty Arbuckles,* 26 St Georges Shopping & Leisure Centre, St Ann's Rd, Harrow, HA1 1HS (8861 0007); *New American Fried Chicken* [TA], 317 Northolt Rd, Harrow, HA2 8JA (8930 0241).

Hillingdon *Woods Coffee Co,* 396 Long La, Uxbridge UB10 9PG (01895 253100).

Hounslow *American Take-Out* [TA], 267 Cromwell Rd, TW3 3QU (8570 0809); *American Dream* [TA], 33 St. Johns Rd, Isleworth, TW7 6NY (8560 0717); *Coyote Café,* 2 Fauconberg Rd, Chiswick W4 (8742 8545); *Fatty Arbuckles,* Browells Lane, Feltham, TW13 7LX (8890 8880); *Mr T's American Burgers* [TA], 173 Hanworth Rd, TW3 3TT (8577 3260).

Islington *American Coffee Traders Ltd* [café], 25a Upper St, Islington, N1 0PQ (77041944); *Shillibeers Brasserie Bar,* North Rd, Holloway, N7 9EF (7700 1858).

Kensington & Chelsea *American Cafe Bar Restaurant,* 7 Fulham Broadway, Fulham, SW6 1AA (7385 9474); *American Café, The,* Unit 21 Gloucester Arcade, Gloucester Road, South Kensington, SW7 4SF (7244 9585); *Cactus Blue,* 86 Fulham Rd, Chelsea SW3 (7823 7858); *Chicago Rib Shack, The,* 1 Raphael St, South Kensington, SW7 1DL (7581 5595); *Dakota,* 127 Ledbury Rd, Notting Hill Gate W11 2AQ (7792 9191); *Ed's Easy Diner,* 362 Kings Rd, Chelsea, SW3 5UZ (7352 1952); *Montana Restaurant & Lounge,* 125-129 Dawes Rd, Fulham, SW6 7EA (7385 9500); *New York New York,* 154 Warwick Rd, West Kensington W14 8PS (7371 1411); *Shoeless Joe's Bar Restaurant Club,* 555 Kings Rd, Fulham, SW6 2EB (7610 9346); *Texas Lone Star Saloon,*154 Gloucester Rd, South Kensington, SW7 (7370 5625); *Tootsies,* 107 Old Brompton Rd, South Kensington, SW7 3LE (7581 8942); *Tootsies,* 177 New Kings Rd., Fulham, SW6 4SW (7736 4023); *Tootsies,* 120 Holland Park Av., Notting Hill, W11 4UA (7229 8567).

Lambeth *Ewing's Classic American Bakers,* Unit 16, Sleaford St, Nine Elms, South Lambeth, SW8 5AB (7498 0550).

Newham *American Fried Chicken T/A,* 69 Plashet Grove, East Ham, E6 1AD (8552 6662); *Zar Zar's,* 405 High St, Stratford, E15 4QZ (8519 6449).

Redbridge *Herman's Bar & Restaurant,* 142 Herman Hill, South Woodford, E18 1QH (8532 2526); *Jailhouse Rock Restaurant,* 90 High Rd, South Woodford, E18 2NA (8518 8007).

Richmond *Canyon,* Tow Path, Riverside, Richmond TW10 6US (8948 2944); *Tootsies,* 147 Church Rd, Barnes, SW13 9HR (8748 3630).

Southwark *American Success Pizza Co* [TA], 43 York Rd, SE1 7NJ (7928 0808); *Arbuckles,* Mast Leisure Centre, Surrey Quays Rd, SE16 2XU (7232 1901).

Tower Hamlets *American Success Pizza Co,* 819-821 Commercial Rd, Poplar, E14 7HG (7515 1100); *Arkansas Cafe,* Unit 12, Old Spitalfields Market, E1 (7377 6999); *Babe Ruth's,* 172-176 The

Highway, Wapping, E1 (7481 8181); *Chili's Grill & Bar*, 2nd fl, Cabot Place East, Canary Wharf, E14 (7363 5678).

Waltham Forest *American Pizza* [TA], 293 High Rd, Leytonstone, Wanstead, E11 4HH (8532 8222).

Wandsworth *American Pizza & Pasta,* 173 Battersea High St, SW11 3JS (7585 1718); *American Pizza & Pasta* [TA], 173 Battersea High St, Battersea, SW11 3JS (7585 0885); *Dixie's,* 25 Battersea Rise, Battersea, SW11 1HG (7228 7984); *Palmares* [Pizza & Pasta] [TA] 40 Upper Richmond Rd, Putney, SW15 2RX (8875 1231).

Westminster *Ma Potters Chargrill,* 3rd fl, Whiteleys Shopping Centre, Queensway, Bayswater W2 4YN (7792 2318); *Minsky's New York Deli,* Jarvis International Regents Park, 18 Lodge Rd, St John's Wood NW8 7JT (7722 7722); *TGI Fridays,* 96-98 Bishops Bridge Rd, Bayswater, W2 5AA (7229 8600).

SHOPS

General *American Excess* [second-hand shop], 19a Buckingham Rd, Islington, N1 4DG (7241 1991); *American Paint Company* [art & craft materials], 4c Athelstane Mews, Finsbury Park, N4 3EH (7272 0171); *American Retro Ltd* [gift Shop], 35 Old Compton St, W1V 5PL (7734 3477); *American Retro* [fashion accessories], 67-74 Saffron Hill, Clerkenwell, EC1N 8QX (7405 3135); *North American Bear Co* [Toys & Games], 4a Spenston Mews, Ladbroke Grove, W10 6HX (7706 1138, 8960 7744).

Clothing *American Active Wear Corp Ltd,* Sidney Smith Buildings, 38 Kings Rd, Chelsea, SW3 4UD (7584 2123); *American Classics,* 20 Endell St, WC2H 9BD (7831 1210); *American Classics,* 398-400 Kings Rd, SW10 0LJ (7352 2853); *American Classics,* 20 Endell St, Holborn, WC2H 9BD (7831 1210); *American Classics,* 398-400 Kings Rd, West Brompton, SW10 0LJ (7352 2853); *American Collections UK Ltd,* 41 Oldhill St, Stoke Newington, N16 6LR (8806 0702); *American Connection Ltd,* 139a Fonthill Rd, Finsbury Park, N4 3HF (7281 9111); *American Fashions* [clothing & fabrics], 41 Oldhill St, Stoke Newington, N16 6LR (8806 0702); *American Influence Ltd,* 75 Commercial Rd, Whitechapel, E1 1RD (7377 0303); *American Pie Ltd* [menswear], 200 Chiswick High Rd, Chiswick, W4 1PD (8995 1942); *American Pie Ltd* [menswear], 15 The Broadway, Ealing, W5 2NH (8933 3377); *American Gear,* 131 Whitechapel Rd, Whitechapel, E1 1DT (7247 6692); *J Simons,* 2 Russell St, WC2 (7379 7353); *Native American Trading Post,*

[second-hand shop], 40 Middle Yard, Camden Lock Place, Camden, NW1 8AF (7284 2089).

SPECIAL *American Appliance Centre Ltd,* 5 The Dencora Centre, Dundee Way, Enfield, EN3 7SX (8443 9999); *American Appraisal Ltd* [valuers], 65-66 Queen St, St Paul's, EC4R 1EB (7329 1776); *American Big Chauffeur,* 10b Westwood Hill, Sydenham, SE26 6QR (8244 5324); *American Limo Scene,* 5 Shirehall Park, Hendon, NW4 2QJ (8556 5718); *American Limousine Service,* 19 Honinster Pl, Stanmore, HA7 2EL (8909 9609) (8907 7779); *American Percussion* [musical instruments], 120 Bermondsey St, SE1 3TX (7403 3200); *American Peanut Council,* Grosvenor Gdns Ho, Grosvenor Gdns, SW1W 0BS (7828 0838); *American Stretch Limousine Co, The,* 57 Coburg Rd, Wood Green, N22 6UB (8889 4848); *Au Pair In America,* 37 Queens Gate, South Kensington, SW7 5HR (7581 7322); *Rock Garden,* 6-7 The Piazza, Holborn, WC2E 8HA (7836 4052); *North American Bear Co* [Toys & Games], 4a Scampston Mews, Ladbroke Grove, W10 6HX; *American Party Store* [Party Goods & Novelties], 16 Woodstock St, W1R 1HE (7493 2678).

TRANSLATION *American Pie,* 3 Caledonian Rd, N1 9DX (7278 9490).

TRAVEL *1st American Travel,* 198 Weir Rd, Balham, SW12 0NW (8673 8888); *Air America ,* 4 Buckingham Parade, The Broadway, Stanmore, HA7 4EB (8385 9008); *America Plus Ltd ,* 508 Linen Hall, 162 Regent St, W1R 5TB (7470 0707); *America West* [Airline], Cargo Service Centre, Sirius Ho, Bedfont Rd, Staines, TW19 7NL (01784 266210); *American & Latin Travel Ltd,* 198 Weir Rd, SW12 0NW (8673 8888); *American Airlines Inc,* 23-59 Staines Rd, Hounslow, TW3 3HE (8572 5555); *American Dream Tour Operators, The* [ski], Station Chambers, High St North, East Ham, E6 1JE (8552 1201); *American Express Travel Service,* 78 Brompton Rd, Knightsbridge, Chelsea, SW3 1ER (7584 6182); *American Express Travel Service,* Epworth House, 25 City Rd, Clerkenwell, EC1Y 1AS (7638 7244); *American Passenger Consolidates,* 28 Davies St, W1Y 1LG (7499 0743); *American Travel,* 19 Lawn Rd, Hampstead, NW3 2YR (7722 7202); *American Travel,* 598 Green Lanes, Palmers Green, N13 5RY (7722 0202); *Anglo American Travel Ltd,* Tour Guides & Sightseeing, 35 Spencer Rd, Raynes Park, SW20 0QN (8947 3416); *Boston-Gateway to New England* [tourist information], 421a Finchley Rd, NW3 6HJ (7431 3434); *Camp America,* 37a Queens Gate, South Kensington, SW7 5HR (7581 7373); *Daytona Beach C & V B Tourist Information,* 121 Gloucester Pl, W1H 3PJ (7935 7756); *Delaware Tourism,* Garden Studios, 11-15 Betterton St, WC2H 9BP (7470 8802); *Fort Lauderdale Visitors' Bureau,* Roebuck Ho, Palace St, SW1E 5BA (7630 9442); *Great Lakes of North America,* 110 St. Martins La, Holborn, WC2N 4DY (7379 7526); *Holland America Line,* 77-79 Great Eastern St, Moorgate, EC2A 3HU (7613 3300); *Kentucky Tourism,* Garden Studios, 11-15 Betterton St, WC2H 9BP (7470 8804);

Kentucky Tourist Information, Molasses Ho, Plantation Wharf, Battersea SW11 3TN (7228 0782); *Key To America* , 21-47 High St, Feltham, TW15 2UW (01784 248777); *Key To America,* 79 Brent St, Hendon, NW4 2EA (8202 2196); *New York Travel Advisory Bureau,* 29 Elsham Rd, West Kensington W14 8HB (7610 4982); *New York City Visitor Information Centre,* 33-34 Carnaby St, W1F 7DW (7437 8300); *North America Travel Service,* 243 Kensington High St, Kensington, W8 6SA (7938 3737); *Pennsylvania Tourism,* Garden Studios, 11-15 Betterton St, WC2H 9BP (7470 8801); *West Virginia Tourism Office,* Molasses Ho, Plantation Wharf, Battersea SW11 3TN (7978 5822).

Amerindian

Amerindian refers to the indigenous peoples of the Americas and their languages, particularly those of Central and South America. Such people and their languages are poorly represented in London but include *Guarani*, *Maya*, and *Quechua*.

Amharic

EDUCATION Mother-tongue education for children in Amharic is available in several places in London; see <www.resourceunit.com> for details. For adults, courses in Amharic are available at *SOAS Language Centre* (7898 4888).

LANGUAGE *Amharic* is a Semitic language with official status in Ethiopia. It is written in the Ethiopic semi-syllabic script. The *Multilingual Capital* (2000) survey reported that there were 431 Amharic-speaking schoolchildren in London of whom the highest proportion lived in the adjoining boroughs of Kensington & Chelsea and Westminster. The main locations of Amharic-speakers in London are shown on Map 5 at <www.global-london.com/gallery>.

RELIGION Christian services in Amharic are held at *St Vedast Church,* 4 Foster Ct, EC2 (7606 3998).

Anaang

Anaang is a Benuic language, closely related to *Efik* and *Ibibio,* spoken in Nigeria. The *Multilingual Capital* (2000) survey reported *Anaang*-speakers only in the borough of Southwark.

Anatolian

Anatolia refers to the main, Asian part of Turkey (and thus excludes the smaller European part of the country where the city of Istanbul is situated). All organizations and services whose names include the words Anatolia or Anatolian (or a variant of these) are listed under *Turkish.*

Andorran

BUSINESS *Andorran Trade Delegation,* 63 Westover Rd, SW18 2RF (8874 4806).

GOVERNMENT *Andorran Delegation,* 63 Westover Rd, SW18 2RF (8874 4806).

LANGUAGES *Catalan* is the official language of Andorra but both *Spanish* and *French* are also spoken there.

RELIGION Most Andorrans are Roman Catholics.

TRAVEL *Andorra Tourist Delegation,* 63 Westover Rd, SW18 2RF (8874 4806).

Angolan

ASSOCIATIONS *Angolan Community Association,* Room 8, Selby Centre, Selby Rd, N17 8JL (8885 1666); *Organisation of the Angolan community in the UK,* Bond Way Commercial Centre, Unit 415, 71 Bond Way, SW8 1SQ (75871679) and Christ Church, Mowll St, SW9 6DF.

BUSINESS *Hull Blyth (Angola) Ltd,* Coldbath Sq, EC1R 5HL (7696 9688).

GOVERNMENT *Embassy of the Republic of Angola,* 22 Dorset St, W1U 6QY (7486 7747).

LANGUAGES The overwhelming majority of Angolans speaks one of five Bantuic languages: Umbundu (38%), Kimbundu (27%), *Kikongo* (12%), Cilunda/Cokwe (9%) and Ciluimbi (8%). (All these figures are estimates given by Mann & Dalby 1987.) Portuguese is the official language and is widely known as a second language.

MEDIA & INFORMATION *Angola News,* c/o Angolan Embassy, 98 Park Lane, W1Y 3JA (7495 1752).

SPECIAL *Mozambique-Angola Committee,* 25 Endymion Rd, N4 1EE, (8348 8463).

TRAVEL *TAAG Angolan Airlines,* 200 Buckingham Palace Rd, SW1W 9TA (7707 4580).

WELFARE *Angolan Refugee Project,* William Wallace Community Centre, Greenleaf Rd E17 6QQ (8223 0818).

Anguillan

GOVERNMENT Anguilla is administered as an overseas territory of the UK.

TRAVEL *Anguilla Tourist Office,* 3 Epirus Mansions, Epirus Rd, Fulham SW6 7UJ (7937 7725).

Antiguan

GOVERNMENT *Antigua and Barbuda High Commission,* 15 Thayer St, W1U 3JU (7486 7073).

LANGUAGES Antiguans speak English, the official language, and Antiguan Creole English.

TRAVEL *Antigua & Barbuda Tourist Office,* 15 Thayer St, W1M 5LD (7486 7073).

Anyi

LANGUAGE *Anyi* is an Aframic language of the Ivory Coast. Although not mentioned in the *Multilingual Capital* (2000) survey, the presence of a few *Anyi*-speaking schoolchildren in Lambeth has been reported within the past decade.

Arab

Arab is the word generally used to designate the Arab peoples and their culture but both *Arabic* and *Arabian* are occasionally used in this sense so entries under these headings should also be consulted. (*Arabic* is for the most part restricted to the **Arabic** language. In modern usage, *Arabian* is sometimes an abbreviation of **Saudi Arabian**.)

ACCOMMODATION *Arab Property Management Ltd,* 21 Gloucester Pl, W1U 3PB (7935 7725); *Arab Trading and Investment Co. Ltd,* 136 George St, W1H 5LD (7724 1656) [estate agents]; *Babylon Estate Agents,* 84 Queensway, W2 (7727 6465).

ARTS & CULTURE *Kufa Gallery,* 26 Westbourne Grove, W2 5RH (7229 1928); *Mathaf Gallery Ltd,* 24 Motcomb St, SW1X 8JU (7235 0010).

ASSOCIATIONS *Arab Club of Britain,* P O Box 2101, W13 8BT (8997 0541); *Arab Community Association in Brent,* 116 Salmon St, NW9 8NL (8205 2190); *Arab-British Centre Ltd,* 21 Collingham Rd, SW5 0NU (7373 8414); *Arab Club of Great Britain,* P O Box 2101, West Ealing, W13 8BT (8997 0541); *Arab Women's Association,* 211 Linen Hall, 162-168 Regent St, W1B 5TG (7287 4606); *Friends of the Arab League,* P O Box 2315, London W1A (01895 613459); *Syrian Arab Association,* 8 Comeragh Rd, W14 9HP (7381 9788).

BUSINESS

Banking: *Arab African International Bank,* 19 Berkeley St, W1J 8DZ (7495 4881); *A r a b Bangladesh Bank Ltd,* Unit 1.2.1, 75 Whitechapel Rd, E1 1DU (7426 0723); *Arab Bank plc,* 118 Kensington High St, W8 7RL (7937 3547); *Arab Bank plc,* 13-15 Moorgate, EC2R 6AD (7315 8500); *Arab Bank plc,* 131 Park La, W1K 7AE (7408 1505); *Arab Bankers Association,* 27 Berkeley Sq, W1J 6EL (7499 6090); *Arab Banking Corporation,* Arab Banking Corporation House, 1-5 Moorgate, EC2R 6AB (7726 4599); *Arab International Trust Co. Ltd,* 6 Cork St, W1S 3LJ (7434 4141); *Arab National Bank,* 47 Seymour St, W1H 7HT (7878 5300); *British Arab Commercial Bank Ltd,* 8-10 Mansion House Pl, EC4N 8BJ *and* 30 Gresham St, EC2V 7LP (7648 7777).

Shipping: *United Arab Chartering Ltd,* Challenger House, 42 Adler St, E1 1EN (7377 5200); *United Arab Shipping Co,* Cardinal Court, 23 Thomas More St, E1 9YY (7369 6700).

Other: *Al Afiya Foods Ltd,* Unit 11, Westway Industrial Centre, 69 St Mark's Rd, W10 6JG (8969 8562); *Arab British Chamber of Commerce,* 6 Belgrave Sq, SW1X 8PH (7235 4363); *Arab Cargo Co Ltd,* 280B Earls Court Rd, SW5 9AS (7373 5018); *Arab Finance Focus Ltd,* 2 London Wall Buildings, EC2M 5PP; *Arab Finance International,* 83 Monega Rd, Forest Gate, E7 8EN; *Arab Investments & Trading Co,* 136-138 George St, W1H 5LD (7724 1656); *Arab Pan American Overseas Investments,* 14 Tiller Rd, E14 8PX (7345 5020); *Arab-world Internet Ltd,* 4 Wellington Rd, NW8 9SP.

EDUCATION *Arab Cultural Foundation,* Flat 24 Princes Court, 88 Brompton Rd, SW3 1ES; *Arab Research Centre,* 76 Notting Hill Gate, W11 3HP (7221 2425); *Centre for Arab and Iranian Studies,* 5 Stratham St, WC1A 1JB (7637 9639); *London Centre Of Arab Studies Ltd,* 63 Gt Cumberland Pl, W1H 7LJ (7724 5324).

FREIGHT *Gulf Arab Express,* 280b Earls Court Rd, SW5 9AS (7373 1034).

HEALTH & BEAUTY *Ten out of Ten Barber,* 7 Bell St, NW1 (7723 4009).

LANGUAGE See **Arabic**.

LEGAL *Arab Lawyers Association,* 28 Lings Coppice, SE21 8SY (8670 3698).

MEDIA & INFORMATION *Arab News,* 184 High Holborn, WC1V 7AP (7831 8181); *Arab News Network Ltd,* 14-17 Wells Mews, W1T 3HF (7323 9920); *League of Arab States Information Office,* 52 Green St, W1K 6RH (7629 0044); *Maghreb Arab Press,* 35 Westminster Bridge Rd, SE1 7JB [news agency] (7401 8146); *Al Arab Publishing House Ltd,* 159 Acre Lane, SW2 5UA.

SPECIAL *Arab League Office,* 52 Green St, W1K 6RH (7629 0732); *Council for the Advancement of*

Arab-British Understanding, 21 Collingham Rd, SW5 0NU (3737 8414).

TRAVEL *Arab Tours Ltd,* 60 Marylebone La, W1U 2NU (7935 3273); *Syrian Arab Airlines,* Birkett Ho, 27 Albemarle St, W1S 4BJ (7493 2851).

WELFARE *Arab National Council against Addiction of Narcotics,* 1 Thorp Close, W10 5XL (8969 2220).

Arabian

See also **Arab, Arabic,** and **Saudi Arabian.**

BUSINESS *Arabian Indonesian Corporation,* 37 Marylebone High St, W1M 3AB (7486 7577); *Arabian Oil Co Ltd* [London office], 61 Brook St, W1Y 2HN (7499 6438); *South Arabian Securities (UK) Ltd,* 5-7 Luke St, EC2A 4PX.

EDUCATION *Society for Arabian Studies,* c/o British Academy, 10 Carlton House Terrace, SW1Y 5AH (01372 842788).

EMPLOYMENT *Arabian Careers Ltd* [employment agency], 7th fl, Berkeley Square Ho, Berkeley Sq, W1X 6LS (7495 3285); *Arabian Careers Ltd* [employment agency], 115 Shaftesbury Ave, WC2H 8AD (7379 7877).

FREIGHT *Trans Arabian Air Transport* [air freight], 103 Mount St, W1Y 5HE (7495 6688).

SHOPS *Arabian Oud,* 439 Oxford St, W1.

Arabic

Although modern usage generally applies **Arabic** only to the dominant language of the Arab peoples, it is occasionally employed in other contexts where **Arab** would generally be preferred, as indicated by several of the entries below.

ASSOCIATIONS *Arabic Group in Hounslow,* 12 School Rd, Hounslow, TW3 1QZ (8577 3226).

BUSINESS *Arabic Trading & Investment,* 136-138 George St, W1H 5LD (7724 9133).

EDUCATION There are some 45 places in London which offer mother tongue education in Arabic. Visit <www.resourceunit.com> for full details.

Arabic classes for adults are available at *SOAS Language Centre* (7898 4888), the *University of Westminster* (7911 5000 x4901), and many other places in London. See *Floodlight* or visit its website at <www.floodlight.co.uk> for full details. Other relevant educational organisations are: *Arab-British Chamber of* Commerce (7235 4363); *Arabic*

Language Centre, 19 New Quebec St, Marble Arch W1H 7DG (7723 4202); *Arabic Tutorial Centre,* Marqueen Ct, Kensington Church St, W8 4DQ (7376 9991); *Key Languages,* Douglas Ho, 16-18 Douglas St, SW1P 4PB (7630 6113).

LANGUAGE **Arabic** is ranked 6th in the world with 200m first-language speakers (250m including competent second-language speakers). However, while there exists a "modern standard Arabic" language with a common standard written form from Morocco to the Persian Gulf, modern colloquial Arabic differs very considerably from one place to another, to the extent that several different but related spoken Arabic languages might be recognised. Particularly important among these are Maghrebi ("western colloquial Arabic" of Morocco, Algeria and Tunisia) and Mashriqi ("eastern colloquial Arabic", spoken from Egypt to the Persian Gulf). Nevertheless, most Arabic-speakers seem disposed to regard all varieties of Arabic as forms of one language, a view probably influenced by the existence of a common written standard form of Arabic.

Arabic is a **Semitic** language written in its own consonantal script. (The same script is also used, with some modifications, for a number of non-semitic languages such as Farsi and Urdu.) The *Multilingual Capital* (2000) survey found that there were 11,023 pupils in London whose first language was Arabic. The borough with the largest number of Arabic-speaking children is Westminster (1,666). Maps showing the distribution of Arabic speakers across London (Map 6) and within the City of Westminster (Map 7) can be viewed at <www.global-london.com/gallery>.

MEDIA & INFORMATION *Al Ahram International (Newspapers),* 203-209 North Gower St, NW1 2NJ (7388 1155); *Al Hawadeth UK Ltd* [magazine], 183-185 Askew Rd, W12 (8740 4500); *Al Hayat Newspaper,* 66 Hammersmith Rd, W14 8YT (7602 9988); *Al Jamilla,* 184 High Holborn, WC1V 7AP (7831 8181); *Al Majallah* [weekly magazine], 184 High Holborn, WC1V 7AP (7831 8181); *Al Quds Al Arabi,* 164-166 King St, W6 0QU (8741 8008) [daily newspaper]; *Al Arab Newspaper,* 159 Acre La, SW2 5UA (7272 9381); *Arabic Centre,* 37 Edgware Rd, W2 2JE (7706 1717) [newspapers]; *Arrajul,* 184 High Holborn, WC1V 7AP (7831 8181) [magazine]; *Asharq Al Awsat,* 184 High Holborn, WC1V 7AP (7831 8181) [newspaper & magazine]; *BBC Arabic Service,* P O Box 76, Bush Ho, Aldwych, WC2B 4PH; *Hiya,* 184 High Holborn, WC1V 7AP (7831 8181) [magazine]; *Sayidaty,* 184 High Holborn, WC1V 7AP (7831 8181) [magazine]; *Spectrum Radio,* International Radio Centre, 4 Ingate Pl, SW8 3NS (7627 4433) [broadcasting in Arabic 21.00 - 23.00 daily].

SHOPS

Bookshops *Agape Arabic Christian Centre,* 11 Porchester Rd, W2 5DP (7221 4355); *Al-Hoda,* 76 Charing Cross Rd, WC2H 0BB (7240 8381); *Al Kitab,* 128c London Rd, Kingston KT2 6QJ (8549

4479); *Al Noor,* 82 Park Rd, NW1 4SH (7723 5414); *Al Saqi Books,* 26 Westbourne Grove, W2 5RH (7229 8543, fax 7229 7492); *Dar al Dawa,* 97 Westbourne Grove, W2 (7221 6256) [Arabic, Islam, Middle East history]; *Dar Al Dawa,* 97 Westbourne Grove, W2 4UW (7221 6256); *Dar Al Hikma,* 88 Chaltin St, NW1 (7383 4037); *Dar Al-Taqwa,* 7a Melcombe St, NW1 6AE (7935 6385, fax 7224 3894).

Other shops *Arabic Sweet Centre,* 45 Churchfield Rd, W3 6AY (8993 4830); *Mayal Arabic Videos and Music,* 46 Westbourne Grove, W2 5SH (7243 8642); *Trehantiri Greek and Arabic Music,* 365-367 Green Lanes, N4 1DY (8802 6530) [record shop].

TRANSLATION *Acuda,* 42-44 Carter La, EC4V 5EA (7236 3377); *A Harb Arabic Translators,* Hanovia House, 28-29 Eastman Rd, W3 7YG (8743 4243); *All Languages Ltd,* Nelson Ho, 362-364 Old St, EC1V 9LT (7739 6641); *Anglo Arabic Translation Services,* 66 Devonshire Rd, Ealing W5 4TP (8566 1173); *APT Transtelex plc,* 585a Fulham Rd, SW6 5UA (7381 0967); *Arabic Advertising & Publishing Co. Ltd,* 1 Hyde Park Gate, SW7 5XE (7584 7000); *Arabic Graphics,* 148-150 Curtain Rd, EC2A 3AT (7739 8000); *Arabic Interpreting & Translating,* 61 Chippenham Rd, W9 2AB (7286 7351); *Arab Legal & Technical Translations,* 74 Maida Vale, W9 5FS (8993 3010); *Arabic Linguistic Services,* 459 Finchley Rd, NW3 6HN (7431 1815); *Arabic Translation Centre,* 4 Old Oak Common La, W3 7EJ (8743 9900); *Arabic Word Processing & Translation Services,* 29 Wendover Court, Western Ave, W3 0TG (8993 6770); *Aradco VSI Ltd,* 132 Cleveland St, W1P 6AB (7692 7000); *Associated Translators,* Macmillan Ho, 96 Kensington High St, W8 4SG (7937 7733); *Caspian Iranian-Arabic Interpreting Services,* 14 Haven Green, W5 2UU (8998 8236); *Jarrar Translations,* 74 Springfield Ave, SW20 9JU (8542 1421); *Kern (UK) Ltd,* 45-46 New Ho, 67-68 Hatton Garden, EC1N 8JY (7831 5600); *Lotus Arab Graphic Ltd,* 245a Acton La, NW10 7NR (8961 2888); *N Mikail,* 10 Barley Mow Passage, W4 4PH (8747 1486); *Oryx (Arabic Graphics),* Trinity House Business Centre, Heather Park Drive, Wembley, HA0 1SU (8795 1727).

WELFARE *Enfield Arab Community Welfare Association,* c/o Mr A Kaptan, PO Box 424, Enfield EN3 7ZN (07940 735056) [languages: Arabic, English].

Aramaic

EDUCATION Mother-tongue education for children in Aramaic is available in Ealing; see <www.resourceunit.com> for details.

LANGUAGE *Aramaic* (also called *Assyrian;* see separate entry below*)* is a **Semitic** language spoken in Palestine, Syria, Lebanon, Iran, Iraq, Turkey and Azerbaijan. (The choice between the names Assyrian and Aramaic among respondents remains to be investigated but may perhaps be related to religious affiliation.) Aramaic has long been, and continues to be, written in a number of consonantal scripts. The *Multilingual Capital* (2000) survey recorded the presence of 263 Aramaic-speaking London schoolchildren, almost all of whom lived in Ealing (246).

Argentinian

ARTS *Academia Nacional del Tango (UK) Ltd,* "Las Estrellas", 2-3 Inverness Mews, W2 3JQ (7221 5038).

ASSOCIATIONS *Anglo Argentine Society,* 2 Belgrave Sq, SW1X 8PJ (7235 9505).

BUSINESS *Banco de la Nacion Argentina,* Longbow Ho, 14-20 Chiswell St, EC1Y 4TD (7588 2738), *British Argentine Chamber of Commerce,* 2 Belgrave Sq, SW1X 8PJ (7245 6661).

GOVERNMENT *Argentine Embassy,* 65 Brook St, W1K 4HX (7318 1300), *Argentine Embassy,* 27 Three Kings Yard, W1Y 1FL (7318 1330).

LANGUAGE The official and principal language of Argentina is *Spanish*.

RECREATION *Academia Nacional del Tango (UK) Ltd.,*"Las Estrellas", 2-3 Inverness Mews, W2 3JQ (7221 5038).

RESTAURANTS

Camden *Gaucho Grill,* 64 Heath St, Hampstead, NW3 (7431 8222).

Wandsworth *La Pampa Grill,* 4 Northcote Rd, SW11 (7924 1167).

SPECIAL *Wines of Argentina,* 58 Jermyn St, SW1Y 6LX (7915 4799).

TRAVEL *Aerolineas Argentinas,* 54 Conduit St, W1S 2YY (7494 1001); *LAPA (Argentina),* 200 Buckingham Palace Rd, SW1W (7707 4576).

Armenian

BUSINESS *International Armenian Community Finance Ltd,* Kemp Ho, 152-160 City Rd, EC1V 2HH.

EDUCATION Mother-tongue education for children in **Armenian** is available in Acton; see <www.resourceunit.com> for details.

Training for adults in **Armenian** is available at *Key Languages,* Douglas Ho, 16-18 Douglas St, SW1P 4PB (7630 6113).

GOVERNMENT *Embassy of the Republic of Armenia,* 25a Cheniston Gdns, W8 6TG (7938 5435).

LANGUAGE *Armenian* is an Indo-European language but is not closely related to any other language. It is spoken mainly in Armenia and Azerbaijan and written in its own (non-Roman) alphabet. There are about 4m speakers in all. The *Multilingual Capital* (2000) survey recorded the presence of 189 Armenian-speaking pupils of whom 83 lived in the borough of Ealing.

RELIGION Most Armenians are Armenian Orthodox Christians. Religious facilities for them in London include *St Sarkis Armenian Church,* Iverna Gdns, W8 6TP (7937 0152), and *St Peters Armenian Church,* Cranley Gdns, South Kensington SW7 3BB (7373 3565).

RESTAURANTS

Westminster *Erebuni Armenia Russian Restaurant,* 36 Lancaster Gate, W2 3NA (7402 6067).

TRANSLATION *Associated Translators,* Macmillan Ho, 96 Kensington High St, W8 4SG (7937 7733).

TRAVEL *Armenian Airlines,* 7 Buckingham Gate, SW1E 6JP (7939 1210).

WELFARE *Armenian Information and Advice Centre,* Hayashen, 105a Mill Hill Rd, W3 8JF (8992 4621); *Life-aid Armenia Ltd,* 8 Baker St, W1M 1DA.

Ashanti

The **Ashanti** are one of the **Akan** peoples of Ghana but the Ashanti kingdom was formerly separately administered as a British protectorate. The **Ashanti** language is today generally considered to be a variety of **Twi**, itself one of the **Akan** group of languages.

BUSINESS *Ashanti Goldfields Co. Ltd,* 3rd fl, Roman Ho, Wood St EC2Y 5HQ (7256 9938).

EDUCATION See **Twi.**

HEALTH & BEAUTY *Ashanti Hair Salon,* 161 Hoe St, Walthamstow E17 3AL (8925 1133).

LANGUAGE see **Akan**

RECREATION *Ashanti Shotokan Karate International,* 46 Broxholm Rd, SE27 0LZ (8761 2218).

Asian

While the word **Asian** properly applies to the whole continent of Asia, it is frequently restricted, in some contexts in current British usage, to the peoples and cultures of the Indian subcontinent, as reflected in the following entries.

ARTS *Art Asia,* 14 Brocklebank Industrial Estate, Brocklebank Rd, SE7 7SX (8858 4855); *Asia Contemporary Art,* 49 Lambs Conduit St, Bloomsbury, WC1N 3NG (7611 5252); *Asian Art,* 37 Bury St, SW1Y 6AU (7839 3414); *Asian Art Gallery,* Dalmeny Ct, 8 Duke St, SW1Y 6BN (7930 0204); *Asian Art in London,* 32 Dover St, W1S 4NF (7499 2215); *Asian Music Circuit Ltd,* Ground fl, Unit E33-34, Warple Way, W3 0RX (8742 9911); *Beagle*

Gallery & Asian Antiques, 303 Westbourne Grove, W11 2QA (7229 9524); *Circle of Inner Asian Art,* Department of Art & Archaeology, SOAS, Thornhaugh St, Russell Sq, WC1H 0XG (7691 3417); *Greenwich Asian Women's Art Group,* Burrage Rd, SE18 7JZ (8317 4904); *John Siudmak Asian Art,* 15 Mount St, W1K 2RB (7493 7195); *Rau (Central Asian Ethno Graphic),* 36 Islington Green, N1 8DU (7359 5337).

ASSOCIATIONS *Royal Asiatic Society,* 60 Queens Gdns, Bayswater, W2 3AF (7724 4742); *Royal Society for Asian Affairs,* 2 Belgrave Sq, SW1X 8PJ (7235 5122).

BUSINESS

Banking *Bank of East Asia,* 75 Shaftesbury Ave, W1D 5BB (7734 3434).

Computing *Euro Asia Systems Ltd,* 301-303 Kennington La, SE11 5RQ (7820 7718).

Import/Export *Business Development Asia plc,* 10 Crown Pl, EC2A 4BT (7655 3660); *Dan Asia Services,* 295-297 High Rd, Leytonstone E11 4HH (8558 6545); *London Asiatic Import Export,* 241 Maida Vale, W9 1QJ (7372 7829); *Temple Asian Imports Ltd,* 18 Temple Cl, Wadley Rd, Leytonstone E11 1JN (01279 306575).

Insurance *Asia Insurance Brokers Ltd,* 64-66 Mark La, EC3R 7HS (7488 4881).

Marketing *Access Asia,* 19 Bramford Ct, High St, Southgate N14 6LA (8350 7150); *Asian Pages UK Ltd,* 548 Barking Rd, Greengate E13 9JU (8552 9891); *Mail Asia,* Unit 41, Waterside Trading Centre, Trumpers Way, W7 2QD (8893 6863).

Oil *Euro Asian Oil UK Ltd,* 1-11 Hay Hill, W1J 6DH (7491 7424).

Textiles *Asia Textile,* 2nd fl, 14-15 D'Arblay St, W1F 8DZ (7494 4594).

EDUCATION *Central Asia Research Forum,* SOAS, Thornhaugh St, Russell Sq, WC1H 0XG (7898 4343).

FREIGHT *Asia Pacific Express Ltd,* London Heathrow Airport, TW6 3JJ (8754 8559).

LEGAL *African, Caribbean and Asian Lawyers Group,* 100-113 Chancery La, Holborn WC2A 1PL.

MEDIA & INFORMATION *Asian Biz,* 4 Outram Rd, E6 1JR (8471 4210) [internet services]; *Asian Marketing Group Ltd,* 1 Silex St, SE1 0DW [publishers] (7928 1234); *Asian on Line plc,* Crown Ho, North Circular Rd, NW10 7PN [internet services] (8965 6333); *Asian Sky,* Crown Ho, North Circular Rd, NW10 7PN (8838 1566); *Asian Xpress,* Bow House Business Centre, Bow Rd, E3 2SE (8981 6333); *Concept Asian Media,* Clerkenwell Ho, 67 Clerkenwell Rd, EC1R 5BL (7693 8400); *Image Asia Photo Video* 359 Roman Rd, Bow E3 5QR (8983 3311); *Sony Entertainment TV Asia,* 34 Fouberts Pl, W1F 7PX (7534 7575); *Trans Asia Ltd,* 235a High St North, East Ham London E6 1JG (8470 1068).

RECREATION *Asian Music Circuit Ltd,* Ground fl, Unit E33-34, Warple Way, W3 0RX (8742 9911).

RELIGION *Asian Chaplaincy,* St Augustine's Church, Fulham Palace Rd, W6 8AU (8563 9102);

Asian Funeral Directors, Ealing Rd, Wembley HA0 (8900 9252).

RESTAURANTS

East Central *Cicada,*132-136 St John St, Clerkenwell, EC1 (7608 1550); *Suan Neo,* 31 Broadgate Circle, EC2 (7256 5045).

West 1 *Noho,* 32 Charlotte St, Fitzrovia, W1 (7636 4445); *Rasa W1,* 16 Dering St, Mayfair W1 (7629 1346).

West Central *Asia de Cuba* [Asian/Cuban fusion], 45 St Martins La, WC2N 4HX (7300 5588).

Brent *Asian T/A,* 43 Kilburn High Rd, NW6 5SB (7328 7132).

Camden *Cafe Bintang*, 93 Kentish Town Rd, NW1 (7813 3393); *Lemongrass,* 243 Royal College St, NW1 (7284 1116).

Greenwich *Curry Asia Tandoori,* 40 Thomas St, SE18 6HT (8855 2951).

Hackney *Anglo-Asian Tandoori*, 60-62 Stoke Newington Church St, N16 0NB (7254 3633); *Rasa,* 55 Stoke Newington, N16 (7249 0344).

Haringey *Asia Spice,* 1 Queens Parade, Green Lanes, N8 0RD (8340 4797).

Kensington & Chelsea *New Asia,* 7 Hogarth Pl, SW5 0QT (7373 0112).

Merton *Cinnamon*, 10 Merton Park Parade, Kingston Rd, SW19 (8540 1717).

Tower Hamlets *Pride of Asia,* 207 Mile End Rd, E1 4AA (7780 9321).

Westminster *Asian Fusion*, The Lawns, Paddington Station, London W2 1HW (7402 9388).

SHOPS

Books/Magazines/Newspapers *Asian Book-shop,* 112 Whitfield St, W1P 5RU (7387 5747); *Asiatic Vision Ltd*, 114 Shaftesbury Ave, W1V 7DJ (7734 3171).

Clothes *Asian Fashions,* 755 Romford Rd, E12 5AW (8514 7975); *Inaya Contemporary Asian Clothing*, 38 Watney Market, E1 2PR (7791 3311); *Mohini (Asian),* 162 Cannon Street Rd, E1 2LH (7791 0821).

Food *Afro Asian Foods,* 3 Arndale Walk, Arndale Centre, Wandsworth SW18 4BX (8870 5060); *Asian Food Centre,* 544 Harrow Rd, W9 3QG (8960 3731); *Asian Oriental Supermarket,* 14 Selkirk Rd, SW17 0ES (8682 2155); *Asian Stores*, 58 Westbourne Grove, W2 5SH (7727 5033); *Asiatic Carpets Ltd,* Buiding O, The Occ, 105 Eade Rd, Finsbury Park, N4 1TJ (8800 2000); *Asiatic Trading*

Centre, 632 Bath Rd, Hounslow TW5 9TL (8759 2939); *Cheap Store,* 157 Green St, E13 (8472 7224).

SPECIAL *Asian Funeral Directors,* Ealing Rd, Wembley HA0 (8900 9252); *Asia House,* 105 Piccadilly, W1V 9FN (7499 1287) [promotes cultural understanding]; *Asian Introduction Agency,* Suite 501, International Ho, 223 Regent St, W1B 2EB (0800 0742392); *Asian Introductions*, 100 Gaskarth Rd, Balham, SW12 9NW (8688 0940); *Asian Wedding Service,* 24 Plashet Grove, E6 1AE (8470 1177); *Asian Conservation Awareness Programme (ACAP),* 5 St Peters St, N1 8JD (7359 3543).

TRAVEL *Asian Travel (UK)*, 35 Kensington Park Rd, W11 2EU (7221 0900); *Dan Asia Travel,* 295-297 High Rd, Leytonstone E11 4HH (8558 6645); *East of Suez Ltd,* 32 Rowan St, W6 (7602 9970); *Lakbay Asia Pilgrimages,* 52 Pembroke Rd, W8 6NX (7602 7171).

WELFARE

Barnet *Barnet Asian Old Peoples Association,* Barnet Multi-Cultural Community Centre, Algernon Rd, NW4 3TA (8202 4414); *Barnet Asian Women's Association,* 1 Friern Park, N12 9DE (8446 9897); *Barnet Elderly Asians Group,* 1 Friern Park, N12 9DE (8445 3644).

Brent *Asian Kitchen,* Kensal Rise Senior Club, 181 Mortimer Rd, NW10 5TN (8968 0317); *Asian People with Disabilities Alliance*, Disabilities Alliance Centre, Central Middlesex Hospital NW10 7NS (8961 6778); *Asian Respite Care Project,* Old Refectory, Central Middlesex Hospital, Acton La, Park Royal, NW10 7NS (8961 6773); *Asian Women's Resource Centre*, 108 Craven Park, NW10 8QE (8961 6549).

Greenwich: *Asian Welfare Centre,* 6 Anglesea Ave, SE18 6EH (8855 2222); *Sahara Asian Carers Project Unit,* F2 Macbean Centre, Macbean St, SE18 6LW (8855 0172).

Enfield *Asian Club of Enfield*, c/o Mr Fokrul Meah, Ponders End Youth Centre, 129 South St, Ponders End EN3 4PX (8804 5908) [[languages: Bangladeshi, English]; *Asian Culture and Welfare Centre* [Enfield] (8363 5693) [languages: Gujarati, Hindi, English]; *Community Aid (Asian Project),* c/o Rina Choudhury, Ponders End Area Housing Office, Curlew Ho, 4 Napier Rd, Enfield EN3 4QW (8443 4361) [languages: Bengali, Hindi, Urdu, English]; *Enfield Asian Welfare Association,* 129-139 South St, Ponders End EN3 4RJ (8443 1197) [languages: Bengali, Gujarati, Hindi, Punjabi, Urdu, English]; *Enfield Saheli,* Community House, 311 Fore Street, Edmonton N9 0PZ [advice for Asian women on legal matters (8373 6218), mental health (8373 6220), general (8373 6219); languages: Gujarati, Hindi, Punjabi, Urdu, English].

Hackney *Asian Women's Advisory Service,* 161 Mare St, E8 3RH (8533 5796); *Asian Women's Support Group,* 161 Mare St, Hackney E8 3RH (8986 4804).

Haringey *Asian Action Group,* 30 Willoughby Rd, N8 0JG (8341 3802); *Asian Centre,* 8 Caxton Rd, Haringey N22 6TB (8889 6938); *Asian Womens Forum,* 2nd fl, Wood Green Shopping City, High Rd, N22 6YA (8888 2446).

Islington *Anand Mandal Asian Elderly Group*, Caxton Ho, 1/9 St John's Way, N19 3RQ (7272 4450).

Kensington & Chelsea: *Association of Blind Asians*, Garrow Ho, 190 Kensal Rd, North Kensington W10 5BN (8962 2633); **Lambeth:** *Lambeth Asian Day Centre*, 7 Coburg Crescent, SW2 3HS (8674 5225).

Merton *Asian Elderly Group of Merton,* 28 St Georges Rd, SW19 4DP (8944 9545).

Newham *British Asian Womens Association,* 455 Romford Rd, Forest Gate E7 8AB (8221 0877); *Newham African Caribbean and Asian Advocacy Project Office,* 8 Stratford Advice Arcade, 107-109 The Grove, Stratford E15 1EN (8519 8311); *Newham Asian Womens Association,* 661 Barking Rd, Plaistow, E13 9EX (8552 5524).

Southwark *Aawaz Southwark Asian Women's Association,* Troy Town Flats, Peckham Rye SE15 4NS (7252 9290); *Salam Bhano Asian Girls & Young Womens Group*, Aylesbury Youth Club, Inville Rd, SE17 2HY (7252 4616).

Tower Hamlets *British Asians' Welfare Association,* 29 Commercial Rd, E1 1LD (7247 2035).

Waltham Forest: *Asian Family Resource Centre,* Truro Rd, E17 7BY (8521 7831); *Asian Mothers Group,* 2a Boundary Rd, E17 8JU (8520 0373); *Consortium for Asian People with Disabilities,* 1a Warner Rd, E17 7DY (8520 1748); *Waltham Forest Asian Blind Association,* 210 Church Rd, E10 7JQ (8556 0355); *Waltham Forest Asian Centre,* 18a Orford Rd, Walthamstow E17 9LN (8520 4511).

Wandsworth *Asian Elderly Project,* Mantle Court, Mapleton Rd, SW18 4AU (8875 9465).

Westminster *Asia House,* 105 Piccadilly, W1J 7NJ [charitable organization] (7499 1287).

Assamese

Assamese is an Indic language spoken in the Indian state of Assam by perhaps 5m people and written in a semi-syllabic script very similar to that used for **Bengali**. The *Mutlilingual Capital* (2000) survey reported the presence of only one **Assamese**-speaking pupil, living in the borough of Brent.

Assyrian

See also **Aramaic.**

ASSOCIATIONS *Assyrian Society of Great Britain,* Temple Rd, Ealing W5 4SN (8567 3768).
EDUCATION See **Aramaic.**
LANGUAGE See **Aramaic.**
RELIGION *Assyrian Church of the East,* Westminster Rd, W7 3TU (8567 1814); *Holy Apostolic Catholic Assyrian Church of the East - St Mary's Church* – UK Representative: V Rev Younan Y Younan, 66 Montague Rd, W7 3PQ (8579 7259).

WELFARE *Assyrian Cultural & Advice Centre,* PO Box 1314, Ealing W5 5QH (8579 0192); *Assyrian Refugees Relief Foundation,* 1 York Parade, Great West Rd, Brentford TW8 9AA (8569 7328).

A-Teso

A-Teso (Teso) is a **Nilotic** language spoken in Uganda. It was recorded as the first language of 14 London schoolchildren in the *Multilingual Capital* (2000) survey.

Australasian

As a geographical term, Australasia comprises minimally Australia, New Guinea, and New Zealand but there is a lack of concensus on the extent to which this word also embraces other South Pacific islands.

BARS & NIGHT-CLUBS *Walkabout Inn,* 58 Shepherds Bush Green, W12 8JG (8740 4339).

EMPLOYMENT *Australasian Temp Co Ltd,* 128-129 Cheapside, EC2V 6LL (7600 1709); *Southern Cross Employment Agency Ltd,* 4 Pelham St, South Kensington SW7 2NG (7589 9005).

FREIGHT *Australasian Forwarding Agency,* The Adventure Travel Centre, 131-135 Earls Court Rd, SW5 9RH (7244 7878); *1st Southern Cross*

Shipping Worldwide, Hampton Business Centre, 7 Mount Mews, High St Hampton-on-Thames, TW12 2SH (8751 2244).

MEDIA & INFORMATION *TNT Magazine & Southern Cross Newspaper,* 14-15 Childs Pl, Earl's Court SW5 9RX (7373 3377).

MOTORING *Southern Cross Motorcycle Engineers,* 14 Arches, Loveridge Rd, Kilburn NW6 2DS (7328 1428).

RESTAURANTS
Hammersmith & Fulham *Southern Cross,* 65 New Kings Rd, Fulham SW6 4SG (7736 2837).

Australian

ACCOMMODATION *Roberts Estates Wines Ltd,* 1st fl, 5 London Wall Buildings, Moorgate, EC2R 6AQ (7600 2244); *Sydney & London Properties Ltd,* 25 Harley St, West End, W1N 2BR (020920 387 364).

ASSOCIATIONS *Australian Trade Commission,* Australia Ho, The Strand, Holborn, WC2B 4LA (7887 5326); *Australian Tourist Commission,* Gemini Ho, 10-18 Putney Hill, Putney, SW15 6AA (8780 2229); *Britain/Australia Society,* Swire Ho, 59 Buckingham Gate, SW1E 6AJ (7630 1075).

BARS & NIGHTCLUBS *Australian* [pub], 29 Milner St, SW3 2QD (7589 6027); *Bar Oz,* 51 Moscow Rd, Bayswater W2Ê4AL (7229 0647).

BUSINESS *Australian Business in Europe Corporate Leisure,* 5 Chancery La, Holborn, WC2A 1LF (7320 6868); *Australian Connection Marketing Consultants,* 6 Jacobs Well Mews, West End, W1H 5PD (7935 0123); *Australian Crawl Ltd Business Consultants,* FLAT 9 Heber Mansions, Queens Club Gardens, West Kensington, W14 9RL ; *Australia & New Zealand Banking Group,* Minerva Ho, Montague Cl, SE1 9DA (7378 2121); *Australia & New Zealand Chamber of Commerce UK,* 393 Strand, WC2R 0LT (7379 0720); *Australian Business in Europe,* 5 Chancery La, WC2A 1LF (7320 6868); *Australian European Consulting Services,* 84 Kynance Gardens, Stanmore, HA7 2QI ; *Australian Hardwood Floors Ltd,* 43 Cloudesdale Rd, Tooting, SW17 8ET ; *Australia Mining Consultants,* Gainsbourough Ho, 33 Throgmorton

St, Moorgate, EC2N 2BR (7861 9535); *Australian Shareholder Services,* 7th fl, Jupiter Ho, Triton Court, 14 Finsbury Sq, EC2A 1BR (7628 4406); *Bank of Western Australia,* 42 New Broad St, EC2M 1SB (7256 5600); *Barclays Global Investors Australia,* 2nd fl, Aldermary Ho, 15 Queen St, St. Paul's, EC4N 1TX; *Chase Securities Australia Ltd,* 200 Aldersgate St, Clerkenwell, EC1A 4HD ; *Chemical Australia Ltd,* 200 Aldersgate St, Clerkenwell, EC1A 4HD ; *Commonwealth Bank of Australia,* Senator Ho, 85 Queen Victoria St, EC4V 4HA (7710 3999); *Commonwealth Bank of Australia,* 3rd fl, 1 Kingsway, Holborn, WC2B 6DU (7379 0955); *Deutche Morgan Grenfell Securities Australia Ltd,* 115 Houndsditch, EC3A 7BU (7283 9133); *Information Services,* Australia Ho, Strand, Holborn, WC2B 4LA (7887 5259); *London & Canberra Investment Company,* 3-4 Bentnick St, West End, W1M 5RN (7935 3144); *National Australia Bank,* 6-8 Tokenhouse Yard, Moorgate, EC2R 7AJ (7710 2100); *National Australia Bank,* 88 Wood St, EC2V 7QQ (7710 2100); *National Westminster Finance Australia Ltd,* 200 Aldersgate St, Clerkenwell, EC1A 4HD; *New South Wales Government Trade & Investment Office,* The Australian Centre, Strand, WC2B 4LG (7887 5871); *Reserve Bank of Australia,* 7 Moorgate, EC2R 6AQ (7600 2244); *South Australian Tourism Commssion Marketing Consultants,* Beamont Ho, Lambton Rd, Raynes Pk, SW20 0LW (8944 5375).

EMPLOYMENT *Australian Staff Connections,* 96 Kensington High St, W8 4SG (7938 4777);

FREIGHT *Advanced Shipping,* 17 Commercial Way, Abbey Rd Ind Est, Willesden, NW10 7XF (8838 3883); *Advanced Australian Removals,* 168 Earls Court Rd, Earl's Court, SW5 9QQ (7373 3900).

GOVERNMENT *Agent General for Western Australia,* 5th fl, Australia Centre, Melbourne Pl, WC2B 4LG (7240 2881); *Australia & New Zealand Chamber Of Commerce Uk,* 393 Strand, Holborn WC2R 0LT (7379 0720); *Australian Consulate,* Australia Ho, Strand, WC2B 4LA (0131 555 4500); *Australian Film Commission,* 2nd fl, Victory Ho, 99-101 Regent St, West End, W1R 7HB (7734 9383); *State of South Australia,* Australia Centre, Strand, WC2B 4LA (7836 3455)**.**

LANGUAGES English is the official and dominant language of Australia but many other languages are spoken there. Some of the formerly large number of Aboriginal languages survive but most have few speakers today. There are also many different languages spoken by immigrant groups, mainly from Europe and Asia. In addition a variety of Creole

English known as Kriol is spoken in the Northern Territory.

LEGAL *Ian Harrop & Associates* [Australian visas], 232 Merton Rd, South Wimbledon, SW19 1EQ (8540 8448); *New Zealand, Australia & Canada Migration Bureau,* Hyde Park Ho, 5 Manfred Rd, SW15 2RS (8874 2844).

MEDIA & INFORMATION *Australian Associated Press,* 12 Norwich St, EC4A 1BP (7353 0153); *Australian Broadcasting Corporation,* 54 Portland Pl, W1B 1DY (7631 4456); *Australian Consolidated Press Bureau,* 3rd fl, 35 Soho Sq, W1D 3QX (7261 7688); *Australian Financial Review,* 95 Fetter La, St. Paul's, EC4A 1HE (7242 0044); *Channel 9 Australia,* The Interchange, Oval Rd, NW1 7DE (7482 4949); *Channel 9 Australia Inc,* 4 Millbank, Westminster, SW1P 3JA (7976 0909); *Film Graphics Australia,* 6a Poland St, W1F 8PR (7734 9029); *News Limited of Australia,* P O Box 481, 1 Virginia St, E1W 2ZZ (7702 1355); *Seven Network Australia,* The Interchange, Oval Rd, NW1 7DZ (7428 4950);. *Seven Network Australian Television,* Grant Way, Isleworth, TW7 5QD (7705 6727); *Sydney Morning Herald,* 95 Fetter La, St Paul's, EC4A 1HE (7242 0044).

RECREATION *British Australian Rules Football League,* 98A Earls Court Rd, Kensington, W8 6EG (7376 2863); *British Australian Rules Football League,* 264 Acton High St, Acton, W3 9BH (8752 1823); *British Australian Rules Football League,* PO Box 6237, West Kensington, W14 9GA (7376 2863); *Outback Sports Ltd,* 137 Earl's Court Rd, SW5 9RH (7460 0298).

RESTAURANTS

Islington *Monitor,* 201 Liverpool St, N1 (7607 7710).

SHOPPING *Also Aussie,* 41 Beauchamp Pl, SW3 1NX [women's clothes] (7584 0231); *Australian Cultural Experience,* 30c Camden Lock Pl, NW1 8AL (7267 6530); *Australian Dried Fruits Ltd,* 786 Salisbury Ho, London Wall, EC2M 5QQ (8566 2944); Australian *Emu Oil,* 49 Portland Rd, Ashford, TW15 3BU (7842 554000); *Australia Shop,* 26 Henrietta St, WC2E 8NA (7836 2292, fax 7385 7253) [books and gifts]; *Australian Wine Bureau,* Australia Ho, Strand, WC2B 4LA (7887 5259).

SPECIAL *Sydney Brassieres Ltd,* 199 Munster Rd, Fulham, SW6 6BY (7381 8821).

TRAVEL *AAT Kings Australian Tours,* 15 Grosvenor Pl, SW1X 7HH (8784 2801); *Ansett Airlines Australia,* Unit 4, Heathrow International Trading Est, Green La, Hounslow, TW4 6HB (7240 2881); *Australian Affair,* Hillgate Ho, 13 Hillgate St, W8 7SP (7616 9193); *Australian Pacific Tours (UK) Ltd,* 2nd fl, William Ho, 14 Worple Rd, SW19 4DD (8879 7444); *Australia's Northern Territory Tourist Commission,* 1st fl, Beaumont Ho, Lambton Rd, Raynes Park SW20 0LW (0906 4799994); *Australian Scenic Tours,* 11-15 Betterdon St, Covent Garden, Holborn, WC2H 9BP (7470 8747); *Australian Tourist Commission,* Gemini Ho, 10-18 Putney Hill, SW15 6AA (8780 2229); *Oz Experience,*

Suite 104-105 Regent House Business Centre, W1H 5YN (7569 3075); *Oz Flights,* 410 Edgware Rd, W2 1ED (7724 9999); *Queensland Tourist & Travel Corporation,* 392-393 Strand, olborn, WC2R OLZ (7240 0525); *Tourism Victoria Australia,* Victoria Ho, 29-31 Melbourne Pl, Holborn, WC2B 4LF (7240 7176).

Austrian

ACCOMMODATION *Austrian Catholic Centre,* 29 Brook Green, W6 7BL [hostel] (7603 2697).

ASSOCIATIONS *Anglo-Austrian Society,* 46 Queen Annes Gate, SW1H 9AU (7222 0366); *Austrian Cultural Institute,* 28 Rutland Gate, SW7 1PQ (7584 8653).

BUSINESS *Austrian Trade Commission,* 45 Princes Gate, SW7 2QA (7584 4411); *Bank Austria Credit Anstalt International AG,* 125 London Wall, EC2Y 5DD (7382 1000); *First Austrian International Ltd,* Eldon Ho, 2 Eldon St, EC2M 7BX (7247 7626); *RZB-Austria,* 36-38 Botolph La, EC3R 8DE (7929 2288).

FREIGHT *Austrian Airlines Cargo,* Building 582, London Heathrow Airport, Hounslow TW6 3EF (8897 1866).

GOVERNMENT *Austrian Embassy and Consular Section,* 18 Belgrave Mews West, SW1X 8HU (7235 3731).

LANGUAGE **German** is the principal language but the linguistic rights of minorities who speak **Slovene** or **Croat** are protected.

MEDIA & INFORMATION *Austrian Radio & Television,* 19 Newman St, W1P 3HB (7631 0860).

RELIGION Roman Catholicism the religion of the overwhelming majority of Austrians.

RESTAURANTS

West 1 *Kerzenstuberl,* 9 St Christopher's Pl, W1M 5HB (7486 3196).

Westminster *Tiroler Hut,* 27 Westbourne Grove, W2 (7727 3981).

SHOPS *Anglo Austrian Patisserie Ltd,* 16 Ravensbury Terrace, Wandsworth SW18 4RL (8947 8607); *Austrian Bedding Co,* 205 Belsize Rd, West Hampstead NW6 4AA (7372 3121); *Austrian Sausage Centre,* 10a Belmont St, NW1 8HH (7267 3601).

TRAVEL *Anglo-Austrian Society,* 46 Queen Annes Gate, SW1H 9AU (7222 0366); *Austrian Airlines,* 10 Wardour St, W1D 6PB (7434 7350); *Austrian Holidays,* 10 Wardour St, W1V 4BQ (7434 7399); *Austrian National Tourist Office,* 14 Cork St, W1S 3NS (7629 0461).

Azerbaijani

BUSINESS *Azerbaijan International Operating Co,* Burdette Ho, Buckingham St, WC2N 6DU [oil and gas exploration] (7451 4100).

EDUCATION See **Azeri.**

GOVERNMENT *Azerbaijan E m b a s s y,* 4 Kensington Ct, W85DL (7938 5482).

LANGUAGE See **Azeri.**

RESTAURANTS

Kensington & Chelsea *Azerbaijan,* 59 Marloes Rd, Kensington W8 6LE (7376 9550).

TRAVEL *Azerbaijan Airlines,* 30 Dover St, Mayfair W1S 4NB (7493 2281).

Azeri

EDUCATION Courses in **Azeri** are available at *SOAS Language Centre* (7898 4888).

LANGUAGE *Azeri,* also known as *Azerbaijani,* is a language of the **Trans-Asia** geozone (in Dalby's 1999-2000 classification) which is related to **Turkish** and spoken in Azerbaijan. It is currently written in an adaptation of the Cyrillic alphabet. The *Multilingual Capital* (2000) survey reported that this was the first language of two London schoolchildren.

TRANSLATION *Associated Translators,* Macmillan Ho, 96 Kensington High St, W8 4SG (7937 7733).

B

Baha'i

MEDIA **&** INFORMATION *Baha'i Information Centre,* 98 Brunswick Park Rd, Friern Barnet N11 1JJ (8361 7093).

RELIGION *Baha'i Community of Ealing,* P O Box 1392, Ealing W5 2QX (8932 5033); *Baha'i Faith,* 1043 Garratt La, Tooting SW17 0LN (8682 3394); *Baha'i Faith,* 111 Nursery Gdns, Staines, TW18 1EL (01784 880913); *Baha'i Faith,* P O Box 392, Wembley HA9 8AW (8621 4943); *Baha'is of Havering,* 12 Lytton Rd, Romford, RM2 5SL (01708 446297); *National Office of the Baha'is of the UK* (7584 2566); *Spiritual Assembly of the Bahá'ís in the UK,* 27 Rutland Gate, SW7 1PD.

Bahamian

ASSOCIATIONS *Friends of the Bahamas Ltd,* Centurion Ho, 37 Jewry St, EC3N 2ER.

GOVERNMENT *Bahamas High Commission,* 10 Chesterfield St, W1X 8AH (7408 4488); *Bahamas Maritime Authority,* 10 Chesterfield St, W1X 8AH (7290 1500).

TRAVEL *Bahamas Reservation Service,* 79 Dean St, W1V 6HY (7434 9915).

Bahraini

ASSOCIATIONS *Bahrain Society,* Sceptre Ct, 40 Tower Hill, EC2N 4DX (7269 2000).

BUSINESS *Bahrain Middle East Bank,* 40 Queen St, EC4R 1DD (7236 0413).

EDUCATION *Bahrain-British Foundation,* The Glassmill, 1 Battersea Bridge Rd, SW11 3BG (7223 3431).

GOVERNMENT *Embassy of the State of Bahrain,* 98 Gloucester Rd, South Kensington SW7 4AU (7370 5132).

LEGAL *Clifford Chance,* 200 Aldersgate St, E1A 4JJ (7600 1000) [office in Bahrain]; *Fairmays,* 10 Babmaes St, SW1Y 6HD (7959 0202) [office in Bahrain]; *Trowers & Hamlins,* Sceptre Ct, 40 Tower Hill, EC3N 4BN (7423 8000) [office in Bahrain].

Baining

Baining is a language of Papua New Guinea. The *Multilingual Capital* (2000) survey identified this as the language of only one London pupil living in Brent.

Bajan

Bajan is a popular abbreviation of *Barbadian*, with reference to the people of Barbados in the West Indies and their way of speaking. See **Barbadian.**

Bali

Bali is among the names of languages which have been reported as the mother tongue of some London schoolchildren within the past decade. According to Dalby (1999-2000), there are seven different languages of this name spoken around the world so the precise language or languages concerned cannot be correctly identified without information on the place of origin of speakers. (Bali is the name of a Tanzanian language of the Rift-Valley geozone, a Hesperonesic language spoken on the Indonesian island of Bali (= **Balinese**), a Manusic language of Papua New Guinea, and four different Bantuic languages three of which are spoken Congo/Zaire and one in Cameroon.)

Balinese

====
ARTS *Indonesian & Balinese Art Ltd,* 3 Blore Ct, W1V 3RG (7494 9666).

BUSINESS *Bali (Design) Ltd* [interior designers], 13 Walpole Gdns, Chiswick W4 4HG (8742 7626); *Bali Financial Services,* 239 Ilford La, IG1 2SB (8478 4454).

RESTAURANTS
Greenwich *Bali,* 180 Trafalgar Rd, SE10 9TZ (8858 7609).

Kensington & Chelsea *Bali Sugar,* 33 All Saints Rd, W11 1HE (7221 4477).

Westminster *Bali,* 101 Edgware Rd, W2 2HX (7262 9100).

SHOPS *Bali Boutique,* 1 Craven Park Rd, Willesden NW10 8SE (8965 1544).

SPECIAL [not yet categorized] *Bali Express Ltd,* 39 Willesden La, NW6 7RF (7372 3443); *Bali-Hi,* 230 Kingston Rd, New Malden KT3 3RN (8942 9252).

Balkan

====
ACCOMMODATION *Hotel Balkan,* 33 Shepherd's Bush Rd, Hammersmith W6 7LU (7603 3706).

FREIGHT *Balkan & Black Sea Shipping Company.Ltd,* 72 Wilson St, EC2A 2DH (7572 7272); *Euro Balkan Freight Lines (UK) Ltd,* Park Royal Business Centre, 9-17 Park Royal Rd, NW10 7LQ (8930 5036).

TRAVEL *Balkan Alpine Holidays Ltd,* 12 Anerley Station Rd, SE20 8PT (8289 0844); *Balkan & Bulgarian Airlines,* 322 Regent St, W1R 5AB (7637 7637); *Balkan Holidays,* Sofia Ho, 19 Conduit St, W1S 2BH (7543 5555); *Balkan Tourist UK Ltd,* Osborne Ho, 111-113 Bartholomew Rd, Kentish Town NW5 2BJ (7485 5280).

Balochi

===
EDUCATION Courses in Balochi are available at *SOAS Language Centre* (7898 4888).

LANGUAGE Balochi (also spelled *Baluchi*) is an Iranic language related to **Farsi** which spoken in Baluchistan (Pakistan) and written in an adaptation of the consonantal Arabic script. This was reported as the first language of 24 London schoolchildren in the *Multilingual Capital* (2000) survey.

Baltic

===
BUSINESS *Baltic Food & Beverages Ltd,* Unit 3, 2a Knightsbridge Rd, Barking IG11 0BP (8591 9928); *Baltic Financial Services Ltd,* 25 Albemarle St, West End, W1X 3FA (7493 9899); *Baltic Fund 1 LLC Financial Consultants,* 17 Hill St, West End, W1X 3FA (7493 3014); *Baltic Timber Products Ltd,* P O Box 2292, West End, W1A 1PH (7491 0441); *Baltic plc* [financial consultants], 25-26 Albemarle St, West End, W1X 7FB (7355 3014).

FREIGHT *Baltic Distribution & Publishing Ltd* [road haulage], 83 Leonard St, EC2A 4QS; *Euro Baltic UK Agency,* 78 Cannon St, St Paul's, EC4N 6HH (7929 3799).

MEDIA & INFORMATION *Baltic Distribution & Publishing Ltd,* 83 Leonard St, EC2A 4QS; *Baltic Publishing Ltd,* Regal Ho, London Rd, Twickenham, TW1 3QS (8891 1199).

RESTAURANTS
South East 1 *Baltic,* 74 Blackfriars Rd, SE1 8EN (7928 1111).

Waltham Forest *Baltika,* 32 High St, Walthanstow E17 (8521 8669).

TRAVEL *Air Baltic Corporation,* 5 Hobart Pl, Westminster, SW1W OHU (7828 4223).

Baluchi

Baluchi is a variant spelling of **Balochi,** which should be consulted.

Bangladeshi

The word **Bangladeshi** comprises three elements: *Bangla* 'Bengal', *desh* 'country', and the suffix *-i* meaning 'of', 'belonging to'. While all the entries below relate to people who - or whose ancestors - came to Britain from what is now Bangladesh, or to its culture, other relevant entries will be found under **Bengali,** a word which is applied to the people and culture of the Indian state of West Bengal (which includes Calcutta) as well as Bangladesh.

ACCOMMODATION *Samad Bangladesh,* c/o Senator Estates, 154 High Road Leyton, E15 2BX (8556 7367).

ASSOCIATIONS *Bangladesh Womens Association,* Mitalee Centre, Stanley Rd, N15 3HB (8365 7498); *Bangla Housing Association Ltd,* 243 Lower Clapton Rd, E5 8EG (8985 1124); *North London Bangladeshi Association,* c/o Mr. Haji Matin,

30 Beverley Close, Winchmore Hill, N21 3JB (8360 9195) [language: **Bengali,** English]; *Queens Park Bangladesh Association,* Athens Gdns, Harrow Rd, W9 3RS (7286 3154); *Wapping Bangladesh Association,* Wapping Youth Club, Tench St, E1 2QD (7702 1708); *Youth Muslim Organisation* [**Bangladeshi**], 74a High Street, Ponders End, Enfield EN3 4ER [Sundays 10.00 - 14.00; contact: Haji Abdul Sattar (8443 2140); languages: **Bengali,** English];

BUSINESS *Arab Bangladesh Bank Ltd,* Unit 1.2.1, 75 Whitechapel Rd, E1 1DU (7426 0723); *Bangla Catering Equipment,* 437 Railway Arches, Huddart St, Bow E3 4AT (8981 1415); *Bangladesh Export & Import Co. Ltd,* 307 Finchley Rd, NW3 6EH (7435 4943).

EDUCATION See **Bengali.**

GOVERNMENT *Bangladesh High Commission,* 28 Queen's Gate, SW7 (7584 0081).

LANGUAGES The great majority of schoolchildren for whom **Bengali** is recorded as the home language are descendents of immigrants from Bangladesh. (Some others are from the Indian state of West Bengal.) A substantial proportion of the Bangladeshis came from Sylhet in the eastern part of that country where **Sylheti**, a language related to Bengali, is spoken. Many Bangladeshis in London thus speak Sylheti rather than Bengali at home. However, it is not easy to determine the proportion of speakers of Sylheti. One reason is that everyone who speaks Sylheti also knows Bengali to a greater or lesser extent and tends to regard Bengali as the cultural language of all Bangladeshis. For further information, see **Bengali** - LANGUAGE.

MEDIA & INFORMATION *Bangla TV,* 150 High St, E15 2NE (8519 3200) [satellite tv]; *Betar Bangla,* Wickham Ho, 43 Cleveland Way, E1 4TZ (7791 3399) [broadcasting].

RESTAURANTS (See also **Bengali**)

South East 1 *Rajdoot,* 158 Westminster Bridge Rd, SE1 (7928 7684).

West Central *Char Bar,* Cromer St, WC1; *Dacca Tandoori Restaurant,* 46 Bedford St, WC2E

9HA (7379 7623); *Hot Chilli,* 52 Tavistock Pl, WC1H 9RG (7713 0903).

Barnet *Dacca Tandoori T/A,* 1 Dancastle Ct, Arcadia Ave, Finchley Central N3 2JU.

Bromley *Bangla Bolaaka T/A,* 49 Maple Rd, SE20 8LA (0800 1699236).

Haringey *Dhaka Tandoori T/A,* 10 Crescent Rd, Wood Green N22 4RS (8889 1786).

Lewisham *Dilraj (Bangladeshi & Indian) Take Away,* 33 Staplehurst Rd, SE13 5ND (8297 8989).

Merton *Dacca Tandoori Restaurant,* 306 Kingston Rd, Wimbledon Chase SW20 8LX (8542 7717).

Newham *Dhaka Express T/A,* 62 Hermit Rd, Canning Town E16 4LF (7474 0400).

Southwark *Joy Bangla Curry House T/A,* 39 Denmark Hill, Camberwell SE5 8RS (7703 3149);

Tower Hamlets *Bangla,* 128, Brick La, E1 6RU (7247 7885); *Dhaka Cafe,* 65 New Rd, Whitechapel E1 1HH; *Dilchad Indo-Bangla Resturant,* 24 Widegate St, E1 7HP (7247 8930); *Le Taj,* 134 Brick La, E1 (7247 4210).

Wandsworth *Bangladesh Curry Mahal,* 294 Upper Richmond Rd, Putney SW15 6TH (8789 9763).

SHOPS *Bangla Bazaar,* 125-127 Cannon Street Rd, Whitechapel E1 2LX (7481 3409); *Bangla Bazaar,* 117 Upper Tooting Rd, SW17 7TJ (8767 8868) [groceries]; *Bangla Bazar Foodstore,* 99 Turnpike La, N8 0DY (8348 0098); *Bangladesh Commercial Centre Ltd* [clothing], 55-59 Hanbury St, E1 5JP (7377 2770); *Bangladesh Resource & Multicultural Book Centre,* 1st fl, 23-25 Hessel St, E1 2LR (7488 4243); *Bangla Superstore,* 17-19 Brick La, E1 6PU (7247 1009); *Bangla Sweets,* 163 Cannon Street Rd, E1 2LX (7488 1977); *Bangla Town Carpets,* 236 Brick La, Bethnal Green E2 7EB (7729 8910); *Bangla Town Cash & Carry,* 67 Hanbury St, E1 5JP (7377 1770); *Planet Bangla,* Arch 146-148, Martha St, E1 2PG (7791 3143)

[supermarket]; *Ruposhi Bangla Ltd,* 220 Tooting High St, SW17 0SG (8672 7843) [bookshop]; *Saree Place,* 100 Cromer St, WC1 (7278 2887).

TRAVEL The national airline is *Bangladesh Biman Airlines,* 17 Conduit St, W1 (7629 0252). Other Bangladeshi organizations concerned with local or international travel are: *Bangla Minicab Service,* 566 Butcher Row, Poplar E14 8EE (7790 5580); *Bangla Minicab Service,* Simon Ho, 566 Cable St, Whitechapel E1 9HB (7790 5559); *Bangla Town Mini Cabs,* 4 Hessel St, Whitechapel E1 2LP (7481 1400); *Bangla Town Travel International,* Unit 2b, 63 Princelet St, Whitechapel E1 5LP (7375 0713); *Eastern Travel,* 155 Bethnal Green Rd, E2 (7729 0708); *Sonar Bangla Travels,* 150 Green St, Forest Gate, E7 8JQ (8548 1414).

WELFARE *Bangladesh Centre,* 24 Pembridge Gdns, W2 4DX (7229 9404); *Bangladesh Welfare Association,* 39 Fournier St, E1 6QE (7247 2105); *Bangladesh Welfare Association,* 12 School Rd, Hounslow TW3 1QZ (8577 2694); *Bangladesh Welfare Association of Enfield,* 6 Napier Rd, Enfield EN3 4QJ (8804 9573); *Bangladesh Womens Association,* 58 Hanley Rd, Finsbury Park N4 3DR (7263 7005)); *Bangladesh Youth Movement,* 21-23 Henriques St, E1 1NB (7488 1831); *North London Bangladesh Welfare Association,* 251 Pentonville Rd, Islington N1 9NG ((7278 0877); *Enfield Bangladesh Welfare Association,* 74a High St, Enfield EN3 4ER (8804 4006); *Marylebone Bangladesh Society,* 19 Samford St, St John's Wood NW8 8ER (7724 7427); *South Islington Bangladesh Association,* 71 Caledonian Rd, N1 9BT (7833 2608).

Bantu

Languages of the **Bantu** family, collectively termed Bantuic by Dalby (1999-2000), are spoken throughout most of Central, East, and Southern Africa. There are several hundred Bantu languages in all and, of these, the three with the largest number of speakers in London are **Lingala** (of the Congo (Kinshasa), **Luganda** (of Uganda) and **Swahili** (of East Africa). See individual entries for these for more information.

The *Multilingual Capital* (2000) survey found that the overall distribution of pupils across London who spoke a **Bantu** language was rather similar and published a map of this which can be seen at <www.global-london.com/gallery> (Map 8). This shows that their speakers are clustered mainly in two areas: from Barnet to Westminster north of the Thames, and from Merton to Greenwich south of the Thames.

A particular problem with the names of most Bantuic languages is that they are variably written both with and without class prefixes, e.g. Luganda is Ganda (plus the prefix lu-), Kingwana is Ngwana (with the prefix ki-), etc. While there are similarly pairs of names for almost all Bantuic languages, only variants spellings known to be in use in London are included in this listing.

Barawan

Barawan was among the names of languages spoken by some London school-children identified by the *Multilingual Capital* (2000) survey. This word probably designates the language spoken by the *Baraawe* people of the *Brava* area of Somalia who speak a distinctive Bantu language, sometimes called *Brava* or **Bravanese** whose Bantu name is *Cimiini.* There are numerous refugees from Brava living in London.

See also the entry for **Bravanese.**

Barbadian

ACCOMMODATION *Belvedere (Barbados) Ltd [property development],* 33a Churchfield Rd, Acton W3 6AY.

BUSINESS *Barbados International Trading Associates,* 92 St Johns Rd, Wembley HA9 7JN (8795 0253).

EDUCATION *Friends of Codrington College Barbados,* 12a Upper Berkeley St, W1H 7PE.

GOVERNMENT *Barbados High Commission,* 1 Great Russell St, WC1B 3ND (7631 4975).

LANGUAGE The official and de facto language of Barbados is English. Nevertheless, the English of Barbados, known popularly as *Bajan,* has its own local characteristics and is related to the English lexicon Creoles of Jamaica and other Caribbean islands. In the *Multilingual Capital* (2000) survey, the two schoolchildren reported as speakers of Bajan were added to the figures for English-based Creoles.

SPECIAL *Barbados Ships Registry,* P O Box 315, WC1B 3JY (7636 5739).

TRAVEL *Barbados Only Barbados,* 125 East End Rd, East Finchley N2 0SZ (8442 0100); *Barbados Tourism Authority,* 263 Tottenham Court Rd, W1P 9AA (7636 9448).

Bari

EDUCATION Mother-tongue instruction for children in Bari is available at one location in London; see <www.resourceunit.com> for details.

LANGUAGE *Bari* is a Nilotic language spoken in Sudan. Though not appearing in the *Multilingual Capital* (2000) survey, there are currently known to be speakers of this in London (see EDUCATION).

Bariba

Bariba is a Voltaic language spoken in Benin and Nigeria which has been reported as the first language of a few London schoolchildren within the past decade but not were recorded at the time of the *Multilingual Capital* (2000) survey.

Basque

The *Londreseko Euskal Elkartea / London Basque Society* (see under ASSOCIATIONS) is a non-political organization which may be contacted about any aspect of Basque culture. The society receives funding from *Euskal Gizatalde Harremanetara* – the Basque country governmental body responsible for external relations.

ARTS *Euskal Elkarteko Musika Taldea* (The London Basque Society's music group), Oxford Ho, Derbyshire St, Bethnal Green E2 6HG (7739 7339).

ASSOCIATIONS *Londreseko Euskal Elkartea / London Basque Society,* Oxford Ho, Derbyshire St, Bethnal Green E2 6HG (7739 7339).

EDUCATION A Basque-speaking playgroup meets at the London Basque Society (see above for address and telephone number).

Basque language classes are held every Saturday morning at *London Guildhall University,* Calcutta Ho, Old Castle St, E1 7NT (for details, phone 7739 7339).

LANGUAGE *Basque,* spoken in the Spanish and French Pyrenees, is not related to any other language. The *Multilingual Capital* (2000) survey listed the presence of only one Basque-speaking pupil but the existence of a Basque playgroup in London (see EDUCATION, above) suggests that there must be several more at least.

MEDIA *Hemen* [newsletter of the London Basque Society - see ASSOCIATIONS for address and phone no.].

RECREATION An official London-based Athletic Club Bibao supporters group is being set up; details from Ibon (07956050871). For other recreational activities, contact *Londreseko Euskal Elkartea / London Basque Society,* Oxford Ho, Derbyshire St, Bethnal Green E2 6HG (7739 7339),

RESTAURANTS
Brent *Mesón Bilbao,* 33 Malvern Rd. NW6 5PS (7328 1744) [This restaurant specialises in Basque food but the staff are not Basque speakers.]

Tower Hamlets The *London Basque Society* (see WELFARE below for address and telephone number) organizes Basque lunches on Saturdays which interested persons may attend by prior arrangement.

Catering The *Basque Mobile Restaurant* provides food for weddings, parties, etc. (7739 7339 for details).

SHOPS The following are among the shops in London which stock food products from the Basque country: *De la Fuente,* 288 Portobello Rd, W10 (8960 5687); *Garcia & Son,* 250 Portobello Rd, W11 (7221 6119).

SPECIAL *Basque Campaign,* P O Box 33597, E2 8WF; *Karlos* [gardening and removals] (0796 009 3782).

WELFARE *Londreseko Euskal Elkartea / London Basque Society,* Oxford Ho, Derbyshire St, Bethnal Green E2 6HG (7739 7339).

Bassa

Bassa was reported as the first language of six schoolchildren in the *Multilingual Capital* (2000) survey. This probably refers, in most if not all cases, to the Kruic language of this name, spoken in Liberia. However, there is also an unrelated language of the same name spoken in Nigeria by fewer people.

Bata

Bata is a Mandaric language spoken in Nigeria and Cameroon. The presence of *Bata*-speaking pupils has been reported in one London borough in recent years but none were found at the time of the *Multilingual Capital* (2000) survey.

Bavarian

ACCOMMODATION *Bavaria Property & Building Ltd,* 665 Finchley Rd, NW2 2HN.

BUSINESS *Bavarian Invest Ltd,* 4 Queen Anne Terrace, Sovereign Close, E1W 3HH.

MOTORING *Bavarian Autos,* Unit 4, Gordon Rd, Southall UB2 5QE (8813 8800); *Bavarian Autos,* Unit 4, Squirrels Trading Estate, Viveash Close, Hayes UB3 4RZ (8561 6644); *Bavarian Motors,* 207 West Hendon Broadway, NW9 7DE (8201 5389).

Beja

Beja is a language spoken in Sudan and Eritrea. The *Multilingual Capital* (2000) survey found 13 *Beja*-speaking London schoolchildren of whom 9 lived in Lewisham.

Belarusian

Belarusian is one of several spellings currently in use for the people and language of the Republic of Belarus. Other spellings include Belarussian and Byelorussian.

EDUCATION Courses in *Belarusian* are available at *SSEES* (7862 8634).

GOVERNMENT *Embassy of the Republic of Belarus,* 6 Kensington Ct, W8 5DL (7937 3288) and 1 St Stephens Crescent, Bayswater W2 5QT (7221 3941).

LANGUAGE *Belarusian* is a **Slavonic** language which has official status in Belarus. The *Multilingual Capital* (2000) survey noted the presence of only one Belarusian-speaking pupil, in Haringey.

RELIGION *Byelorussian Catholic Mission,* Marian Ho, Holden Ave, North Finchley N12 8HY (8445 1938).

TRAVEL *Belavia Belarussian Airways,* 5 Hobart Pl, SW1 (7393 1201).

Belgian

ASSOCIATIONS *Anglo-Belgian Club,* 60 Knightsbridge, SW1X 7LF (7235 5642).

BUSINESS *Bank Brussels Lambert,* 6 Broadgate, EC2M 2AJ (7247 5566); *Belgium-Luxembourg Chamber of Commerce,* 73 Upper Richmond Rd, Putney, SW15 2SZ (8877 9263); *Flanders Export Promotion Agency,* 103 Eaton Sq, SW1W 9AB (7823 1607).

GOVERNMENT *Belgian Embassy,* 103 Eaton Sq, SW1W 9AB (7470 3700); *Belgian Tourist Office for Brussels & Ardennes,* 225 Marsh Wall, Poplar, E14 9FW (0800 954 5245).

LANGUAGES *Dutch (Flemish)* and *French* are the dominant languages of northern and southern Belgium, respectively in addition to which there is a small, *German*-speaking area adjoining the German border.

RELIGION *Belgian Evangelical Mission,* 20 Vicarage Farm Rd, Hounslow, TW3 4NW (8577 3023).

RESTAURANTS
West Central *Belgo Centraal,* 50 Earlham St, WC2H 9LA (7813 2233); *Belgo Ventures T/A,* 1 Neal's Yard, WC2H 9DP (7916 5300).

Camden *Belgo Noord,* 72 Chalk Farm Rd, NW1 8AN ((7267 0718).

Kensington & Chelsea *Belgo Zuid,* 124 Ladbroke Grove, W10 (8982 8400).

SHOPS *Belgian Chocolates,* 51 The Broadway, Mill Hill, NW7 3DA (8906 4953); *Natalie Belgian Chocolates,* 12 Sicilian Ave, WC1A 2QD (7242 3227); *P & D's Luxury Belgian Ice Cream Ltd,* 82 Hillside Rd, Northwood, HA6 1QB (01923 822048).

TRAVEL *Belgian National Railways,* Suite 439 Premier Ho, 10 Greycoat Pl, SW1; *Belgian Tourist Office for Brussels-Ardennes,* 31 Pepper St, Poplar E14 9RW (7458 2888); *Flanders the Experience Ltd,* 29 Princes St, W1R 7RG.

Belizean

GOVERNMENT *Belize High Commission,* 22 Harcourt Houses, 19 Cavendish Square, W1G 0PN (7499 9728).

LANGUAGES *English* is the official language but an *English Creole* and *Spanish* are the main languages spoken while there are also important minorities which speak *Maya* or Garifuna.

RELIGION Most Belizeans are Christian and there are considerably more Roman Catholics than Protestants.

Bemba

Bemba is a Bantuic language spoken in Zambia and Congo (Kinshasa). In the *Multilingual Capital* (2000) survey, Bemba was reported to be the first language of 131 London schoolchilden, of whom a quarter lived in Lewisham.

Bende

Bende is a **Bantuic** language of Tanzania. The *Multilingual Capital* (2000) survey reported that this was the first language of one pupil in Lambeth.

Bengali

Within the Indian subcontinent, the *Bengali* people and speakers of the *Bengali* language are located on both sides of the border between India (West Bengal) and Bangladesh. Although there is no doubt that people of *Bangladeshi* descent greatly outnumber those who – or whose ancestors - came from West Bengal, the precise proportions of the two groups has not been determined. For that reason, all organizations whose names include the words Bengal or *Bengali* are listed here rather than under *Bangladeshi.*

ARTS *N Bengali* [music management], 43d Ferme Park Rd, Finsbury Park N4 4EB (8342 9220).

ASSOCIATIONS *Asian Club of Enfield,* c/o Mr Fokrul Meah, Ponders End Youth Centre, 129 South St, Ponders End EN3 4PX (8804 5908) [[languages: *Bengali,* English]; *Bengal Club,* 128 Shakespeare Crescent, Manor Park E12 6LP; *Bengali Cultural Association,* Dryburgh Hall, Alderney St, SW1V 4ET (7828 3360); *Bengali Institute London,* 85 York St, W1H 1DU (7723 4520); *Bengali Womans Group,* Rockingham Community Centre, Rockingham St, SE1 6PD (7357 0623); *Bengali Workers Action Group,* 1 Robert St, NW1 3JU (7388 7313); *Bethnal Green Bengali Voluntary Community Association,* 49 Braintree St, E2 0EX (8983 3409); *Bethnal Green Bengali Association,* 1 Cornwall Ave, E2 0HW (8983 3409); *Consortium of Bengali Associations,* Gatesden, Argyle St, WC1H 8EA (7713 8610); *Eastern Cultural Society - North London,* c/o Mr S Mazumdar, 20 Orchard Ave, Southgate N14 4ND (8886 4231) [languages: Bengali, English]; *Hammersmith Bengali Association,* 61 Briony Rd, W12 0SP (8746 0913); *North London Bangladeshi Association,* c/o Mr. Haji Matin, 30 Beverley Close, Winchmore Hill, N21 3JB (8360 9195) [language: *Bengali,* English]; *Overseas Bengali Association,* c/o Mr. Sukumar Mazumdar, 20 Orchard Ave, Southgate, N14 4ND (8886 4231) [*Hindu* religious matters; languages: *Bengali,* English]; *Sisters in*

Islam (**Muslim** Girls Club), c/o Mrs. Rahana Hassan, Ponders End Youth Centre, 129 South St, Ponders End EN3 4PX (8804 5908) [languages: **Bengali, Urdu**, English]; *Youth Muslim Organisation* [Bangladeshi], 74a High Street, Ponders End, Enfield EN3 4ER [Sundays 10.00 - 14.00; contact: Haji Abdul Sattar (8443 2140); languages: **Bengali**, English].

BUSINESS *Bengal Group* [food & drink suppliers], 31a Hartfield Rd, Wimbledon SW19 3SG (8542 9090).

EDUCATION Nearly 100 places in London offer mother-tongue classes for children in **Bengali**. For full details, visit <www.resourceunit.com>. Courses for adults are available at *SOAS Language Centre* (7898 4888), *Tower Hamlets College* (7510 7777) and *Tower Hamlets Lifeling Learning Service* (8983 1047).

Bengali Community Education Centre, 106 High Rd, NW10 2PP (8451 6800).

HEALTH & BEAUTY General information on cancer in Bengali is available at *Asian Cancer Information Line* (freephone 08088 080000). An information leaflet on *breast cancer* is available in Bengali from the *Women's Nationwide Cancer Control Campaign*, 1st fl, Charity Ho, 14-15 Perseverence Works, EC2 8BD (7729 4688, fax 7613 0771).

Quitline [in **Bengali / Sylheti**; for help with stopping smoking] (0800 002 244).

Leaflets on Caring for Dementia are available in Bengali from the *Alzheimer's Disease Society*, Gordon Ho, 10 Greencoat Pl, SW1P 1PH (7306 0606).

LANGUAGE **Bengali** is an Indic language which has official status both in Bangladesh and the Indian state of West Bengal (which includes the city of Calcutta). It is written in a semi-syllabic script. There are about 250m speakers of **Bengali** worldwide of whom it is the primary language of about 190m.

According to the *Multilingual Capital* (2000) survey, the great majority of schoolchildren for whom Bengal*i* is recorded as the home language are descendents of immigrants from Bangladesh (but some others are from the Indian state of West Bengal). A substantial proportion of the **Bangladeshi** immigrants came from Sylhet in the eastern part of that country where **Sylheti**, a language related to Bengali, is spoken. Many Bangladeshis in London thus speak Sylheti rather than **Bengali** at home. However, it is not easy to determine the proportion of speakers of Sylheti. One reason is that everyone who speaks Sylheti also knows Bengali to a greater or lesser extent and tends to regard Bengali as the cultural language of all Bangladeshis. The survey found that six London boroughs recorded separate figures for Sylheti and Bengali, seven overtly combined Bengali and Sylheti in a single figure, while the rest recorded only Bengali. For those reasons, *Multilingual Capital* amalgamated the figures for **Bengali** and **Sylheti** and found that these were the first languages of 40,459 London schoolchildren of whom almost half (19,149) lived in Tower Hamlets.

The combined figures for Bengali and Sylheti make this the home language of more London schoolchildren than any other language (apart from **English**), This displayed on Map 9 at <www.global-london.com/gallery>, which reveals that speakers are largely concentrated in an area stretching from Westminster to Newham.

MEDIA & INFORMATION *Notundin* [Bengali newspaper], Brady Centre, Hanbury St, E1 5HU (7247 6280); *Surma* is a Bengali-language weekly newspaper published in London (8981 8832); *Spectrum Radio,* International Radio Centre, 4 Ingate Pl, SW8 3NS (7627 4433) [broadcasting in Bengali 00.00 - 01.00 Tue-Sat]; *Sunrise Radio Ltd*, Sunrise Ho, Sunrise Rd, Southall, UB2 4AU (8574 6666) [broadcasting in Bengali 00.00 - 01.00 Mon-Sat].

RELIGION Bengalis living in the Indian state of West Bengal are mainly Hindus while those in Bangladesh are overwhelmingly Muslims.

RESTAURANTS Note that, in addition to the restaurants listed below, many of the resturants listed separately under **Indian** are run by Bengalis and/or have Bengali chefs.

South East 1 *Bengal Clipper,* 31 Shad Thames, Southwark SE1 2YR (7357 9001).

West 1 *Bay of Bengal,* 26 Greek St, W1V 5LL (7734 0384).

West Central *New Shaha Bhag Bengal & Indian,* 52 Tavistock Pl, Bloomsbury WC1H 9RG (7833 8160).

Barnet *Bengal Bertie's,* 355 Ballards La, North Finchley N12 8LJ (8343 8332); *Bengal Brasserie T/A,* 40 Grants Close, Mill Hill NW7 1DD; *Golden Bengal T/A,* 96 Audley Rd, Hendon NW4 3HG.

Brent *Golden Bengal Tandoori,* 12-13 Empire Parade, Empire Way, Wembley HA9 0RQ (8902 8082/8147); *Standard Bengal,* 33 High Rd, Willesden NW10 2TE (8459 1999).

Camden *Bengal Lancer,* 253 Kentish Town Rd, NW5 2JT (7485 6688); *Bengal Village,* 2 Elm Terrace, Constantine Rd, NW3 2LL (7485 9921).

Croydon *Haweli of West Wickham T/A,* 576 Wickham Rd, Croydon CR0 8DN (8777 0881).

Enfield *Bengal Lancer T/A,* 187 Hertford Rd, Lower Edmonton N9 7EP.

Hammersmith & Fulham *Bengal Heritage T/A,* 26 Filmer Rd, Fulham SW6 7BW (7381 6123).

Haringey *Kamil Bengal,* 153 Tottenham La, Hornsey N8 9BT (8341 2964, 8348 5309).

Islington *Bengal Balti House,* 6 Brecknock Rd, Holloway N7 0DD (7609 7075); *Bengal Brasserie,* 85 Junction Rd, Archway N19 5QU (7263 0831).

Lambeth *Bengal Balti House T/A,* 58a Morrish Rd, Brixton SW2 4EG (8674 6100); *Lancer of Bengal,* 220 Brixton Hill, Brixton SW2 1HE (8674 4736);

Lewisham *Bengal Brasserie,* 79 Springbank Rd, Lewisham SE13 6SS (8244 2442); *Bengali Spice,* 144 Sydenham Rd, SE26 5JZ (8778 0146); *Star of Bengal T/A,* 26 Deptford High St, Deptford SE8 4AF (8691 6425).

Merton *Taste of Bengal T/A,* 147 Kingston Rd, Wimbledon SW19 1LJ (8542 0560).

Richmond *Bengal Brasserie,* 162 Stanley Rd, Teddington TW11 8UD (8977 7332).

Tower Hamlets *Bengal Clipper T/A,* 250 Bethnal Green Rd, E2 0AA; *Bengal Cuisine,* 12 Brick La., E1 6RF (7377 8405); *Bengal Lancer T/A,* 250 Bethnal Green Rd, E2 0AA; *Bengal Trader,* 1 Parliament Ct, 44 Artillery La, Spitalfields, E1 (7375 0072); *Empress of Bengal,* 141 Leman St., E1 8EY (7702 1168); *Spice of Bengal T/A,* 203 Mile End Rd, E1 4AA; *Tamanna Bengal Cuisine T/A,* 65 New Rd, Whitechapel E1 1HH.

Waltham Forest *Bengal Curry House,* 24 St James's St, Walthamstow E17 7PF (8520 4434/0385).

Westminster *Paradise of Bengal,* 187-189 Queensway, Bayswater W2 5HL (7229 1640).

SHOPS *Bengali Books,* 45 Brick La, E1 6PU (7375 0236); *Bengal Pisces* [fishmongers], 291a Hertford Rd, Lower Edmonton N9 7ES (8805 8842); *Bengal Pride* [frozen food], 65a Vyner St, Bethnal Green E2 9DQ (8981 7172); *Bengal Spice,* 604 Holloway Rd, N19 3PH (7561 1107); *Bengal Vegetable Supplier,* 12 Colchester Rd, Leyton E10 6HA (8988 0778);

Bondor Bazar Cash & Carry, 130 Green St, E13 (8503 4104); *Ridwan Fashion,* 294 Bethnal Green Rd, E2 (7729 6872);

Ruposhi Bangla Ltd [Bengali books and handicrafts], 220 Tooting High St, SW17 0SG (8672 7843).

TRANSLATION *Choudhury's Bengali Translation,* 7 Skipsea Ho, Fitzhugh Grove, Wandsworth SW18 3SF (8874 3135).

TRAVEL Local *Bengal Mini Cabs,* 215 Plashet Rd, Plaistow E13 0QU (8471 3181); **International** *Bengal Enterprise,* 68 Brick La, E1 6RL (7375 3291).

WELFARE *Community Aid (Asian Project),* c/o Rina Choudhury, Ponders End Area Housing Office, Curlew Ho, 4 Napier Rd, Enfield EN3 4QW (8443 4361) [languages: *Bengali,* Hindi, Urdu, English]; *Enfield Asian Welfare Association,* 129-139 South St, Ponders End EN3 4RJ (8443 1197) [languages: Bengali, Gujarati, Hindi, Punjabi, Urdu, English]; *Enfield Bangladesh Welfare Association,* 74a High St, Ponders End EN3 4ER (8804 4006) [languages: *Bengali,* English]; *Newham Bengali Community Trust,* 2 Barking Rd, E6 3BP (8552 9777); *St Dunstans Bengali Resource Centre,* 73 Shandy St, E1 4LX (7790 6607); *Wandsworth Bengali Welfare Association,* 57 Trinity Rd, SW17 7SD (8672 9308).

Benin

As well as being the name of an independent country (previously known as Dahomey, see *Beninois* below), Benin is also the name of an important Nigerian city and of the language spoken in that area. As a language name, Benin is a variant of Bini, itself an alternative name for *Edo* (see under this name).

Beninois

GOVERNMENT *Benin Consulate,* 16 The Broadway, Stanmore HA7 4DW (8954 8800).

LANGUAGES The most important languages of Benin, according to estimates by Guédou (1980), are Fon (spoken by about 30% of the population), *Yoruba* (about 10%), with about 10% each for *Bariba, Ewe* and Goun. *French* has official status.

Benuic

Benuic is a term coined by Dalby (1999-2000) for an important group of *Kwa* languages located in Nigeria and adjoining states. These include both *Yoruba* and *Igbo* among the most widely spoken African languages in London. A map showing the distribution of the *Benuic* languages (collectively) across London can be viewed at <www.global-london.com/gallery> (Map 10).

Berber

Berber is the collective name in English for a number of different but related Tamazic languages which together have around 10m speakers who live mainly in Morocco and Algeria. (Speakers of *Berber* languages do not use the word 'Berber' themselves and this is sometimes considered a pejorative term, being historically related to the word 'barbarian'.) Most North-African-born Berbers in London also speak *Arabic* which is generally accorded more status.

The *Multilingual Capital* (2000) survey, which found only 10 London schoolchildren whose first language was given as **Berber**, suggested that **Arabic** rather than **Berber** may have been misreported as the home language in many cases.

Bermudan

BUSINESS *Bank of Bermuda Representative Office*, 3rd fl, Austin Friars Ho, 2-6 Austin Friars, EC2N 2HE (7296 4000); *Bermuda International Business Association*, Haymarket Ho, 28-29 Haymarket, SW1Y 4SP (7839 5545); *H A & E Smith (Bermuda) Ltd* [import & export agents], 47 Brook St House, Davies St, W1Y1FJ (7493 7422).

GOVERNMENT Bermuda is administered as a an Overseas Territory of the UK.
The Bermuda Society and Secretariat, Five Trees, Wood La, Stanmore HA7 4JZ (8954 0652).

MEDIA & INFORMATION *Live From Bermuda* [film & TV studios], 1 Lower John St, W1R 3PD (7437 7335).

TRAVEL *Bermuda Tourism,* 1 Battersea Church Rd, SW11 3LY (7771 7001).

Berri

Speakers of **Berri** have been reported among London schoolchildren in the recent past but none were recorded at the time of the *Multilingual Capital* (2000) survey. *Berri* is the name of two languages spoken in Sudan, one Saharic and the other Nilotic.

Bihari

Bihari is an Indic language, spoken in the state of Bihar and adjoining areas of India by some 50m people, which is written in the Devanagari semi-syllabic script. Although Bihari-speakers have been noted among London's schoolchildren within the past decade, none were reported in the *Multilingual Capital* (2000) survey.

Bimoba

Bimoba is a Voltaic language spoken in Ghana. The *Multilingual Capital* (2000) survey noted the presence of only one Bimoba-speaking pupil, living in Brent.

Bini

Bini is one of three names given to a language spoken in and around Benin City in Nigeria. See under the alternative name of **Edo** for details.

Bisayan

Bisayan is the name of a group of Hesperonesic languages (which also includes **Cebuano** and **Hiligaynon**). All of these are spoken on various islands in the Philippines. Only two London schoolchilden were reported as speakers of Bisayan at the time of the *Multilingual Capital* (2000) survey (but separate figures were given for Cebuano and Hiligaynon).

Black

ACCOMMODATION *Black Roof Community Housing Association Ltd,* Unit 2, The Stableyard, Broomgrove Rd, Brixton SW9 9TL (7733 6646); *Ebony People's Association,* c/o Patricia Obichukwu Community House, 311 Fore St, Edmonton N9 0PZ (8884 3098) [*Black* mental health]; *Federation of Black Housing Organisations,* 137 Euston Rd, NW1 2AA (7388 1560); *Federation of Black Housing Organisations,* 374 Grays Inn Rd, WC1X 8BB (7837 8288).

ARTS *Afro-Ebony Arts & Craft,* 77f Elgin Ave, W9 2DB (7266 5695); *Black Arts Consultant Ltd,* Shakespeare Business Centre, 245a Coldharbour La, Brixton SW9 8RR; *Black Audio Film Collective,* Bowman Ho, 7-12 Greenland St, Camden NW1 0ND (7267 0846); *Black Productions,* 391 Harrow Rd, W9 3NF (7229 7483); *Black Theatre Co-op,* Unit 3p, Leroy Ho, 436 Essex Rd, Islington N1 3QP (7226 1225); *Black Theatre Forum,* 52 Kennington Oval, Lambeth SE11 5SW (7735 1395); *Black Women in the Arts,* Unit B20, Metropolitan Business Centre, Islington N1 5AZ (7923 7658); *Ebony Promotions,* 103 Talbot Rd, W11 2AT (7221 0652); *Innovative Black Women,* 62d Stamford Hill, Stoke Newington N16 6XS (8801 9226).

ASSOCIATIONS *Association of Black Photographers Ltd,* 5 Hoxton Sq, Islington N1 6NU.

BUSINESS *Black Business Association (Haringey),* 81 Seaford Rd, N15 5DX.

EDUCATION *Black Education Today Ltd,* 24 Parkholme Rd, Hackney E8 3AG (7249 9278); *Camden Black Parents & Teachers Association,* 27-30 Cheriton. Queens Crescent, Kentish Town NW5 4EZ (7284 0030); *Ebony Education Ltd,* 1 5 Dunvegan Rd, Eltham SE9 1RZ.

EMPLOYMENT *Black Employment Initiative,* Unit K 111, Business Design Centre, 52 Upper St, Islington N1 0QH (7288 6806).

HEALTH & BEAUTY

Hair *Black American Hair Centre,* 147 Dawes Rd, SW6 7EB (7386 8932); *Black Rod* [men], 3 Boundaries Rd, Balham SW12 8ET (8673 1192); *Black Rod* [women], 5 Boundaries Rd, Balham SW12 8ET (8673 4332); *Blanc et Noir,* 103 Hamlets Way, Bow E3 4TL (8983 3731); *Concept Noir,* 200 Blackstock Rd, Highbury N5 1EN (7359 9318); *Ebony,* 404 Green St, Plaistow E13 9JJ (8552

8613); *Ebony & Ivory,* 186 Clapham High St, Clapham SW4 7UG (7622 9414).

Massage *Ebony Massage,* 39a Faversham Rd, Catford SE6 4XE (8690 8413).

Medical *Cancer Black Care,* 16 Dalston La, Hackney E8 3AZ (7249 1097); *London Black Women's Health Action Project,* Cornwall Ave, Bethnal Green E2 0HW (8980 3503).

LEGAL *Black Quest for Justice,* 506 Brixton Rd, SW9 8EN (7733 5996); *Mediation Bureau for Black Families* [legal advice], Suite 20, Avenue Ho, East End Rd, Finchley N3 3QE (8343 1944); *Society of Black Lawyers,* Room 9, Winchester Ho, 11 Cranmer Rd, Kennington Park, SW9 6EJ (7735 6592).

MEDIA & INFORMATION

Advertising and public relations *Black Agency* [public relations], Unit 26, 10 Acklam Rd, W10 5QZ (8932 5245); *Black Sponsorship,* Unit 51, Buspace Studios, Conlan St, W10 5AP (7460 8494); *Little Black Book* [advertising directory], P O Box 12886, Battersea SW11 1ZU (7223 1984); *U K Black Links* [advertising], Rivington Ho, 82 Great Eastern St, EC2A 3JF (7749 7244).

Books *Black Book Publishing Ltd,* 25a Kensington Church St, W8 4LL; *Black Film Maker Publications Ltd* [publishing], 2nd fl, Sentinel Ho, Ashley Rd, Tottenham N17 9LZ (8885 6435); *Black Press,* Unit 221 16 Ashley Rd, Leigh Valley Techno Park, Tottenham N17 9LN (8880 4262); *Black Spring Press Ltd,* 126 Cornwall Rd, Southwark SE1 8TQ (7401 2044); *Black Sun plc,* 9 Burlington Lodge Studios, Rigault Rd, Fulham SW6 4JJ (7736 0011); *UK Black Links Ltd,* 1st fl suite, 80 Scrubs La, Willesden NW10 6RF (8964 9649).

Broadcasting *Black Film Maker Publications Ltd* [audio-visual services], Suite 9, 5 Blackhorse La, Walthamstow E17 6DS (8527 9582); *Black Island Studios* [film & TV], Heron Trading Estate, Alliance Rd, Acton W3 0RA (8752 1700).

Magazines *Black Beauty & Hair,* 13 Park Ho, 140 Battersea Park Rd, SW11 4NB (7720 2108); *Black Beauty Professional Magazine,* New Citizen Publications Ltd, 120 High Rd, Willesden Green, NW10 2PN (8459 7201); *Black Echo,* Black Volunteering, 183 Eversholt St, NW1 1DD; *Black Education Today,* 24A Parkholme RD, E8 3AG (72499278); *Black Enterprise Insight,* 3 Stamford St, SE1 9NT (79289955); *Black Perspective,* PO Box 246, SE13 7DL (86926986); *Black to Black,* Southbank Technopark, 90 London Rd, SE1 6LN (77171579); *Blackworld,* JBK Foundation Trust, 441 New Cross Rd, SE14 6TA (8692 5847).

Other *Black Cultural Archives,* 378 Coldharbour La, Brixton SW9 8LF (7738 4591); *Black Net Communications Ltd,* Torrington Ho, High Rd, North Finchley N12 8JW.

SHOPS

Books *Soul of Black Folks* [secondhand books], 407 Cold Harbour La, Brixton SW2 1JH (7738 4141).

Music *Blacker Dread Music Store,* 406 Coldharbour La, Brixton SW9 8LF (7274 5095); *Black Market Records,* 25 D'Arblay St, W1V 3FH (7287 1932); *Black on Black Records,* 1st fl, 44a Charlotte Rd, EC2A 3PD (7613 0404); *Red Records* [Black music specialists], 500 Brixton Way, SW9 (7274 4476).

Other *Black Treasure,* 14 Conlan St, W11 1WD (8960 9997).

SPECIAL *Black Market* [fashion agents], Studio 84, 49 Effra Rd, Brixton SW2 1BZ (7924 9132); *Black Tracing & Investigation Services* [detective agency], 59 Trevelyan Cresent, Harrow HA3 0RG (8909 1911); *Operation Black Vote,* 16-24 Underwood St, Islington N1 7JQ (7684 3860).

WELFARE *Black and Ethnic Minority Community Care Forum,* System Ho, 3 Deanery Rd, Stratford E15 4LT (8221 2386); *Black Cultural Centre,* Gliddon Rd, West Kensington W14 9BL (8741 1119); *Black Drug Workers' Forum,* 30-31 Great Sutton St, EC1V 0DX (7490 4338); *Black Elderly Group,* 86 Bellenden Rd, Peckham SE15 4RQ (7639 8655); *Black Environment Network,* 65-69 White Lion St, Islington N1 9PP (7278 2322); *Black European Community Development Federation,* 150 Townmead Rd, Fulham SW6 2RA (7384 1502); *Black Roof Community Housing Association Ltd* [nursing home], 17 Groveway, Brixton SW9 0AH (7582 4436); *Black Lesbian & Gay Centre,* 5 Westminster Bridge Rd, Southwark SE1 7XW (7620 3885); *Black Womens Mental Health Project,* 12 Donovan Ct, Exton Crescent, Willesden NW10 8DB (8961 6324); *Camden Black Sisters Group,* 2c Falkland Rd, Kentish Town NW5 2PT (7284 3336); *Craig Park Youth Centre (Black Youth Projects),* Asha Urhobo, Lawrence Rd, Edmonton N18 2HN (8803 8292) [languages: **French, Somali,** English]; *East London Black Women's Organisation,* ELBWO Centre, Clinton Rd, Forest Gate E7 0HD (8534 7545); *Ijeoma Black Women's Project,* 628 High Rd, Tottenham N17 9TP (8885 5227); *Mediation Bureau for Black Families* [welfare], 8 Layfield Rd, Hendon NW4 3UG (8202 3980); *National Black Development Agency for the Black Voluntary Sector,* Winchester Ho, 9 Cranmer Rd, Brixton SW9 6EJ (7735 9010); *National Coalition for Black Volunteering,* 35-37 William Rd, NW1 3ER (73871681); *Nehanda Black Womens Organisation,* Knights La, Lower Edmonton N9 0PG (8803 9397); *Resource Unit for Black Volunteering,* 183 Eversholt St, NW1 1BU (7388 8542); *Southall Black Sisters,* 52 Norwood Rd, Southall UB2 4DW (8571 9595);*Southwark Black Women's Centre,* 76 Elsted St, Elephant and Castle SE17 1QG (7708 1643); *Waltham Forest Black People Mental Health Association,* 2 Priory Ave, E17

7QP (8509 2646); *Wandsworth Black Elderly Project,* 966 Garratt La, Tooting SW17 0ND (8767 8426).

Bolivian

BUSINESS *Bolivian and General Tin Trust plc,* 31 Royal Exchange, EC3V 3LP.

GOVERNMENT *Embassy of Bolivia,* 106 Eaton Sq, SW1W 9AD (7235 4248).

LANGUAGES The official language is *Spanish* but significant minorities speak indigenous languages such as *Quechua* and *Aymará*.

RELIGION The population is mainly Christian (Roman Catholic).

RESTAURANTS
Islington *Café Latino* [Bolivian], Holloway Rd, N7.

SHOPS *Amano* [knitware from Bolivia], Highgate Business Centre, 4th fl, 33 Greenwood Pl, NW5 1LB (7267 6918).

TRAVEL *Aerosur Bolivia,* 200 Buckingham Palace Rd, SW1W 9TA (7707 4585); *Magic of Bolivia,* Caelt Gallery, 182 Westbourne Grove, W11 2RH (7221 7310).

Bosnian

ASSOCIATIONS *Bosnia Herzegovina Association in London,* 1st fl, 24 Churton St, Westminster SW1V 2LP (7976 5393); *Bosnian Institute,* 14 St Marks Rd, W11 1RQ (7243 2900).

GOVERNMENT *Embassy of Bosnia and Hercegovina,* Morley Ho, 320 Regent St, W1B 3BB (7255 3758).

LANGUAGE All the main population groups of Bosnia speak varieties of the language formerly known as *Serbo-Croat* and for which there is currently no universally accepted name. Muslims and Roman Catholic Croats write their varieties in the Roman alphabet while Orthodox Serbs employ the Cyrillic alphabet.

RELIGION The three main religions are Islam (44%), Christian - Orthodox (33%), and Christian - Roman Catholic (17%; *Whitaker's* 2002).

WELFARE *Bosnia and Herzegovina Community Biblioteka,* Cricklewood Broadway, NW2; *Bosnia Herzegovina Heritage Rescue,* Omnibus Business

Centre, 39-41 North Rd, N7 9DP (7700 8469); *Bosnian Refugee Information Centre,* 62 Mill La, NW6 1NJ (7433 3834).

Botswana

Botswana is the name of a country whose national language is *Setswana* and whose people are termed *Batswana* (plural; *Motswana* singular). The people and, to a lesser extent, their language, are frequently termed in English by the root common to all these words, *Tswana* which should be consulted.

There are some 5m Tswana people in all of whom about one third live in Botswana while two thirds live in South Africa.

GOVERNMENT *Botswana High Commission,* 6 Stratford Pl, W1C 1AY (7499 0031).

LANGUAGES *Setswana* is the first language of more than 90% of the population. Several other Bantuic and Khoisanic languages are spoken by small minorities. *English* has official status.

Brass

Details of *Brass,* a language spoken in Nigeria, will be found under its alternative name of *Nembe.*

Bravanese

Bravanese is the word currently most often used to designate the *Baraawe* people of the *Brava* area of Somalia who came to London as refugees, and this word is also applied to their language.

EDUCATION Mother-tongue instruction for children in *Bravanese* is currently available in Barnet; see <www.resourceunit.com> for further information.

LANGUAGE *Bravanese* is a distinctive Bantuic language, also known in London as *Brava* or *Barawan,* but whose Bantu name is *Cimiini*. This language is quite closely related to *Swahili* and, in the *Multilingual Capital* (2000) survey, the figures for *Bravanese* included with those for Swahili.

WELFARE *Somali Bravanese Action Group,* 340 High Road Leyton, E10 5PW (8558 2204).

Brazilian

ARTS *Brazilian Contemporary Arts,* 241 King St, W6 9LP (8741 9579); *Brazilian Music & Dance,* 2 Orford Ho, 1 Rawlings St, SW3 2LR (07956 659440).

ASSOCIATIONS *Anglo Brazilian Society,* 32 Green St, W1Y 3FD (7493 8493); *Hispanic and Luso Brazilian Council,* Canning Ho, 2 Belgrave Sq, SW1X 8PJ (7235 2303)

BARS & NIGHT-CLUBS *Terra Brasil - Barzinho,* 36-38 Chalton St, NW1 (7388 6554) [Fri & Sat nights only].

BUSINESS *Banco do Brasil S.A.,* 34, King St, EC2V 8ES (7606 7101); *Banco Mercantil de São Paulo,* 24 Bruton St, W1J 6QQ (7499 6867); *Banespa,* Trinity Tower, 9 Thomas More Sq, E1 (7959 5555).

EDUCATION Mother-tongue instruction for children in Portuguese is available in more than 20 locations in London and, of these, one in Hammersmith specifies that this is Brazilian Portuguese; see <www.resourceunit.com> for details.

More than 60 courses in Portuguese for adults are available in London at a wide range of levels. Of these, a minority specify that instruction is in Brazilian Portuguese; see *Floodlight*, <www.floodlight.co.uk> for details.

FREIGHT *Mina Travel & Freight Ltd,* 33 Westbourne Grove, W2 (7792 4690); *Sheikha Freight,* 6 Shepherds Bush Rd, W6 7PJ (8746 1113).

GOVERNMENT *Brazilian Aeronautical Commission in Europe,* 16 Great James St, WC1N 3DP (7405 5062); *Brazilian Consulate General,* 6 St Albans St, SW1Y 4SQ (7930 9055); *Brazilian Embassy,* 32 Green St, W1K 7AU (7499 0877); *Brazilian Embassy,* 54 Mount St, W1K 2SQ (7629 5435); *Brazilian Naval Commission,* 170 Upper Richmond Rd, Putney, SW15 2SH (8246 4400).

HEALTH AND BEAUTY *Hair Brasil,* 469 Fulham Rd, SW6 (7385 6671); *Hair Brazil,* 48 Harrowby St, W1 (7724 2422); *London School of Capoeira,* Units 1-2, Leeds Pl, Tollington Park, N4 (7281 2020).

LANGUAGES ***Portuguese*** is the official and dominant language of Brazil but a range of indigenous languages are spoken by minorities and some immigrant groups retain their traditional languages.

Brazilian Portuguese differs from varieties spoken in Portugal in a number of respects. See EDUCATION for details of specifically Brazilian Portuguese language courses available in London.

MEDIA & INFORMATION *Brasilnet* [monthly magazine in Portuguese], PO Box 21276, W9 3YL (8964 5077); *Leros* [monthly magazine in Portuguese], PO Box 19037, N7 9WU (7687 0173); *SPI Publicações Brasileiras,* Shop E3, Queensway Market, 23-25 Queensway, W2 4QJ (7792 2931).

RECREATION *London School of Capoeira,* Units 1-2, Leeds Pl, Tollington Park, N4 (7281 2020).

RELIGION Although most Brazilians are Roman Catholics, no Catholic church catering specifically for Brazilians has yet been identified. Other Christian groups which hold services for Brazilians ibnclude: *Assembléia de Deus Brasileira em Londres,* 14 New Cross Rd, SE14 (7732 0999); *Assembléia de Deus de Londres,* 182b Kensington Park Rd, W11 (8451 9501); Hampden Chapel, Lauriston Rd, E9; *Comunidade Evangélica Pão da Vida,* 116 Bramley Rd, W10 6SU (8964 4306); *Comunidade Pentecostal de Londres,* 1a Tubbs Rd, NW10 (8961 5453); *Igreja Presbiteriana Renovada,* 620 Harrow Rd, W9 (8621 7784).

RESTAURANTS

West 1 *Touch Café,* 40-42 Oxford St, W1 (7636 7222).

Camden *Terra Brasil,* 36-38 Chalton St, NW1 (7388 6554) [Mon - Fri lunch only; Sun 12.30–6.30].

Hammersmith & Fulham *Brazil Pizzaria & Restaurante,* 511 Fulham Rd, SW6 (7385 2244); *Brazilian Paulo's,* 30 Greyhound Rd, W6 (7385 9264).

Westminster *Rodízio Rico,* 111 Westbourne Grove, W2 4UW (7792 4035).

SHOPS *Mercearia Brasil* [groceries], 773 Harrow Rd, NW10 (8962 0252); *São Paulo Imports (SPI),* Shop E3, Queensway Market, 23-25 Queensway, W2 4QJ (7792 2931).

SPECIAL *Hispanic & Luso Brazilian Council,* 2 Belgrave Sq, SW1X 8PJ (7235 2303).

TRAVEL *Brazil Air,* 23 Eccleston St, SW1W 9LX (7730 3024); *Mina Travel & Freight Ltd,* 33 Westbourne Grove, W2 (7792 4690); *Varig Brazilian Airlines,* 63 Conduit St, W1R 0HG (7287 3131); *Veloso Tours,* 34 Warple Way, W3 0RG (8762 0616).

British

ACCOMMODATION *British Hotel Reservation Centre,* Victoria Station, Buckingham Palace Rd, SW1W 0SH (7730 5296).

ARTS & CULTURE *Association of British Orchestras,* Francis Ho, Francis St, SW1P 1DE (7828 6913); *British Cartoon Centre* [and galleries], 7 & 60 Brunswick Sq, WC1 (7278 7172/8337);

British Film Institute, 21 Stephen St, W1P 2LN (7255 1444); *British Library,* 96 Euston Rd, NW1 2DB (7412 7000).; *British Museum,* Great Russell St, Bloomsbury WC1B 3DG (7636 1555); *Composers Guild of Great Britain,* The Penthouse, 4 Brook St, W1Y 1AA (7629 0886); *Federation of British Artists,* 17 Carlton House Terrace, SW1Y 5BD (7930 6844); *Imperial War Museum,* Lambeth Rd, SE1 6HZ (7416 5000); *National Youth Jazz Orchestra of Great Britain,* 11 Victor Rd, Harrow HA2 6PT (8863 2717); *National Youth Theatre of Great Britain,* 443-445 Holloway Rd, N7 6LW (7281 3863); *Paul Mellon Centre for Studies in British Art,* 16 Bedford Sq, Bloomsbury WC1B 3JA (7580 0311); *Royal Society of Musicians of Great Britain,* 10 Stratford Pl, W1N 9AE (7629 6137); *Royal Society of British Sculptors,* 108 Old Brompton Rd,

South Kensington SW7 3RA (7244 7788); *World Monuments Fund in Britain,* 39-40 St James's Pl, SW1A 1NR (7499 8254); *Writers' Guild of Great Britain,* 15 Britannia St, WC1X 0JN (7833 0777).

ASSOCIATIONS *British Astronomical Association,* Burlington Ho, Piccadilly, W1J 0DU (7734 4145); *British Ecological Society,* 26 Blades Ct, 121 Deodar Rd, Putney SW15 2NU (8871 9797); *British Interplanetary Society,* 27 South Lambeth Rd, SW8 1SZ (7735 3160); *Restaurateurs' Association of Great Britain,* 28 Kingsway, WC2B 6JR (7831 8727).

BUSINESS *Association of British Insurers,* 51-55 Gresham St, EC2V 7HQ (7600 3333); *British Bankers Association,* Pinners Hall, 105-108 Old Broad St, EC2N 1AP (7216 8800); *British Linen Bank Ltd,* 8 Fredericks Pl, EC2R 8AB (7601 6840).

EDUCATION *Association of British Language Schools,* 11 Golders Green Rd, Golders Green NW11 8DY (8455 6528); *British Association for Early Childhood Education,* 111 City View Ho, 463 Bethnal Green Rd, E2 9QY (7739 7594); *British Association for Literacy in Development,* 14 Dufferin St, EC1Y 8PD (7426 5828).

FREIGHT *Cross Britain Express Couriers,* RAB Bermondsey Trading Estate, Rotherhithe New Rd, SE16 3LL (7233 0001).

HEALTH & BEAUTY

British Acupuncture Council, Park Ho, 206-208 Latimer Rd, W10 6RE (8964 0222); *British Deaf Association,* 1 Worship St, EC2A 2AB (7588 3529); *British Diabetic Association,* 10 Queen Anne St, W1M 0BD (7323 1531); *British Dyslexia Association,* 29 Carlton Rd, N11 3EX (8361 3013); *British Geriatrics Society,* 1 St. Andrews Pl, NW1 4LB (7935 4004); *British Heart Foundation,* 14 Fitzhardinge St, W1H 4DH (7935 0185); *British Lung Foundation,* 78 Hatton Gdn, EC1N 8JA (7831 5831); *British Medical Association,* BMA Ho, Tavistock Sq, WC1H 9JP (7387 4499); *British Sleep Foundation,* 40-42 Osnaburgh St, Camden NW1 3ND (7546 1580); *British Society for Rheumatology,* 41 Eagle St, WC1R 4AP (7242 3313); *British Society for Surgery of the Hand,* Royal College of Surgeons, 35-43 Lincolns Inn Fields, WC2A 3PN (7831 5162); *British Society of Clinical Hypnotherapists,* 229a Sussex Gdns, W2 2RL (7499 2813); *British British Society of Gastroenterology,* 3 St. Andrews Pl, Camden NW1 4LB (7387 3534); *British Stammering Association,* 15 Old Ford Rd, Bethnal Green E2 9PJ (8983 1003); *Multiple Sclerosis Society of Great Britain & Northern Ireland,* 83 Dalmeny Ave, Streatham SW16 4RR (8679 7819).

LEGAL *British Institute of Human Rights,* 8th fl, 75-79 York Rd, Southwark SE1 7AW (7401 2712); *British Irish Rights Watch,* 20-21 Tooks Ct, EC4A 1LB (7405 6415); *Malik Law Chambers,* 233 Bethnal Green Rd, E2 6AB (7613 5454) [human rights, immigration, nationality].

MEDIA & INFORMATION *BBC,* Broadcasting Ho, Portland Pl, W1A 1AA (7580 4468); *BBC,* Television Centre, Wood La, W12 7RJ (8743 8000);

MOTORING *Association of British Drivers,* P O Box 19608, Upper Norwood SE19 2ZW (07000 781544); *John Reeves British Motorcycle Repairs & Restoration,* 37 Hamilton Rd, Twickenham TW2 6SN (8894 9749).

RECREATION *British Armwrestling Association,* 21 Sheringham Rd, Penge SE20 7YH (8778 4463); *British Association of Leisure Parks, Piers & Attractions,* 25 Kings Terrace, NW1 0JP (7383 7942); *British Dance Council,* Terpsichore Ho, 240 Merton Rd, South Wimbledon SW19 1EQ (8545 0085); *British Darts Organisation Ltd,* 2 Page's La, Muswell Hill N10 1PS (8883 5544); *British Field Sports Society,* 367 Kennington Rd, Lambeth, SE11 4PT (7582 5432); *British Greyhound Racing Board,* 32 Old Burlington St, W1X 1LB (7292 9900); *British Horseracing Board Ltd,* 42 Portman Sq, W1H 0EN (7396 0011); *British Institute for Chinese Martial Arts,* Mill Hill Boys School, The Ridgeway, Mill Hill NW7 1QS (8455 6636); *British International Rowing Office,* 6 Lower Mall, Hammersmith W6 9DJ (8741 7580); *British Karate Kyokushinkai,* 97 Tyneham Rd, Battersea SW11 5XG (7350 0881); *British Karate Shikukai,* 24 Brookdale Rd, Walthamstow E17 6QL (8521 7791); *British Ki Aikido Association,* 17 Langland Gdns, Hampstead NW3 6QE (7435 1330); *British Sub-aqua Club,* Seymour Leisure Centre, Seymour Pl, W1H 5TJ (7723 8336); *British Tae Kwon-Do Council,* 58 Wiltshire La, Pinner HA5 2LU (8429 0878); *British Tai Chi Chuan Centre,* 208 Maybank Rd, South Woodford E18 1ET (8502 9307); *British Tennis Foundation,* Queens Club, Palliser Rd, West Kensington W14 9EG (7381 7000); *British Water Ski Federation,* 390 City Rd, EC1V 2QA (7833 2855); *Martial Arts Academy Great Britain,* 10 Northumberland Park, Tottenham N17 0TX (8801 9970); *Shorinji Kempo British Federation,* 11 Bishops Close, Archway N19 5YJ (7281 8907); *Theatregoers Club of Great Britain,* Harling Ho, 47-51 Great Suffolk St, SE1 0BS (7450 4040).

RELIGION *British Council of Protestant & Christian Churches,* 258-260 Bedfont La, Feltham TW14 9NU (8844 2152); *Council of Churches for Britain & Ireland,* 35-41 Lower Marsh, Southwark SE1 7RL (7620 4444).

RESTAURANTS

East Central *Bill Bentley's* [fish], Swedeland Ct, 202 Bishopgate, EC2 (7283 1763); *City Rhodes,* 1 New Street Sq, EC4 (7583 1313); *Fish Central* [fish and chips], 149-151 Central St, EC1V 8AP (7253 4970); *Futures* [vegetarian], 2 Exchange Sq, EC2 (7638 6341); *Home,* 100-106 Leonard St, EC2 (7684 8618); *P O S H British Colonial Restaurants Ltd,* 7a Leonard St, EC2A 4AQ; *Prism,* 147 Leadenhall St, EC3 (7256 3888); *Quality Chop House,* 92-94 Farringdon Rd, EC1 (7837 5093); *St John,* 26 St John St, EC1 (7251 0848); *Sweetings,* 39 Queen Victoria St, EC4 (7248 3062); *The Place Below* [vegetarian], St Mary-le-Bow, Cheapside, City, EC2 (7329 0789); *Vic Naylor,* 38-40 St John St, EC1 (7608 2181).

South East 1 *Butler's Wharf Chop House,* Butlers Wharf Bldg, 26E Shad Thames, SE1 (7403 3403); *Honest Cabbage,* 99 Bermondsey St, Bermondsey, SE1 (7234 0080).

South West 1 *Fifth Floor,* Harvey Nichols, Knightsbridge, SW1 (7235 5250); *Tate Gallery Restaurant,* The Tate Gallery, Millbank, Pimlico,SW1 (7887 8877); *Wiltons,* 55 Jermyn St, St James's, SW1 (7629 9955).

West 1 *Alastair Little,* 49 Frith St, Soho, W1 (7734 5183); *Atlantic Bar & Grill,* 20 Glasshouse St, Soho W1B 5DJ (7734 4888); *Connaught,* 16 Carlos Pl, Mayfair, W1 (7499 7070); *Circus,* 1 Upper James St, Soho, W1 (7534 4010); *Greenhouse,* 27A Hay's Mews, W1 (7499 3331); *Lindsay House,* 21 Romilly St, W1 (7439 0450); *Red Room,* Downstairs at Waterstone's, 203-206 Piccadilly, W1 (7851 2464); *R K Stanley's,* 6 Little Portland St, W1 (7462 0099); *Sotheby's Café,* 34-35 New Bond St, Mayfair, W1 (7293 5077); *Titanic,* 81 Brewer St, Soho, W1 (7437 1912); *Zinc Bar & Grill,* 21 Heddon St, Mayfair W1 (7255 8800).

West Central *Bank Aldwych,* 1 Kingsway, WC2 (7379 9797); *British Museum Court Restaurant,* Great Russell St, WC1 (7323 8978); *Cafe in the Crypt,* St Martin-in-the-Fields, Duncannon St, Trafalgar Square, WC2 (7839 4342); *Cooper's,* 49a Lincoln's Inn Fields, WC1 (7831 6211); *North Sea Fish Restaurant,* 8 Leigh St, WC1 (7837 5892) [fish and chips]; *Rock & Sol Plaice, The,* 47 Endell St, Covent Garden WC2 (7836 3785); *Rules,* 55 Maiden La, Covent Garden WC2 (7836 5314) *Rules,* 35 Maiden La, Covent Garden WC2 (7379 0258); *Savoy Grill,* The Strand, WC2 (7836 4343); *Simpson's in the Strand,* 100 The Strand, WC2 (7836 9112); *Union Tavern,* 52 Lloyd Baker St, King's Cross, WC1 (7278 0111).

Camden *Sauce,* 214 Camden High St, NW1 (7482 0777); *The Engineer,* 65 Gloucester Ave, Primrose Hill, NW1 (7722 0950).

Hackney *Boulevard,* 91 Lauriston Rd, Victoria Park E9 (8533 3341); *Cafe Booze,* 87 Lauriston Rd, Victoria Park E9, (8985 8941); *Faulkner's,* 424-426 Kingsland Rd, Dalston, E8 (7254 6152) [fish and chips]; *Frocks,* 95 Lauriston Rd, Victoria Park E9 (8986 3161).

Hammersmith & Fulham *Anglesea Arms,* 5 Wingate Rd, W6 (8749 1291); *Stonemason's Arms,* 54 Cambridge Gr, W6 (8748 1397); *The Gate* [vegetarian], 51 Queen Caroline St, W6 (8748 6932).

Islington *Euphorium,* 203 Upper St, Islington N1 (7704 6909); *Harbour,* 302 Upper St, Islington N1 (); *Kavanagh's,* 26 Penton St, N1 (7833 1380).

Kensington & Chelsea *Maggie Jones's,* 6 Old Court Pl, Kensington Church St, W8 (7937 6462); *New Restaurant at the V&A,* The Victoria & Albert Museum, Cromwell Rd, South Kensington, SW7 (7942 2506).

Richmond *The Depot,* Tideway Yard, Mortlake High St, SW14 (8878 9462); *The Glasshouse,* 14 Station Parade, Kew, TW9 (8940 6777).

Tower Hamlets *Cherry Orchard,* 241-247 Globe Rd, E2 (7890 6678); *Landy's at the Space,* 269 Westferry Rd, Isle of Dogs, E14 (7515 7799); *Quayside,* World Trade Centre, 1 St Katharine's Way, E1 (7481 0972).

Wandsworth *Buchan's,* 62-64 Battersea Bridge Rd, Battersea, SW11 (7228 0888); *Chez Bruce,* 2 Bellevue Rd, SW17 (8672 0114); *Ship,* 41 Jews Row, SW18 (8870 9667).

Westminster *Veronica's British Restaurant,* 3 Hereford Rd, Bayswater W2 4AB (7229 5079).

SHOPS

Books *British Library Book Shop,* 96 Euston Rd NW1 2DB (7412 7735);

Clothing *British Boot Co.* [footwear], 5 Kentish Town Rd, NW1 (7485 8505); *British Designer Knitwear,* Unit 4, The Ritz Arc, Piccadilly W1V 9DQ (7629 6614); *The British Hatter,* 36 Kensington Church St, W8 4BX (7361 0000).

Food *A Gold*, 42 Brushfield St, E1 (7247 2487); *The Cheesemonger* [British farm-made cheeses], 148 Westway, Raynes Park SW20 9LS (8395 6082); *Two Figs* [British farmhouse cheeses], 101 Newington Green Rd, N1 0JL (7690 6811).

SPECIAL *Association of British Introduction Agencies*, 25 Abingdon Rd, Kensington W8 6AH (7937 2800).

TRAVEL *Britain Tours Ltd,* The Colonnades, 34 Porchester Sq, Bayswater W2 6AT (7262 6061); *British Airways,* 200 Buckingham Palace Rd, SW1W 9TA (7707 4587); *British Airways Travel,* 156 Regent St, W1R 5TA (7434 4700); *British Mediterranean Airways,* Cirrus Ho, Bedfont Rd, Staines (01784 266301); *British Tourist Authority* [head office], Thames Tower, Blacks Rd, Hammersmith W6 9EL (8846 9000); *British Tours Ltd,* 49 Conduit St, W1R 9FB (7734 8734); *Great British Tours,* 22-22a Wardour St, W1V 3HH (7434 1843); *Hello Britain Ltd,* 8-10 Neals Yard, WC2H 9DP (7240 4206); *Historic Homes of Britain,* 21 Pembroke Sq, Kensington W8 6PB (7937 2402).

WELFARE *Asylum Aid,* 28 Commercial St, E1 6LS (7377 5123); *Institute of Race Relations,* 2 Leeke St, Wc1X 9HS (7837 0041).

British Sign Language

See under **BSL Signer**

British Virgin Islander

GOVERNMENT The British Virgin Islands are administered as an overseas territory of the UK.

TRAVEL *British Virgin Islands Club,* 7-8 Upper Sq, Isleworth TW7 7BJ (8232 9781); *British Virgin Islands Tourist Board,* 110 St Martins La, WC2N 4DY (7240 4259).

Bruneian

GOVERNMENT *Brunei Darussalam High Commission,* 19-20 Belgrave Sq, SW1X 8P (7581 0521).

LANGUAGE The official and dominant language of Brunei is *Malay.*

TRAVEL *Royal Brunei Airlines,* 49 Cromwell Rd, SW7 2ED (7584 6660).

BSL Signer

British Sign Language (BSL) was reported as the language of only seven schoolchildren in the *Multilingual Capital* (2000) survey but it was suggested that the true figure must be far greater than that and that many boroughs may have felt that only the recording of spoken languages was required. In fact, more than 100 pupils in three London schools receive education through the medium of *BSL* and facilities also exist for training instructors of this language. For more information, contact the British Deaf Association, <www.bda.org.uk>.

TRANSLATION Islington Council Social Services Sign Language Interpreting, 166 Upper St, N1 1XU (7527 3396).

Buddhist

ARTS *London Buddhist Arts Centre,* Eastbourne Ho, Bullards Pl, E2 0PT (8983 6134).

ASSOCIATIONS *Buddhist Association (British),* 11 Biddulph Rd, W9 1JA (7286 5575); *Buddhist Society,* 58 Eccleston Sq, SW1V 1PH (7834 5858) <www.thebuddhistsociety.org.uk>; *Friends of the Western Buddhist Order,* 96 High St, Croydon CR0 1ND (8688 8624); *Friends of the Western Buddhist Order,* 3 Plough La, Purley CR8 3QB (8660 2542); *Friends of the Western Buddhist Order,* 51 Roman Rd, E2 0HU (8980 1960); *Friends of the West London Buddhist Order,* 94 Westbourne Park Villas, W2 5PL (7727 9382); *International Buddhist Progress Society (UK),* 84 Margaret St, W1W 8TD (7636 8394).

RELIGION

Buddhist centres *Buddhapadipa Temple,* 14 Calonne Rd, Wimbledon SW19 5HJ (8946 1357); *Buddhist Center London* [Tibetan, Karma Kagyu (Diamond Way)], c/o Steven James, 27 Johns Mews, WC1N 2NS (7916 2282); *Burmese Buddhist Vihara* [Burmese Theravada], 1 Old Church La, NW9 8TG (8200 6898); *Central London/St James Sangha* [Vietnamese Mahayana], 34 Kennington La, SE11 4LS (7820 9703); *Chua Linh Son,* 89 Bromley Rd, Catford SE 6 (8461 1887); *Croydon Buddhist Centre,* 98 High St, Croydon CR0 1ND (8688 8624); *Dorjechang Buddhist Centre,* 12 Springfield Rd, SW19 7AL (8946 5140); *Drukpa London (Drukpa Kargyud Trust)* [Tibetan, Kagyu, Drikung], 114 Harvist Rd, NW6 6HJ (8964 2337); *Heruka Buddhist Centre,* 13 Woodstock Rd, NW11 8ES (8455 7563); *Jamyang Buddhist Centre,* Lambeth Magistrates Court, Renfrew Rd, SE11 4NB (7820 8787); *Kagyu Samye Dzong Tibetan Buddist Centre,* Carlisle La, Southwark SE1 7LG (7928 5447); *London Buddhist Centre,* 51 Roman Rd, E2 0HU (8981 1225); *London Buddhist Vihara* [Theravada], The Avenue, W4 1UD (8995 9493); *London Ch'an Group* [Chinese Zen], 20 Goodhall St, NW10 6TU (8961 7802); *London Diamond Way Centre,* 27 Johns Mews, WC1N 2NS (7916 2282); *London Group of the International Zen Association UK (North)*

[Japanese Soto], Highbury Roundhouse Community Centre, 71 Ronalds Rd, N7; *London Group of the International Zen Association UK (South)* [Japanese Soto], 4a Park St, off Stoney St, SE1; *London Group of the International Zen Association UK (West)* [Japanese Soto], Shiatsu College, Unit 62, Pall Mall Deposit, 126-128 Barlby Rd, W10; *London Shambhala Centre,* 27 Belmont Close, SW4 6AY (7720 3207); *London Soto Zen Group* [Japanese Soto], 23 Westbere Rd, NW2; *London Zen Group* [Korean Chogye], 13 Rodney Pl, SW19 2LQ (8542 5826); *North London Buddhist Centre,* St Marks Studio, Chillingworth Rd, N7 8TJ (7700 3075); *Quan Am Ni Tu Temple* [Vietnamese Mahayana], 8 Fenn St, Hackney E9 6JN (8985 1122); *Redbridge Buddhist Cultural Centre* [Theravada (Sri Lanka)], 9 Balfour Rd, Ilford, IG1 4HP (8478 8286); *RIGPA Buddhist Centre* [Tibetan Nyingmapa], 330 Caledonian Rd, N1 1BB (7700 0185); *ROKPA - London* [Tibetan Kagyu], c/o Ramos-Gonzales, 67 Parkholme Rd, Dalston E8 3AQ (8254 5004); *Zen London* [Korean Zen], 11 Dorchester Ct, Leigham Court Rd, SW16 2PH (8696-7601); *Saint James's Church Sangha* [Vietnamese Zen], 7 Sundorne Rd, SE7 7PR (8293 1775); *Satipanna - City Buddhist Meditation Centre* [Burmese Vipassana (Mahasi)], 156 Morton Way, Southgate, N14 (8886 0076); *South London Sangha,* 102 Alleyn Rd, SE21 8AH (8670 6388); *Sri Saddhatissa International Buddhist Centre* [Burmese Theravada], 309-311 Kingsbury Rd, NW9 9PE (8204 3301); *Zen Practice Centre* [Japanese Soto/Rinzai], 22 Nettlewood Rd, SW16 5DX (8679 5412).

Temples *Linh Sonh Phat Duong Temple* [Vietnamese Mahayana], 11 Ermine Rd, Tottenham N15 (8809 1566); *Linh Son Tu Temple* [Vietnamese Mahayana], 76 Beulah Hill, Upper Norwood SE19 3EW (8771 5933/5484); *London Zendo Hannya Temple,* 10 Belmont St, NW1 8HH (7485-9576); *Thich Ca Temple* [Vietnamese], 185a Victoria Rise, Clapham (8627 0393).

RESTAURANTS *Wild Cherry,* 241-245 Globe Rd, Bethnal Green E2 0JD (8980 6678).

SHOPS *Jambala Bookshop,* 247 Globe Rd, Bethnal Green E2 0JD (8981 4037); *London Buddhist Centre,* 51 Roman Rd, E2 0HU (8981 1225); *Wisdom Books,* 402 Hoe St, E17 9AA (8520 5588); *Wisdom Books Distribution Ltd* (books on Buddhism), 25 Stanley Rd, Ilford IG1 1RW (8553 5020); *Zam Tibetan Buddhist Shop,* 330 Caledonian Rd, Islington N1 1BB (7700 0334).

SPECIAL *Buddhist Cooperative,* 5 Hindmans Rd, SE22 9NF (8693 9951).

WELFARE *Britain Burma Buddhist Trust,* 1 Old Church La, NW9 8TG (8200 6898); *Buddhist Interhelp* [Vietnamese Zen], 12 Shell Rd, SE13 7TW (8692 1737).

Bukusu

Bukusu is a Bantuic language of Kenya, reported among the languages spoken by schoolchildren in Southwark by the *Multilingual Capital* (2000) survey.

Bulgarian

ASSOCIATIONS *British Bulgarian Friendship Society,* c/o Finsbury Library, 245 St. John St, Clerkenwell EC1V 4QJ (7837 2304);

BUSINESS *British Bulgarian Chamber of Commerce,* 186 Queens Gate, South Kensington SW7 5HL (7584 8333); *Bulgarian Foreign Trade Bank,* 1 Gracechurch St, EC3V 0DD (7626 1888); *Bulgaria House Ltd* [import agents], 85 Upwood Rd Lewisham SE12 8AL (8265 2266); *Bulgarian Vintners Co Ltd,* Nazdrave Ho, 154 Caledonian Rd, N1 9RD (7841 6500).

EDUCATION *SSEES* (7862 8634) offers university courses in **Bulgarian**.

GOVERNMENT *Republic of Bulgaria Embassy,* 186-188 Queens Gate, SW7 5HL (7584 9400).

LANGUAGE **Bulgarian**, the official language of Bulgaria, is a Slavonic language written in the Cyrillic alphabet. The *Multilingual Capital* (2000) survey reported that there were 248 Bulgarian-speaking pupils in London schools.

RELIGION The great majority of Bulgarians are Christians belonging to the Bulgarian Orthodox Church but a significant minority, about 13%, are Muslims.

TRANSLATION *Bulgarian Language & Business Services Ltd,* 71 Glen Albyn Rd, SW19 6HB (8788 3646).

Buli

Buli is among the languages reportedly spoken by London schoolchildren in recent years, although none were recorded in the *Multilingual Capital* (2000) survey. Unfortunately, **Buli** is the name of three different languages so it cannot be correctly identified without knowing the speakers' place of origin. (These languages are spoken in Nigeria, Indonesia, and Ghana.)

Buma

Although not recorded in the *Multilingual Capital* (2000) survey, **Buma** has been reported as the language of a few London schoolchildren within the past decade. Unfortunately, Buma is the name of three different languages – a language of the Solomon Islands, a Bantuic language of Congo/Kinshasa, and a Nilotic language of Ethiopia. Thus the precise language spoken cannot be correctly identified without knowing the speakers' place of origin.

Burmese

Although Burma officially changed its name to Myanmar in 1989 (*Whitaker's Almanack 2002*), the words Burma (for the country) and Burmese (as the adjective, and as the name for the people of Burma) remain in general use in Britain and are preferred here.

EDUCATION Courses in **Burmese** are available at *SOAS Language Centre* (7898 4888).

GOVERNMENT *Embassy of the Union of Myanmar*, 19a Charles St, W1J 5DX (7499 8841).

LANGUAGES **Burmese** is the official language of Burma and the first language of about 60% of its population. Burmese is an Irriwadic languages which is written in its own semi-syllabic script. The *Multilingual Capital* (2000) survey found that there were then 39 **Burmese**-speaking schoolchildren in London.

More than 100 other languages are spoken in Burma but, of these, only the Karen languages (collectively), Arakanese, and Shan are spoken by more than 5% of the population (*Ethnologue*).

RELIGION About 90% of the population of Burma is Buddhist. The remaining 10% comprises Christians, Muslims, and Hindus.

Burmese Buddhist Vihara [Burmese Theravada], 1 Old Church La, NW9 8TG (8200 6898); *Satipanya - City Buddhist Meditation Centre* [Burmese Vipassana (Mahasi)], 156 Morton Way, Southgate, N14 (8886 0076); *Sri Saddhatissa International Buddhist Centre* [Burmese Theravada], 309-311 Kingsbury Rd, NW9 9PE (8204 3301).

RESTAURANTS

Westminster *Mandalay*, 444 Edgware Rd, W2 1EG (7258 3696).

WELFARE *Britain Burma Buddhist Trust,* 1 Old Church La, NW9 8TG (8200 6898); *Burma Campaign UK Ltd*, Bickerton Ho, 25-27 Bickerton Rd, N19 5JT (7281 7377); *Burma Star Association*, 4 Lower Belgrave St, SW1W 0LA (7823 4273).

Burundi

Burundi is a nationality but not an ethnic name. More than 80% of íthe people of Burundi are Hutus, the remainder Tutsis.

GOVERNMENT Burundi interests in Britain are represented from its embassy in Belgium at Maria-Louizaplein 46, B-1040 Brussels (+32 2 230 4535).

LANGUAGES The official languages of Burundi are **Kirundi** and **French. Swahili** is also widely known.

Burushaski

Burushaski is among the language names which have been reported as spoken by some London schoolchildren within the past decade although none were found by the *Multilingual Capital* (2000) survey. According to Dalby's (1999-2000) classification, **Burushaski** is the collective name for three languages of the South-Asia geozone spoken in Pakistan and Kashmir.

Byelorussian

For all entries relation to the people, culture, and language of Belarus, see under **Belarusian**.

Calabari

The word **Calabari** refers both to the town of Calabar on the Niger Delta in Nigeria and to the dominant language of that area.

LANGUAGE **Calabari**, for which the spelling *Kalabari* is often preferred as a language name, is a Deltic language spoken in Nigeria. At the time of the *Multilingual Capital* (2000) survey, this was reported as the first language of 17 pupils in London, most of whom lived in Lambeth.

RESTAURANTS

Barnet *Mama Calabar*, 25-27 Watford Way, Hendon Central NW4 3JH (8202 2003).

Southwark *Calabar Kitchen*, 54 Camberwell Church St, SE5 8QZ (7252 5477, 7771 7225).

Cambodian

BUSINESS *Khmer Consulting Ltd,* Flat 46, Yale Ct, Honeybourne Rd, Kilburn NW6 1JG.

EDUCATION Language courses in Cambodian (Khmer) are available at *SOAS Language Centre* (7898 4888).

GOVERNMENT Cambodian interests in the UK are represented from its embassy in Paris at 4 rue Adolphe Yvon, F 75116 Paris, France (+33 1 45 03 47 20).

LANGUAGES The principal language of Cambodia is **Khmer** (sometimes referred to as "Cambodian").

Cameroonian

ASSOCIATIONS *Anglo-Cameroon Society*, 330 Kilburn High Rd, NW6; *Cameroons International Friendship Society*, 199 Gloucester Pl, NW1 6BU, (7729 6672);

GOVERNMENT *Cameroon High Commission*, 84 Holland Park, W11 3SB (7727 0771).

LANGUAGES Cameroon is one of the most multilingual countries in the world and only two of its many languages, **Ewondo** and **Fula**, are the mother tongues of more than 5% of its population. **Pidgin English** is known as a second language by at least 20% of Cameroonians.

RESTAURANTS

Hackney *Mbangang*, 237 Lower Clapton Rd, E5 (8519 3557).

Canadian

BUSINESS

Banking *Bank of Nova Scotia*, Scotia Ho, 33 Finsbury Sq, EC2A 1BB (7638 5644); *Canadian Imperial Bank of Commerce*, Cottons Centre, Cottons La, SE1 2QL (7234 6000); *Royal Bank of*

Canada, 71 Queen Victoria St, EC4V 4AY (7489 1188).

Insurance *Canada Life Ltd,* Martin Ho, 5 Martin La, EC4R 0DP (7955 0155); *Sun Life Financial of Canada,* 131-139 The Broadway, Wimbledon SW19 1QJ and 4th fl, 18 Buckingham Gate, SW1E 6LB (0870 1613333).

Other *Canadian Bank Note International Ltd,* Suite 210, 164-180 Union St, SE1 0LH (7620 2774); *Canadian Shipbuilding & Engineering Ltd,* 9 Artillery La, E1 7LP (7377 6237); *Forest Alliance of British Columbia,* 1 Regent St, SW1Y 4NS (7839 5118).

GOVERNMENT *Agent General for British Columbia,* 1-3, Regent St, SW1Y 4NS (7930 6857); *Canadian High Commission,* Canada Ho, 5 Trafalgar Sq, SW1Y 5BJ and Macdonald Ho, 1 Grosvenor Sq, W1K 4AB (7258 6600); *Quebec Government Office,* 59 Pall Mall, SW1Y 5JH (7766 5900).

LANGUAGES The official languages of Canada are **English** and **French**, and these are the first languages of about 60% and 24% of the population, respectively. There are in addition many indigenous languages as well as a large number of languages introduced by immigrants.

MEDIA & INFORMATION *Canada Post,* 6 Pembridge Rd, W11 3HL (7243 4243); *Canadian Press,* 12, Norwich St, EC4A 1EJ (7353 6355); *Canadian Television Network (CTV) Ltd,* 200 Grays Inn Rd, WC1X 8SJ (7278 4191).

SPECIAL *New Zealand, Australia & Canada Migration Bureau,* Hyde Park Ho, 5 Manfred Rd, SW15 2RS (8874 2844).

TRAVEL *Canadian Affair,* 13, Hillgate St, W8 7SP (7616 9999); *Frontier Travel (Canada),* 6 Sydenham Ave, SE26 6UH (8776 8709); *Go Fishing Canada,* Voyager Ho, 5 The Lanchesters, 162-166, Fulham Palace Rd, W6 9ER (8748 8367).

Cantonese

The word **Cantonese** derives from *Canton,* the European form of the name of Chinese city and province which is today spelled *Guangzhou.* In Britain, the word **Cantonese** is most often applied to (a) the distinctive Chinese language spoken in that province (and also in Hong Kong and Macau) and (b) to a particular style of cooking associated with that region.

EDUCATION Mother tongue classes for Cantonese-speaking children are available in at least a dozen locations in London. Details can be found at <www.resourceunit.com>. Both SOAS Language Centre and the University of Westminster offer courses in **Cantonese**. Other courses are available elsewhere in London. For details, see *Floodlight,* <www.floodlight.co.uk>.

HEALTH & BEAUTY An information leaflet on breast cancer is available in Cantonese from the Women's Nationwide Cancer Control Campaign, 1st fl, Charity Ho, 14-15 Perseverence Works, EC2 8BD (7729 4688, fax 7613 0771).

LANGUAGE **Cantonese** is a Sinitic language ranked 19th in the world with 70m speakers. The Chinese name for this language is *Yue.* As a spoken language, Cantonese is very different from - and not mutually intelligible with - the official **Mandarin** (Putonghua) variety. However, written Cantonese is virtually identical with written Mandarin (see **Chinese** for more information).

In London, Cantonese was found to be the 11th most widely spoken language among London schoolchildren in *Multilingual Capital,* being the home language the home language of 6,922 pupils (of whom the largest number, 674, live in Southwark). A map showing the distribution of speakers of Cantonese within the borough of Westminster can be seen on Map 11 at <www.global-london.com/gallery>.

RESTAURANTS Most of the Chinese restaurants in London serve Cantonese food. The short list which follows includes only those which overtly identify their cuisine as Cantonese in the sources consulted. Others are simply listed in the general **Chinese** entry.

West 1 *Chuen Cheng Ku,* 20 Rupert St & 17 Wardour St, W1 (7734 3281, 7437 1398); 20 *Harbour City,* 46 Gerrard St, W1 (7439 7859); *Oriental,* Dorchester Hotel, Park La, W1 (7317 6328).

West Central *Canton,* Newport Pl, WC2H 7JR (7437 6220).

Croydon *Wong Kei T/A* [Cantonese & Pekingese], High St, Thornton Heath, CR7 8RW (8684 1485); *My Old China,* 2 Godstone Rd, Purley CR8 2AN (8668 7455).

Islington *Beijing* [Cantonese / Peking / Szechuan], 205 Holloway Rd, N7 8DL (7609 1312).

Lambeth *Golden Canton T/A,* 218 Railton Rd, SE24 0JT (7274 5681).

Newham *Canton Chinese T/A,* 6a Leytonstone Rd, E15 1SE (8534 4339).

Waltham Forest *Kwunwah Cantonese Peking Cuisine,* 308 High Rd Leyton, E10 5PW (8539 6300).

Carib

Carib is both a language and an ethnic group. This word is also occasionally used as an alternative to *Caribbean* and, in all such cases, these are included under *Caribbean.*

LANGUAGE **Carib** is a language formerly spoken on many of the Caribbean islands and which is still spoken in parts of Venezuela, the Guianas and Brazil. In the *Multilingual Capital* (2000) survey, *Carib* was reported as the language of 16 London schoolchildren but this was probably intended as an alternative name for *(Afro-Caribbean) Patwa.*

Caribbean

ACCOMMODATION *Caribbean Resource Association,* 1 Cambus Rd, Canning Town E16 4AY; *Carib Housing Association Ltd* [nursing homes], Lee Samuel Ho, 2/23 Nealden St, Brixton SW9 9RA (7738 3785).

ASSOCIATIONS *Anglo Caribbean Society,* 66-68 West End Rd, Southall UB1 1JL (8843 1147); *Caribbean Cultural Organisation,* 134 Minet Ave, Willesden NW10 8AP (8961 9293); *Enfield Caribbean Association,* Memorial Hall, Maldon Road, Edmonton N9 0PD (8351 1328) ["a vibrant luncheon club for the elderly" Fridays 13.00]; *United Anglo Caribbean Society,* Berrymead School, Osborne Rd, Acton W3 8SJ (8992 0307).

BARS & NIGHT-CLUBS *Brixtonian Havana Club* [Caribbean/Cuban], 11 Beehive Pl, SW9 (7924 9262); *Orbital Bar,* 144 Clerkenwell Rd, EC1R 5DP (7278 9584).

BUSINESS *Anglo Caribbean Insurance Agents Ltd,* 201-203, City Rd, EC1V 1QH (7490 5586); *British Caribbean Junior Chamber of Commerce,* 2 Anne Boleyn Ho, Prusom St, E1W 3RD (7481 2137); *Caribbean Trade & Advisory Group,* Westminster Palace Gdns, 1-7 Artillery Row, SW1P 1RR (7839 0899); *Mutual Services Caribbean Ltd,* 15 Cambridge Ct, 210 Shepherds Bush Rd, Hammersmith W6 7NL (7371 4497).

EDUCATION *Foods of Africa & the Caribbean Educational Trust (FACET),* 48 Endlesham Rd, SW12 8JL (8874 3662); *Francophone Africa, Caribbean, & the Pacific Research Group,* SSHS, University of Westminster, 309 Regent St, W1B 2UW (7911 5000 x2078);

FREIGHT *Anglo Caribbean Shipping Co. Ltd,* 14 Skylines Village, Limeharbour, E14 9TS (7537 7420); *Eastern Caribbean Shipping & Exporting,* 111A Green St, Forest Gate E7 8JF (8470 5503);

GOVERNMENT *Eastern Caribbean Commission,* 10 Kensington Ct, Kensington W8 5DL (7937 9522).

LEGAL *African, Caribbean and Asian Lawyers Group,* 100-113 Chancery La, Holborn WC2A 1PL

MEDIA & INFORMATION *Data Caribbean Ltd,* 83 Clerkenwell Rd, EC1R 5AR; *UK Afro & Caribbean News Magazine,* 313 Romford Rd, Forest Gate E7 9HA (8257 5672);

RELIGION *Caribbean Hindu Society,* 16 Ostade Rd, SW2 2BB (8674 0755).

RESTAURANTS

East Central *Orbital,* 144 Clerkenwell Rd, EC1R 5DP (7278 9584);

West 1 *Mr Jerk,* 189 Wardour St, W1.

Brent *Lionness Caribbean T/A,* 94a Willesden La, Kilburn NW6 7TA (7624 8696); *Oasis,* 108 Cricklewood Broadway, NW2 3EJ (8452 0463); *Planet Caribbean Cuisine,* 11 Malvern Rd, Kilburn NW6 5PS (7372 4980).

Bromley *Carib Vibe Cafe T/A,* Flat above 150 High St, Penge SE20 7EU (8659 9525).

Camden *Mango Room,* 10 Kentish Town Rd, NW1 (7482 5065).

Ealing *B B's Crabback Caribbean Restaurant,* 3 Chignell Pl, West Ealing W13 0TJ (8840 8322); *Spice Shack,* 5 Drayton Green Rd, West Ealing W13 0NG (8840 9186); *Uncle's Favourite Caribbean T/A,* 5 Drayton Green, W13 0JE (8840 9186).

Greenwich *Sunjam Caribbean T/A,* 13a Spray St, Woolwich SE18 6AG (8317 2174).

Hackney *Junior's T/A,* 63 Nevill Rd, Stoke Newington N16 8SW (7275 7244); *Moon Walk,* 100-102 Hoxton St, N1 6SG (7613 4071).

Haringey *Hibiscus,* 93 West Green Rd, N15 (8211 8268).

Hammersmith & Fulham *Lion Head,* 773 Harrow Rd, NW10 5PA (8964 8031); *Oche Caribbean T/A,* 226 Uxbridge Rd, Shepherd's Bush W12 7JD (8742 9620).

Haringey *Beewee's,* 96 Stroud Green Rd, Finsbury Park N4 3EN (7263 4004); *Elliott's,* 110 High Rd, N15 6JR (8880 1440).

Lambeth *Spice of the Caribbean,* 203 Streatham High Rd, SW16 6EG (8677 0708); *Tropical Waves,* 56 Morrish Rd, Brixton SW2 4EG (8671 4714).

Lewisham *2001 Africaribbean,* 199 Lewisham Way, Brockley SE4 1UY (8694 9955); *Cummin Up Caribbean T/A,* 9 George La, Lewisham SE13 6HQ (8694 1745); *Tropicana,* Eros Ho, Brownhill Rd, Catford SE6 2EG (8695 9188).

Waltham Forest *Carib T/A,* 698 High Road Leyton E10 6JP (8556 2102).

Wandsworth *Jamdish Caribbean T/A,* 116 Plough Rd, Battersea SW11 2AL (7924 4359); *Klaro T/A,* 4 Upper Richmond Rd, Junction West Hill, SW15 2SD (8874 7250).

Westminster *DJ's Caribbean T/A,* 616 Harrow Rd, W10 4NJ (8968 6619).

SHOPS *Caribbean Cut Price* [off licence], 83 Evering Rd, Stoke Newington N16 7SJ (7254 1721); *Caribbean Market* [greengrocery], 29 Chatsworth Rd, Clapton E5 0LH (8985 2154); *Caribbean Super Shop,* Unit 10, The Broadway Shopping Centre, Southall UB1 1QB (8917 9313); *New Beacon Books,* 76 Stroud Green Rd, N4 3EN (7272 4889; fax 7281 4662); *Nyam Foods,* 423 Coldharbour La, Brixton (7738 4030); *Soma Books,* 38 Kennington La, SE11 4LS (7735 2101; fax 7735 3076).

TRAVEL *Caribbean Connection,* 93 Newman St, W1P 4DT (7344 3004); *Caribbean Experience Ltd,* 70 Pembroke Rd, Kensington W8 6NX (7602 4021);

Caribbean Expressions, 104 Belsize La, Hampstead NW3 5BB (7431 2131); Caribbean Holidays & African Safaris, 79 Sefton Ave, Harrow Weald HA3 5JP (8424 0917); Caribbean Link Travel Accommodation, Tress Ho, 3-7 Stamford St, Southwark SE1 9NT (7401 8112); Caribbean Reunion Club, 93 Newman St, W1P 4DT (7344 0101); Caribbean Tourism Organisation, 42 Westminster Palace Gdns, Artillery Row SW1P 1RR (7222 4335); Carib Cars [mini cabs], 193 Stanstead Rd, Forest Hill SE23 1HP (8699 5555); CaribJet - LIAT - the Caribbean Airline, 8 Manor Ho, The Green, Southall UB2 4BJ (8571 7553); Hammock Leisure Caribbean Holidays, Wickham Ho, 10 Cleveland Way, E1 4TR (7423 9400).

WELFARE Caribbean Community Centre, 416 Seven Sisters Rd, N4 2LX (8802 0550); Caribbean Day Nursery, 416 Seven Sisters Rd, N4 2LX (8802 0550); Caribbean Development Foundation, 35 Horton Rd, Hackney E8 1DP (7254 8480); Caribbean Links, 628 High Rd, Tottenham N17 9TP (8880 9300); Caribbean Pensioners and Friends [day centre], 91 Tollington Way, Holloway N7 6RE (7263 3501); Caribbean Senior Citizens Centre [day centre], Chesnut Rd, Tottenham N17 9EU (83651593); Carib Housing Association Ltd [nursing homes], Lee Samuel Ho, 2/23 Nealden St, Brixton SW9 9RA (7738 3785); East London African & Caribbean Counselling Service, Stratford Advice Arc, 107-109 The Grove, Stratford E15 1HP (8221 1233); Hackney Caribbean Elderly Organisation, c/oS N C A, 61 Leswin Rd, Stoke Newington N16 7NX (7923 3536); Hibiscus Caribbean Elderly Association [day centre], Community Centre, Buckingham Rd, Stratford E15 1SP (8519 6159); United Anglo Caribbean Society Day Centre, 23 Hanbury Rd, Acton W3 8RF (8993 3306); Unity African Caribbean Project, Prah Rd, N4 2RA (7359 8111).

Catalan

BUSINESS Catalan Trade Centre, 17 Fleet St, EC4Y 1AA (7583 4000).

EDUCATION Courses in **Catalan** have been provided by King's College London – check <www.floodlight.co.uk> for details.

LANGUAGE Catalan is a Romanic language with official status in Andorra. It is also spoken in southwestern France, northeast Spain, and the Balearic islands by perhaps 11m people in all. In London, it was reported as the first language of 12 pupils in the Multilingual Capital (2000) survey.

SHOPS Casa Catalan, 15 Chalk Farm Rd, NW1 8AG (7916 1824); Casa Catalan, 16 Heath St, Hampstead, NW3 6TE (7431 6002).

TRAVEL Catalan Tourist Board, 16 Fleet St, EC4Y 1AA (7583 8855).

Cayman Islander

FREIGHT Cayman Islands Shipping Office, 7th fl, Dudley Ho, 169 Piccadilly, W1J 9EH (7491 2858).

GOVERNMENT Department of Cayman Islands, 6 Arlington St, SW1A 1RE (7491 7771).

TRAVEL Cayman Airways, 6 Arlington St, SW1A 1RB (7491 7771); Cayman Islands Department of Tourism, 6 Arlington St, SW1A 1RB (7491 7771).

Cebuano

Cebuano is a **Hesperonesic** language of the Philippines with some 17m speakers. It is one of the languages known collectively as **Bisayan** (see this for further details). The Multilingual Capital (2000) survey noted the presence of 5 Cebuano-speaking London pupils, of whom 4 lived in Barnet.

Celtic

ACCOMMODATION Celtic Hotel, 61-63, Guilford St, WC1N 1DD (7837 6737).

ARTS Celtic Association [Irish dancing], 41 Hertfoed Rd, Barnet EN4 9BH (8449 6291); London Celtic Harp Society, 31 Allenby Rd, SE23 2RQ (8699 8342).

BUSINESS Celtic Fabrication Ltd, Acton Business Centre, School Rd, NW10 6TD (8838 5355); Celtic Resources Holdings plc, Enterprise Ho, 59-65 Upper Ground, SE1 9PQ (7593 0001).

MEDIA & INFORMATION Celtic Films Ltd, Government Bldgs, Bromyard Ave, W3 7XH (8740 6880).

RECREATION Celtic Association [Irish dancing], 41 Hertfoed Rd, Barnet EN4 9BH (8449 6291).

SHOPS Celtic Bakery, 42b Waterloo Rd, Cricklewood, NW2 7UH (8452 4390); Celtic Designs, inside the Thistle Hotel, 100 Kings Cross Rd WC1X 9DT (7837 2162).

SPECIAL Celtic Division, Unit 1f1 2, Michael Rd, SW6 2ER (7384 3190).

TRAVEL Celtic Line Travel Ltd, 11 Rays Rd, N18 2NX (8807 9309).

Central African

RELIGION *Universities Mission to Central Africa,* 157 Waterloo Rd, SE1 8UU (7928 8681).

Central American

LEGAL *Central America Human Rights Coordination,* 83 Margaret St, W1N 7HB (7631 4200).

Chadian

GOVERNMENT Chadian interests in the UK are represented from the *Republic of Chad*'s embassy in Belgium at Lambermontlaan 52, B 1030 Brussels (+32 2 215 1975).

Channel Islander

BUSINESS *Westminster & Guernsey,* 25 Old Broad St, EC2N 1HT (7229 6060);
TRAVEL *Jersey Tourism & Information Office,* 7 Lower Grosvenor Pl, SW1W 0EN (7630 8787); *Jersey Travel Services,* 43-57 London Rd, Twickenham TW1 3SZ (8939 5401);

Che

C h e is a Benuic language of Nigeria. In the *Multilingual Capital* (2000) survey, this was reported as the language of two London schoolchildren, both living in Lewisham.

Chewa

Chewa (full name *Chichewa*) which, with minor geographical differences, is essentially the same entity as *Nyanja*, is a Bantuic language spoken in Malawi, Zambia and Mozambique by several million people. The *Multilingual Capital* (2000) survey reported that this was the language of 50 London school-children, of whom 20 were living in Barnet.

Chiga

Chiga (also known as *Kiga*) is a Bantuic language of Rwanda and Uganda. This was reported as the first language of only one pupil in London in the *Multilingual Capital* (2000) survey.

Chilean

ASSOCIATIONS *Anglo Chilean Society*, 12 Devonshire St, W1N 2DS (7580 1271).
BUSINESS *British Chilean Chamber of Commerce,* 12 Devonshire St, W1N 2DS (7323 3053); *Chile Copper Ltd*, York Ho, 23 Kingsway, WC2B 6UJ (7240 0221); *Wines of Chile,* Premier Ho, 10 Greycoat Pl, SW1P 3SB (7222 2073).
GOVERNMENT *Chilean Consulate,* 6 St Albans St, SW1Y 4SZ (7930 4160); *Chilean Embassy,* 12 Devonshire St, W1N 2DS (7580 6392); *Embassy of Chile*, 49 Albemarle St, W1S 4JL (7495 6700).
LANGUAGE The official language is *Spanish.*
RELIGION Chileans are overwhelmingly Roman Catholic.
TRAVEL *Chile Tours Ltd,* 62-63 Fenchurch St, EC3M 4AQ.

Chinese

ARTS *British Chinese Artists Association,* Interchange Studios, Dalby St, Kentish Town, NW5 3NQ (7267 6133); *Percival David Foundation of Chinese Art*, 53 Gordon Square, WC1H 0PD (7387 3909).

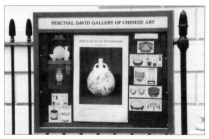

ASSOCIATIONS *Association of Traditional Chinese Medicine* 22 Rupert Street, W1V 7FN; *British Chinese Artists Association,* Interchange Studios, Dalby St, Kentish Town, NW5 3NQ (7267 6133); *Great Britain-China Centre,* 15 Belgrave Sq, SW1X 8PS (7235 6696); *Lambeth Chinese Community Association,* 69 Stockwell Rd, Brixton, SW9 9PY (7733 4377); *Lambeth Vietnamese and Chinese Youth Association,* 56b Courland Grove, South Lambeth, SW8 2PU (7498 8531); *Lewisham Indo Chinese Community & School,* 171a Deptford High St, Deptford, SE8 3NU (8692 2772); *London Chinatown Chinese Association,* 3 Gerrard St, W1D 5PD (7434 4226); *Waltham Forest Chinese Association,* 547-551 High Rd Leytonstone, Wanstead, E11 4PB (8558 0182).
BUSINESS
Banking *Agricultural Bank of China – London Representation Office,* 18th fl, Royex Ho, Aldermanbury Sq, EC2V 7HR (7606 0100); *Bank of China International (UK) Ltd,* 90 Cannon St, EC4N 6HA (7022 8888); *Bank of China – London Branch,* 90 Cannon St, EC4N 6HA (7282 8000); *Bank of Communications – London Representative Office,* 18th fl, Royex Ho. Aldermanbury Sq, EC2V 7HR (7606 1808); *China Construction Bank – London Representative Office,* 6th fl, 29/30 Cornhill, EC3V 3ND (7220 7871); *Industrial and Commercial Bank of China – London Representative Office,* 18th fl, Royex Ho, Aldermanbury Sq, EC2V 7HR (7600 7622); *Oversea-Chinese Banking Corporation Ltd,* 111 Cannon St, EC4N 5AR, (7337 8822).
Insurance *China Insurance Co (UK) Ltd,* Communications Bldg, 48 Leicester Sq, WC2H 7LT (7839 1888); *China Reinsurance Company – London Office,* 6 Lloyds Ave, EC3 (7481 8240); *People's Insurance Company of China – European Representative Office,* 4th fl, 38 Leadenhall St, EC3A 1AT (7680 0668).
Other *CATIC Trading Development (UK) Ltd,* Unit 9 Iron Bridge Ho, Bridge Approach, NW1 8BD (7586 3854); *CCIC London Company Ltd,* Premier Ho, 112 Station Rd, Edgware HA8 7BJ (8905 6689); *CCPIT/CCOIC Representative Office in the UK,*

40/41 Pall Mall, SW1Y 5JQ (7321 2044); *China Apollo Group (Europe) Ltd,* 12 College Fields Business Centre, Prince Georges Rd, SW19 2PT (8640 3212); *China Britain Trade Group,* 4th fl, Abford Ho, 15 Wilton Rd, SW1V 1LT (7828 5176); *China Shipping (UK) Agency Co Ltd,* 2 Abbey Rd, Barking IG11 7AX (8709 1095); *China Worldbest Group Co Ltd – UK Office,* 12 Angel Mews, 240 Cable St, E1 0BL (7791 2453); *COSCO (UK) Ltd,* Cosco Ho, Vicarage Drive, Barking IG11 7NA (8594 8688); *Erdos Cashmere Group (Europe) Ltd,* 2 Closemend Close, Northwood HA6 2RZ (01707 266658); *Fujian FTC - London Office,* 74 Oversley Ho, Alfred Rd, W2 5HF (7289 6132); *Hebei Light (UK) Ltd,* 21 Lansdowne Rd, E17 8QT (8521 5885); *Minmetals (UK) Ltd,* Mimet Ho, 5A Praed St, W2 1NJ (7411 4012); *Shanghai General Electronics (UK) Ltd,* 9 Churchill Ct, 58 Station Rd, North Harrow (8863 6607); *Sinochem Europ Holding plc* and *Sinochem (United Kingdom) Ltd,* 17th fl, New Zealand Ho, Haymarket, SW1Y 4TE (7930 7060); *Sinochem International Oil (London) Co Ltd,* 11th fl, Westminster Tower, 3 Albert Embankment, SE1 7SP (7735 7878); *S Seasons Co Ltd,* 28 Ash Grove, W5 4AX (8567 6651); *Sunry Import & Export Co Ltd,* Sunry Ho, 76 St Helen Gdns, W10 6LH (8968 4250); *Temax (UK) Ltd,* 23 Collingham Rd, Earl's Court, SW5 0NU (7373 7728); *Top Glory (London) Ltd,* 6th fl, 9 St Clare St, EC3N 1LQ (7481 9997); *UNIPEC UK Co Ltd,* 20th fl, Marble Arch Tower, 55 Bryanston St, W1H 7AA (7616 9888).

EDUCATION More than 30 places in London offer mother tongue education in "Chinese" (of which 11 specify that this is in **Cantonese** and a further 11 that this is in **Mandarin**). For fuller details, visit <www.resourceunit.com>.

Both SOAS Language Centre and the University of Westminster offer courses for both Cantonese and Mandarin Chinese. Other courses in both of these are available elsewhere. For details, see *Floodlight,* <www.floodlight.co.uk>.

One other educational organization is *Tienyi Chinese Medical & Training Centre Ltd,* 83 Leonard Street, EC2A 4QS.

EMPLOYMENT *China Association for International Exchange of Personnel - London Office,* 78 Gordon Rd, Ealing W5 2AR (8991 5779).

GOVERNMENT *Chinese Embassy*, 49 Portland Pl, W1B 1JL (7299 4049**).**

HEALTH & BEAUTY

South East 1 *SJY Chinese Medicine & Acupuncture,* 96 Tower Bridge Rd, Southwark, SE1 4TP (7252 0698).

West 1 *Acupont Herbalist Centre*, 42 Goodge St, W1T 2QR (7436 9735); *Association of Traditional Chinese Medicine* 22 Rupert Street, W1V 7FN; *Chinese Medical Centre,* 1 Marlborough Ct, Carnaby St, W1F 7EF (7437 5147); *Chinese Medicine Practice,* 16 Balderton St, W1Y 1TF (7355 4036); *London Chinese Health Resource Centre,* 29-30 Soho Sq, W1V 5DH (7287 0904); *Zhai Clinic*

[acupuncture and Chinese herbal medicine for infertility], 10 Harley St, W1G 9PF (7467 8420).

West Central *East West Herbs,* 3 Neal's Yard, Covent Garden WC2H 9DP (7379 1312); *Hing Ning Co Ltd,* 15 Little Newport St, WC2H 7JJ (7437 4910); *Institute of Chinese Medicine,* 44-46 Chandos Place, WC2N 4HS (7836 5220); *Register of Chinese Herbal Medicine,* Office 4, Garden Studios,11 Betterton St, WC2H 9BP (7470 8740).

Barnet *Chinese Medical Centre,* 77 The Broadway, Mill Hill, INW7 3BU (8959 4979); *Chinese Medical Centre,* 752 Finchley Rd, Golders Green, NW11 7TH (8731 9997); *London Chinese Medical College Ltd,* 7 Lorian Close, North Finchley, N12 7DW; *San Ling Chinese Medical Centre,* 97b Golders Green Rd, Golders Green, NW11 8EN (8731 8687); *Virtue Chinese Medical Centre Ltd,* Sheaveshill Pde, Sheaveshill Ave, Colindale, NW9 6RS (8200 8118).

Brent *Chinese Medical Centre of London,* 337 Kilburn High Rd, NW6 (7372 2184).

Camden: *Acumedic Centre* [acupuncture and Chinese medical treatments], 101-105 Camden High St, NW1 7JN (7388 5783/6704) *Chinese Medical Centre,* 2 Regency Parade, Finchley Rd, NW3 5EG (7722 0922).

Ealing: *Chinese Herbal Medicine & Healthcare Ltd*, Herbal King, 92 High St, Acton W3 6QX (8992 2888).

Enfield: *Chinese Medical Centre (Enfield Branch),* 10 The Concourse, Edmonton Green, N9 0TY (8803 0950).

Greenwich *The Chinese Shop,* 150 Sandy Hill Rd, Woolwich, SE18 7BA (8855 0771).

Hackney: *Chinese Medical Centre,* 16 Kingsland High St, E8 2JP (7249 1300); *Herbal Inn Clinic,* 527 Kingsland Rd, Hackney E8 (7249 9888).

Hammersmith & Fulham: *Eastern Chinese Herbal Medicine Clinic,* 16 Fulham High St, SW6 3LQ (7731 7888); *Hammersmith Acupuncture & Chinese Herbal Clinic,* 3 Pleydell Av, Stamford Brook, W4 2NW (8741 3556).

Haringey: *Chinese Natural Herbal Centre,* 93 Turnpike La, N8 0DY (8348 0568); *SJY Chinese Medicine,* 545c High Rd, London N17 6SB (8801 6618).

Harrow *Hong Tao Acupuncture & Chinese Herbal Clinic,* 21 St Thomas Dr, Pinner, HA5 4SX (8421 2668).

Hounslow *Chinese Medical Centre of London,* 90 Kingsley Rd, Hounslow, TW3 1QA (8570 9998).

Lambeth: *Chinese Herbal Medicine Centre,* 34 Knights Hill, West Norwood SE27 0HY (8670 7477).

Lewisham: *Chinese Health Centre,* 359 New Cross Rd, SE14 6AT (8694 7987); *Chinese Herbal Medicine & Healthcare Ltd,* Herbal King, 193 Rushey Green Catford, SE6 4BD (8695 9898).

Southwark: *SJY Chinese Medicine,* 4 Camberwell Rd, SE5 0EN (7703 6663); *Traditional Chinese Medicine & Acupuncture,* 315 Camberwell Rd, Camberwell, SE5 0HQ (7703 8198).

Tower Hamlets: *Chinese Herbal Remedy Centre,* 305 Bethnal Green Rd, E2 6AH (7729 5100).

Waltham Forest *Harmony Chinese Medicine Centre,* 629 High Rd, Leytonstone, E11 4PA (8518 7337).

Wandsworth: *Chinese Herbal Medicine and Healthcare Ltd,* Herbal King, 6 Tooting High St, SW17 0RG (8682 4808); *Herbary Chinese Medicine Centre,* 26a Upper Tooting Rd, SW17 7PG (8672 3388).

LANGUAGES Various languages are spoken in China, all of which share a common logographic written form. There is thus a single written language which can legitimately be called **Chinese** but this word cannot be applied unambiguously to any single language spoken in China. The most important Sinitic languages of China are **Mandarin** (which has official status and for which the government prefers the name *Putonghua,* 'commonly understood language'), **Wu**, **Cantonese** (known as *Yue* within China), **Hokkien**, **Xiang** and **Hakka**. All of the latter are regarded as dialects of **Mandarin** by the Chinese government even though they are not mutually intelligible with it. In addition a number of relatively small minorities speak other, non-Sinitic languages.

Within London, speakers of **Cantonese** appear to outnumber speakers of **Mandarin** and other Sinitic languages of China by at least 3 to 1.

LEGAL *Nadine Wong & Co,* Westbourne Grove, W2 (7243 8888).

MEDIA & INFORMATION *China National Publication I & E Corporation - London Office,* Unit 4, 55-57 Park Royal Rd, NW10 7LR (8961 9283); *Cypress Book Co (UK) Ltd,* Unit 13 Park Royal Metro Centre, Britannin Way, London NW10 (8453 0687); *Spectrum Radio,* International Radio Centre, 4 Ingate Pl, SW8 3NS (7627 4433) [broadcasting for Chinese listeners 18.00 - 19.00 daily and 23.00 - 00.00 weekdays]; *Wen Tai Sun Chinese News Agency,* 80 Dean St, W1V 5AD (7437 5188).

RECREATION *British Institute for Chinese Martial Arts,* Millhill Boys School, The Ridgeway, Millhill NW7 1QS (8455 6636); *Martial Arts Institute Wing*

Chun Kung Fu, PO Box 628, Richmond TW9 1FF (8332 1078); *Meijin,* 141 Goldhawk Rd, W12 8EN (8749 0158); *Shaolin Way,* 10 Little Newport St, WC2H 7JJ (7734 6391); *Tao Sports* [martial arts], 523 Green Lanes, N4 1AN (8348 0870); *Ving Tsun Kung Fu* [martial arts], 218 Lambeth Rd, SE1 7JY (0860 638 854); *Wu Shu Kwan Chinese Boxing,* The Colonnades, Porchester Square Mews, W2 6AG (7229 6354).

RELIGION *King's Cross Methodist Church,* 58a Birkenhead St, WC1 (7833 8820); *London Ch'an Group* [Chinese Zen], 20 Goodhall St, NW10 6TU (8961 7802); *London Fo Kuang Temple,* Margaret St, W1.

RESTAURANTS (see also *Cantonese, Hainanese, Hunanese, Pekingese, Szechuan*)

East Central *China-e-Restaurant,* 285, City Rd, EC1V 1LA (7250 1600); *China Silk,* 14 Exmouth Market, EC1R 4QE (7837 6000); *Cicada,* 132-136 St Johns St, EC1V 4JT (7608 1550); *Dim Sum,* 5-6 Deans Ct, St Pauls EC4V 5AA (7236 1114); *East One,* 175-179, St John St, EC1V 4LW (7566 0088); *Ming Court,* 54-56, Ludgate Hill, EC4M 7HX (7248 4303); *Moorgate Oriental,* 45 London Wall, EC2M 5TE (7638 2288); *New Man Loong,* 71 Compton St, EC1V 0BN (7253 0222); *Orchid Inn,* 37 Farringdon Rd, EC1M 3JB (7242 6008); *Poons in the City,* Minster Pavement, Minster Ct, Mincing La, EC3R 7PP (7626 0126); *Red Mandarin,* 9 Dallington St, EC1V 0BQ (7566 9410); *Royal Inn,* 95 Leather La, EC1N 7TS (7405 4669); *Tao,* 11-11a Bow La, EC4M 9AL (7248 5833); *Yeungs City Bar,* 70-74, City Rd, EC1Y 2BJ (7250 0608).

South East 1 *Bandong,* 97 Newington Butts, SE1 6SF (7252 6747); *Golden Chopsticks,* 128 Tooley St, SE1 2TU (7407 5276); *Golden City,* 159 Borough High St, SE1 1HR (7378 8100); *Great Wall,* 90 Tooley St, SE1 2TH (7357 0200); *Hing Lee,* 32 Curlew St, SE1 2ND (7403 7919); *New Peking Inn,* 9 Milroy Walk, SE1 9LW (7928 8770); *Sino Thai* [Chinese/Thai], 127-128 Lower Marsh, SE1 7AE (7401 9002); *Tall House,* 134 Southwark St, SE1 0SW (7401 2929); *Waterloo Dumpling Inn,* 57 Baylis Rd, SE1 7AU (7928 9972); *Wok U Like,* 31 Baylis Rd, SE1 (7401 8899).

South West 1 *Hunan*, 51 Pimlico Rd, SW1W 8NE (7730 5712); *Jenny Lo's Teahouse*, 14 Eccleston St, SW1W 9LT (7259 0399); *Ken Lo's Memories of China*, 67 Ebury St, SW1 (7730 7734); *Kym's*, 70-71 Wilton Rd, SW1V 1DE (7828 8931); *Mandarin House*, 26 Buckingham Palace Rd, SW1W 0RE (7834 0192); *Mr Chow*, 151 Knightsbridge, SW1 (7589 7347).

West 1 *Aroma*, 118 Shaftesbury Ave, W1D 5EP (7437 0377); *Cam Phant* [Chinese / Vietnamese], 12 Macclesfield St, W1D 5BP (7437 5598); *Chiang Mai*, 48 Frith St, W1V 5TE (7437 7444); *Dorchester Hotel*, 55 Park La, W1 (7317 6328); *Far East*, 13 Gerrard St, W1D 5PS (7437 6148); *Gerrard's Corner*, 30 Wardour St, Soho W1 (7437 0984); *Harbour City*, 46 Gerrard St, W1V 7LP (7439 7859); *Ho Ho*, 29 Maddox St, W1R 9LD (7493 1228); *Kai*, 65 S Audley St, W1 (7493 8988); *Kowloon*, 21-22 Gerrard St, W1V 7LA (7437 1694); *Mandarin*, 8 Gerrard St, W1D 5PJ (7734 0078); *New Hoo Wah*, 37-38 Gerrard St, W1V 7LP (7434 0540); *New Mayflower*, 68-70 Shaftesbury Ave, W1 (7734 9207); *New World* [Chinese / Malaysian], 1 Gerrard St, W1 (7734 0396); *Wong Kei*, 41-43 Wardour St, Soho, W1 (7437 6833).

West Central *Canton*, 11 Newport Pl, WC2H 7JR (7437 6220); *China City*, 25a Lisle St, WC2H 7BA (7734 3388); *China House*, 51 Marchmont St, WC1N 1AP (7713 0866); *Drury Lane Diner*, 176 Drury La, WC2B 5QF (7405 2911); *Fung Shing*, 15 Lisle St, WC2H 7BE (7437 1539); *Golden Harvest*, 17 Lisle St, WC2H 7BE (7287 3822); *Golden House*, 15 Leigh St, WC1 (7383 3135); *Hing Loon*, 25 Lisle St, WC2H 7BA (7437 3602); *Joy King Lau*, 3 Leicester St, WC2H 7BL (7437 1132); *Kam Fung*,

27 Red Lion St, WC1R 4PS (7242 5821); *London Hong Kong*, 6-7 Lisle St, WC2H 7BG (7287 0324); *Mr Au*, 47-49 Charing Cross Rd, WC2H 0AN (7437 7472); *Mr Kong*, 21 Lisle St, WC2H 7BA (7437 7341); *New Diamond*, 23 Lisle St, WC2H 7BA (7437 2517); *New Shu Shan*, 36 Cranbourn St, WC2H 7AD (7836 7501); *Poon and Co*, 26-27 Lisle St, WC2H 7BA (7437 4549); *Poon's*, 4 Leicester St, WC2H 7BL (7437 1528); *Poon's*, 50 Woburn Pl, WC1H 0JZ (7580 1188); *Sheng's Tea House*, 68 Millman St, WC1N 3EF (7405 3697); *Wing Ki*, 59 Charing Cross Rd, WC2H 0NE (7734 5951); *Woo Sang*, 34 Lisle St, WC2H 7BD (7437 2524); *Young Cheng*, 22 Lisle St, WC2H 7BA (7287 3045).

Barnet *Chai* [vegetarian], 236 Station Rd, Edgware HA8 7AU (8905 3033); *Golden Villa*, 18 Varley Parade, NW9 6RR (8205 8489); *Good Earth*, 143-145 The Broadway, Mill Hill, NW7 4RN (8959 7011); *Gourmet Garden*, 59 Watford Way, NW4 3AX (8202 9639); *Hainanese*, 63 Golders Green Rd, NW11 8EL (8455 0704); *Happy Valley*, 87-89 Church Rd, NW4 4DP (8203 5010); *Hee's*, 27 The Broadway, NW7 3DA (8959 7109); *Jun Peking-Chinese*, 12 Sutton Parade, Hendon, NW4 1RR (8203 3388); *Kaifeng Kosher Oriental*, 51 Church Rd, Hendon NW4 4DU (8203 7888); *Kung's*, 30 Temple Fortune Parade, NW11 0QS (8458 3558); *Man Chui Three*, 84 Ballards La, N3 2DL (8349 2400); *Mandarin*,152 High Rd, N2 9ED (8444 0012); *Man Fu*, 68 Greyhound Hill, Hendon NW4 4JB (8203 1234); *Mr Kan's*, 29 Market Pl, NW11 6JY (8455 8861); *Oriental Hawkers Delight*, 20 Vivian Ave, NW4 3XP (8202 3889); *Peking Gardens*, 1174 High Rd, Whetstone, N20 0LH (8445 6406); *Saigon Vietnam & Chinese*, 340 Regents Park Rd, N3 2LN (8343 4149); *Sakonis*, 114 Station Rd, Edgware HA8 7AA (8951 0058); *Shanghai Shanghai*, 132 High Rd, N2 9ED (8883 2138); *Water Margin*, 96 Golders Green Rd, NW11 8HB (8458 5815); *Welcome*, 682 High Rd, N12 9PT (8445 3718); *Xian*, 862 High Rd, N12 9RH (8445 8125).

Brent *China City*, Oriental City Plaza, Edgware Rd, NW9 0JJ (8201 3838); *China Dragon*, 24 Willesden La, NW6 7ST (7624 5773); *Dumpling*, 9 Kilburn High Rd, NW6 5SD (7624 3338); *Kilburn Park Restaurant*, 9 Malvern Rd, Kilburn, NW6 5PS (7328 9218); *Mandarin Chef T/A*, 110 High St, NW10 4SL (8965 0237); *Sakonis*, 127-129 Ealing

Rd, Wembley HA0 4BP (8903 9601); *Sino Thai* [Chinese/Thai], 9 High Rd, NW10 2TE (8459 1622); *Vegan Chinese Buffet,* 405 Kilburn High Rd, NW6 5LP (8201 8556).

Bromley *Beijing,* 188 High St, Penge, SE20 7QB (8776 7559); *Mandarin Palace,* 31 Widmore Rd, Bromley BR1 1RW (8466 0018).

Camden *Cheng-Du,* 9 Parkway, NW1 (7485 8058); *Dim T,* 3 Heath St, Hampstead, NW3 6TP (7435 0024); *Feng Shang,* Cumberland Basin, Prince Albert Rd, NW1 7SS (7485 8137); *Happy House,* 18 Fortess Rd, NW5 2HB (7485 0152); *Jubilee,* 186 Broadhurst Gdns, NW6 3AY (7624 7548); *Mulan,* 91 Haverstock Hill, NW3 4RL (7722 3993); *New Culture Revolution,* 43 Parkway, NW1 7PN (7267 2700); *Oriental Star,* 134 Finchley Rd, NW3 5HS (7435 8488); *Regent,* 333 Euston Rd, NW1 3AD (7388 7568); *Speedy Noodle,* 238 Kilburn High Rd, NW6 2BS (7328 9528); *Street Hawker,* 237-239 West End La, NW6 1XN (7431 7808); *Table Fashion,* 96 West End La, NW6 2LU (7624 8897); *Welcome,* 68 Belsize La, NW3 5BJ (7794 9217); *Weng Wah House,* 240 Haverstock Hill, NW3 2AE (7794 5123); *Yen,* 40 Doric Way, NW1 1LH (7387 2518); *ZEN W3,* 83 Hampstead High St, NW3 1RE (7794 7863).

Croydon *Mr Kai,* 11 Central Hill, SE19 1BG (8670 6384); *New Moon,* 5 Portland Rd, South Norwood SE25 4UF (8654 6551); *Sun Sun,* 10 Church Rd, Upper Norwood SE19 2ET (8653 3404); *Wong Kei T/A* [Cantonese & Pekingese], High St, Thornton Heath, CR7 8RW (8684 1485).

Ealing *August Moon,* 7 Ashbourne Parade, Ealing W5 3QS (8997 5120); *Dragon Inn,* 179 South Ealing Rd, W5 4RH (8568 8838); *Happiness Garden,* 22 Boston Parade, Boston Rd, Hanwell W7 2DG (8579 5033); *Lee's New Peking,* 139 Northfield Ave, Ealing W13 9QT (8579 9935); *Maxim,* 153-155 Northfield Ave, West Ealing W13 9QT (8567 1719); *Mr Wong,* 4 Elliott Rd, W4 1PE (8987 8877); *New Leaf,* 35 Bond St, Ealing, W5 5AS (8567 2343); *New Fu On,* 152 Broadway, W13 0TL (8840 4106); *North China,* 305 Uxbridge Rd, Acton, W3 9QU (8992 9183); *Peking Duck,*146 Uxbridge Rd, West Ealing, W13 8SB (8579 1489); *PK Wong,* Kendal Ave, Park Royal, W3 (8896 3861); *Premier Peking,* 25 The Avenue, West Ealing, W13 8JR (8991 9145).

Enfield *Good Food,* 93 Bramley Rd, N14 4EY (8886 8204); *Honeymoon,* 84 Crown La, N14 5EN (8886 3509); *Magical Wok,* 64 Fore St, Edmonton, N18 2SW (8345 5540); *Oakwood Palace,* 113-115 Bramley Rd, N14 4UT (8886 6639); *Tip Top,* 8 Dennis Parade, Winchmore Hill Rd, N14 6AA (8882 7764).

Greenwich *China Noodles,* 21-22 Elm Terrace, SE9 5DW (8850 8660); *Jaya House* [Chinese/Malaysian], 754 Sidcup Rd, SE9 3NS (8857 2188); *Kings,* 12 Spray St, SE18 6AG (8855 2791); *Mandarin House,* 67 Avery Hill Rd, SE9 2BJ (8850 2716); *Mandarin Palace T/A* [Chinese/Malaysian], 56 Charlton Church La, SE7

7AB (8853 1706); *Mr Chung,* 166 Trafalgar Rd, SE10 9TZ (8858 4245); *Peninsular* within Holiday Inn, Bugsbys Way, SE10 0QJ (8858 2028); *Regent Palace,* 5 Lee Rd, SE3 9RQ (8318 0791); *Sun Ya,* 9-10 Stratheden Parade, SE3 7SX (8858 0728); *Wingsing,* 27-29 Charlton Church La, SE7 7AG (8269 1029).

Hackney *East* [Chinese/Vietnamese], 54-64 Kingsland Rd, E2 8DP (7729 5544); *Fang Cheng of China,* 241 Mare St, E8 3NS (8986 0072); *ITTO,* 226 Stoke Newington High St, N16 7HU (7275 8827); *Shanghai,* 41 Kingsland High St, E8 2JS (7254 2878); *Thang Long,* 9 Chatsworth Rd, E5 0LH (8533 9566).

Hammersmith & Fulham *Eat Well,* 313-317 King St, W6 9NH (8748 4390); *Formosa,* 1 Walham Green Ct, Fulham Rd, SW6 2DH (7381 0735); *Mandarin,* 6a Beaconsfield Terrace Rd, W14 0PP (7603 8145); *Mandarin Star T/A,* 115 Munster Rd, SW6 6DH (7736 2064); *Mao Tai,* 58 New King's Rd, SW6 4LS (7731 2520); *Oriental Garden,* 616 Fulham Rd, SW6 5RP (7736 9171); *Treasure Pot,* 45 Fulham High St, SW6 3JJ (7371 7839).

Haringey *Evergreen,* 75 West Green Rd, N15 5DA (8802 8868); *Honeymoon,* 33-35 Park Rd, Crouch End, N8 8TE (8341 5113); *Jade,* 82 High St, N8 7NU (8341 5096); *Jade Palace,* 20 Broadway Parade, Tottenham La, N8 9DE (8347 8594); *Khin Lee,* 19 Westbury Ave, N22 6BS (8881 4251); *Wonderful Palace,* 275 Archway Rd, N6 5AA (8348 5385); *Wood Green Chinese,* 138 High Rd, N22 6EB (8888 8830); *Yien,* 15-17 Muswell Hill Broadway, N10 3HA (8444 6830).

Harrow *Mandarin T/A,* 207 Headstone La, Harrow HA2 6ND (8428 3308); *Mister Ho's Harrow Rendezvous,* 152 Station Rd, Harrow, HA1 2RH (8863 2702); *Rickshaw,* 124 High St, Harrow, HA3 7AL (8861 3637); *Sakonis,* 5-8 Dominion Parade, Station Rd, Harrow HA1 (8863 3399).

Hillingdon *Beijing,* 32 Oxford Rd, Uxbridge UB9 4DQ (01895 814484); *Harefield Chinese Take-away,* 7 Moorhall Rd, Uxbridge, UB9 6PE (01895 823735); *Mulberry Chinese Take Away & Fish Bar,* 1 Mulberry Pde, West Drayton, UB7 9AE (01895 444331).

Hounslow *Hyatt Peking Cuisine,* 82 The Centre, Feltham, TW13 4BH (8890 2648); *Mandarin Express,* 157 Thornbury Rd, Isleworth TW7 4QG (8560 8898/1988); *Mandarin T/A,* 40 Brook Rd South, Brentford TW8 0PH (8560 8036).

Islington *Beijing,* 205-207 Holloway Rd, N7 8DL (7609 1312); *Eastern Chinese T/A,* 156

Canonbury Rd, Islington N1 2UP (7226 5032); *Nam Bistro,* 326 Upper St, N1 2XQ (7354 0851); *New Culture Revolution,* 42 Duncan St, N1 8BW (7833 9083); *Waterlands,* 151 Upper St, N1 1RA (7704 9308); *Wok Wok,* 67 Upper St, N1 0NY (7288 0333); *Young's,* 154 Upper St, N1 1RA (7226 8760).

Kensington & Chelsea *China Kitchen,* 36a Kenway Rd, Earl's Court SW5 0RA (7370 2533); *Choy's,* 172 Kings Rd, Chelsea SW3 4UP (7352 9085); *City Lounge,* 160 Portobello Rd, W11 2EB (7727 6170); *Dragon Palace,* 207 Earls Court Rd, SW5 9AN (7370 1461); *Emperor,* 366-370 Kings Rd, SW3 5UZ (7823 3368, 7352 6797); *Ho Ho,* 11 King's Rd, SW3 4RP (7730 4629); *Golden Chopsticks,* 1 Harrington Rd, SW7 3ES (7584 0855); *Lee Gardens,* 29 Kensington High St, W8 5NP (7937 8448); *Lotus Garden,* 15 Kenway Rd, SW5 0RP (7244 8984); *Mandarin,* 197c Kensington High St, W8 6BA (7937 1551); *Mr Chow,* 151 Knightsbridge, SW1X 7PA (7589 7347); *Mr Wing,* 242 Old Brompton Rd, SW5 0DE (7370 4460); *New Culture Revolution,* 305 Kings Rd, SW3 5EP (7352 9281); *New Culture Revolution,* 157 Notting Hill Gate, W11 3LF (7313 9688); *Paper Tiger,* 10 Exhibition Rd, SW7 2HF (7225 0776); *Singapore Mandarin,* 120 Holland Park Ave, W11 4UA (7727 6341); *Stick & Bowl,* 31 Kensington High St, W8 5NP (7937 2778); *Ta-Krai,* 100 North End Rd, West Kensington W14 9EX (7386 5375); *Veg Veg* [vegetarian], 8 Egerton Gdn Mews, Knightsbridge SW3 2EH (7584 7007); *Wok Wok,* 140 Fulham Rd, SW10 9PY (7370 5355); *Wok Wok,* 7 Kensington High St, W8 5NP (7938 1221); *Zen,* Chelsea Cloisters, 85 Sloane Ave, Chelsea SW3 3DX (7589 1781).

Kingston *Mandarin,* 31 Upper Ham Rd, Kingston, KT2 5QX (8541 4140); *Man's,* 92 Coombe La, Raynes Park SW20 0AY (8946 9959).

Lambeth *Abacus,* 38 Clapham High St, SW4 7UR (7622 3114); *Chinese Chef,* 191 Streatham High Rd, SW16 6EG (8769 1607); *Golden Bowl,* 195 Gipsy Rd, SE27 9QY (8761 1132); *Golden Canton,* 218 Railton Rd, SE24 0JT (7274 5681); *Hung's,* 2 Sunnyhill Rd, SW16 2UH (8769 0176); *Kong Lam,* 57 Abbeville Rd, SW4 9JW (8673 2791); *Mr Kai Peking Cuisine,* 11 Central Hill, SE19 1BG (8670 6384); *Mrs Wong's,* 179 Streatham High Rd, SW16 6EG (8769 0126); *New Jade,* 16 Greyhound La, SW16 5SD (8769 5293); *New Lotus,* 161 Streatham High Rd, SW16 6EG (8769 0149); *Noodle Bar,* 426 Coldharbour La, SW9 8LF (7274 1492); *Pang's Chinese Food,* 184 Tulse Hill, SW2 3BU (8674 9923); *Rejoice,* 36 Norwood High St, SE27 9NR (8766 6432); *Sun Sun,* 94 Clapham High St, SW4 7UL (7622 9696).

Lewisham *Eastern Queen,* 85a Rushey Green, Lewisham SE6 4AF (8697 4677); *Golden City,* 58 Sydenham Rd, SE26 5QE (8778 6172); *Golden Pearl,* 15-16, Royal Parade, Blackheath Vale, SE3 0TL (8852 7777); *Good Friend,* 2a Douglas Way, SE8 4AG (8692 6383); *King's Chow Mein,* Eros Ho, Brownhill Rd, Catford, SE6 2EG (8695 9188);

Mandarin House T/A, 16 Rushey Green, SE6 4JF (8690 3250); *Matahari,* 75 Springbank Rd, SE13 6SS (8695 8823); *Noodle King,* 36 Deptford Broadway, SE8 4PQ (8692 9633); *Shen Xiang Yuan,* 318 Lewisham High St, SE13 6JZ (8690 0032); *Tai Wu,* 82 Brockley Rise, SE23 1LN (8690 8790); *Tse's,* 54 London Rd, SE23 3HF (8291 0019); *Welcome Noodles House,* 47-49 Lee High Rd, SE13 5NS (8297 5268).

Merton *Happiness Chinese T/A,* 278 Haydons Rd, Wimbledon, SW19 8TT (8540 5924); *Mai's Kitchen,* 264 The Broadway, Wimbledon SW19 1SB (8542 5007); *Wimbledon Palace Chinese Restaurant,* 88 The Broadway, Wimbledon SW19 1RH (8540 4505).

Newham *Canton Chinese T/A,* 6a Leytonstone Rd, E15 1SE (8534 4339); *Chinese Overseas,* 411 High St, E15 4QZ (8534 1987); *Eastern Palace,* 278 Romford Rd, E7 9HD (8534 3719); *Golden Gate,* 146 Barking Rd, E6 3BD (8472 8637).

Redbridge *Grace's,* 299 High Rd, Leytonstone E11 4HH (8539 8284); *Mandarin Palace,* 559 Cranbrook Rd, Ilford IG2 6JZ (8551 5599).

Richmond *Lotus Palace,* 331 Upper Richmond Rd, West Sheen, SW14 8QR (8878 2612).

Southwark *Chinese Chequers,* 176-178 Lower Rd, Surrey Quay, SE16 2UN (7231 7774); *Dragon Wok,* 40 Peckham Rd, SE15 8PX, (7708 3898); *Ginseng Noodle,* 4 Coldharbour La, SE5 9PR (7733 4006); *Gracelands Palace,* 881-883 Old Kent Rd, SE15 1NL (7639 3961); *Mr Liu,* 148 Lordship La, SE22 8HB (8693 8266); *Oriental Noodle Hut,* 18 Peckham High St, SE15 5DT (7639 1888); *Rainbow,* 33-37 Brunel Rd, SE16 4LA (7231 0028); *Supernoodle,* 1a Rotherhithe Old Rd, SE16 2PP (7232 1323); *Yun Hai,* 4 Gwent Ct, Rotherhithe St, SE16 5SW (7231 5073).

Tower Hamlets *Eat & Drink,* 11 Artillery Passage, E1 7LJ (7377 0557); *Good Friends,* 139 Salmon La, E14 (7987 5498); *Jade Harbour,* 1-2 Admirals Way, E14 9XL (7987 0771); *Lotus Floating Restaurant,* 38 Limeharbour, E14 9RH (7515 6445); *Millennium Chinese,* 222 Whitechapel Rd, E1 1BJ (7247 6788); *Noodle King,* 185 Bethnal Green Rd, E2 6AB (7613 3131); *Old Friends,* 659 Commercial Rd, E14 7LW (7790 5027); *River View,* New Crane Wharf, Wapping High St, E1W 3TU (7480 6026); *Sea Palace,* 278 Bethnal Green Rd, E2 0AG (7739 2140); *Sinh Le,* 41 Mile End Rd, E1 (7790 0773).

Waltham Forest *Chong's,* 170 Station Rd, N Chingford E4 6AN (8529 3988); *Hong Kong,* 218 Chingford Mount Rd, Chingford, E4 8JL (8529 7655); *King's Chef,* 178 Hoe St, E17 (8520 5918); *King Wai,* 554 High Rd, Leytonstone E11 3DH (8539 2573); *New Mandarin,* 65 Orford Rd, E17 9NJ (8520 6219); *Noodle Express,* 216 High St, Walthamstow, E17 (8520 6622); *Oriental Spices,* 23 Winchester Rd, Highams Park, E4 (8527 0777).

Wandsworth *David Wong,* 108 Mitcham Rd, SW17 9NG (8672 9886); *Jasmin,* 50 Battersea Rise, SW11 1EG (7228 0336); *Little House,* 545 Battersea Park Rd, SW11 3BL (7738 0712);

Mandarin House, 205 Merton Rd, SW18 5EE (8871 1662); Mei, 6-8 West Hill, Wandsworth SW18 1SB (8870 0177); Ning Fung, 75 Upper Tooting Rd, SW17 7TW (8672 5237); Ocean City, 183/185, Battersea Park Rd, SW11 4LB (7720 9928); Rasa Penang, 315 Putney Bridge Rd, Putney, SW15 2PP (8789 3165); Royal China, 3 Chelverton Rd, Putney, SW15 1RN (8780 1520); Yum Yum [Chinese/Malaysian], 112 St Johns Hill, SW11 1SJ (7585 1802).

Westminster Four Seasons, 84 Queensway, W2 3RL (7229 4320); Hsing, 451 Edgware Rd, W2 1TH (7402 0904); Hung To, 51 Queensway, W2 (7727 5753); Kam Tong, 59-63 Queensway, W2 4QH (7229 6065); Lee Fook, 98 Westbourne Grove, W2 5RU (7727 0099); Magic Wok, 100 Queensway, W2 3RR (7792 9767); Mandarin, 33 Craven Rd, Bayswater, W2 3BX (7723 8744); Mr Wu's Bayswater, 54 Queensway, W2 3RY (7243 1017); New Culture Revolution, 442 Edgware Rd, W2 1EG (7402 4841); Park Inn, 6 Wellington Terrace, Bayswater Rd, W2 4LW (7792 2472); Peking, 113-115 Praed St, W2 1RL (7723 9550); Phoenix Palace, 3 Glentworth St, NW1 5PG (7486 3515); Poon's, 205 Whiteleys Centre, 151 Queensway W2 4YJ (7792 2884); Royal China, 68 Queens Grove, NW8 6ER (7586 4280); Royal China [dim sum], 13 Queensway, W2 4QJ (7221 2535); Southeast W9, 239 Elgin Ave, W9 1NJ (7328 8883); Street Hawker, 166 Randolph Ave, W9 1PG (7286 3869).

SHOPS Guanghwa Co. Ltd, 7 Newport St, WC2H 7JR (7437 3737, fax 7831 0137) [arts, crafts, books]; Helen's Chinese Shop, 35 Green Lanes, Palmers Green, N13 4TN (8365 7911); Loon Fung Supermarket, 42 Gerrard St, W1 (7437 7179); Priestley & Ferraro Chinese Art, 17 King St, SW1Y 6QU (7930 6228); Shanghai Tang, 6 Sloane St, SW1 (7235 8778);

Soo San Chinese Furniture, 239a Fulham Rd, Chelsea, SW3 6HY (7352 8980); Wen Tai Sun Chinese Arts & Crafts, 80 Dean St, W1V 5AD (7437 5188); Wing Tai Supermarket, 13 Electric Ave, SW9 (7738 5898); Wing Yip, 395 Edgware Rd, NW2 (8450 0422); Ying Hwa, 14 Gerrard St, W1V (7439 8825) [books and magazines].

TRANSLATION Anglo-Chinese Translations, 29 Winchelsea Rd, NW10 8UN (8838 6288); Chinese & Mandarin Translation Services, The Moorings, 164 Brindley Close, Wembley HA0 1BU (8991 6761).

TRAVEL Air China, 41 Grosvenor Gdns, SW1W 0BP (7744 0789); Cultural Tours Ltd, 320 Regent St, W1B 5BB (7636 7906); Cathay Pacific Airways Ltd, 7 Apple Tree Yard, SW1Y 6LD (7747 8888); China Eastern Airlines, 7 Buckingham Gate, SW1E 6JP (7393 1231); China Holidays, 14 Broadwick St, W1F 8HW (7287 6727); China Hotel Reservations, 124 Euston Rd, NW1 (7388 8828); China National Tourist Office, 4 Glentworth St, NW1 (0891 600188); China Travel Service (UK) Ltd, CTS Ho, 7 Upper St Martin's La, WC2H 9DL (7836 9911); China Travel Service and Information Centre, 124 Euston Rd, NW1 2AL (7388 8838); China Travel Service and Information Centre, 78 Shaftesbury Ave, W1D 6NG (7439 8888); China UK Information Centre Ltd, 3rd fl, 45 Gerrard St, W1D 5QQ (7734 9529); Cultural Tours Ltd, 320 Regent St, W1R (7636 7906); East Asia Travel, Unit 20, Angerstein Business Park, Horn Lane, Greenwich SE10 (8293 4048); Hong Kong Tourist Association, 125 Pall Mall, SW1Y (7930 4775); Macau Tourism, 1 Battersea Church Rd, SW11 (7771 7006); Orient Travel Service, 100 Brick La, E1 (7247 5932); Universal Travel, 80 Shaftesbury Ave, W1 (7734 3172).

WELFARE Camden Chinese Community Centre, 173 Arlington Rd, NW1 (7267 3019); Chinese in Britain Forum, Suite 109, Davina Ho, 137-149 Goswell Rd, EC1V 7ET (7253 8585); Hackney Chinese Community Services, Ellingfort Rd, Hackney,E8 3PA (8986 6171); Haringey Chinese Centre, c/o Raymond Yip, 211 Langham Rd, N15 3LH (8881 8649) [languages: **Chinese,** English];

Lambeth Chinese Community Association, 69 Stockwell Rd, Brixton, SW9 9PY (7733 4377); *Southwark Vietnamese / Chinese Refugee Community,* Thomas Carlton Centre, Alpha St, SE15 4II (7635 0022).

Chokwe

Chokwe is a Bantuic language spoken in Angola, Congo/Kinshasa and Zambia. In the *Multilingual Capital* (2000) survey it was reported as the home language of only one pupil, in Westminster.

Christian

ACCOMMODATION *Catholic International Student Chaplaincy* [hostel], 16c Portland Rise, Finsbury Park N4 2PP (8802 9673); *Christian Alliance Housing Association Ltd,* Christian Alliance Centre 2, Secker St, SE1 8UF (7450 4601); *Young Men's Christian Association –* see *YMCAs* (below) *Young Women's Christian –* see *YWCAs* (below).

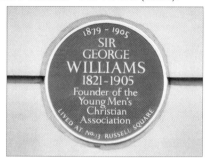

YMCAs offering accommodation: *YMCA Barbican,* Fann St, EC2 (7628 0697); *YMCA Earl's Court,* 10 West Cromwell Rd, SW5 (7373 0787); *YMCA Hornsey,* 184 Tottenham La, N8 (8340 2345); *YMCA Kingston* (8390 0148); *YMCA Lambeth,* 40 Stockwell Rd, SW9 (7501 9795); *YMCA City of London,* 8 Errol St, EC1 (7628 8832); *YMCA Waltham Forest,* 642 Forest Rd, E17 (8520 0931); *YMCA Wimbledon,* 200 The Broadway, SW19 (8542 9055); see also entries under *German* and *Indian.*

YWCAs offering accommodation: *YWCA Bayswater,* 13 Palace Ct, W2 (7727 3009); *YWCA Central Club,* 63 Camden High St, NW1 (7388 7737); *YWCA Devonshire St,* 2 Devonshire St, W1 (7580 5323); *YWCA Ealing,* 9 North Common Rd, W5 (8567 9588); *YWCA Earl's Court,* 227 Earl's Court Rd, SW5 (7373 2851); *YWCA Euston,* 14 Endsleigh Gdns, WC1 (73887 3378); *YWCA Finchley & Friern Barnet,* 69 Gainsborough Rd, N12 (8446 2550); *YWCA Hampstead,* 6-8 Kemplay Rd, NW3 1SY (7435 5730); *YWCA Highgate,* Roden Ct, Hornsey La, N6 (7272 2373); *YMCA Holborn,* Helen Graham Ho, Great Russell St, WC1 (7430 0834); *YMCA King's Cross,* 13 Lloyd Sq, WC1 (7837 2601).

ASSOCIATIONS *Christian Socialist Movement,* Westminster Central Hall, SW1H 9NH (7233 3736).

EDUCATION *Carmena Christian Nursery School,* 38 Mitcham La, Streatham SW16 6NP (8677 1376).

MEDIA & INFORMATION *Christian Broadcast International* [TV, film & video production services], 341, Brixton Rd, SW9 7DA (7924 9263); *Church of England Newspaper,* 10 little College St, SW1 (7878 1549).

RELIGION There are several thousand churches and other places of Christian worship in London. It is beyond the scope of this book to attempt to list these here. Instead each of the main branches of Christianity represented in London is listed below with one address and telephone number which could be contacted. These details are drawn from *Whitaker's Almanack 2002* which is a useful source of further information.

African and Afro-Caribbean Churches *Afro-West Indian United Council of Churches,* c/o New Testament Church of God, Arcadian Gdns, High Rd, N22 5AA (8888 9427); *Council of African and Afro-Caribbean Churches UK,* 31 Norton Ho, 31 Sidney Rd, SW9 0UJ (7274 5589).

Baptist Church *Baptist Central Church,* 235 Shaftesbury Ave, WC2 (7836 6843).

Christadelphianism *Christadelphian Information Service,* 116 Greenvale Rd, SE9 (8859 8061).

Church of Christ, Scientist *Christian Science Committee on Publication,* 9 Elysium Gate, 126 new Kings Rd, SW6 4LZ (7384 8600).

Church of England *Church of England, Church Ho,* Great Smith St, SW1P 3NZ (7898 1000), *Saint Paul's Cathedral,* EC4 (7236 4128) *Southwark Cathedral, Westminster Abbey,* SW1 (7222 5152).

Church of Jesus Christ of the Latter-Day Saints ("Mormons") *England London Mission,* 64 Exhibition Rd, SW7 (7584 7553).

Church of Scotland *Church of Scotland,* Crown Ct, Russell St, London WC2 (7836 5643); *Saint Columba's Church,* Pont St, SW1 (7584 2321).

Eastern Orthodox Church *Patriarchate of Antioch Representative:* Rev Samir Gholam, St George's Cathedral, 1a Redhill St, NW1 4BG (7383 0403); *Patriarchate of Moscow Representative:* Metropolitan Anthony of Sourozh, 67 Ennismore Gdns, SW7 1NH (fax 7584 9864); *Russian Orthodox Church Outside Russia Representative:* Archbishop Mark, c/o 57 Harvard Rd, W4 4ED (8742 3493).

Free Church of Scotland *Free Church of Scotland,* 114 Queen Victoria St, EC4 (7248 5213).

Holy Apostolic Catholic Assyrian Church of the East *UK Representative* V Rev Younan Y Younan, 66 Montague Rd, W7 3PQ (8579 7259).

Jehovah's Witnesses *British Isles HQ,* Watchtower Ho, The Ridgeway, NW7 1RN (8906 2211).

Lutheran Church *Lutheran Council of Great Britain,* 30 Thanet St, WC1H 9QH (7554 2900).

Methodist Church *Methodist Central Hall Westminster,* Storey's Gate, SW1 (7222 8010); *Methodist Church Administrative Headquarters,* 25 Marylebone Rd, NW1 5JR (7486 5502).

New Church [Swedenborgian] *General Conference of the New Church,* 20 Bloomsbury Way, WC1A 2TH (7229 9340).

Oriental Orthodox Churches *Council of Oriental Orthodox Churches,* Chertsey Rd, Church Sq, Shepperton TW17 9LF (8368 8447). See also RELIGION under **Armenian, Coptic, Eritrean, Ethiopean, Keralite** and **Syrian.**

Pentecostal Churches *Pentecostal Church Enquiry,* 30 Blomfield Villas, W2 (7286 9261).

Religious Society of Friends (Quakers) *Central Offices,* Friends Ho, 173 Euston Rd, NW1 2BJ (7663 1000).

Roman Catholic Church *Bishops' Conference Secretariat for England and Wales,* 39 Eccleston Sq, SW1V 1PD (7630 8220); *Westminster Cathedral,* Victoria St, SW1 (7798 9055).

Salvation Army *Territorial Headquarters,* 101 Newington Causeway, SE1 6BN (7367 4500).

Seventh-Day Adventist Church *South England Conference,* 25 St Johns Rd, Watford (01923 232728).

Unitarian and Free Christian Churches *General Assembly of Unitarian and Free Christian Churches,* Essex Hall, 1-6 Essex St, WC28 3HY (7240 2384).

United Reformed Church *Headquarters,* 86 Tavistock Pl, WC1H 9RT (7916 2020).

SHOPS *Agape Arabic Christian Centre* [books], 11 Porchester Rd, W2 5DP (7221 4355); *Chapter Two Christian Bookshop,* 199 Plumstead Common Rd, SE18 2UJ (8316 4972); *Christian Books & Music,* Kensington Temple, Kensington Park Rd, W11 3BY (7727 8684); *Cornerstone Christian Bookshop,* 299 Lavender Hill, SW11 1LN (7924 2413).

TRAVEL *Christian Travel Worldwide,* 317 Greenford Ave, W7 1JH (8357 0986);

WELFARE *Action by Christians Against Torture,* Quex Rd Methodist Church, NW6 4PR (7372 7347); *Catholic Institute for International Relations,* 190 New North Rd, Islington N1 7BJ (7354 0883).

Cockney

BARS & NIGHT-CLUBS *Cockney's,* 610 Old Kent Rd, SE15 1JB (7252 9090).

BUSINESS *Cockney Rebel plc,* 97 Mortimer St, W1W 7ST [clothing manufacturers].

RESTAURANTS

Croydon *Cockney's,* 82 Church St, Croydon CR0 1RB (8680 4512).

Kensington & Chelsea *Cockney's Pie and Mash Shop,* 314 Portobello Rd, W10 5RU (8960 9409).

Redbridge *Cockney Grub House,* 823 High St, Goodmayes IG3 8TD (8597 8545).

Southwark *Cockney Hut Cafe,* 218 Camberwell Rd, SE5 0ED (7701 8587).

Tower Hamlets *Cockney Frier* [fish and chips], 222 Devons Rd, Bow, E3 3PN (7515 7736).

SHOPS *Cockney Touch* [clothes], 113 Fonthill Rd, Finsbury Park N4 3HH (7263 0343); *Cockney Touch Clothing* [clothes], 30 Wentworth St, E1 7TF (7377 5373); *Gricks Jellied Eels,* Rear of 316a High St North, Manor Park E12 6SA (8472 2502).

TRAVEL *Cockney Cab Co Ltd,* 15 Bohemia Pl, Mare St, E8 1DU (8533 9599).

Colombian

ASSOCIATIONS *Colombian Peace Association,* Cleveland Ho, 55 Cleveland Sq, W2 6DB.

GOVERNMENT *Colombian Consulate,* 3rd fl, 15-19 Gt Titchfield St, W1W 8AZ (7637 9893); *Colombian Embassy,* 3 Hans Crescent, SW1X 0LN (7589 9177); *Proexport-Colombian Government Trade Bureau,* 9 Berkeley St, W1X 5AD (7491 3535).

LANGUAGE The principal and official language of Colombia is **Spanish.**

RECREATION *Colombia FC Association,* 17 Purdon Ho, Oliver Goldsmith Estate, Peckham, SE15 5EF.

RELIGION the established religion is Roman Catholicism.

RESTAURANTS

Islington *Café Colombia,* 236 St Pauls Rd, N1 2LJ (7704 8227); *Tienda Tropical,* 217 Holloway Rd, N7 (7607 6002).

SHOPS *La Bodeguita* [food], Unit 256, Upper Level, Elephant & Castle Shopping Centre, SE1 (7708 5826); *La Tienda* [food], 81 Praed St, W2 (7706 4695).

TRAVEL *Avianca Airline,* 15-17 Col Walk, 151 Buckingham Palace Rd, SW1W 9SH (0870 576 7747).

Commonwealth

ARTS & CULTURE *Commonwealth Arts & Cultural Foundation Ltd,* Tempo Ho, Falcon Rd, SW11 2PJ (7924 1449).

ASSOCIATIONS *British Commonwealth Ex-Services League,* 48 Pall Mall, SW1Y 5JG (7973 7263); *Commonwealth Association of Architects,* 54 Old St, EC1V 9AL (7490 3024); *Commonwealth Journalists Association,* 17 Nottingham St, W1U 5EW (7486 3844); *Commonwealth Magistrates & Judges Association,* Uganda Ho, Trafalgar Sq, WC2N 5DS (7976 1007); *Royal Agricultural Society of the Commonwealth,* 2 Grosvenor Gdns, SW1W 0DH (7259 9678); *Royal Commonwealth Society,* 18 Northumberland Ave, WC2N 5BJ (7766 9200); *Victoria League for Commonwealth Friendship,* 57 Leinster Sq, W2 4PW (7243 2633).

BUSINESS *Commonwealth Invest Ltd,* 10 White Horse St, W1Y 7LB (7491 2112).

EDUCATION *Association of Commonwealth Universities,* 36 Gordon Sq, WC1H 0PF (7380 6700); *Commonwealth Science Council,* Marlborough Ho, Pall Mall, SW1Y 5HX (7839 3411); *Council for Education in the Commonwealth,* 7 Lion Yard, Tremadoc Rd, SW4 7NQ (7498 1202); *Commonwealth Youth Exchange Council,* 7 Lion Yard, Tremadoc Rd, SW4 7NF (7498 6151).

GOVERNMENT *Commonwealth Local Government Forum,* 59 and a half Southwark St, SE1 0AL (7401 6864); *Commonwealth Parliamentary Association – United Kingdom Branch,* Houses of Parliament, SW1A 0AA (7219 5373); *Foreign & Commonwealth Office,* King's Charles St, SW1A 2AH (7270 1500).

LEGAL *Commonwealth Legal Advisory Service,* Senate Ho, Malet St, WC1E 7HU (7862 5151).

MEDIA & INFORMATION *Commonwealth Broadcasting Association,* 17 Fleet St, EC4Y 1AA (7583 5550); *Commonwealth Press Union,* 17 Fleet St, EC4Y 1AA (7583 7733); *Commonwealth Telecommunications Organisation,* 26 Oxendon St, SW1Y 4EL (7930 5511).

RECREATION *Commonwealth Games Federation,* 26 Upper Brook St, W1K 7QE (7491 8801).

RELIGION *Commonwealth Christian Fellowship,* St Mark's Church, North Audley St, W1Y 2DP (7409 0251).

SPECIAL *Commonwealth Foundation,* Marlborough Ho, Pall Mall, SW1Y 5HX (7930 3783); *Commonwealth Human Ecology Council,* Church Ho, Newton Rd, W2 5LS (7792 5934); *Commonwealth Institute,* Kensington High St, W8 6NQ (7603 4535); *Commonwealth Trade Union Council,* Congress Ho, Great Russell St, WC1B 3LP (7467 1301).

WELFARE *Commonwealth Society for the Deaf,* 34 Buckingham Palace Rd, SW1W 0RE (7233 5700); *Commonwealth Welfare Immigration Advisory,* 479 High Road Leytonstone, E11 4II (8558 9597).

Comoran

GOVERNMENT Comoran interests in Britain are represented from its embassy in France at 20 rue Marbeau, F-75016, Paris (+33 1 4067 9054).

LANGUAGES Arabic and French have official status but the dominant local language, sometimes termed *"Komoro"*, is closely related to Swahili.

RELIGION Virtually the entire population is Muslim.

Congolese-Brazzaville

ASSOCIATIONS *London Congo Brazza Association,* 3 Bradbury St, N16 8JN (7249 7730).

GOVERNMENT *Honorary Consulate of Congo Brazzaville,* Unit 4, Wendle Ct, 131-137 Wandsworth Rd, SW8 2LH (7622 0419).

LANGUAGES The majority of the population speak varieties of *Kongo.* Several other Bantuic languages are also spoken of which *Lingala* is particularly important as a second language in the northern part of the country.

Congolese-Kinshasa

Since Zaïre changed its name to the Democratic Republic of Congo there have in effect been two Congos, the other being the Republic of Congo-Brazzaville. The current tendency is to term these, respectively, Congo-Kinshasa and Congo-Brazzaville, as was formerly the case prior to the adoption of the (now abandoned) name of Zaïre for the Democratic Republic.

ASSOCIATIONS *Congolese-Kinshasa Community Association,* 54 Selby Centre, N17 8JN (8365 1665); *South London Congolese Association,* Unit 203, Croydon Ho, 1 Peall Rd Croydon CR0 3EX (8664 9580); *Zairean Community Association,* 307 Selby Centre, N17 8JN (8365 1665); *Zairean Refugee Womens Association,* 7-8 Romford Rd, Manor Park E12 6BT (8478 2839).

FREIGHT *Congo Freight Services,* Marc Ct, West Green Rd, N15 5NR (8800 8023).

GOVERNMENT *Embassy of the Democratic Republic of Congo,* 38 Holme Chase, N2 0QQ (8458 0254).

LANGUAGES About 150 different languages are spoken in Congo-Kinshasa. The four with the largest number of speakers are *Luba, Kongo, Swahili,* and *Lingala,* all of them *Bantuic.* None of these is the mother tongue of more than 7% of the population but *Swahili* and *Lingala* are both widely known as a second languages.

RESTAURANTS

Haringey *Leopoldville chez José Apula,* 78 West Green Rd, N15 (8800 8160); *Ma Mapasa,* 62 West Green Rd, N15 (8802 7084).

WELFARE *Congolese-Kinshasa Action Group*, 375 High St, E15 (8555 7508); *Tower Hamlet Zairean Refugees Group,* Alpha Grove Community Centre, Millwall, Poplar E14 8LH (7987 0022); *Zairean Advice & Support Project,* Battle Bridge Centre, 226 Battle Bridge Rd, NW1 2TL (7278 4546).

Continental

BUSINESS *Continental Research*, 37-42 Compton St, EC1V 0AP (7490 5944).

FREIGHT *A & B Continental Transport,* 8 9 Lytchet Way, Enfield EN3 5XS (8443 3091); *Continental Freight Distributors Ltd,* Unit 3 Ascot Rd, Feltham, TW14 8QH (01784 420030); *Sterling Continental Services Ltd,* Unit 1, The Heston Centre, International Ave, Hounslow TW5 9NZ (8573 9443).

HEALTH & BEAUTY *Aphrodite Continental Hairdressing Co Ltd*, 89 Landor Rd, SW9 9RT (7274 6324); *Continental Cosmetics Centre,* 51 Atlantic Rd, Brixton SW9 8JL (7738 7655); *Modern Gents Continental Hairstylists,* 99 Upper Tooting Rd, SW17 7TW (8767 7037); *Nicola Continental Hair Fashions,* 37 Hamilton Rd, Brentford TW8 0QF (8560 8837).

MOTORING *Continental Autos,* 10 Daleham Mews, NW3 5DB (7794 7701); *Continental Autos,* 715 North Circular Rd, NW2 7AH (8450 0555); *Continental Cars & Commercial Ltd*, 2a Bridgewater Rd, Wembley, HA0 1AJ (8900 1766); *Continental Cars Centre Ltd,* Campdale Rd, N7 0ED (7281 4444); *Continental Coachworks*, 112-114 North End Rd, W14 9PP (7381 3338); *Continental Motors,* Bamborough Gdns, Shepherd's Bush W12 8QN (8740 0327); *Continental Motors Kilburn,* Arch 19, Loveridge Rd, Kilburn NW6 2DS (7624 2184); *Motor Continental,* 73 Crouch Hall Rd, Hornsey N8 8HD (8340 9217).

RESTAURANTS
West Central *Continental Touch,* 137 Grays Inn Rd, WC1X 8TZ (7831 8200).

Barnet *Continental Sandwich Bar,* 757 High Rd, N12 8LD (8445 3229).

Enfield *Caterina's Continental Restaurant,* 147 Green Lanes, Palmers Green N13 4SP (8889 1847).

Islington *Continental Café,* 154 Blackstock Rd, N4 2DY (7704 1902); *Continental Café,* 121 Stroud Green Rd, N4 3PX.

Lewisham *Sam's English & Continental Restaurant,* 134 Hither Green La, Lewisham SE13 6QA (8463 0777).

Southwark *Continental Café,* 403a Walworth Rd, SE17 2AW (7701 7982).

Westminster *Erra Continental Cuisine,* 65 Praed St, W2 (7402 8048).

SHOPS
Books *Continental Books Ltd*, 57 Grosvenor St, W1X 9DA.

Food:

Barnet *Fritzsch Continental Bakery,* 25 Queens Parade, Friern Barnet Rd, N11 3DA (8368 1866).

Brent *Springfield Continental Patisserie,* 171 Edgware Rd, NW9 6LP (8200 7690).

Camden *English & Continental Groceries,* 3 Camden Park Rd, NW1 9AU (7485 8959); *Taz Continental Store,* Unit A, 31 Pratt St, NW1 0BG (7916 7709).

Enfield *Continental Grocer,* 54 Hoppers Rd, N13 4DB (8886 0551); *Demos Continental Greengrocers,* 8 Green Lanes, N13 6JR (8889 2682); *Ideal Continental Delicatessen Ltd,* 184-186 High St, Enfield, EN3 4EU (8443 3528); *Kayas Continental Store,* 263 Hertford Rd, Enfield, EN3 5JL (8805 4749); *Michaels Continental Groceries,* 26 Market Sq, N9 0TZ (8807 8022); *P & J Continental Foods,* Unit 4, Shaftesbury Rd, N18 1SW (8803 6611).

Greenwich *Continental Supermarket,* 7 Plumstead Rd, SE18 7BZ (8317 0902).

Hackney *Camlic Continental Grocers,* 13 Green Lanes, N16 9BS (7226 5925); *Henry's Continental Stores,* 35 Marsh Hill, E9 5QA (8986 2257); *Max's Eight Till Late Continental Store,* 98a Kingsland High St, E8 2NS (7241 2777); *Terry's Continental Stores,* 88 Ridley Rd, E8 2NR (7254 1357).

Hammersmith & Fulham *Continental Food Stores,* 167 Railway Arches, Shepherds Bush Market, W12 8DF (8743 1191); *Mimi's Continental Patisserie,* 76 Goldhawk Rd, W12 8HA (8749 5922); *Pak Continental Foodstore,* 191 Shepherds Bush Market, W12 8DF (8743 5389).

Haringey *Continental Delicatessen & Bakery,* 192 Archway Rd, N6 5BB (8348 8090); *Continental Delicatessen,* Markethall, Wood Green Shopping City, High Rd, N22 6YE (8889 9995); *Continental Meat Supply,* 17 Turnpike Lane, N8 0EP (8348 5250); *Omonia Continental Patisserie,* 129-133 High Cross Rd, N17 9NU (8801 0986).

Islington *Continental Stores,* 3 Campdale Rd, N7 0EA (7272 3512); *KC Continental Stores,* 26 Caledonian Rd, N1 (7837 0201); *King's Cross Continental Stores Ltd,* 26 Caledonian Rd, N1 9DU (7837 0201); *Motta Continental Patisserie,* 7-7a Eden Grove, N7 8DX (7700 1430).

Lambeth *Continental Fruit Stores,* Unit C, 16 Fruit & Vegetable Market, New Covent Garden Market, SW8 5JJ (7720 4233); *New Continental Store Delicatessen,* 401 Coldharbour La, SW9 8LQ (7274 2020); *Rosedale Continental Foods,* 272 Brixton Hill, SW2 1HP (8671 7244).

Southwark *Paul's Continental Greengrocers,* 62 Camberwell Church St, SE5 8QZ (7703 0156); **Tower Hamlets** *Continental Grocers,* 7 West India

Dock Rd, E14 8EZ (7538 1457); *Toynbee Continental Groceries*, 21-23 Toynbee St, E1 7NE (7247 8115).

Waltham Forest Ammas Continental Food Shop, 34 Capworth St, E10 7HA (8558 6788); *Angel Continental Bakeries*, 44 Fairways Business Park, Lammas Rd, E10 7QB (8539 5252).

Westminster *Sadia Continental Foodstore*, 218 Edgware Rd, W2 1DH (7723 6421).

Other *English & Continental Pigeon Supplies*, Unit 1b St Marks Industrial Estate, North Woolwich Rd, E16 2BS (7476 5806).

Coptic
====

RELIGION *Coptic Orthodox Church*, Allen St, Kensington W8 6UX (7937 9455); *Coptic Orthodox Church*, 594 Great West Rd, Hounslow TW5 0TH (8577 7222); *Coptic Orthodox Church*, 14 Newton Mansions, Queens Club Gdns, West Kensington W14 9RR (7385 1991).

Cornish

BUSINESS *Ginsters Cornish Pasties Ltd*, Unit 21 Airlinks Industrial Estate, Spitfire Way, Heston TW5 9NW (8848 7268); *Cornish Springwater Company (London) Ltd*, 44 Upper St, N1 0PN (7354 3815).

EDUCATION A beginners' course in **Cornish** has been offered in recent years at City Lit, 16 Stukeley St, WC2B 5LJ (7831 9631).

MEDIA & INFORMATION *Cornish Guardian*, 31 John St, WC1N 2QB (7400 1100) *and* [editorial department], Northcliffe Ho West, Bouverie St, EC4 (7353 6000).

RESTAURANTS
West Central *West Cornwall Pasty Co*, Old Covent Garden, WC2.

Camden *Cornish Oggy Oggy Pasty Company*, 14 Station Colonnade, Euston Station, NW1 2SE (7380 0223).

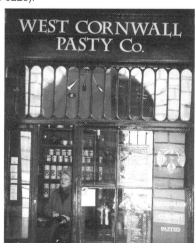

Corsican
====

TRAVEL *Corsican Affair*, 5-7 Humbolt Rd, Hammersmith W6 8QH (7385 8438); *Simply*

Corsica, Chiswick Gate, 598-608 Chiswick High Rd, Chiswick W4 5RT (8747 3580).

Costa Rican
====

GOVERNMENT *Embassy of Costa Rica*, 14 Lancaster Gate, W2 3LH (7706 8844).

LANGUAGE The official language is **Spanish.**

Creole

The word **Creole** has a very wide range of meanings in London. It is applied primarily (1) to certain people born in former colonies of European countries; (2) to a diverse group of languages which developed in those territories; and (3) to styles of cooking associated with those areas.

With regard to (1), **Creole** is applied to people partly or wholly of African descent in Mauritius and the Seychelles as well as in some parts of the Caribbean but in other parts of the Caribbean it can conversely refer to those of mainly or wholly European descent who were born and raised locally.

See LANGUAGES for the meanings of (2) and RESTAURANTS for (3).

EDUCATION *Creole Linguistics Research Group*, Dept. of English & Linguistics, SSHL, University of Westminster, 309 Regent St, WW1B 2UW (7911 5000 x2396).

LANGUAGES **Creole** languages are languages which developed in colonial contact situations such as the slave plantation societies which formerly existed in the Caribbean and elsewhere. They are generally grouped, according to the source of most of their vocabulary, as **English Creoles, French Creoles, Portuguese Creoles,** etc. – see these entries for more information.

RESTAURANTS **Creole** cuisine normally refers to spicy food from either (a) Louisiana and former French colonies in the Caribbean area, or from (b) Mauritius and the Seychelles in the Indian Ocean.

Brent *Tabanka Creole & Afro Caribbean T/A*, 8 Chamberlayne Rd, NW10 3JD (8969 3286).

Croydon *Nu-Bar Creole Restaurant*, 300 High St, Croydon CR0 1NG (8667 0007).

Westminster *Fats* [Cajun Creole Caribbean cuisine], 178 Shirland Rd, W9 3JE (7266 7878).

SHOPS *Elegance Creole Ltd* [clothing], 126 Commercial Rd, E1 1NL (7488 4750).

Croatian
====

EDUCATION Mother-tongue instruction for children in "Serbo-Croat" (see LANGUAGE) is available in a few places in London, see <www.resourceunit.com>. A range of courses in **Croatian** is available at the *Croatian Language School*, 65 St Mary's Rd, W5 5RG (8579 1910). University courses in **Croatian** are taught at *SSEES* (7636 8000).

GOVERNMENT *Embassy of the Republic of Croatia*, 21 Conway St, W1T 6BW (7387 2022; 7387 1790).

LANGUAGE Croatian and Serbian are nearly identical as spoken languages but are written, respectively, in the Roman and Cyrillic alphabets. In the past, they were known collectively in English as "Serbo-Croat", a name which was never popular with Serbians or Croatians and which has become increasingly unacceptable since the political separation of these states. (See also the entry for **Bosnian**.)

At the time of the *Multilingual Capital* (2000) survey, a combined total of 659 schoolchildren were reported as having Bosnian, Croatian, Serbian, "Serbo-Croat" or "Serbian/Croatian" as their first language. A large proportion of these lived in the adjoining boroughs of Hammersmith & Fulham, Kensington & Chelsea, and Westminster.

RELIGION *Croatian Catholic Church,* 17 Boutflower Rd, SW11 1RE (7223 3530).

TRANSLATION *Anglo-Croatian Translation Services,* Flat 3a, Buckingham Mansions, 353 West End La, NW6 1LR (7794 4897).

TRAVEL *Croatia Airlines,* Unit 2, Lanchesters, 162-164 Fulham Palace Rd, W6 9ER (8563 0022); *Croatian National Tourist Office,* 2 Lanchesters, 162-164 Fulham Palace Rd, W6 9ER (8563 7979); *Croatia Tours,* 21 Sawley Rd, W12 0LG (7379 6249).

Cuban

ARTS & CULTURE *Cuban Music Specialist,* Flat 93, Latham Ho, Chudleigh St, E1 0RD (7790 4693); *Havana Connections Ltd* [music publishers], 6 Heath Close, Ealing W5 3EG (8998 5859).

ASSOCIATIONS *Cuban Solidarity Campaign,* 129 Seven Sisters Rd, Holloway, N7 7QG (7263 6452); *Havana Cigar and Travel Club Ltd,* 26 Crown Rd, Twickenham TW1 3EE; *Havana Club Ltd,* Kemp Ho, 152-160 City Rd, EC1V 2NX.

BARS & NIGHT-CLUBS *Brixtonian Havana Club* [Caribbean/Cuban], 11 Beehive Pl, SW9 (7924 9262); *Havana,* 17 Hanover Sq, W1R 9AJ (7629 2552); *Havana Bar,* 72 Upper St, Islington, N1 0NY (7354 9998).

BUSINESS *Cuba Consultants (UK) Ltd,* 196-197 Upper St, Islington, N1 1RQ; *Havana International Bank Ltd,* 20 Ironmonger La, EC2V 8EY (7606 0781).

GOVERNMENT *Cuban Embassy & Consulate,* 167 High Holborn, WC1V 6PA (7240 2488, 7420 3100).

LANGUAGE the dominant and official language of Cuba is **Spanish.**

RESTAURANTS
East Central *Havana Cafe T/A,* Kemp Ho, 152-160 City Rd, EC1V 2NX.
West 1 *Havana,* 17 Hanover Sq, W1R 9AJ (7629 2552).
West Central *Asia de Cuba* [Asian/Cuban fusion], 45 St Martins La, WC2N 4HX (7300 5588); *Little Havana,* Queen's Ho, 1 Leicester Pl, WC2H 7BP (7287 0101/7601).

Hammersmith & Fulham *Havana,* 490 Fulham Rd, SW6 (7381 5005).

Islington *Cuba Libre,* 72 Upper St, Islington, N1 0NY (7354 9998).

Kensington & Chelsea *Cuba,* 11-13 Kensington High St, W8 5NP (7938 4137); *Havana Cafe,* 69 Golborne Rd, W10 5NP (8960 4445).

SHOPS *C Gars,* [Havana cigar merchant], 18 Kingsgate Pl, NW6 4TA (7372 1865); *Havana Cigars Organisation Ltd,* 63 Burlington Arcade, W1J 0QS (7409 0250); *Havana Club* [tobacconists], 165 Sloane St, SW1X 9QB (7245 0890); *Havana Cigar Shop,* 165 Sloane St, SW1X 9QB (7245 0890); *Havana Supermarket,* 243 Plaistow Rd, E13 0AL (8503 1639).

SPECIAL *Havana Horse Ltd* [bloodstock agents], 20 Kinnerton St, SW1X 8ES (7235 5704).

TRAVEL *Captivating Cuba,* 26 Crown Rd, Twickenham, TW1 3EE (8744 9494); *Cuba Experience,* 240 West End La, NW6 1LW (7431 0670); *Cuba Salsa Holidays,* Unit 30, DRCA Business Centre, Charlotte Despard Ave, SW11 5HD (7498 8444); *Cuba Tourist Board,* 154 Shaftesbury Ave, WC2 (7240 6655); *Cuba Tourist Board,* 167 High Holborn, WC1V 6PA (7240 6655); *Havana Cigar and Travel Club Ltd,* 26 Crown Rd, Twickenham TW1 3EE; *Scuba en Cuba,* 7 Maybank Gdns, Pinner, HA5 2JW (01895 624100).

Cypriot

Although Cyprus became independent in 1960 as a unitary state, one third of the island has been administered as the Turkish Republic of Northern Cyprus for more than 20 years. Turkey is the only country to have recognised the latter.

Entries specifically identified as *Greek Cypriot* or *Turkish Cypriot* are listed under those headings and follow *Greek* and *Turkish*, respectively. The entries which follow immediately relate to Cyprus as a whole or, at least, are not identified by name as being limitted to just one of the island's two ethnolinguistic groups.

ASSOCIATIONS *Islington Cypriot Community Association,* 15 Hercules St, N7 6AT (7272 4142).

BARS & NIGHT-CLUBS *Cyprus Nights Club,* 419 Green Lanes, N4 1EY (8340 5955).

BUSINESS
Banking & Finance *Bank of Cyprus (London) Ltd - Head Office,* 27-31 Charlotte St, W1T 1RP (7304 5800); *Bank of Cyprus Ltd,* 14-16 Denmark Hill, Camberwell SE5 8RZ (7274 2189, 7346 5900); *Bank of Cyprus (London) Ltd,* 87-93 Chase Side, Southgate N14 5BU (8267 7200/7201); *Bank of*

Cyprus (London) Ltd, 56-57 Grand Parade, Green Lanes, Harringay, Finsbury Park N4 1AF (8802 1773); Bank of Cyprus (London) Ltd, 131 Green Lanes, Palmers Green N13 4SP (8829 0010); Bank of Cyprus (London) Ltd, 23 Highgate Hill, Archway N19 5LP (7561 8700); Bank Of Cyprus (London) Ltd, 160-162 Seven Sisters Rd, Holloway N7 7PT (7561 8000); Cyprus Credit Investments, 32-33 Grand Parade, Green Lanes, Finsbury Park N4 1LG (8800 3085); Cyprus Credit Investments Ltd, 119 Kingsland High St, Hackney E8 2PB (7241 0707); Cyprus Popular Bank, 19 Fitzroy St, W1P 6BQ (7307 8400); Cyprus Popular Bank Ltd, 246 Green Lanes, Palmers Green, N13 5XT (8920 1000); Cyprus Popular Bank Ltd, 995 High Rd, North Finchley N12 8QX (8492 2000); Cyprus Popular Bank Ltd, 95 Seven Sisters Rd, Holloway N7 6BZ (7561 7000).

Other Cyprus Fisheries Ltd, 23 Billingsgate Fish Market, Trafalgar Way, Poplar E14 5SY (7537 9945); Cyprus Fruit Sales (London) Ltd, Ingersoll Ho, 7-9 Kingsway, Holborn WC2B 6XF (7720 8733); Cyprus Fruit Sales (London) Ltd, Row B, Fruit and Vegetable Market, New Covent Garden SW8 5HH (7720 8733); Cyprus Potato Marketing Board, 14 Wordsworth Parade, Green Lanes, Hornsey N8 0SJ (8889 8822); Cyprus Upholstery, 163 Clarence Rd, Clapton E5 8EE (8986 4929).

GOVERNMENT Cyprus High Commission, 93 Park St, W1Y 4ET (7499 8272, 7629 5350); Cyprus High Commission Trade Centre, 29 Princes St, 3rd fl, W1R 7RG (7629 6288);

RELIGION The Greek population is predominantly Christian (Greek Orthodox Church) and the Turkish population mainly Muslim. See entries under Greek Cypriot and Turkish Cypriot, respectively.

RESTAURANTS Cyprus Fish Bar, 12 East Ham Manor Way. East Ham E6 5NG (7511 9203); Cyprus Grapevine T/A, 50 Cannon Hill, Southgate N14 6LH (8886 0825); New Cyprus Pizza T/A, 269 Bethnal Green Rd, E2 6AH (7739 7454).

SHOPS Cyprus Supermarket, 400 High Rd, Tottenham N17 9JB (8801 6580).

TRAVEL Cyprus Airways Ltd, 5 Brent Cross Gdns, Hendon NW4 3RJ (8359 1333); Cyprus Car Services, 29a High St, Hornsey N8 7QB (8348 4422); Cyprus Car Services, 2 Queens Parade, Green Lanes, Hornsey N8 0RD (8341 6624); Cyprus Paradise, 689 High Rd, North Finchley, N12 0DA (8343 8888); Cyprus Tourist Office, 213 Regent St, W1R 8DA (7734 9822); Cyprus Travel (London) Ltd, 42 Hampstead Rd, Camden NW1 2PY (7387 7854).

WELFARE Cypriot Advisory Service, 26 Crowndale Rd, NW1 1TT (7387 6617); Cypriot Centre, Earlham Grove, N22 5HJ (8881 2329); Cypriot Community Centre (London) Ltd, 94 Camden Rd, NW1 9EA (7485 4052); Cypriot Women's Group, 94 Camden Rd, NW1 9EA (7267 7194); Hackney Cypriot Association, 5 Balls Pond Rd, N1 (7249 4494); Southwark Cypriot Day Centre, 12a Asylum Rd, Peckham SE15 2RL (7277 8690).

Czech

EDUCATION City Lit (7831 9631), SSEES (7636 8000), and the University of Westminster (7911 5000) provide courses in **Czech**.

GOVERNMENT Czech Embassy, 26 Kensington Palace Gdns, W8 4QY (7243 1115).

LANGUAGE **Czech** is a Slavonic language which has official status in the Czech Republic. The Multilingual Capital **(2000) survey found that there were** 224 Czech-speaking schoolchildren in London.

RESTAURANTS

Camden Czech and Slovak House, 74 West End La, NW6 (7372 5251).

SHOPS Orbis Books, 66 Kenway Rd, Earl's Court, SW5 0RD (7370 2210, fax 7742 7686);

TRANSLATION Tramont Translation Management, 57 Upper Park Rd, NW3 2UL (7692 6319; 7504 8638);

TRAVEL Czech Airlines, Margaret St, W1 (7255 1898).

WELFARE Anglo-Czechoslovak Trust, 23 Stonefield St, Islington, N1 0HW (7278 8459); Europe-Roma [refugee organization, currently mainly Czech. Open meetings Thursdays 19.00 in North London (phone 8802 7496 for address). Advice available at Chestnuts Community Centre, 280 St Anns Rd, N15 (Mon - Fri 11.00 - 14.30)].

D

Dagari

Dagari is a Voltaic language spoken in Ghana and Burkina Faso. The presence of Dagari-speaking children has been reported in some boroughs within the past decade but none were recorded at the time of the *Multilingual Capital* (2000) survey.

Dagbane

Dagbane is a Voltaic language of Ghana and Togo. This was reported as the first language of six schoolchildren in the *Multilingual Capital* (2000) survey.

Damara

Damara is a Khoisanic language spoken in Namibia. The *Multilingual Capital* (2000) survey recorded this as the language of only one London pupil, living in Islington.

Dangme

Dangme is a variant spelling of **Adangme**, which should be consulted.

Danish

ACCOMMODATION *Danish YWCA*, 43 Maresfield Gdns, NW3 5TF (7435 7232);

BUSINESS *Danish Catering*, Unit 77e, King Henrys Rd, NW3 3QU (7586 8050); *Danish Express Laundry*, 16 Hinde St, W1U 2BB (7935 6306); *Danish Reinsurance Syndicates Ltd*, 16 Eastcheap, EC3M 1BD (7337 8600); *Danish UK Chamber of Commerce Ltd*, 55 Sloane St, SW1X 9SR (7259 6795);

EDUCATION Courses in **Danish** are available at *Morley College,* 61 Westminster Bridge Rd, SE1 7HT (7928 8501) and the *University of Westminster* (7911 5000).

GOVERNMENT *Royal Danish Embassy*, 55 Sloane St, SW1X 9SR (7333 0200).

LANGUAGE **Danish** is a Germanic language with official status in Denmark. The *Multilingual Capital* (2000) survey reported that there were 67 **Danish**-speaking London schoolchildren.

RELIGION *Danish Church*, 5 St Katherine's Precincts, Regents Park NW1 4HH (7935 7584);

Danish Seaman's Church, 322 Rope St, SE16 7TY (7232 2227);

RESTAURANTS
Kensington & Chelsea *Lundum's,* 119 Old Brompton Rd, SW7 (7373 7774).

SHOPS *Danish Patisserie*, 156 Munster Rd, SW6 5RA (7731 3877).

TRAVEL *Maersk Air A/S*, 52 Grosvenor Gdns, SW1W 0AU (7333 0066).

Dari

EDUCATION Mother-tongue classes in **Dari** are available in Acton; see <www.resourceunit.com> for details.

LANGUAGE **Dari** is an Iranic language spoken in Afghanistan which is closely related to *Farsi*. In the *Multilingual Capital* (2000) survey Dari was recorded as the first language of only 38 London schoolchildren but it was suspected that others may have been reported as **Persian** or **Farsi** in some boroughs.

Dhivehi

Dhivehi (alternatively written *Divehi* and also known as *Maldivian*) is an Indic language whose closest relative is **Sinhala** (of Sri Lanka), and which has official status in the Maldive islands. It is written in its own unique, basically consonantal script which consists mainly of characters derived from numerical symbols of both Arabic and local origin. The presence of a few Dhivehi-speaking schoolchildren in London has been noted within the past decade although none were recorded at the time of the *Multilingual Capital* (2000) survey.

Dhopadhola

LANGUAGE **Dhopadhola** is a Nilotic language of Uganda and Kenya. This is closely related to one of the two languages both of which are variably spelled **Luo** and **Lwo**. In view of this ambiguity, the *Multilingual Capital* (2000) survey chose to record **Dhopadhola** as a separate language. The presence of only one pupil speaking this language, in Lambeth, was noted.

Dhopaluo

See **Luo**.

Dinka

EDUCATION Mother-tongue instruction for children in Dinka is available in Camden; see <www.resourceunit.com> for details.

LANGUAGE *Dinka* is the name of a group of Nilotic languages spoken in Sudan. This was recorded as the first language of 54 London schoolchildren in the *Multilingual Capital* (2000) survey, most of whom lived in Camden.

Dioula

See under the alternative spelling, Dyula.

Dominican *(Island of Dominica)*

Note that *DomiNIcan*, with reference to the island of DomiNIca, has the stress on the third syllable and is thus distinguished in pronunciation from *DoMInican*, referring to the DoMInican Republic, where the stress falls on the second syllable.

GOVERNMENT *Dominica High Commission*, 1 Collingham Gdns, SW5 0HW (7370 5194/1937).

TRAVEL *Dominica Tourist Office*, 1 Collingham Gdns, SW5 0HW (7835 1937).

Dominican *(Dominican Republic)*

Note that *DoMInican*, with reference to the DoMInican Republic, has the stress on the second syllable and is thus distinguished in pronunciation from *DomiNIcan*, referring to the island of DomiNIca, where the stress falls on the third syllable.

GOVERNMENT *Embassy of the Dominican Republic*, 139 Inverness Terrace, W2 6JF (7727 6214/6285)

TRAVEL *Dominican Republic Tourist Board*, 18-22 Hand Ct, WC1V 6RZ (7242 7778).

Druze

ARTS & CULTURE *Druze Heritage Foundation*, 48 Park St, W1K 2JH (7629 7761).

Dubaian *(Dubaiite)*

BUSINESS *Dubai Commerce & Tourism Promotion Board*, 125 Pall Mall, SW1Y 5EA (7839 0580); *Dubai Natural Gas Co Ltd*, 150 Regent St, W1R 5FA (7432 0367); *National Bank of Dubai* [Head Office], 207 Sloane St, SW1X 9QX (7245 6923); *National Bank of Dubai*, 45 Edgware Rd, W2 2HZ (7706 8544).

GOVERNMENT Dubai is one of the seven territories which form the United Arab Emirates.

LEGAL *Allen & Overy*, 1 New Change, Ec4M 9QQ (7330 3000) [office in Dubai]; *Clifford Chance*, 200 Aldersgate St, E1A 4JJ (7600 1000) [office in Dubai]; *Trowers & Hamlins*, Sceptre Ct, 40 Tower Hill, Ec3N 4BN (7423 8000) [office in Dubai].

TRAVEL *Dubai Commerce & Tourism Promotion Board*, 125 Pall Mall, SW1Y 5EA (7839 0580).

Dutch

BUSINESS *Netherlands-British Chamber of Commerce*, The Dutch House, 307-308 High Holborn, WC1V 7LS (7242 1064); *Rotterdam Finances Ltd*, 3 Cochrane Rd, Wimbledon SW19 3QP.

EDUCATION Courses in *Dutch* are available in London at a wide range of levels and at about a dozen locations – see <www.floodlight.co.uk> for details.

FREIGHT *Air Holland Cargo*, Unit 6a Ascot Rd, Feltham TW14 8QH (0845 608 0363).

GOVERNMENT *Netherlands Embassy*, 38 Hyde Park Gate, SW7 5DP (7590 3200).

LANGUAGES *Dutch* is a **Germanic** language with official status in the Netherlands and Belgium (with reference to which the name Flemish is often used). The *Multilingual Capital* (2000) survey indicated the presence of 210 Dutch-speaking schoolchildren (A further 11 recorded their language as Flemish).

RELIGION *The Dutch Church*, 7 Austin Friars, EC2N 2HA (7588 1684).

RESTAURANTS
Hackney
Dutch Pots T/A, 27 Homerton High St, E9 6JP (8985 0157).

SHOPS *Holland Fashion Centre*, 91 High St, Walthamstow E17 7DB (8520 0438); *Rob of Amsterdam (London) Ltd* [leather clothing], 24 Wells St, W1P 3FG (7735 7893).

TRANSLATION *Arabic Chinese Danish Dutch Finnish French German Greek and more*, 585a Fulham Rd, SW6 5UA (7381 0967).

TRAVEL *Holland America Line*, 77-79 Great Eastern St, EC2A 3HU (7613 3300); *KLM Royal Dutch Airlines*, Plesman Ho, 2a Cains La, Feltham, TW14 9RL (8750 9200); *Martinair Holland NV*, 9 The Courtyard, 76-88 High St, Staines, TW18 4DP (01784 441180).

Dyula

Dyula (also written *Dioula*) is a Mandic language spoken in the Ivory Coast. No speakers of this were identified at the time of the *Multilingual Capital* (2000) but a few *Dyula*-speaking pupils have recently been identified in Lambeth.

E

East African

ASSOCIATIONS *British Institute In Eastern Africa,* 10 Carlton House Terrace, SW1Y 5AH (7969 5201); *Eastern Africa Association,* 2 Vincent St, SW1P 4LD (7828 5511).

BUSINESS *East Africa Enterprises,* 7 Minerva Rd, NW10 6HJ (8537 1190).

MEDIA & INFORMATION *East African Standard,* 11 Holborn Viaduct, EC1 (7489 0063); *Eastern Africa Review,* Renaissance Publications, 30 Sturrock Close, N15 5JA (8292 0076).

MOTORING *East Africa Garage,* 25 Watsons Rd, N22 4TZ (8826 0642).

SPECIAL *Liberty East Africa Ltd,* 8 Upper Grosvenor St, W1X 9PA (7518 8000).

Eastern

The word *Eastern* sometimes refers to the Asian continent as a whole but, in the names of London restaurants and other businesses, is it variably applied to (a) the Indian subcontinent, (b) South East Asia, and (c) the Far East. Only those businesses whose areal links have not yet been established are listed here.

ARTS *Eastern Art Gallery,* 40 Bloomsbury Way, WC1A 2SA (7430 1072).

ASSOCIATIONS *Eastern Cultural Society - North London,* c/o Mr S Mazumdar, 20 Orchard Ave, Southgate N14 4ND (8886 4231) [languages: **Bengali**, English].

HEALTH & BEAUTY *Eastern Health & Beauty Centre,* 136 Holloway Rd, N7 8DD (7607 3331);

MEDIA & INFORMATION *Eastern Art Publications,* P O Box 13666, SW14 8WF (8392 1122); *Eastern Film Club* [video library], 64 Hanbury St, E1 5JL (7247 8501).

RESTAURANTS

Barnet *Eastern Aroma,* 60 Vivian Ave, Hendon NW4 3XH (8202 2494).

Enfield *Eastern Gold,* 10 Station Rd, Winchmore Hill N21 3RB (8360 9543).

Harrow *Eastern Delight T/A,* 15 Love La, Pinner HA5 3EE (8868 8484).

Islington *Eastern Eye T/A,* 295 Pentonville Rd, Islington N1 9NP (7713 1244).

Merton *Eastern Delight T/A,* 286 Haydons Rd, Wimbledon SW19 8JZ (8540 6804).

Newham *Eastern Delight T/A,* 574 Barking Rd, Plaistow E13 9JU (8472 7837).

Tower Hamlets *Eastern Cafe,* 807 Commercial Rd, Poplar E14 7HG (7987 2687); *Eastern Eye,* Brick La, E1 6QL (7375 1696); *Eastern Fried Chicken,* 117 Cannon Street Rd, E1 2LX ((7481 0909).

SHOPS *Eastern Food Centre,* 67 Old Oak Common La, Acton W3 7DD (8742 9969); *Eastern Foods,* 165 Green St, E7 8JE (8472 0030); *Eastern Food Stores,* 812 High Rd, Leyton E10 6AE (8558 2862); *Eastern Gate Market,* 122-124 Hammersmith Rd, W6 7JG (8741 4344); *Eastern Grocers,* 53 Hanbury St, E1 5JP (73771824); *Eastern Halal Service* [butchers], 104 Lower Clapton Rd, E5 0QR (8985 0224); *Eastern Paradise* [records, tapes, CDs], 258 Green St, Forest Gate E7 8LF (8552 7413).

East European

ASSOCIATIONS *British Association for Central & Eastern Europe,* 50 Hans Crescent, SW1X 0NB (7584 0766); *School of Slavonic & East European Studies,* Senate Ho, Malet St, WC1E 7HU (7862 8575).

RESTAURANTS

Camden *Trojka,* 101 Regent's Park Rd, NW1 (7483 3765); *Zamoyski,* 85 Fleet Rd, NW3 (7794 4792).

Kensington & Chelsea *Wodka,* 12 St Alban's Gr, W8 (7937 6513).

TRANSLATION *Russian & East European Translation & Interpreting,* 32 Paget Rise, SE18 3QQ (8854 5521).

Ebira

Ebira (also known as *Igbira*) is a **Benuic** language of Nigeria. The *Multilingual Capital* (2000) survey found that this was the first language of five London schoolchildren.

Ecuadorian

BARS & NIGHT-CLUBS *Rincón Ecuadorian Bar & Restaurant,* 235 Holloway Rd, N7 8HG (7700 3670).

GOVERNMENT *Embassy of Ecuador,* 3 Hans Crescent, SW1X 0LS (7584 1367).

LANGUAGES The two main languages of Ecuador are **Spanish** and **Quechua.**

RESTAURANTS

Islington *Rincón Ecuadorian Bar & Restaurant,* 235 Holloway Rd, N7 8HG (7700 3670).

TRAVEL *Ecuador Travel Ltd,* Palladium Ho, 1-4 Argyll St, W1V 1AD (7439 7794).

Edo

EDUCATION Mother tongue education in **Edo** is available for young children in at least three places in London – visit <www.resourceunit.com> for details.

LANGUAGE *Edo* (also known as both *Bini* and *Benin*) is a **Benuic** language spoken in Nigeria. In the *Multilingual Capital* (2000) survey, 140 London pupils from *Edo*-speaking homes were identified.

Efik

Efik and *Ibibio* are two very closely related Benuic languages of Nigeria as also is *Anaang*, For the purposes of the *Multilingual Capital* (2000) survey, all three were considered varieties of a single language and a total of 238 pupils in London were reported to be speakers of one of these.

Efutu

Efutu is an Aframic language spoken in Ghana. The *Multilingual Capital* (2000) survey reported that there were five *Efutu*-speaking pupils in London, all living in Lambeth.

Eggon

Eggon is a Benuic language spoken in Nigeria. Although no *Eggon*-speakers were found among London's schoolchildren at the time of the *Multilingual Capital* (2000) survey, their presence has been reported in at least one London borough within the past decade.

Egyptian

ASSOCIATIONS *Association for the Study of Travel in Egypt and the Near East,* St Paul's Lodge, 97 Larkhall Rise, SW4 6HR (7622 9407); *British Egyptian Society,* c/o Egyptian-British Chamber of Commerce, P O Box 4EG, W1A 4EG (7499 3100); *Egypt Exploration Society,* 3 Doughty Mews, WC1N 2PG (7242 1880); *Egyptian Association in Great Britain Ltd,* 106 Frampton St, NW8 8NB; *Egyptian Community Association,* 100 Redcliffe Gdns, SW10 (7244 8925); *National Bank of Egypt,* Park Ho, 16 Finsbury Circus, EC2M 7DJ (7374 6446); *Petrie Museum of Egyptian Archaeology,* University College London, Malet Pl, WC1E 6BT (7504 2884).

BARS & NIGHT-CLUBS *Cairo's Bar*, 10 Beak Street W1 (7439 4258).

BUSINESS *Egyptian-British Chamber of Commerce,* P O Box 4EG, 299 Oxford St, W1A 4EG (7499 3100); *Egyptian Producers Consortium Ltd,* 2nd floor, Crusader Ho, 145-157 St John St, EC1V 4PY; *Egyptian Reinsurance Co Ltd,* 6 Lloyds Ave, EC3N 3AX (7481 4678).

EDUCATION *Egyptian Education Bureau*, 4 Chesterfield Gdns, W1Y 8BR (7491 7720).

Colloquial *Egyptian Arabic* is taught at *SOAS Language Centre* (7898 4888).

GOVERNMENT *Consulate of the Arab Republic of Egypt,* 2 Lowndes St, SW1X 9ET (7235 9719); *Egyptian Defence Office* 24 South St, W1Y 6DN (7493 2649); *Embassy of the Arab Republic of Egypt,* 26 South St, W1K 1DW (7499 3304).

LANGUAGE *Arabic* is the language of the overwhelming majority of the population and has official status.

RELIGION The population is mainly Sunni Muslim with a small minority of Coptic Christians.

RESTAURANTS

Kensington & Chelsea *Valley of the Kings,* 162 Cromwell Rd, SW5 (7370 4282).

Lambeth *Cafe Cairo,* 88 Landor Rd, Clapham North SW9 9PE (7771 1201).

Westminster *Abohammed*, 102 Queensway, W2 3RR (7727 0830); *Ali Baba*, 32 Ivor Pl, Marylebone NW1 (7723 7474).

SHOPS *Al Mustafa*, 133 Edgware Rd, W1 (7402 7707) [groceries]; *Egyptian Bazaar*, 19 Bury Place, WC1A 2JB (7831 3296); *Egyptian House Ltd.*, 77 Wigmore St, W1H 9LJ (7935 9839).

TRAVEL *Egyptair,* 29-31 Piccadilly, W1V 0PT & Walmer Ho, 296 Regent St, W1R 6PH (7734 2864 / 2395); *Egyptian State Tourist Office*, 170 Piccadilly, W1V 0JL (7493 5283).

Ekpeye

Ekpeye is a Benuic language spoken in Nigeria. Although no *Ekpeye*-speakers were found among London's schoolchildren at the time of the *Multilingual Capital* (2000) survey, their presence has been reported in at least one London borough within the past decade.

Eleme

Eleme is a Benuic language spoken in Nigeria. The *Multilingual Capital* (2000) survey reported the presence of two *Eleme*-speaking pupils in the London borough of Greenwich.

Emai

Emai is a Benuic language of Nigeria which, although not found as one of the languages spoken by London's schoolchildren at the time of the *Multilingual Capital* (2000) survey, has been reported in at least one London borough within the past decade.

Emirates

See **United Arab Emirates** for all entries.

English

ACCOMMODATION *English Villages Housing Association Ltd*, 35 Belgrave Sq, SW1X 8QB.

ARTS & CULTURE *Dickens House Museum,* 48 Doughty St, WC1 (7405 2127); *English Bach Festival Trust*, 15 South Eaton Pl, SW1W 9ER

(7730 5925); *English Chamber Orchestra Ltd*, 2 Coningsby Rd, W5 4HR (8840 6565); *English Folk Dance & Song Society*, Cecil Sharp Ho, 2 Regents Park Rd, NW1 7AY; *English Heritage,* Ranger's Ho, Chesterfield Walk, Blackheath SE10 8QX (8853 0035); *English National Ballet Ltd*, Markova Ho, 39 Jay Mews, SW7 2ES (7581 1245); *English National Opera*, London Coliseum, St Martin's La, WC2N 4ES (7632 8300); *English Schools Orchestra*, Churchill Ho, 137 Brent St, NW4 4DJ (8457 2606); *English Shakespeare Company International*, Unit 13.1.1, Leather Market, Weston St, SE1 3ER (7403 1515); *English Speaking Union*, Dartmouth Ho, 37 Charles St, W1X 8AB (7493 3328); *English Touring Opera*, 250 Kennington La, SE11 5RD (7820 1131).

ASSOCIATIONS *English Club*, 26 Savage Gardens, EC3N 2AR (7480 7065); *English Nature Conservation*, Ormond Ho, 26-27 Boswell St, WC1N 3JZ (7831 6922); *English Speaking Union*, Dartmouth Ho, 37 Charles St, W1J 5ED (7493 3328).

BUSINESS *Bank of England,* Threadneedle St, EC2R 8AL (7601 4444);

EDUCATION A huge range of courses in English at many different levels and for people of diverse backgrounds and needs is available in London. Consult *Floodlight* or visit <www.floodlight.co.uk> for full details.

English Gardening School, 66 Royal Hospital Rd, SW3 4HS (7352 4347); *English National Ballet School*, Carlyle Building, Hortensia Rd, SW10 0QS (7376 7076).

HEALTH & BEAUTY *Classic English Roses* [medicines & therapies], Suite 401, Langham Ho, W1R6HH (7580 6005); *Health Service Ombudsman for England,* Millbank Tower, 21-24 Millbank, Westminster SW1P 4QP (7217 4051).

LANGUAGE **English** is a Germanic language with 1000m speakers worldwide (of whom this is the first language of 400m). It is the first language of the majority of the population in the UK, USA, Canada, Australia, New Zealand, and a number of other countries but its international importance stems from the fact that it is known as a second or additional language by far more people than any other, making it by far the most international of languages.

RECREATION *All England Lawn Tennis & Croquet Club*, Church Rd, Wimbledon SW19 5AE (8944 1066); *Amateur Boxing Association of England*, Ledrington Rd, Upper Norwood SE19 2BB (8778 0251); *Disability Sport England,* 13 Brunswick

Pl, Islington N1 6DX (7490 4919); *England & Wales Cricket Board, Lords Cricket Ground, St Johns Wood Rd, NW8 8QZ (7432 1200); English First Division Rugby Ltd*, Fairfax Ho, Fulwood Pl, WC1V 6UB; *English Sports Council*, 16 Upper Woburn Pl, WC1H 0QP (7273 1500); *South of England Athletic Association,* 36 London Fruit Exchange, Brushfield St, E1 6EU (7247 2963).

RESTAURANTS

Southwest 1 *Old English Coffee House*, 1a Montrose Pl, SW1X 7DU (7235 3643).

West Central *Browns*, 82-84 St Martin's La, Covent Garden WC2 (7497 5050); *Porter's*, 17 Henrietta St, WC2E 8QH (7379 3556).

Camden *George & Niki's*, 38 Parkway, NW1 (7485 7432).

Ealing *English and International T/A,* 50 South Ealing Rd, W5 4QY (8451 4883).

Hackney *F Cooke,* 9 Broadway Market, London Fields, E8 (7254 6458) [pie and mash].

Islington *Albert's Pie and Mash,* 1 7 4 Copenhagen St, N1 (7278 5690).

Kensington & Chelsea *English Garden*, 10 Lincoln St, SW3 2TS (7584 7272); *English House*, 3 Milner St, SW3 2QA (7584 3002); *The Collection,* 264 Brompton Rd, SW3 (7225 1212).

Lewisham *Sam's English & Continental Restaurant,* 134 Hither Green La, Lewisham SE13 6QA (8463 0777).

Tower Hamlets *G Kelly*, 526 Roman Rd, E3 (8980 3165) [pie and mash] and 414 Bethnal Green Rd, E2 (7739 3603) [pie and mash].

Waltham Forest *M Manze*, 76 High St, Walthamstow, E17 (8520 2855) [pie and mash].

SHOPS

English & Continental Pigeon Supplies, Unit 1b St Marks Industrial Estate, North Woolwich Rd, E16 2BS (7476 5806); *English Art Works Ltd* [gold & silversmiths], 50 Jermyn St, SW1Y 6LX (7493 0807); *English Art Works Ltd* [jewellery repair], 50 Dover St, W1X 3RG (7493 0807); *English Cheesecake Co*, Unit 55 Pall Mall Deposit, 124-128 Barlby Rd, W10 6BL (8964 9556); *English Furniture Co*, Metropolitan College of Craftsmen, Enfield Rd, N1 5AZ (7937 9809); *English Garden Co* [landscape contractors], 30b Henslowe Rd, SE22 0AP (8693 4176); *English Tailoring*, 14 South Colonnade, E14 4PZ (7512 9991); *English Traditional Jewellery*, 22 Hatton Garden, EC1N 8BA (7405 1471); *Hive Honey Shop,* 93 Northcote Rd, SW11 6PL (7924 6233); *Olde English Furniture Ltd*, 26 Loampit Hill,

SE13 7SW (8694 2966); *Old English Ltd* [furnishings], 190 Westbourne Grove, W11 2RH (7727 2699); *Traditional English Conservatory Co*, 91-93 Buckingham Palace Rd, SW1W 0RP (7730 7999); *Ye Old English Organic Greengrocer*, 77 Junction Rd, Archway N19 5QU (7263 8565).

TRAVEL *English Tourism Council*, Thames Tower, Black's Rd, W6 9EL (8563 3000).

WELFARE *Council for the Protection of Rural England*, 5 Cowcross St, EC1M 6DR (7253 0300);

English Creole

LANGUAGE **English Creole** is an abbreviation of *English-based Creole* or *English lexicon Creole*, meaning a Creole language which draws its vocabulary mainly from English and its grammar from a range of sources often including African languages.

The **English-based Creoles** spoken in London are those spoken in Jamaica, in most of the East Caribbean islands from the Virgin Islands down to Trinidad, and in Guyana. All of these are very closely related historically (Baker 1999). **Krio**, spoken in Sierra Leone, is also an English-based Creole and has its own entry under K.

As all the English Creoles of the wider Caribbean area are mutually intelligible, they may justifiably be considered varieties of a single language. However, the figures obtained for speakers of English-based Creoles in London in the *Multilingual Capital* (2000) survey are unsatisfactory for several reasons:

(a) Apart from **Krio** (see separate entry), English Creoles are mostly recorded as **Patwa** (sometimes written *Patois* or *Patua*) but this word is often preceded by *Afro-Caribbean* or a name relating to a particular territory (e.g. Jamaican Patwa). The word **Creole** is also sometimes used. Both **Patwa** and **Creole** are potentially ambiguous in that they can be applied to both English-based and French-based Creole languages. (In the islands of Dominica and St Lucia both a **French Creole** and an **English Creole** are spoken.) In Guyana, the term *Creolese* is often used.

(b) Six boroughs did not record any speakers of **English Creoles** under any of the names listed above while a further five acknowledged the presence only of some Krio speakers. It is virtually certain that all eleven of these boroughs have schoolchildren from homes in which **English Creole** is the principal language. It would appear that all such children were counted as monolingual speakers of English. At the opposite extreme, Lewisham reported that almost 30% of its schoolchildren were from *Afro-Caribbean Patwa*-speaking homes. In this case it appears that all children considered to be ethnically Afro-Caribbean were recorded as speakers of *Afro-Caribbean Patwa*.

(c) A further complication is that, among many London schoolchildren, the word **Patwa** seems to be increasingly and loosely applied to what might more accurately be termed "Afro-Caribbean London English". 25 years ago, the parents of most locally-born Afro-Caribbean children spoke the English Creole of their place of birth. Today's London-born Afro-Caribbean children are more likely to hear such speech from their grandparents than from their parents. What many seem to call *Patwa* today includes words and expressions from the Caribbean, as well as others which seem to have been adopted from Black American English, but this is grammatically very similar to the informal English of most young Londoners regardless of their ethnicity.

For all these reasons, it was not possible to give a reliable estimate of the number of London schoolchildren who speak **English Creole**.

Equatorial Guinean

GOVERNMENT Equatorial Guinean interests in the UK are represented from its embassy in Paris at 6 rue Alfred de Vigny, 75008 Paris (+33 1 47 66 44 33).

LANGUAGES Although both Spanish and French have official status, the first language of 75% of the population is **Fang**, a Bantu language. Bubi, another Bantu language, is spoken by 6%.

Eritrean

ASSOCIATIONS *Eritrean Association*, Palingswick Ho, 241 King St, Hammersmith W6 9LP (8748 0547); *Eritrean Community Association*, 266-268 Holloway Rd, N7 6NE (7700 7995); *Eritrean Parents & Children Association*, 1 Thorpe Close, W10 5XL (8964 5535).

BUSINESS *Asmara Ltd* [business research], Eggington Ho, Buckingham Gate, SW1E 6LD (7808 5880).

GOVERNMENT *Consulate of the State of Eritrea*, 96 White Lion St, N1 9PF (7713 0096).

LANGUAGES The principal language of Eritrea is **Tigrinya** *(Tigray)* which has official status as does **Arabic**. Other languages spoken in the country include 'Afar, Bilin, Hadareb, Kunama, Nara, **Saho**, and **Tigre**. (Only the last two of these are among the languages reported to be spoken by some London schoolchildren in the *Multilingual Capital* (2000) survey.)

MEDIA & INFORMATION *Eritrean Community in the UK* [information services], 266-268 Holloway Rd, N7 6NE (7700 7995);

MOTORING *Asmara Cars*, 73 Lansdowne Way, SW8 2EA (7640 9777).

RELIGION About half the population is Christian while the other half is Muslim.

RESTAURANTS

73

Camden *Selam,* 12 Fortess Rd, NW5 (7284 3947).

Lambeth *Asmara,* 386 Coldharbour La, Brixton SW9 (7737 4144).

TRANSLATION *Associated Translators,* 96 Kensington High St, W8 4SG (7937 7733).

WELFARE *Eritrean Advice & Information Centre,* 73 Stockwell Rd, Brixton SW9 9PY (7501 9605); *Eritrean Community in Haringey,* c/o Tesfay Gebremichael, Selby Centre, Selby Rd, London N17 8JN (8365 0819) [language: Tigrinya]; *Eritrean Relief Association,* 96 White Lion St, Islington N1 9PF (7837 9236); *Eritrean Support Group,* 7 Thorpe Close, W10 5XL (8964 3856).

Esan

Esan, also known as *Ishan*, is a Benuic language of Nigeria. The *Multilingual Capital* (2000) reported this as the language of 47 London schoolchildren.

Estonian

EDUCATION A course in **Estonian** is provided by *SSEES* (7862 8631).

GOVERNMENT *Estonian Embassy,* 16 Hyde Park Gate, SW7 5DG (7589 3428).

LANGUAGE **Estonian** is a **Uralic** language related to Finnish and is the official language of Estonia. The *Multilingual Capital* (2000) survey recorded this as the language of 8 London schoolchildren. A significant minority of Estonians speaks **Russian** as its first language.

RELIGION Most Estonians are Lutherans but there are other Christian minorities. Occasional services in Estonian are held at the *Church of St Anne & St Agnes,* Gresham St, EC2 (7606 4986).

SPECIAL *Estonian House Ltd,* 18 Chepstow Villas, W11 2RB (7229 6700).

TRANSLATION *Tramont Translation Management,* 57 Upper Park Rd, NW3 2UL (7692 6319; fax 7504 8638).

TRAVEL *Estonian Air,* Terminal Ho, 52 Grosvenor Gdns, SW1W 0AW (7333 0196).

Ethiopian

ASSOCIATIONS *Anglo-Ethiopian Society,* 154 Connell Crescent, W5 3BP (8997 4447, 01403 264879); *Ethiopian Community Association,* 66 Hampstead Rd, NW1 2NT (7388 4944/3984); *Ethiopian Community in Britain,* 2a Lithos Rd, Hampstead NW3 6EF (7794 4265).

GOVERNMENT *Ethiopian Embassy,* 17 Princes Gate, SW7 1PZ (7589 7212)

LANGUAGES More than 50 languages are spoken in Ethiopia of which the three most extensively spoken are **Amharic**, **Oromo**, and **Tigrinya.**

MEDIA & INFORMATION *News from Ethiopia,* 17 Princes Gate, SW7 1PZ (75897212); *Spectrum Radio,* International Radio Centre, 4 Ingate Pl, SW8 3NS (7627 4433) [broadcasting for Ethiopian listeners 17.00 - 18.00 Saturdays only].

RELIGION Most Ethiopians are Christians but a significant minority of the population is Muslim.

Ethiopian Christian Fellowship Church in the UK, 105 Foundling Ct, Brunswick Centre, WC1N 1AN (7833 3309);

RESTAURANTS

South East 1 *Ambasel,* 280 Old Kent Rd, SE1 5UL (7703 9840),

Brent *Abyssinia,* 9 Cricklewood Broadway, NW2 3JX (8208 0110).

Camden *Addis Ababa,* 23 Pratt St, NW1 (7209 3501).

Hammersmith & Fulham *Piassa,* 129 Askew Rd, W12 (8622 0234).

Haringey *Roha,* 407 Lordship La, N17 6AG (8808 1227, fax 8809 3924).

Islington *Fasika,* 152 Seven Sisters Rd, N7 (7272 7572), *Menelik,* 277 Caledonian Rd, N1 3EF (7700 7774), *Merkato,* 193a Caledonian Rd, N1 (7837 1838); *Senke,* 1b-1c Rock St, N4 (7359 7687).

Lambeth *Axum,* 266 Wandsworth Rd, SW8 2JR (7622 0455),

Westminster *Blue Nile Ethiopia 2001,* 1 Woodfield Pl, W9;

SHOPS *Ethio Stores,* 120 Judd St, WC1H 9NS (7837 8607) [injera, kibe, berbre, and fresh khat; videos and music cassettes],

ARTS Chamber Orchestra of Europe, 8 Southampton Pl, WC1A 2EA (7831 2326); European Computer Network for the Arts Ltd, Leroy Ho, 436 Essex Rd, N1 3QP (7226 8181); European Theatre Company, 39 Oxford Av, SW20 8LS (8544 1994); European Union Youth Orchestra, 6a Pont St, SW1X 9EL (7235 6641); Europe Music Group Ltd, 59 Great Portland St, W1N 5DH (7580 6308); First European Artists, 100a Chalk Farm Rd, NW1 8EH (7482 2825).

ASSOCIATIONS British Association for Central & Eastern Europe, 50 Hans Cres, SW1X 0NB (7584 0766); East European Partnership, Carlton Ho, 27a Carlton Drive, SW15 2BS (8780 2841); European Foundation, 61 Pall Mall, SW1Y 5HZ (7930 7319); European Wind Energy Association, 26 Spring St, W2 1JA (7402 7122); Young European Movement, Dean Bradley Ho, 52 Horseferry Rd, SW1P 2AF (7222 0915).

BUSINESS East European Import & Export Corporation Ltd, 11 Cold Harbour, E14 9NS (7515 0081); East European Trade Council, 10 Westminster Palace Gdns, Artillery Row, SW1P 1RL (7222 7622); European Bank for Reconstruction & Development, 1 Exchange Sq, EC2A 2JN (7338 6000); European Federation of Pharmaceutical Industries, 1 Canada Sq, E14 5AA (7513 0466); European Fishing Tackle Trade Association, Forde Ho, 51 Cloth Fair, EC1A 7JQ (7606 0555); European Investment Bank, 68 Pall Mall, SW1Y 5ES (7343 1200); Federation of European Marketing Research Associations, Wimbledon Stadium Business Centre, Riverside Rd, SW17 0BA (8944 0315); Institute of European Trade & Technology, 29 Throgmorton St, EC2N 2AT (7628 3723); Research Europe Ltd, 10 Warple Way, W3 0UE (8743 4242); SBI European Bank PLC, 1 Milk St, EC2P 2JP (7600 4535).

EDUCATION Anglo-European Study Tours Ltd, 8 Celbridge Mews, W2 6EU (7229 4435); European Association of Teachers, 7 Greenland St, NW1 0ND (7284 3748); European College, 7 Whitechapel Rd, E1 1DU (7377 8962); European Vocational College, 32-38 Dukes Pl, EC3A 7LP (7648 8530).

EMPLOYMENT European Recruitment Services, 7 Academy Buildings, Fanshaw St, N1 6LQ (7739 6444); Network Europe Associates [employment consultants], Suite 11 Beaufort Court, Admirals Way, E14 9XL (7531 6600).

FREIGHT Anglo European Transport Ltd, Falcon Ho, Feltham, TW14 0XQ (8890 4442); Europe Express, 1 Cargreen Rd, SE25 5AD (8771 6282); Freight Europe (UK) Ltd, 10 Leake St, SE1 7NN (7203 7020); Inter Europe Forwarding Services Ltd, Unit 9 Thameside Industrial Estate, Factory Rd, E16 2HB (7474 6611); Whittle East European Logistics Ltd, 65-66 Woodrow, SE18 5DH (8316 6000).

GOVERNMENT European Parliament UK Office, 2 Queen Anne's Gate, SW1H 9AA (7227 4300); European Parliamentary Labour Party, 2 Queen Anne's Gate, SW1H 9AA (7222 1719).

HEALTH & BEAUTY European Academy of Anaesthesiology, 48 Russell Sq, WC1B 4JP (7637 4188); European Academy of Esthetic Dentistry, 57a Wimpole St, W1M 7DF (7224 1488); European Association for the Treatment of Addiction, 375 Kennington La, SE11 5QY (7582 6732); European Congress of Chemotherapy, 7 William Rd, NW1 3ER (7232 1080); European Dialysis & Transplant Association, St. Thomas' Hospital, Lambeth Palace Rd, SE1 7EH (7633 0636); European Journal of Herbal Medicine, 5 Christchurch Rd, N8 9QL (8340 2900); Sino European Clinics Ltd, 33 Bolingbroke Rd, W14 0AJ (7602 7504).

LEGAL Alliance of European Lawyers, Royex House, Aldermanbury Sq, EC2V 7HR (7796 2599); European Law Chambers, 5 Paper Buildings, EC4Y 7HB (7583 9275); European Legal Directory, 11 Coldbath Sq, EC1R 5HL (7972 0790).

MEDIA & INFORMATION Business News Europe, 10 Fleet Pl, EC4M 7RB (7653 9300); Channel 7 Europe, 3-11 Dod St, E14 7EQ (7510 0011); Discovery Networks Europe, 160 Great Portland St, W1W 5 QA (7462 3600); Essential European Information Ltd, 15 Cecil Rd, E11 3HF (8558 3850); European Media Forum, 29 Pall Mall, SW1Y 5LP (7839 7896); European Policy Forum, 125 Pall Mall, SW1Y 5EA (7839 7565); European Publishing Ltd, 21 Grafton St, W1X 3LD (7495 3210); European Publishing Ltd, 112-114 Great Portland St, W1N 5PF; European Telecommunications Services Ltd, Beaufort Court, Admirals Way, E14 9XL (01494 465217); European Telecommunications Services Ltd, 2 London Wall Buildings, EC2M 5PP (7628 4500); Europe Media Ltd, Acre Ho, 11-15 William Rd, NW1 3ER (7452 0453); Europe Media Ltd, 130 City Rd, EC1V 2NJ (7452 0453); European Mobile Communications Ltd, 57-61 Mortimer St, W1N 8JX; European Mobile Communication Services Ltd, 50 Queen Anne St, W1M 0HQ; Information Access Company Europe, Watergate Ho, 13-15 York Buildings, WC2N 6JU (7930 3933); Marie Claire European Magazines Ltd, 2 Hatfields, SE1 9PG (7261 5240); Network Europe Telecommunications, Telecom Ho, Thackaray Rd, SW8 3TG (7344 4700); New European Publications Ltd, 14-16 Carroun Rd, SW8 1JT (7582 3996); Tele Europe, 52 Broadwick St, W1V 1FF (7437 6167); The European Ltd, 200 Grays Inn Rd, WC1X 8NE (7418 7777); Video Europe plc, Unit 5, Albion Wharf, SW11 4AN (7585 0555); Video Europe (Soho) Ltd, 8 Golden Sq, W1R 3AF (7439 2277); Vidfilm Europe, North Orbital Rd, Uxbridge, UB9 5HL (01895 835555).

MOTORING European Car Rental, 178 Strand, WC2R 1EH (7240 4711); Europe Car Sales & Self Drive Hire, 103 Colney Hatch La, N10 1LR (8444 1455).

RECREATION European Grand Prix Circuit Ltd, 48 Grays Inn Rd, WC1X 8LT (7831 5297).

RELIGION European Board of World Union for Progressive Judaism, The Montagu Centre, 21 Maple St, W1P 6DS (7637 7442); European Council *of Jewish Communities*, 74 Gloucester Pl, W1H 3HN (7224 3445).

RESTAURANTS

East Central *The Don,* The Courtyard, 20 St Swithins La, EC4N 8AD (7626 2606).

South East 1 *Apprentice,* Cardamom Bldg, 31 Shad Thames, Butlers Wharf, SE1 (7234 0254); *Blue Print Café*, Design Museum, 28 Shad Thames, Butlers Wharf, SE1 (7378 7031); *Delfina Studio Café*, 50 Bermondsey St, SE1 (7357 0244); *Le Pont de la Tour*, Butlers Wharf Bldg, 36d Shad Thames, SE1 (7403 8403); *Oxo Tower Restaurant*, Oxo Tower Wharf, Barge House St, South Bank, SE1 (7803 3888).

West 1 *Attica,* Foubert's Pl, W1 (7287 6983); *Bali Sugar Aurora*, 49 Lexington St, W1 (7494 0514); *Coast,* 26B Albemarle St, W1 (7495 5999); *Leith's Soho*, 41 Beak St, W1 (7287 2057); *Mash*,19-21 Great Portland St, W1 (7637 5555); *Mezzo*, 100 Wardour St, W1 (7314 4000); *Orrey*, 55 Marylebone High St, W1 (7616 8000); *Stephen Hill*, 5-7 Blandford St, W1 (7486 9696); *Stockpot*, 18 Old Compton St, W1 (7287 1066).

West Central *Bank*, 1 Kingsway, WC2 (7234 3344 , 7379 9797); *Saint Tropez*, 1a Shorts Gdns, WC2 (7379 3355); *Stephen Hill*, 12 Upper St Martin's La, WC2 (7379 7811); *The Ivy*, 1 West St, Covent Garden, WC2 (7836 4751).

Brent *William IV*, 786 Harrow Rd, NW10 (8969 5944).

Camden *Odette's*, 130 Regent's Park Rd, NW1 (7586 5486); *P J's Grill*, 82 Hampstead High St, NW3 (7435 3608); *Solo,* 20 Inverness Terrace, NW1 (7482 4611).

Greenwich *Time Bar Gallery*, 7a College Approach, Greenwich, SE10 (8305 9767);

Islington *Art to Zen*, 27 Upper St, N1 (7226 5300); *Lola's,* The Mall Bldg, Camden Passage, 359 Upper St, N1 (7359 1932); *Dining Room*, 169 Hemingford Rd, N1 (7609 3009); *Independence*, Upper St, N1 (7704 6977).

Kensington & Chelsea *Beach Blanket Babylon*, 45 Ledbury Rd, Notting Hill, W11 (7229 2907); *Bibendum,* Michelin Ho, 81 Fulham Rd, SW3 (7581 5817); *Bluebird*, 350 King's Rd, SW3 (7559 1000); *Chepstow*, 39 Chepstow Place, W2 (7229 0323); *Pharmacy Restaurant & Bar,* 150 Notting Hill Gate, W11 (7221 2442).

Lewisham *Belair House*, Gallery Rd, Dulwich, SE21 (8299 9788).

Richmond *Fish Tank*, 45 Sheen La, SW14 (8878 3535).

Wandsworth *Ransome's Dock*, 35-37 Parkgate Rd, SW11 4NP (7223 1611).

SHOPS *European Bakeries Ltd*, 2a Quebec Way, SE16 7LQ (7231 8941); *European Bookshop*, 5 Warwick St, W1R 6BH (7734 5259, fax 7287 1720); *European Charcuterie Ltd*, 54a Minerva Rd, NW10 6HJ (8933 2535); *Grant and Cutler,* 55-57 Gt Marlborough St, W1V 2AY (7734 2012, fax 7734 9272) [books in European languages].

SPECIAL *Institute for European Environmental Policy*, 52 Horseferry Rd, SW1P 2AG (7799 2244).

TRANSLATION *East European Language Agency*, 12 Chepstow Rd, W2 5BD (7229 0116); *Europe Translations*, 34 Hallingbury Court, 644 Forest Rd, E17 3EE (8509 2465).

TRAVEL *All European Travel Ltd*, Alexander Ho, 3 Shakespeare Rd, N3 1XE (8343 1440); *Club Europe Holidays Ltd*, Fairway Ho, 53 Dartmouth Rd, SE23 3HN (8699 7788); *European Express Ltd*, 102 Queensway, W2 3RR (7727 0888); *European Heritage Tours*, 123 Teddington Park Rd, TW11 8NG (8977 5143); *European Rail Ltd*, Tavistock House North, Tavistock Sq, WC1H 9HR (7387 0444); *European Regions Airline*, 7 Buckingham Gate, SW1E 6JP (7393 1211); *European Study Tours*, 100 Chalk Farm Rd, NW1 8EH (7424 3339); *Europe Student Travel*, 6 Campden St, W8 7EP (7727 7647); *European Travel Centre Ltd*, 216 Earls Court Rd, SW5 9QB (7373 8058); *European Travel Network Ltd*, Malvern Ho, Meridian Gate, 199 Marsh Wall, E14 9YT (7987 9988); *European Travel Services*, 52 Ebury St, SW1W 0LU (7730 7182); *Grand European Tours*, 100 Chalk Farm Rd, NW1 8EH (7424 3336); *Inter Europe Travel Ltd*, 83 Buckingham Palace Rd, SW1W 0QJ (7630 5188); *Jet Set Europe*, Kenilworth Ho, 79-80 Margaret St, W1N 7HB (7436 3737); *Jet Set Europe Ltd*, 92 Wimpole St, W1M 8DT (7491 1234); *Rail Europe*, French Railways Ho, 179 Piccadilly, W1V0BA (0870 584 8848); *Rail European*, 10 Leake St, SE1 7NN (7803 3030).

WELFARE *Black European Community Development Federation*, 150 Townmead Rd, SW6 2RA (7384 1502); *Central Council for European Training Research & Arts*, 64 Essex Rd, N1 8LR(7354 4869); *East European Advice Centre*, 240 King St, W6 0RF (8748 3085); *European African & Asian Charitable Association*, 10 Northumberland Park, N17 0TX (8801 1975); *European Children's Trust*, Prince Rupert Ho, 64 Queen St, EC4R 1AD (7248 2424).

Ewe

EDUCATION Mother tongue education in **Ewe** is available for children in two places in London – visit <www.resourceunit.com> for details.

LANGUAGE **Ewe** is an Aframic language of Togo and Ghana. The *Multilingual Capital* (2000) survey found that this was the language of 124 London pupils.

Ewondo

Ewondo *(Yaunde)* is a Bantuic language spoken in Cameroon. It was reported as the language of seven London schoolchildren in the *Multilingual Capital* (2000) survey.

F

Falasha

ASSOCIATIONS *Society for the Study of Ethiopian Jews (Falashas)*, SOAS, Thornhaugh St, Russell Sq, WC1H 0XG (7898 4350).

Falklander

GOVERNMENT *Falklands Islands Government Office*, Falkland Ho, 14 Broadway, SW1H 0BH (7222 2542).

TRAVEL *Falkland Islands Tourism*, Falklands Ho, Broadway, SW1H 0BH (7222 2542).

WELFARE *Falklands Conservation*, 1 Princes Ave, Finchley N3 2DA (8343 0831); *Falkland Island Association*, 16 Douglas St, SW1P 4PB (7592 0022); *Falkland Islands Association*, 2 Greycoat Pl, SW1P 1SB (7222 0028).

Fang

Fang is a Bantuic language spoken in Cameroon, Equatorial Guinea and Gabon. Only one London pupil was reported to be a *Fang*-speaker in the *Multilingual Capital* (2000) survey.

Fante

Fante (also written *Fanti*) is one of the two major *Akan* languages. See *Akan* for details.

Far Eastern

The term *Far Eastern* is generally understood to refer collectively to *Chinese, Japanese*, and *Korean.*

BUSINESS *Far East Agencies Ltd*, 164 Union St, SE1 0LH (7620 3933); *Far East Consortium*, Abercorn Trading Estate, Manor Farm Rd, Wembley HA0 1BD (8902 5566); *Far East Trading & Investment Incorporated*, 35 Gloucester Sq, W2 2TD (7706 3026); *Phoenix Far East Pearls Ltd*, 34 Hatton Gdn, EC1N 8DX ((7831 4299); *Tong Shing International Ltd* [importer from Far East], 384 Lea Bridge Rd, E10 7DY (8556 4033); *TR Far Eastern Income Trust plc*, 3 Finsbury Ave, EC2M 2PA (7638 5757).

FREIGHT *Far Eastern Freight Conference*, Bridge Ho, Borough High St, SE1 9QZ (7403 1700); *Far East Fisheries*, Empire Ho, Empire Way, Wembley HA9 0NA (8970 2189); *Far East Forwarding Ltd*, Hunting Ho, Central Way, Feltham TW14 0UD (8890 9900).

HEALTH & BEAUTY *Massage Far Eastern* [aromatherapy], 8 St Stephens Crescent, W2 5QT (7243 0577).

MEDIA & INFORMATION *Far Eastern Economic Review*, International Press Centre, 76 Shoe La,

EC4A 3JB (7334 0008); *Far East Power Magazine*, 20 Thornton Rd, SW19 4NG (8944 6688).

RESTAURANTS
Haringey *Satay Baba Far Eastern Restaurant*, 82 Fortis Green Rd, N10 3HN (8883 5875).

Wandsworth *Far East*, 11 Alma Rd, SW18 1AA (8870 4588); *Far East T/A*, 128 Upper Richmond Rd, SW15 2SP (8788 5895); *Nancy Lam's Enak Enak Indonesian & Far Eastern Restaurant*, 56 Lavender Hill, SW11 5RQ (7924 3148).

SHOPS *Far Eastern Gems*, 149a Grosvenor Rd, SW1V 3JY (7976 5037); *Far East Supermarket*, 28 High Rd, NW10 2QD (8459 1574/0977).

SPECIAL *About the Far East*, 149a Grosvenor Rd, SWI 3JY (7286 4842); *Far East Expert International*, 17 Penrhyn Rd, Kingston KT1 2BZ (8392 0145); *Far Eastern Agriculture*, 27 Wilfred St, SW1E 6PR (7834 7676); *Far East Direct Ltd*, 92 Warwick Rd, W5 5PT (0870 163 5008).

TRAVEL *Destination Far East Ltd*, 14 Greville St EC1V 7EH (7400 7002); *Far East Travel Centre*, 13a Macclesfield St, W1D 5BS (7437 8164); *Hayes & Jarvis Travel Ltd* [Far East reservations] (0870 898 9890); *Malaysian & Far Eastern Travel Ltd*, 18 Chiltern St, W1U 7QA (7486 8656); *Travelbag plc* [Far East], 52 Regent St, W1A 3BJ (7287 5558); *Worldwide Journeys plc* [Far East discounted air travel], 22 Stephenson Way, NW1 2BU (7388 6000).

Farsi

EDUCATION Mother tongue education in *Farsi* is available for children in at least five places in London - visit <www.resourceunit.com> for details. Courses for adults in *Farsi* are available at *SOAS Language Centre* (7898 4888) and *University of Westminster Language Centre* (7911 5000 x4352).

LANGUAGE *Farsi* (traditionally known as *Persian*, and sometimes called *Iranian*) is an Iranic language with official status in Iran. It is also current in parts of Tajikistan and Afghanistan, with some 40m speakers in all. *Farsi* is written in an adaptation of the consonantal Arabic script.

The *Multilingual Capital* (2000) survey found that this language spoken at home by 3,279 London schoolchildren. A map showing the distribution of speakers of *Farsi* across London can be viewed at <www.global-london.com/gallery> (Map 12).

MEDIA & INFORMATION *Pars Publications & Translations Services*, 4 Beaconsfield Terrace Rd, W14 0PP (7602 0221).

TRANSLATION *Acuda Ltd*, 42-44 Carter La, EC4V 5EA (7236 3377); *All Languages Ltd*, 362-364 Old St, EC1V 9LT (7739 6641); *Associated Translators*, 96 Kensington High St, W8 4SG (7937 7733); *Farsi Publications & Translation Services*, P O Box 18960, London W14 0XF (7602 0221); *Farsi Translation Services*, 62 Fitzgeorge Ave, West Kensington W14 0SW (7602 0221); *Persian - Farsi*, 181 Bream Close, N17 9DJ (8801 4712); *French & Farsi Translators & Interpreters*, 46 Inverness

Terrace, W2 3JA (7243 1855); *Kern (UK) Ltd,* Rooms 45-46, New Ho, 67-68 Hatton Garden, EC1N 8JY (7831 5600); *Key Languages,* 16-18 Douglas St, SW1P 4PB (7630 6113); *Pars Publications & Translations Services,* 4 Beaconsfield Terrace Rd, W14 0PP (7602 0221); *Persian - Farsi,* 181 Bream Cl, N17 9DJ (8801 4712).

Fijian

GOVERNMENT *Embassy of Fiji,* 34 Hyde Park Gate, SW7 5DN (7584 3661).

LANGUAGES The principal languages of Fiji are *Fijian* and a local form of Hindi. *Fijian* is a Transpacific language of which there are a number of regional varieties. The *Multilingual Capital* (2000) survey reported the presence of 78 *Fijian*-speaking pupils in London of whom 36 lived in Lambeth.

Filipino

As well as *Filipino,* the words *Philippine* and *Philippino* are also applied to people and things of the Philippines.

BUSINESS *Allied Bank Philippines (UK) plc,* 114 Rochester Row, Westminster SW1P 1JQ (7233 6311); *Philippine National Bank (Europe) plc,* 128 Queen Victoria St, EC4V 4HR (7653 1400);

EMPLOYMENT *London-Filipino Employment Agency Ltd,* 36 Ritchings Ave, Walthamstow E17 6LB.

GOVERNMENT *Embassy of the Philippines, Trade & Investment Promotion,* 1a Cumberland Ho, Kensington Court, W8 5NX (79371898).

HEALTH & BEAUTY *Salon De Manila,* 11-12 Hogarth Pl, Earl's Court SW5 0QT (7370 7101).

LANGUAGES Two languages have official status in the Philippines – *English* and *Filipino. Filipino* is an alternative name for *Tagalog* (see this entry). Many other languages are spoken in the Philippines and, of these, there are known to be speakers of *Bisayan, Cebuano, Hiligaynon, Ilocano, Pampangan,* and *Pangasinan* living in London – see individual entries of these for information.

RELIGION Most Filipinos are Christians but there is a significant minority of Muslims.

RESTAURANTS

West 1 *Josephine's Restaurant,* 6 Charlotte St, W1 (7580 6551).

Kensington & Chelsea *Filipino,* 10 Kenway Rd, SW5 0RR (7244 0007).

SHOPS *Filipino Cleaning Services* [dry cleaning], 36 Harold Rd, Plaistow E13 0SQ (84721772); *Filipino Supermarket,* 1 Kenway Rd, SW5 0RP; *Manila Market* [supermarket], Plaistow Rd, Stratford E15 3ET (8534 3714); *Manila Supermarket,* 11 Hogarth Pl, SW5 (7373 8305).

TRAVEL *Philippines Department of Tourism,* 17 Albemarle St, W1X 4LX (7499 5443); *Philippines Travel Centre Ltd,* 69 Wigmore St, W1H 9LG (7224 2454).

WELFARE *Centre for Filipinos,* 59 Chalton St, Camden NW1; *Commission for Philipino Migrant Workers,* 57 Chalton St, Camden NW1 1HY (7388 5845); *Kanlungan Filipino Consortium* [community centre], 25-27 Bickerton Rd, Archway N19 5JT (7281 9757).

Finnish

ASSOCIATIONS *Finnish Institute,* 35-36, Eagle St, WC1R 4AJ (7404 3309).

BUSINESS *Finland Trade Centre,* 177-179, Hammersmith Rd, W6 8BS (8600 7260); *Finnish British Chamber of Commerce,* 5 Arlington St, SW1A 1RA (7647 4496).

EDUCATION Courses in *Finnish* are available at *Morley College* (7928 8501), *SSEES* (7862 8635), and the *University of Westminster* (7911 5000).

GOVERNMENT *Finnish Embassy,* 38 Chesham Pl, SW1X 8HW (7838 6200).

LANGUAGES Both *Finnish* and *Swedish* have official status in Finland (although the latter is the first language of less than 6% of the population). *Finnish* is a *Uralic* language. spoken mainly in Finland. [148 pupils (48 Lambeth)].

RELIGION *Finnish Church (Seamen's Mission),* 33 Albion St, SE16 7JG (7237 1261).

TRANSLATION *Finnish Translations,* 2 Admiral Sq, Chelsea Harbour SW10 0UU (7795 2066); *Finnish Translations,* 136a Tanfield Ave, London NW2 7RR (8452 6676).

TRAVEL *Finnish Tourist Board,* PO Box 33213, London W6 8JX (7365 2512).

WELFARE *Finnish Seamen's Mission,* 33 Albion St, London SE16 7JG (7237 4100).

Flemish

In the widest sense, *Flemish* refers to the people and culture of Flanders, the northern part of Belgium. For all relevant entries other than LANGUAGE, see under *Belgian.*

LANGUAGE *Flemish* is a Germanic language with official status in Belgium and about 5m speakers (of whom some live in adjoining areas of northern France). It is very closely related to *Dutch* with which it is generally considered to form a single language. In the *Multilingual Capital* (2000) survey, *Flemish* was recorded as the language of 11 London schoolchildren.

Fon

Fon (full name: *Fongbe*) is an Aframic language spoken in the Republic of Benin. The *Multilingual Capital* (2000) survey identified this as the language of two London schoolchildren.

Frafra

See *Gurenge* for information about this language.

French

ACCOMMODATION Property in France *All France*, 56 Gloucester Rd, SW7 4UB (7370 0129); *Anglo French Properties Ltd*, 111a Walton St, SW3 2HP (7225 0359); *French Property News* [magazine], 6 Burgess Mews, Wimbledon SW19 1UF (8543 3113); *Property Search South of France*; 4 Tideway Yard, 125 Mortlake High St, London SW14 8SN (8878 6611); *Provence Alpes Côte d'Azur Properties*, 61 Holmewood Gdns, SW2 3NB (8671 9293);

ASSOCIATIONS *African Francophone Community Association*, c/o Mr J Nzau-Matomisa, 3rd fl, The Irish Centre, Pretoria Rd, Tottenham N17 8DX (8808 0999) [languages: *French* and *Lingala*]; *Institut Francais Cultural Centre*, 17 Queensberry Place, SW7 2DT (7838 2144).

BARS & NIGHT-CLUBS *Zinc Bar & Grill*, 21 Heddon St, W1 (7255 8800).

BUSINESS *Banque Banorabe*, 195 Brompton Rd, SW3 1LZ (7590 7777); *Banque Edouard Constant*, 2 Studio Pl, SW1X 8EW (7235 4441); *Banque Nationale De Paris plc*, 8-13 King William St, EC4N 7BL (7895 7070); *Banque Nationale de Paris plc*, 20-21 St. James's St, SW1A 1ES (7522 1680); *Banque Transatlantique*, 36, St. James's St, SW1A 1JD (7493 6717); *Caisse Centrale des Banques Populaires*, 76 Cannon St, EC4N 6NH (7827 0066); *Caisse Nationale De Credit Agricole*, 11 Moorfields Highwalk, EC2Y 9DE (7374 5000); *Credit Lyonnais (UK) Ltd*; P.O Box 81, Broadwalk House, 5 Appold St, EC2A 2DA (7374 4014); *French Chamber of Commerce*, 21 Dartmouth St, SW1H 9BP (7304 4040); *Natexis Banque*, 4-6 Throgmorton Ave, EC2N 2DL (7638 0088); *Paris Bourse Ltd*, 4th fl, Cannongate Ho, 64 Cannon St, EC4N 6AE (7332 5932).

EDUCATION *Alliance Francaise de Londres*, 1 Dorset Sq, NW1 6PU (7723 6439); *Club Français*, 235 Nimrod Rd, SW16 6TN (8677 2245); *Club Français*, 6 Spencer Rd, Twickenham TW2 5TH (8893 4690); *Club Français Fun French For Children*, Orpington Rd, Winchmore Hill N21 3PD (8886 6875); *Francophone ACP (Africa, Caribbean*

& the Pacific) Research Group, SSHL, University of Westminster, 309 Regent St, W1B 2UW (7911 5000 x2078); *French and Spanish à la Carte*, 97 Revelstoke Rd, SW18 5NL (8946 4777); *French and Spanish Language Holidays*, 13 Crouch Hall Rd, N8 8HT (8348 2400); *French Online*, 2b Woodstock Rd, NW11 8ER (8922 3578); *Institut Français*, 14 Cromwell Place, SW7 2JR (7581 2701); *Lycée Français Charles De Gaulle School*, 35 Cromwell Rd, SW7 2DG (7584 6322); *Lycee Francais & Charles De Gaulle Wix School*, Wixs La, SW4 0AJ (7738 0287); *Native French Teachers*, 18 Leverton St, NW5 2PJ (7284 1554); *William Boyle English French Tuition*, 95 Hatherley Gdns, E6 3HG (8471 5244).

As well as some of the above, mother tongue education in French is available for children in several other places in London – visit <www.resourceunit.com> for details. In addition, well over 400 courses in French for adults are provided by universities and local education authorities throughout London - see *Floodlight* or visit <www.floodlight.co.uk> for full details.

GOVERNMENT *French Consulate General*, 21 Cromwell Rd, SW7 2EN (7838 2000);

HEALTH AND BEAUTY *French Cosmetic Medical Company Ltd*, 25 Wimpole St, W1G 8GP (7637 0548); *Le Dispensaire Francais*, 6 Osnaburgh St, NW1 3DH (7388 3215); *Medicare Français*, 3 Harrington Gardens, SW7 4JJ (7370 4999); *Paris Beauty Institute*; 32 Thurloe Place, SW7 2HQ (7581 0060); *The French Clinic (Dispensaire Français)*, 6 Osnaburgh St, NW1 3DH (7388 3215).

LANGUAGES *French* is the official and overwhelmingly dominant language of France. It also has official status in at least 20 other countries, particularly those in which there was formerly a colonial French presence. Within France, there are also several regional languages (*Breton, Basque, Catalan,* etc.) as well many languages introduced by settlers from other parts of the world (of which *Arabic* is probably the most important). There are, however, no official figures for the number of speakers of any of these.

In world terms, *French* ranks 12th with 125m speakers of whom 90m are primary speakers. It is a *Romanic* language. According to the *Multilingual Capital* (2000) survey, *French* was the first language 5,609 London schoolchildren (but this figure probably includes some who speak *French Creole* - see this entry for details).

MEDIA & INFORMATION *Agence France-Presse*, 3rd fl, 78 Fleet St, EC4Y 1NB (7353 7461); *France Magazine (London) Ltd*, within French Government Tourist Office, 178 Piccadilly, W1J 9AL (7491 9995);

France Telecom UK Ltd, Wellington Ho, 8 Upper St Martin's La, WC2H 9DL (7343 2424); *France 2 Television*, 66-67 Newman St, W1T 3EQ (7636 4573).

MOTORING *Auto French Spares*, 310 High St, North Manor Park, E12 6SA (8552 9737); *French*

Car Services, 2 Middleton Mews, N7 9LT (7609 1502).

RELIGION *French Protestant Church of London,* 9 Soho Sq, W1D 3QB (7437 5311); *Notre Dame de France,* 5 Leicester Place, WC2H 7BP (7437 9363); *Peniel French Church,* Imperial House, Willoughby Lane, Tottenham N17 0SP (8808 4600).

RESTAURANTS

East Central *Bleeding Heart Bistro,* Bleeding Heart Yard, Hatton Garden, EC1 (7242 8238); *Bubb's Le Restaurant Français,* 329 Central Markets, EC1A 9NB (7236 2435); *Cafe du Marche,* 22 Charterhouse Mews, Charterhouse Sq, EC1M 6AH (7608 1609); *Cafe Flo,* 38-40 Ludgate Hill, EC4M 7DE (7329 3900); *Café Rouge,* Hillgate House, Limeburner La, EC4M 7HY (7329 1234); *Chez Gerard,* 14 Trinity Sq, EC3N 4AA (7480 5500); *Chez Gérard,* 64 Bishopsgate, EC2N 4AJ (7588 1200); *Club Gascon,* 57 West Smithfield, EC1 (7253 5853); *Figaro,* 268 St. John St, EC1V 4PE (7336 8080); *Maison Novelli,* 29 Clerkenwell Green, EC1R 0DU (7251 6606); *Paquerette,* Finsbury Sq, EC2A 1RR (7638 5134); *Paris Grill,* James Capel Ho, 18 Bury St, EC3A 5AX (7626 2158); *Simply Nico Barbican,* 7 Goswell Rd, EC1M 7AH (7336 7677).

South East 1 *Cafe Rouge,* Tooley St, SE1 2LA (7378 0097); *Simply Nico,* 10 London Bridge St, SE1 9SG (7407 4536).

South West 1 *Boisdale,* 15 Eccelston St, SW1 (7730 6922); *Brasserie Roux,* Waterloo Pl, SW1 (7968 2900); *La Tante Claire,* Berkeley Hotel, Wilton Pl, Knightsbridge, SW1 (7823 2002); *Oranger,* 5 St James's St, SW1A 1EF (7839 3774); *Poule au Pot,* 231 Ebury St, SW1W 8UT (7730 7763); *Roussillon,* 16 St Barnabas St, SW1 (7730 5550); *Simply Nico,* 48a Rochester Row, SW1P 1JU (7630 8061); *Vong,* Wilton Pl, SW1 (7235 1010).

West 1 *Artiste Musclé,* 1 Shepherd Market, W1J 7PA (7493 6150); *BamBou,* 1 Percy St W1P (7323 9140); *Boudin Blanc,* 5 Trebeck St, W1J 7LS (7499 3292); *Cafe De Paris,* 3-4 Coventry St, W1D 6BW (7734 7700); *Chez Nico at Ninety Park Lane,* 90 Park La, W1 (7409 1290); *Connaught,* 16 Carlos Pl, W1 (7499 7070); *Criterion,* 224 Piccadilly, W1 (7930 0488); *Dover Street Restaurant & Bar* [French / Mediterranean], 8-10 Dover St, W1X 3PJ (7491 7509); *Frith Street,* 63-64 Frith St, W1 (7734 4545); *Gavroche,* 43 Upper Brook St, W1 (7408 0881); *John Burton Race,* 222 Marylebone Rd, NW1 (7723 7800); *Krusts* [Italian & French], 13 Seymour Pl, W1H 5AN (7724 3446); *L'Escargot,* 48 Greek St, W1 (7437 2679); *Mirabelle,* 56 Curzon St, W1 (7499 4636); *Nico - Central London,* 35 Great Portland St, W1N 5DD (7436 8846); *Oak Room,* Le Meridien, 21 Piccadilly, W1V 0BH (7437 0202); *Odeon,* 65 Regent St, W1 (7287 1400); *Patisserie Valerie,* 44 Old Compton St, W1 (7437 3466); *Pied A Terre,* 34 Charlotte St, W1T 2NH (7636 1178); *Quo Vadis,* 26-29 Dean St, W1 (7437 9585).

West Central *Admiralty,* Somerset House, The Strand, WC2 (7845 4646) [regional French cuisine];

Ahmed Ahmadi, 136 Long Acre, WC2E 9AD (7379 1844); *Alchemy Dining Club,* 21 Gower St, WC1E 6HG (7636 7612); *Bohème,* 27 Catherine St, WC2B 5JS (7240 9705); *Café des Amis du Vin,* 11-14 Hanover Pl, WC2E 9JP (7379 3444); *Cafe du Jardin,* 28 Wellington St, WC2E 7BD (7836 8760); *Café Rouge,* 34 Wellington St, WC2E 7BD (7836 0998); *Chez Gérard,* 119 Chancery La, WC2A 1PP (7405 0290); *Chez Gérard at the Opera Terrace,* 45 The Market, The Piazza, WC2E 8RF (7379 0666); *Connaught's Brasserie,* 61-65 Great Queen St, WC2B 5BZ (7242 9793); *Crêperie Bretonne,* 26 New Row, WC2N 4LA (7240 3603); *Denise's,* 79, Southampton Row, WC1B 4ET (7436 1562); *Estaminet,* 14 Garrick St, WC2E 9BJ (7379 1432); *Estaminet,* 1 Kingsway, WC2B 6UN (7379 9797); *Garrick Wine Bar,* 10 Garrick St, WC2E 9BH (7240 7649); *Mon Plaisir,* 21 Monmouth St, WC2 (7836 7243); *Palais du Jardin,* 136 Long Acre WC2E 9AD (7379 5353); *Piaf,* Southampton Row, WC1B 4ET (7580 7800); *Salieri Theatre Restaurant,* 376 Strand, WC2R 0LR (7836 1318); *Savoir Faire,* 42 New Oxford St, WC1A 1EP (7436 0707); *Tutton's Brasserie,* 11-12 Russell St, Covent Garden WC2B 5HZ (7836 4141).

Barnet *Café Rouge,* 1 Leisure Way, High Rd, Finchley N12 0QZ (8446 4777).

Brent *Cafe M,* 67 Cricklewood Broadway, NW2 3JR (8208 3275); *Marseille,* 45 Kilburn High Rd, NW6 5SB (7624 7477).

Camden *Café Flo,* 205 Haverstock Hill, NW3 4QG (7435 6744); *Café Rouge,* 6-7 South Grove, N6 6BS (8342 9797); *Camden Brasserie,* 216 Camden High St, NW1 8QR (7482 2114); *Casablanca,* 102 Fleet Rd, NW3 2QX (7284 2619); *Chez Didier,* 102 Fortune Green Rd, NW6 1DS (7431 6602); *Chez Nous,* 157 Haverstock Hill, NW3 4QT (7483 3373); *Le Cellier du Midi,* 28 Church Row, Hampstead NW3 6UP (7435 9998); *Lécluse,* 3 Chalk Farm Rd, NW1 8AA (7267 8116); *Little Bay,* 228 Belsize Rd, NW6 4BT (7372 4699); *Mustoe Bistro,* 73 Regents Park Rd, NW1 8UY (7586 0901); *Petit Prince* [French & Moroccan], 5 Holmes Rd, NW5 3AA (7267 3789); *Ravel's Bistro & Wine Bar,* 4 Fleet Rd, Hampstead NW3 2QS (7485 3615); *Vine,* 86 Highgate Rd, NW5 1PB (7209 0038).

Ealing *Lisa's,* 46 Pitshanger La, Ealing, W5 1QY (8810 8668); *Uppercrust Brasserie,* 187 South Ealing Rd, W5 4RH (8569 8933).

Enfield *Cafe Anjou,* 394 Green Lanes, Palmers Green N13 5PD (8886 7267); *Cafe Rouge,* 45-46 Cannon Hill, N14 6LH (8886 3336);

Greenwich *Café Rouge,* Ibis Hotel, Stockwell St, Greenwich, SE10 8EY (8293 6660); *Spread Eagle Antiques,* 8-9, Nevada St, SE10 9JL (8692 1618).

Hackney *Frocks,* 95 Lauriston Rd, Victoria Park E9 7HJ (8986 3161); *LMNT Gastro Bar,* 316 Queensbridge Rd, E8 3NH (7249 6727); *Small and Beautiful,* 171 Blackstock Rd, N4 2JS (7359 9068); *Soulard,* 113 Mortimer Rd, N1 4JY (7254 1314).

Hammersmith & Fulham *Au Coeur de Paris*, 156 Shepherds Bush Rd, W6 7PB (7371 1001); *Balzac Bistro*, 4 Wood La, W12 7DT (8743 6787); *Bibendum Restaurant Ltd*, Michelin House 81, Fulham Rd London 6RD (7581 5817); *Cafe France*, 24b Concord Shopping Centre, Shepherds Bush Green, W12 8PP (8743 5415); Cafe Rouge, 98-100 Shepherds Bush Rd, W6 7PD (7602 7732); *Les Tournesols*, 235 Wood Lane, London W12 0HL (8746 2365); *Pierre Victoire*, 690 Fulham Rd, SW6 5SA (7736 1195).

Haringey *Cafe Rouge*, 66 Crouch End Hill, N8 8AG (8340 2121); *Le Bistro*, 36 High St, Hornsey N8 7NX (8340 2116); *Le Cadre*, 10 Priory Rd, Crouch End N8 7RD (8348 0606); *Le Chardon*, 65 Lordship La, SE22 8EP (8299 1921); *Le Moulin*, 310 Archway Rd, N6 5AU (8348 1214); *Les Associes*, 172 Park Rd, N8 8JT (8348 8944).

Hillingdon *Chez Gérard*, Terminal 3, Heathrow Airport, Hounslow TW6 1QG (8607 5990); *Simply Nico* within Crown Plaza Hotel, Stockley Rd, West Drayton UB7 9NA (01895 437564).

Hounslow *Cafe Rouge*, 85 Strand On The Green, Chiswick W4 3NN (8995 6575);*Christian's*, 1 Station Parade, Burlington La, W4 3HD (8995 0382); *Le Parisien*, 472 Chiswick High Rd, W4 5TT (8995 5129); *le Piaf*, 156 Chiswick High Rd, Chiswick, W4 1PR (8995 1656).

Islington *Bertie's*, 139 Upper St, Islington N1 1QP (7226 3344); *Cafe Flo*, 334 Upper St, Islington Green N1 0PB (7226 7916); *Chase Restaurants*, 106, Islington High St, N1 8EG (7359 1118); *Dome1*, 341 Upper St, N1 0PB (7226 3414); *Frederick's*, Camden Passage, Islington, N1 8EG (7359 2888); *Gill Wing Cafe*, 300 St Pauls Rd, N1 2LH (7226 2885); *La Vie En Rose*, 658, Holloway Rd, N19 3NU (7272 6856); *Le Mercury*, 140a Upper St, N1 1QY (7354 4088); *Paris London Café*, 5 Junction Rd, N19 5QT (7561 0330);*Sacre Coeur Bistro*, 18 Theberton St, Islington N1 0QX (7354 2618).

Kensington & Chelsea *Abingdon*, 54 Abingdon Rd, W8 6AP (7937 3339); *Aix*, 129 Holland Park Ave, W11 3RZ (7727 7288); *Aubergine*, 11 Park Walk, SW10 0AJ (7352 3449); *Bistro at the French Institute*, 17 Queensberry Pl, SW7 2DT (7589 5433); *Brasserie du Marché aux Puces*, 349 Portobello Rd, W10 (8968 5828);

Brasserie St Quentin, 243 Brompton Rd, SW3 2EP (7589 8005); *Café Rouge*, 29-31 Basil St, SW3 1BB (7584 2345); *Café Rouge*, 2 Lancer Sq, Kensington Church St, W8 4EH (7938 4200); *Capital*, The Capital Hotel, 22-24 Basil St. SW3 1AT (7926 3199); *Chez Moi*, 1 Addison Ave, W11 4QS (7603 8267); *Colombier*, 145 Dovehouse St, SW3

(7351 1155); *Dan's*, 119 Sydney St, SW3 6NR (7352 2718); *Dome*, 354 Kings Rd, Chelsea, SW3 5UZ (7352 2828); *Dome*, 35a Kensington High St, W8 5EB (7937 6655); *Francofill*, 1 Old Brompton Rd, SW7 3HZ (7584 0087); *Gordon Ramsay*, 68-69 Royal Hospital Rd, SW3 (7352 4441); *Le Colombier*, 145 Dovehouse St, SW3 6LB (7351 1155); *Le Piaf*, 19-21 Notting Hill Gate, W11 3JQ (7727 8810); *Le Shop*, 329 Kings Rd, London SW3 5ES (7352 3891); *Little French Restaurant*, 18 Hogarth Place, SW5 0QY (7370 0366); *Number 13*, 13-16 Queens Gate, SW7 5EN (7581 4478); *Piaf Restaurant*, 19-21 Notting Hill Gate, W11 3JQ (7727 8810); *Six Clarendon Road*, 6 Clarendon Rd, W11 3AA (7727 3330); *Tray Gourmet*, 240 Fulham Rd, SW10 (7352 7676).

Kingston *Cavendish*, Ace of Spades Roundabout, Hook Rise, North Surbiton KT6 5AT (8288 1810); *Gravier*, 9 Station Rd, Kingston, KT2 7AA (8547 1121).

Lambeth *Cafe Prov*, 16a Coldharbour La, SE5 9PR (7738 5585); *Ivoire*, 40-42 Brixton Rd, SW9 6BT (7582 3771); **Lewisham:** *Café Rouge*, 16-18 Montpelier Vale, SE3 0TA (8297 2727); *Foret Des Amis*, 15 Perry Vale, SE23 2NE (8699 2028); *French Touch*, 40 Lee High Rd, SE13 (8318 0737); *Lobster Pot*, 3 Kennington La, SE11 (7582 5556).

Merton *French Street Cafe*, 190 Merton High St, SW19 1AX (8543 4060); *Le Piaf*, 40 Wimbledon Hill Rd, SW19 7PA (8946 3823).

Richmond *Auberge* at the Kings Head, 123 High St, Teddington TW11 8HG (8943 2259); *Brula*, 43 Crown Rd, Twickenham TW1 3EJ (8892 0602); *Café Flo*, 149 Kew Rd, Richmond TW9 2PN (8940 8298); *Café Rouge*, 291 Sandycombe Rd, Kew TW9 3LU (8332 2882); *Cassis*, 57 Kew Rd, Richmond TW9 2NQ (8948 7898); *Chez Lindsay*, 11 Hill Rise, Richmond TW10 6UQ (8948 7473); *Cigale*, 3 Church Rd, Teddington TW11 8PF (8943 3331); *Dome*, 26 Hill St, Richmond TW9 1TW (8332 2525); *Monsieur Max*, 133 High St, Hampton TW12 1NJ (8979 5546); *Raefil's*, 34 Church St, Twickenham TW1 3NR (8892 6366).

Southwark *Café Provençal*, 4 Half Moon La, SE24 9HU (7978 9228); *Paris Café*, 10 Peckham High St, SE15 5DT (7703 3637); *Piaf*, 75-77 Dulwich Village, SE21 7BJ (8693 9331).

Tower Hamlets *Café Rouge*, 20 Cabot Sq, E14 4QW (7537 9696); *1789 French Restaurant*, 9a, Fairfield Rd, E3 2QA (8980 8233); *Le Tigre et la Grenouille*, 261 Bethnal Green Rd, E2 (7729 0829); *MPW*, 2nd fl, Cabot Place East, Canary Wharf, E14 (7513 0513); *The Light*, 233 Shoreditch High St, E1 6PJ (7247 8989).

Wandsworth *Auberge,* 22 Upper Richmond Rd, SW15 2RX (8874 3593); *Brasserie Metz,* 30 Battersea Rise, SW11 1EE (7228 0611); *Café Rouge,* 39-49, Parkgate Rd, Battersea, SW11 4NP (7924 3565); *Café Rouge,* 200-204 Putney Bridge Rd, SW15 2NA (8788 4257); *Delifrance,* 121 Putney High St, SW15 1SU (8780 3396); *Grafton Restaurant Français,* 45 Old Town, Clapham SW4 0JL (7627 1048); *Le Gothique,* Royal Victoria Patriotic Buildings, Fitzhugh Grove, SW18 3SX (8870 6567); *Le Petit Normand,* 185 Merton Rd, SW18 5EF.

Westminster *Antony's,* 54 Porchester Rd, W2 6ET, (7243 8743); *Bistro Daniel,* 26 Sussex Pl, W2 (7262 6073); *Brasserie,* 272 Brompton Rd, SW3 2AW (7581 3089); *Café Flo,* 51 St Martins La, WC2N 4EA (7836 8289); *Café Rouge,* 2nd floor, Whitleys Centre, Queensway, W2 4YJ (7221 1509); *Cravache,* 26 Leinster Terrace, W2 3ET (7706 1384); *Jason's,* Jason's Wharf, opposite 60 Blomfield Rd, Maida Vale, W9 (7286 6752); *La Cravache,* 26 Leinster Terrace, W2 3ET, (7706 1384); *L'Aventure,* 3 Blenheim Terrace, NW8 0EH (7624 6232); *Oslo Court,* Prince Albert Rd, NW8 7EN (7722 8795); *Peche,* 12-14 Glentworth St, NW1 5PG (7935 0212).

SHOPS

Antiques *Un Francais à Londres,* 202 Ebury St, London SW1W 8UN (7730 1771); *Nicole Fabre French Antiques,* 592 Kings Rd, SW6 2DX (7384 3112); *French Interiors,* 7a Bouverie Mews, London N16 0AE (8809 2927) [antique repair and restoration].

Bookshops *French Bookshop,* 28 Bute St, South Kensington, SW7 (7584 2840); *Librairie La Page,* 7 Harrington Rd, South Kensington, SW7 3ES (7589 5991, fax 7225 2662).

Fashion *An'Ge Paris,* Ames Ho, 44 Mortimer St, W1W 7RJ (7580 7377); Fille De Paris Retail Ltd, 138 Uxbridge Rd, W12 8AA (8743 4446); *French Sole,* 6 Ellis St, SW1X 9AL (7730 3771) [shoes]; *French Wools Ltd,* 106 Brompton Rd, SW3 1JJ (7581 0711); *Hermès,* 176 Sloane St, SW1 (7259 5191); *Lanvin Paris*; 94 Brompton Rd, SW3 1ER (7581 4401); *Lanvin-Paris for Men,* 108 New Bond St , W1S 1EF (7499 2929); *Marciano Paris*; 87 Marylebone High St, W1U 4QW, (7487 5228) [clothing manufacturers and retailers]; *Rodier Paris Ltd,* 106-108 Brompton Rd, SW3 1JJ (7584 6398); *Voyage Paris Ltd*; 50 Mortimer St, W1W 7RJ (7636 1892).

Florists: *Flowers from Paris,* Unit 7, 184-186, Oakleigh Rd, N20 0UA (8523 8814) [florists];

Food: *Comptoir Gascon,* 63 Charterhouse St, EC1 (7608 0851); *Fileric,* 12 Queenstown Rd, SW8 (7720 4844); *Delice de France,* Unit 18, Bow Triangle Business Centre, Eleanor St, E3 4UR (8880 6660); *French & Italian Cuisine* 66 Wallingford Avenue, W10 6PY (8969 6034); *French Tarts,* 28 Battersea Rise, SW11 1EE (7228 6006); *Maison Blanc,* 303 Fulham Rd, SW10 (7795 2663); *Paris Express,* Fruit & Vegetable Market, New Covent Garden Market, SW8 5JJ (7498 4454); *Parisien Coffee,* 40 Lime St, EC3M 5BY (7283 5245); *Tour de France,* 135 Sunnyhill Rd, SW16 2UW (8769 3554); *Truc Vert,* 42 North Audley St, W1 (7491 9988).

Furnishing *Le Tissus Francais Ltd,* 227 Ebury St, SW1W 8UT (7730 5050); *Salon Français,* 32 Edgware Rd, W2 2EH (7262 4991).

Wines: *Bacchus les Vignobles de France,* Bacchus Ho, Unit 4 , Grange Mills, Weir Rd, SW12 0NE (8675 9007); *Classic French* 195 Upper Richmond Rd, SW15 6SG (8788 5778).

SPECIAL *Fille De Paris Ltd,* 202-208 Commercial Rd, E14 7HA (7265 9004) [textile warehouse]; *French Cuisiniers,* Units 1, 2 and 6, Parmiter Industrial Estate,Parmiter St, E2 9HZ (8980 5792) [food manufacturers]; *French National Research Council,* 6 Cromwell Pl, SW7 2JN (7581 3367); *La Cuisine De France,* 47 Barmeston Rd, Catford, SE6 3BH (8695 0892) [caterer]; *Le Peche & Mignon,* 2a Melbourne Grove, SE22 8QZ (8693 3712); *Paris London Co,* 54 Turnmill St, EC1M 5SH (7689 7680) [events organisers]; *Paris Photography,* 7 Charterhouse Works, Eltringham St, Wandsworth, SW18 1TD (8871 2162) [photographers].

TRANSLATION *Alvarez Spanish & French Translations,* 3 The Crest, 21 Ellington Rd, Muswell Hill, N10 3DE (8352 9785); *English-German-French Interpreting,* 17 Davisville Rd, Shepherd's Bush W12 9SH (8740 6440); *French & Farsi Translators & Interpreters,* 46 Inverness Terrace, W2 3JA (7243 1855); *French & German Commerical Translations,* 64 Fielding Rd, Chiswick W4 1HL (8994 7549); *French Italian Translations,* 77 Hotham Rd, SW15 1QW (8788 5011); *French Legal & Commercial Translator,* 64 Fielding Rd, W4 1HL (8994 7549); *French to English Translations,* 35 Courthope Rd, NW3 2LE (7482 2227); *French Translations,* Unit E Thames House, Battersea Park Rd, Battersea, SW11 4NB (7771 6501); *French Translator & Interpreter,* 140 Hindle House, Arcola St, E8 2DY

(7241 6820); *Interpreter Arabic & French*, 61 Chippenham Rd, W9 2AB (7286 7351); *Language Service - French Swahili English*, 124 Tottenhall Rd, Palmers Green, N13 6DG (8365 8342); *Pierre M Beguin French Translations*, 64 Stockwell Rd, SW9 9JQ (7733 5146); *Romanian, French and English Translation Bureau*, 14 Laurel View, N12 7DT (8445 8080); *Russian & French Translations*, 27 South Drive, Ruislip HA4 8EU (01895 637597); *Spanish and French Solutions,* 14 St Augustine's Ct, Mornington Rd, E11 3BQ (8539 4457).

TRAVEL *Club La Vie Francais*, 338 Old York Rd, SW18 1SS (8870 3355); *Disneyland Paris,* 3 Queen Caroline St, W6 9PE (8222 2861); *Fish in France,* 90 Grove Park Rd, Mottingham SE9 4QB (8857 1244); *France Exclusive*, PO Box 36101, SW7 5JD (07720 431029); *French Affair Ltd,* 5-7 Humbolt Rd, W6 8QH (7381 8519); *French Gascony Self-Catering*, 2 Wellington Rd, Ealing, W5 4UH (8579 8026); *French Government Tourist Office,* 178 Piccadilly, W1J 9AL (7491 9995); *French Holiday Service,* 178 Piccadilly, W1J 9AL (7355 4747); *French Holidays Service,* Image Ho, Station Rd, N17 9LR (8324 4043); *French Impressions Holidays,* Image Ho, Station Rd, N17 9LR (8324 4042); *French* Railways *(Rail Europe),* French Railways Ho, 179 Piccadilly, W1 (0870 5848848); *House in France,* 11 Mount View London, NW7 3HT (8959 5182); *Invitation to France,* Kiln Ho, 210 New Kings Rd SW6 4NZ (7751 0990); *Just France,* 10-18 Putney Hill, SW15 6AX (8780 4488); *Picardie*, 39 Neal St, WC2H 9PJ (7836 2232).

WELFARE *Afro - Care Umbrella*, c/o Andy Hammond, 45 North Sq, Edmonton Green N9 0HY (8372 5528) [languages: *French,* Igbo, Swahili, English]; *Craig Park Youth Centre (Black Youth Projects)*, Asha Urhobo, Lawrence Rd, Edmonton N18 2HN (8803 8292) [languages: *French*, Somali, English]; *Franco-British Council,* 47-49 Strutton Ground, SW1P 2HY (7976 8380); *Franco-British Society,* Room 623, Linen Hall, W1R5TB (7734 0815).

French Creole

LANGUAGE *French Creole* is an abbreviation of *French-based Creole* or *French lexicon Creole,* a language which has a largely French vocabulary but a grammar influenced by African and other languages. *French Creole* languages are spoken in London by (the descendents of) immigrants from two widely-separated parts of the world – the Caribbean (mainly the *St Lucian* and *Dominican* varieties) and the Indian Ocean (*Mauritian* and

Seychellois). (See entries under these names for more information. Note also that the Caribbean and Indian Ocean varieties are far from being entirely mutually intelligible even though they do share many features.)

The *Multilingual Capital* (2000) survey had difficulty in obtaining reliable data on the numbers of schoolchildren speaking *French Creole*. Only 12 boroughs listed speakers of these under unambiguous names (such as Creole French, Mauritian Creole, etc.). In other boroughs, speakers of French Creoles may have been returned as 'French' or, particularly in the case of those from the West Indies, 'Patois' (which is more often applied to English Creoles). The total of 1,664 returned from these 12 boroughs is could be as little as one third of the true figure because the boroughs not listing any speakers include two – Islington and Wandsworth – where substantial numbers of *French Creole*-speakers are known to live.

Fula

Fula (also known, especially in Nigeria, by its Hausa name *Fulani*) is an Atlantic language spoken in more than a dozen countries from Senegal to Nigeria to southern Sudan. This was reported as the first language of 10 London schoolchildren in the *Multilingual Capital* (2000) survey.

Fulani

Fulani is the Hausa name for *Fula* (see under this name for information).

G

Gã

EDUCATION Mother tongue education for young children in **Gã** is available in two places in London – see <www.resourceunit.com> for details.

LANGUAGE **Gã** (also written as *Ga* and *Gan*) is an Aframic language spoken by about half a million people in the Accra area of Ghana. The *Multilingual Capital* (2000) survey reported that this was spoken by 831 London schoolchildren, of whom more than a quarter lived in Lambeth.

For the distribution of **Gã** speakers in London, see Map 13 in the Map Gallery at <www.global-london.com>.

Gabonese

GOVERNMENT *Gabonese Embassy*, 27 Elvaston Pl, SW7 5NL, (7823 9986)

LANGUAGES More than 20 Bantuic languages are spoken in Gabon, of which **Fang** is by far the most important, but **French** is the official language.

Gaelic

FREIGHT *Gaelic Freight*, 72 New Bond St, W1S 1RR (7649 9871).

EDUCATION Mother tongue education in (Irish) **Gaelic** for young children is available in about ten places in London – visit <www.resourceunit.com> for full details. Several places provide courses in Irish Gaelic for adults in London – see *Floodlight* or visit its website at <www.floodlight.co.uk> for details. *City Lit* (7831 9631) provides courses in Scottish Gaelic.

LANGUAGE The spelling **Gaelic** refers to two different but related Celtic languages which are also distinguished by pronunciation - Irish Gaelic (pronounced "Gaylic") and Scottish Gaelic (pronounced "Gallic"). In the *Multilingual Capital* (2000) survey, 291 schoolchidren were identified as speakers of **Gaelic**, 98 as speakers of *Irish Gaelic,* and there was no specific mention of *Scottish Gaelic*-speakers.

Galician

BUSINESS *Caja de Ahorros de Galicia,* 3rd fl, 170 Piccadilly, W1J 9EJ (7491 3020); *Galicia y Buenos Aires Securities (UK) Ltd,* 2nd fl, 50 Gresham St, EC2V 7AY (7600 9393);

LANGUAGE **Galician** is a **Romanic** language closely related to *Portuguese*.

MOTORING *Galicia Motors Ltd,* 14-17 Astwood Mews, SW7 4DE (7373 2408);

RESTAURANTS
Croydon *Galicia,* 269-275 High St, Croydon CR0 1QH (8686 0043).

SHOPS *Galicia Ltd* [women's wear], 24 Wellington St, WC2E 7DD (7836 2961);

Galla

Galla is an alternative name for **Oromo** – see **Oromo** for all information on this language.

Gambian

ASSOCIATIONS *The Gambian Association,* Dalston, E8 (7254 4832).

GOVERNMENT *High Commission of the Gambia,* 57 Kensington Ct, W8 5DG (7937 6316).

LANGUAGES **English** has official status. The five main indigenous languages, in descending order, are **Mandinka, Fula, Wolof,** Dyola, and **Soninke. Aku,** a local form of **Krio,** is also spoken in the capital Banjul.

TRAVEL *Gambian National Tourist Office,* 57 Kensington Ct, W8 5DG *(7376 0093).*

Gan

Gan is an alternative spelling of **Gã.** See under **Gã** for details.

Ganda

Ganda is a Bantuic language, better known today with its Bantu prefix as **Luganda** - see under this name for further information.

Gascon

BARS **& NIGHT-CLUBS** *Cellar Gascon,* 59 West Smithfield, EC1A 9DS (7600 7561).

RESTAURANTS
East Central *Club Gascon,* 57 West Smithfield, EC1 (7796 0600).

SHOPS *Comptoir Gascon Ltd,* 63 Charterhouse St, EC1M 6HJ (7608 0851); *Gascon Merchant* [delicatessen], 29 Cheval Pl, South Kensington SW7 1EW (7581 0715).

TRAVEL *French Gascony Self-Catering,* 2 Wellington Rd, Ealing, W5 4UH (8579 8026).

Georgian

GOVERNMENT *Georgian Embassy*, 3 Hornton Pl, Kensington, W8 4LZ (7937 8233).

EDUCATION Courses in **Georgian** are available at *SOAS Language Centre* (7898 4888).

LANGUAGES **Georgian** is the official language of Georgia but **Russian** and **Armenian** are also widely known and **Abkhazian** has joint official status in Abkhazia (Whitaker's 2000).

Georgian is a language of the Caucasus geozone (Dalby 1999-2000). It has about 5m speakers and is written in its own alphabetic script. The *Multilingual Capital* (2000) survey reported that there were 14 **Georgian**-speaking schoolchildren in London.

RELIGION Most Georgians are Orthodox Christians but there is a Muslim minority.

RESTAURANTS

Hackney *Little Georgia,* 2 Broadway Market, E8 (7249 9070).

Islington *Tblisi,* 91 Holloway Rd, N1 (7607 2536).

German

ACCOMMODATION *German YMCA,* 35 Craven Terrace, W2 (7723 9276).

ASSOCIATIONS *British-German Association,* 18 Conduit St. W1S 2XN (7629 4975);

BUSINESS

Banking *Bankgesellschaft Berlin,* 1 Crown Ct, Moorgate, EC2V 6JP (7572 6200); *Berliner Handels- und Frankfurter Bank,* 61 Queen St, EC4R 1AE (7634 2300); *Deutsche Bank,* P O Box 441, Moorgate, EC2P 2AT (7545 8000); *Deutsche Bank Aktiengesellschaft,* 6-8 Bishopsgate, EC2P 2AT (7971 7000); *Deutsche Bank Capital Markets Ltd,* 150 Leadenhall St, EC3V 4RJ (7545 8000); *Deutsche Bank Gilts Ltd,* Winchester Ho, 1 Great Winchester St, EC2N 2DB; *Deutsche Hypo,* City Tower, Level 19, 40 Basinghall St EC2V 5DE (7920 0100); *Deutsche Hypothekenbank Frankfurt Aktiengesellschaft,* 1 Love La, EC2V 7JJ (7600 7575); *Deutsche Pfandbrief-und Hypothekenbank Ag,* Royex Ho, Aldermanbury Sq EC2V 7HR (7606 0656); *Deutsche Schiffs Bank,* Grocers Hall, Princes St, EC2R 8AQ (7726 8726); *Frankfurter Hypothekenbank Centralboden A G,* Winchester Ho, 1 Great Winchester St, EC2N 4DA (7545 2111).

Insurance *Aachen & Munich Insurance Co,* 14 Fenchurch Ave, EC3M 5BS (7623 2488); *Munich Reassurance Co,* 154 Fenchurch St, EC3M 6JJ

(7626 2566); *Munich Re-underwriting Ltd,* St Helens, 1 Undershaft, EC3A 8EE (7886 3900).

Other financial services *Central Marketing Organisation of German Agricultural Industries,* CMA Ho., 17a Church Rd, Wimbledon, SW19 5DQ (8944 0484); *Deutsche Asset Management Life & Pensions Ltd,* Prince George Ho, 20 Finsbury Circus, EC2M 1NB; *Deutsche Finanz Und Investment Ltd,* 72 New Bond St, W1Y 9DD; *Euro Finanz Anlagen Ltd,* Rowlandson Ho, 289-293 Ballards La, North Finchley N12 8NP *Federation of German Industries,* 16 Buckingham Gate, SW1E 6LB (7233 7816). *Finanz-investments & Security Consulting Ltd,* 9-10 College Terrace, Bow E3 5AN; *German-British Chamber of Industry & Commerce,* Mecklenburg Ho, 16 Buckingham Gate, SW1E 6LB (7976 4100); *German Financial Investments Ltd,* 5 North Colonnade, Poplar E14 4BB; *Germany Investments Ltd,* 665 Finchley Rd, NW2 2HN; *Innovatives Finanz-management Ltd,* 788-790 Finchley Rd, Golders Green NW11 7TJ; *Nissay Deutsche Asset Management Europe Ltd,* Prince George Ho, 20 Finsbury Circus, EC2M 1NB; *Project Management (Germany) Ltd,* 28 Church Rd, Stanmore HA7 4XR; *VDL Germany,* 22-26 Albert Embankment, Southwark SE1 7TJ (7582 9644).

Other German businesses *Berlin London Industrial Design,* 1 Leonard St, EC2A 4AQ (7689 3311); *Deutsche Wurlitzer UK* [vending machines], 6 Devonshire Ct, Victoria Rd, Feltham TW13 7LU (8867 0224).

EDUCATION The *Deutsche Schule,* Petersham Rd, Richmond TW10 7AA (8940 2510) provides standard German education from kindergarten to pre-university level.

More than 300 courses in ***German*** are provided for adults by universities and local education authorities in London – see *Floodlight* or visit <www.floodlight.co.uk> for full details.

German Academic Exchange Service, 34 Belgrave Square SW1X 8QB (7235 1736); *German Experience Ltd* (language school), 13 Cumberland Park, Acton W3 6SY (8896 1335); *German Historical Institute,* 17 Bloomsbury Sq, WC1A 2LP (7404 5486); *German Tuition Barbara Classen,* 2 Blackall St, EC2A 4AD (7613 3177); *Institute of Germanic Studies,* 29 Russell Sq., WC1B 5DP (7862 8967); *Goethe-Institut London,* German Cultural Centre, 50 Princes Gate, South Kensington SW7 2PH (7596 4000); *Internationale Management Schule International,* Vicarage Ho, 58-60 Kensington Church St, W8 4DB; *N J S McLauchlan* [German tuition], 1 Woodville Close, Teddington TW11 8NF (8977 1278).

FREIGHT *German Parcel Ltd,* Unit 28g, Southampton Ho, Building 521, London Heathrow Airport, TW6 2AP (8759 7599).

GOVERNMENT *Embassy of the Federal Republic of Germany,* 23 Belgrave Sq, SW1 (7824 1300).

LANGUAGE In terms of total numbers of speakers, **German** is ranked 11th in the world with 125m speakers (of whom this is the first language of

100m, mainly in Germany, Austria and Switzerland). Instruction in **German** is available in all London boroughs at a wide range of levels - see *Floodlight*.

M E D I A & **INFORMATION** *Deutsche Presse-agentur,* 30 Old Queen St, SW1H 9HP (7233 2888); *Frankfurter Allgemeine Zeitung,* 2nd fl, Bedford Chambers, Covent Garden Piazza, Holborn, WC2E 8HA (7836 5540) and 1 Southwark Bridge, Southwark SE1 9HL (7378 1514); *German Advice Centre,* 34 Belgrave Sq., SW1X 8QB (7235 4343); *German Broadcasting,* 10-12 Great Chapel St, W1V 3AL (7734 5740, 7439 7986); *German Film Board,* 4 Lowndes Ct, W1V 1PP (7437 2047); *German Radio SDR SWF BR,* 3 Logan Pl, W8 6QN (7244 7111); *German Television-ZDF,* 30 Old Queen St., SW1H 9HP (7233 4100); *German TV News Agency,* 5 Meldon Cl, Fulham SW6 2AQ (7736 3416); *Neue Zuercher Zeitung,* 18 St Albans Rd, Kentish Town NW5 1RD (7267 2130).

MOTORING *Deutsch Auto Parts,* 1456 London Rd, Streatham SW16 4BU (8765 0618); *German and Swedish Car Centre Ltd,* 284-286, Wightman Rd N8 0LT (8341 7570); *German and Swedish Car Parts Ltd,* 69-75, Robin Hood Way, SW15 3PW (8547 3101); *German Autocare,* 14 Liddell Rd, Kilburn NW6 2EW (7624 2334); *German Auto Works,* Unit 4, Rear of 10-16 Empire Way, HA9 0RQ (8903 8300); *German Car Centre,* 24-28 Boston Pl, NW1 6ER (7723 4699): *German Car Care Centre,* 660 Great Cambridge Rd, Enfield EN1 3SU (8364 5758); *German Car Parts,* 186 Alexandra Ave, Harrow HA2 9BN (8426 6222); *German Direct,* Oxgate Farm Works, Coles Green Rd, Cricklewood NW2 7EX (8452 8001); *German Gate,* 490 West Green Rd N15 3DA (8888 0707); *German Motor Co,* 2 Woodlands Way, Putney SW15 2SX (8871 0922); *GTS (German Car Parts),* Unit 9 South, 176 The Broadway, Colindale NW9 7AA (8201 6081); *Japanese & German Motorcycles,* Rear of 179-183 Staines Rd, Hounslow TW3 3JB (8814 0008).

RELIGION *St Mary-Le-Savoy German Lutheran Church,* 10 Sandwich St, Bloomsbury WC1H 9PL (7388 9586); Services are held in German at the *Deutsche Dietrich-Bonhoeffer Kirche,* Dacres Rd, SE23 (8699 4982); the *Deutsche Evangelische Christuskirche,* 18 Montpellier Pl, SW7 1HL (8876 6366); and the *German Lutheran Church of St Mary-le-Savoy,* 10 Sandwich St, WC1 (7388 9586); *St Boniface RC Church,* 47 Adler St., E1 1EE (7247 9529).

RESTAURANTS

Islington *Schnecke auf den Grün,* 80-82 Upper Stm N1 0NU (7226 6500).

Westminster *Jagerhutte,* 36 Queensway, W2 3RY (7229 7941).

SHOPS Most large supermarkets stock the basic range of foodstuffs the German shopper would expect to find, even if not all the familar brand names. Some of the latter can be found in the growing number of German-owned *Aldi* and *Lidl* supermarkets being established in London. Food outlets specializing in German produce include *German Wurst and Delicatessen,* 127 Central St., EC1V 8AP (7250 1322); *German Lager Importers Ltd,* 86 Roding Rd, E6 6LS (7511 3116); *Lidl Supermarkets,* New Rd, Hanworth TW13 6TQ (8893 7216); *Aldi Stores Ltd,* 18-19 Southampton Pl, Bloomsbury WC1A 2AJ (01827711800).

SPECIAL *Deutsche Interwein,* 1 The Village, North End Way, NW3 (8455 9895), *German Wine Information Service,* Lane House, Parsons Green, SW6 (7331 8800) and 1 Woburn Walk, WC1 (7388 25250).

TRANSLATION *Anglo-German Business & Finance Translations,* 25 Grand Ave, N10 3BD (8365 3778); *Berlin Translation Services,* 21 Hillcrest Rd, South Woodford E18 2JL (8989 3431); *Covac German Translations,* 19 Telford Parade Mansions, Streatham Hill, Brixton SW2 4RG (8671 4546); *English-German-French Interpreting,* 17 Davisville Rd, Shepherd's Bush W12 9SH (8740 6440); *French & German Commerical Translations,* 64 Fielding Rd, Chiswick W4 1HL (8994 7549); *German Accurate Translations,* 81 Chambers La. NW10 2RN (8459 5023); *German Interpreting and Translation Services,* 27 Ecclesbourne Rd, N1 3AF (7226 5549); *German Russian Language Services,* 14 West End La, Pinner HA5 1BT (8429 2943); *German Technical & Scientific Translations,* 5 Dryden St, WC2E 9NB (72401568); *German To English Translations,* 8 Linom Rd, Clapham SW4 7PD (7326 1088); *German Translations and Interpreting,* 61 Carysfort Rd, Stoke Newington N16 9AD (7249 6639); *German Translation Service,* 8 Brendon Ho, 3 Nottingham Pl, W1M 3FN (7486 9964); *German Translation Service,* 47 Popes Grove, Twickenham TW1 4JZ (8892 0232).

TRAVEL *Augsburg (Germany)* [airline], 200 Buckingham Palace Rd, SW1W 9TA (7707 4575); *Deutsche Bahn UK,* 18 Conduit St, W1R 9TD (0870 2435363); *Deutsche Lufthansa Aktiengesellschaft,* Lufthansa Ho, 10 Old Bond St, W1X 4EN (8750 3500); *German Travel Bureau,* 18 Conduit St, W1 (7408 0111); *German Travel Centre Ltd,* 403-409 Rayners La, Pinner HA5 5ER (8429 2900); *Lufthansa German Airlines,* Terminal 2, Heathrow Airport, Hounslow TW6 1EX (8750 3300); *Transline Anglo German Travel,* 28 Langham Gdns, West Ealing W13 8PY (8998 7791); The German national airline is *Lufthansa,* (reservations, flight enquiries 0845 773 7747).

WELFARE *Deutsche Evangelische Synode,* Lancaster Hall Hotel, 35 Craven Terrace, Bayswater W2 3EL (7706 8589); *German Advice Centre,* 34 Belgrave Sq, SW1X 8QB (7235 4343); *German British Forum,* 50 Stratton St, W1X 6NX (7518 3337); *German Old People's Home,* Homelands 33, Homelands Drive, Upper Norwood SE19 2NU (8653 3675).

Ghanaian

ASSOCIATIONS *Ghana Union,* 431 Caledonian Rd, N7 2LT (7700 5634).

BUSINESS *Ghana Cocoa Marketing Co (UK) Ltd,* Unit 5, The Granard Business Centre, NW7 2DQ (8906 4877); *Ghana International Bank,* 69 Cheapside, EC2P 2BB (7248 2384); *Ghana Timber Export Development Board,* Unit 4, Granard Business Centre, Bunns La, NW7 2DQ (8906 9560).

EDUCATION *Universities of Ghana,* 321 City Rd, EC1V 1LJ (7278 7413).

GOVERNMENT *High Commissioner for Ghana,* 13 Belgrave Sq, SW1X 8PS (7235 4142) and 104 Highgate Hill, N6 5HE (8342 8686).

LANGUAGES There are a great many indigenous languages in Ghana of which the most important are the **Akan** languages **Twi** and **Fante** (40%), **Dagari** and **Dagbane** (14%), **Ewe** (13%), **Adangme** (3.5%), **Gā** (3.5%), and **Nzema** (2.7%; estimates from Mann, Dalby et al. 1987). All of these are spoken in London. The official language is **English.**

MEDIA & INFORMATION *Euro-Ghana Courier Express Ltd,* 12 Lavender Rd, SW11 2UG (7924 2277); *Ghana Review International,* 700 High Rd, Tottenham, N17 0AE (8808 5655).

RELIGION *Ghanaian Catholic Chaplaincy,* 212 Sangley Rd, SE6 2JS (8697 0643).

RESTAURANTS

Hackney *Afrikico,* 27A Dalston La, E8 (7254 0201).

Haringey *Lomnava,* 487A Seven Sisters Rd, N15 6EP (8800 3212).

SHOPS *Akwaaba Ghanaian Craft,* 33 London Rd, SW17 9JR (8646 6446); *Eunice Tropical Food Store,* 133a Deptford High St, SE8 (8469 3095).

TRAVEL *Ghana Airways,* 3 Princes St, W1B 2LB (7499 0201); *Travel Ghana,* Berkley Ho, 73, Upper Richmond Rd, SW15 2SZ (8877 9262).

WELFARE *Ghana Welfare Association,* 547-551 High Rd, Leytonstone E11 4PB (8558 9311); *Ghana Union,* 431 Caledonian Rd, N7 9BG (7700 5634).

Gibraltarian

GOVERNMENT *Government of Gibraltar,* Arundell Great Ct, 179 Strand, WC2R 1EH (7836 0777).

MEDIA & INFORMATION *Gibraltar Information Bureau,* 179 Strand, WC2R 1EH (7836 0777).

Gikuyu

Gikuyu (called *Kikuyu* in Swahili) is a Bantuic language of Kenya. The *Multilingual Capital* (2000) survey reported this as the language of 116 London schoolchildren, of whom 24 lived in Barnet.

Goan

LANGUAGE The principal language of Goa is **Konkani,** an Indic language (see separate entry).

RESTAURANTS

West 1 *Palms of Goa,* 12 Charlotte St, W1 (7636 1668); *Palms of Goa,* 4 Meard St, W1F 0EF (7439 2994).

Bromley *Goa Tandoori,* 44a Newlands Park, SE26 5NF (8659 9922).

Greenwich *Goan Cuisine,* 136 Plumstead High St, SE18 1JQ (8317 1966).

Wandsworth *Goa,* 344 Battersea Park Rd, SW11 3BY (7924 4390); *Ma Goa,* 244 Upper Richmond Rd, SW15 6TG (8780 1767); *Ma Goa Express T/A,* 199 Upper Richmond Rd, West East Sheen, SW14 8QT (8876 2288).

TRAVEL *Goa Way (UK) Ltd,* 47 Dorset St, W1U 7ND (7224 3344).

Gogo

Gogo is a Bantuic language of Tanzania. The *Multilingual Capital* (2000) survey indicated that there were two **Gogo**-speaking pupils in London schools, both living in Lewisham.

Gokana

Gokana is a Benuic language of Nigeria. **Gokana** was found to be the language of 15 London schoolchildren by the *Multilingual Capital* (2000) survey, 12 of whom lived in Lewisham.

Gola

Gola is a Melic language spoken in Sierra Leone and Liberia. This was reported as the language of two London schoolchildren, living in Islington, by the *Multilingual Capital* (2000) survey.

Gonja

Gonja is an Aframic language spoken in Ghana. Although not mentioned in the *Multilingual Capital* (2000) survey, the presence of **Gonja**-speaking schoolchildren has been reported in London within the past decade.

Gora

Gora is a Benuic language spoken in Nigeria. The *Multilingual Capital* (2000) survey reported that there were two **Gora**-speaking pupils in London, both living in Barnet.

Greek

ACCOMMODATION *Constantia-Hellenic,* 5a Back La, NW3 1HL (7794 7493); *Greece Accommodation Direct,* 483 Green Lanes, N13 4BS (8886 1011).

ARTS *Theatro Technis,* 26 Crowndale Rd, NW1 (7387 6617).

ASSOCIATIONS *Greek and Cypriot Cultural Community,* Youth, Legal & Computer Centre, Arts & Media School, Turle Rd, N4 3LS (7263 6445); *Greek Parents Association,* c/o Maria Kasamias, 39 Winkfield Rd, N22 5RP (8889 1872) [languages: **Greek,** English]; *Society for the Promotion of Hellenic Studies,* Senate House, Malet St, WC1E 7HU (7862 8730); *Syndesmos Atomon Me Eidikes Anagkes* (Association for Greek and Greek Cypriot People with Special Needs), Cypriot Community Centre, Earlham Grove, Wood Green, London N22 5HJ (contact Mr J Kyriakides 7229 2244 for details; languages: **Greek**, English]; *Turkish and Greek Social Club,* 130 Clarence Rd, E5 8DY (8986 4341).

BARS & NIGHT-CLUBS *Greek Meze Bar*, 247 Upper St, N1 1RU (7288 2779); *Sappho Meze Bar*, 9 Clapham High St, SW4 7TS (7498 9009).

BUSINESS *Commercial Bank of Greece*, Prince Rupert Ho, 64 Queen St, EC4R 1AD (7329 1888); *Commercial Bank of Greece*, Pinners Hall, 105-108 Old Broad St, EC2N 1AP (7426 1400); *Hellenic Bank Ltd,* 406 Holloway Rd, N7 6PZ (7609 3606); *National Bank of Greece,* 7-9 Great Cumberland Pl, W1H 7BE (7724 9191); *National Bank of Greece,* 50 St Mary Axe, EC3A 8EL (7626 3222); *National Bank of Greece,* 208 Tottenham Court Rd, W1T 7LJ (7307 7100); *National Trust for Greece Ltd,* Albany House, 324-326 Regent St, W1R 5AA.

EDUCATION Mother tongue education for young children in Greek is available in at least 25 places in London – visit <www.resourceunit.com> for details. Few of these are included in the list of other Greek language educational facilities which is given below.

About 75 courses in modern Greek are provided by universities and local education authorities in London. There are also a few places which teach Classical Greek. For details, see *Floodlight* or visit <www.floodlight.co.uk>.

Bowes Greek School, Bowes Rd, N11 1AT (8368 5942); *Greek Educational Trust Ltd,* 3 Sylvan Av, Wood Green, N22 5HX; *Greek Parents Association,* 39 Winkfield Rd, N22 5RP (8889 1872); *Greek School of London,* 3 Pierrepoint Rd, Acton W3 9JR (8992 6156); *Greek School of London Nurses School,* 3 Pierrepoint Rd, W3 9JR (8896 3581); *Greek Secondary School of London,* Avenue Lodge, Bounds Green Rd, N22 7EU (8881 9320); *Hellenic College of London,* 67 Pont St, SW1X 0BD (7581 5044); *Hellenic College Nursery of St Michael,* Holy Cross & St Michaels Church, Golders Green Rd, NW11 8HJ (8455 8511); *St Andrews Greek School,* 122 Kentish Town Rd, NW1 9JJ (7485 0198).

FREIGHT *Anglo Greek (UK) Ltd,* 18 Eastbury Rd, E6 6LP (7474 3499); *Greek Shipping Committee,* 6 Middlesex St, E1 7EP (7247 3773); *Greek Shipping Co-operation Committee,* Baltic Exchange Bldgs, 38 St Mary Axe, EC3A 8BH (7626 4545).

GOVERNMENT *Consulate General of Greece,* 1a Holland Park, W11 3TP (7221 6467); *Embassy of Greece,* 1a Holland Park, W11 3TP (7229 3850).

LANGUAGE Greek has about 12m speakers world-wide and its own alphabetic script. The *Multilingual Capital* (2000) survey reported that there were 6,347 **Greek**-speaking London school-children of whom 1,932 were in Enfield. The distribution of **Greek**-speaking schoolchildren across London can be seen at <www.global-london.com/gallery> on Map 14.

MEDIA & INFORMATION *Greek Publishing (UK) Ltd,* Flat 1, 35 Grafton Way, W1P 5LA; *Hellenic TV,* Television Ho, 50 Clarendon Rd, N8 0DJ (8292 7037); *London Greek Radio Ltd,* Florentia Village, Vale Rd, N4 1PP (8800 8001); *London Greek Television,* Progress Ho, Clarendon Rd, N8 0DJ (8888 2808); *Papyrus Greek Press Agents,* 569 Green Lanes N8 0RL (8348 5240); *Parikiaki Haravgi (Greek Language Newspaper),* 534a Holloway Rd, N7 6JP (7272 6777); *London Greek Radio* [103.3], Florentia Village, Vale Rd, N4 1TD (8800 8001).

RELIGION

Barnet *Holy Cross & St Michaels Greek Church,* Golders Green Rd, NW11 (8455 7510).

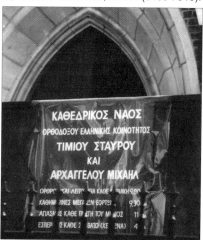

Camden *All Saints Greek Orthodox Church,* Camden St, NW1 0JA (7485 2149); *St Andrews Greek Orthodox Cathedral,* Kentish Town Rd, NW1 9QA (7485 6385).

Croydon *Greek Orthodox Church,* 69a Westow St, SE19 3RW (8653 6824).

Enfield *St Demetrios Greek Orthodox Church,* Logan Rd, N9 0LP (8803 4411); **Haringey:** *St Barnabas Greek Orthodox Church,* Finsbury Rd, N22 8PA (8889 1122); *St John the Baptist Greek Church,* Wightman Rd, N8 0LY (8348 7104); *St Mary's Greek Orthodox Cathedral,* 22 Trinity Rd, N22 8LB (8888 2295);

Hackney *Greek Orthodox Church of St John the Theologian,* 184 Mare St, E8 3RD (8985 5803).

Haringey *Community Of St Barnabas Greek Orthodox Church,* Finsbury Rd, Wood Green, N22 8PA (8889 2295); *St. John The Baptist Greek Church,* Wightman Rd, N8 0LY (8348 3158).

Hammersmith & Fulham *Greek Orthodox Church of St. Nicholas,* Godolphin Rd, W12 8JW (8743 3968); **Harrow:** *Greek Orthodox Church of Panteleimon,* 660 Kenton Rd, HA3 9QN (8732 2833).

Islington *Greek Orthodox Church,* Westbourne Rd, N7 8AB (7609 7020).

Kingston *St George Greek Orthodox Church,* Borough Rd, Kingston Upon Thames, KT2 6BD (8546 9269).

Lambeth *St Mary's Greek Orthodox Church,* 305 Camberwell New Rd, SE5 0TF (7703 0137).

Newham *St. Lazarus & St. Andrews Greek Orthodox Church,* Rutland Rd, E7 8PH (8472 2075).

Waltham Forest *St Eleftherios Greek Orthodox Church,* Ruckholt Rd, E10 5NT (8539 1425).

Wandsworth *St Nectarious Church,* 19 Wycliffe Rd, SW11 5QR (7228 4278).

Westminster *Greek Cathedral,* Moscow Rd, W2 4LQ (7229 7260); *Greek Orthodox Archdiocese of Great Britain,* 5 Craven Hill, W2 3EN (7723 4787).

RESTAURANTS

East Central *Kolossi Grill,* 56-60 Rosebery Ave, EC1R 4RR (7278 5758).

South West 1 *Psistaria,* 82 Wilton Rd, SW1V 1DL (7821 7504).

West 1 *Anemos,* 17 Percy St, W1P 9FE (7580 5907); *Apollonia,* 17a Percy St, W1P 9FE (7580 5907); *Café Greco,* 18 Charlotte St, W1P 1HJ (7436 7411); *Cleopatra,* 56 Maple St, W1T 6HW (7580 4819); *Cosmas Tavern,* 29 Goodge St, W1P 1FD (7636 1877); *Dionysus,* 3-5 Oxford St, W1R 1RF (7434 4204); *Elysée,* 13 Percy St, W1P 9FD (7580 3988); *Four Lanterns,* 96 Cleveland St, W1P 5DP (7387 0704); *Hellenic,* 30 Thayer St, W1U 2QW (7935 1257); *Jimmy's,* 23a Frith St, W1V 5TS (7437 9521); *Karizma,* 43 Crawford St, W1H 1HA (7724 8228); *Mr C,* 49 Tottenham Court Rd, W1P 9RE (7323 1017);

West Central *Farm House Table,* 190 Shaftesbury Ave, WC2H 8JL (7836 2652); *Greek Gods Taverna,* 6 Maiden La, Covent Garden, WC2E (7836 6578); *Kantara Taverna,* 190 Shaftesbury Av, WC2H 8JL (7836 1149); *Konaki,* 5 Coptic St, WC1A 1NH (7580 9730); *Yialousa Greek Taverna,* 18 Woburn Pl, WC1H 0LU (7837 4748).

Barnet *Jack's Greek Restaurant & Nightclub,* 43 Friern Barnet Rd Southgate, N11 1ND (8368 5693); *Onassis Restaurant & Take Away,* 1282 High Rd, N20 9HH (8445 2817); *Sunset,* 22 Ballards La, N3 2BJ (8346 3938);

Brent *D & G,* 2-6 Station Pde, Cricklewood, NW2 4NH (8450 6166); *Eagles,* 1-6 Glengall Rd, Kilburn, NW6 7EP (7461 0330);

Bromley *Grapevine Greek Taverna,* 24 Kingsway, West Wickham, BR4 9JG (8462 9434);

Camden *Andy's Taverna,* 81-81a Bayham St, NW1 0AG (7485 9718); *Artemis,* 327 Euston Rd, NW1 3AD (7388 7565); *Bacchus Greek Taverna,* 37 Heath St, NW3 6TR (7435 1855); *Cafe Corfu,* 7 Pratt St, NW1 0AE (7267 8088); *Daphne,* 83 Bayham St, Camden Town NW1 0AG (7267 7322); *Gemini,* 94 Camden Rd, NW1 9EA (7485 1127); *Karavas,* 87 Plender St, NW1 0JN (7388 4121); *Lemonia,* 89 Regents Park Rd, NW1 8UY (7586 7454); *Marios,* 153-155 Broadhurst Gdns, NW6 3AU (7625 5827); *Nontas,* 14-16 Camden High St, NW1 0JH (7387 1380); *Roullas,* 98 Arlington Rd, NW1 7HT (7388 4888);

Croydon *Aphrodite Greek Taverna,* 19 Westow St, SE19 3RY (8653 9895); *Dionysos,* Station Parade, Sanderstead Rd, CR2 0PH (8651 5445).

Ealing *Acropolis*, 15-16 The Broadway, Gunnersbury La, W3 8HR (8992 1997); *Lantern Taverna*, 5 Grosvenor Pde, W5 3NN (8992 4267); *Pandora*, 86 Northfield Ave, W13 9RR (8567 5953); *Retsina & Mousaka*, 7-8 Culmington Parade, Uxbridge Rd, W13 9BD (8567 7165); *Wine & Mousaka*, 30 Haven Green, W5 2NY (8997 0287).

Enfield *Babinondas*, 598 Green Lanes, N13 5RY (8886 1010); *Fanari*, 62 Aldermans Hill, N13 4PP (8882 8085); *Greek Touch*, 757 Green Lanes, N21 3SA (8364 1144); *La Creveppe Restaurant & Greek Taverna*, 135 Chase Side, EN2 0PN (8363 4452); *Pappa's the Greek House*, 396 Green Lanes, N13 5PD (8245 6095); *Sirtaki Taverna*, 161-163 Bramley Rd, Southgate, N14 4XA (8367 1100); *Taste of Greek*, 414 Green Lanes, N13 5PB (8886 2044); *To Spitiko*, 43 Green Lanes, N13 4TN (8365 7994); *Trios*, 248 Green Lanes, N13 5TU (8886 2985); *Zorba's*, 29 Green Lanes, N13 4TN (8881 3073).

Hackney *Real Greek*, 15 Hoxton Market, N1 6HG (7739 8212); *Zoazan*, 38 Shacklewell La, E8 2EZ (7254 0917).

Hammersmith & Fulham *Bacchus Greek Taverna*, 16 Jerdan Pl, SW6 1BH (7381 1144); *Vine Leaves Taverna*, 71 Uxbridge Rd, W12 8NR (8749 0325).

Haringey: *Crete*, 291 Hermitage Rd, N4 1NT (8376 1780); *Paneri*, 340 High Rd, Wood Green, N22 4JW (8888 3111); *Zeus Greek Banqueting*, 9a The Broadway, High Rd, N22 6DS (8888 0202).

Harrow: *Acropolis*, 2 High St, Harrow, HA3 7AA (8427 1802); *Greek Taverna*, 434 Rayners La, Pinner, HA5 5DX (8868 2723); *Van Antonis*, 254 Uxbridge Rd, Pinner, HA5 4HS (8428 0066).

Hounslow *Kalamari*, 4 Chiswick High Rd, W4 1TH (8994 4727); *Kleftiko*, 293 Chiswick High Rd, W4 4HH (8994 0305); *Plaka*, Odeon Parade, London Rd, Isleworth, TW7 4DE (8560 6900).

Islington: *Greek Garden*, 41 Bavaria Rd, N19 4EU (7561 9376); *Olive Tree Greek Taverna*, 177a/b Blackstock Rd, N5 2LL (7503 5466); *Orexi*, 236 Hornsey Rd, N7 7LL (7607 7098); *Paradise*, 129 Holloway Rd, N7 8LT (7607 2886); *Ta Dilina*, 122 Junction Rd, N19 5LB (7272 0318); *Tavros Taverna*, 156 Seven Sisters Rd, N7 7PL (7281 5231); *Wild Track Greek Taverna*, 7 Hercules St, N7 6AT (7263 7000).

Kensington *Aurum*, 7 Ladbroke Rd, Notting Hill W11 3PA (7727 9720); *Cafe O Ltd*, 163 Draycott Ave, Chelsea SW3 3AJ (7584 5950); *Costas Grill*, 14 Hillgate St, Kensington W8 7SR (7229 3794); *Kleftiko*, 186 Holland Park Ave, W11 4UJ (7603 0807); *Mediterranean Greek Taverna*, 308 Earls Court Rd, SW5 9BA (7373 5012).

Lambeth *Athenian*, 27 Streatham High Rd, SW16 1DS (8769 0860); *Neraida*, 1511 London Rd, SW16 4AE (8764 6725).

Merton *Stage Door Steak House & Greek Taverna*, 92 The Broadway, SW19 1RH (8543 8128); *Village Taverna*, 28 Ridgway, SW19 4QW

(8946 4840); *Zorba's Greek Taverna*, 138 Merton Rd, Wimbledon SW19 1EH (8543 4141).

Richmond *Orpheus Taverna*, 369 Richmond Rd, Twickenham, TW1 2EJ (8892 3103).

Southwark *Lemon Grove*, 58a Camberwell Church St, SE5 8QZ (7703 0224); *Vineyard Greek Taverna*, 3-5 Camberwell Grove, SE5 8JA (7703 2131).

Sutton *Greek Taverna*, 13 Green Wrythe Lane, Carshalton, SM5 2DS (8647 9207).

Waltham Forest *Corfu Greek Taverna*, 417 Lea Bridge Rd, E10 7EA (8539 2447); *Saray Kebab House*, 313 Lea Bridge Rd, E10 7NE (8539 6331).

Wandsworth *Vine Leas*, 44 Northcote Rd, SW11 1NZ (7228 3309).

Westminster *Angelos*, 78 Westbourne Grove, W2 5RT (7221 8843); *Aphrodite Taverna*, 15 Hereford Rd, W2 4AB (7229 2206); *Athens Taverna T/A*, 11 Craven Rd, Bayswater W2 3BP (7706 8886); *Greek Valley*, 130 Boundary Rd, NW8 0RH (7624 3217); *Kalamaras* [organic food], 66 Inverness Mews, W2 3JQ (7727 5082); *Le Pamelco*, 36 Leinster Terrace, W2 3ET (7262 5358); *Niki Taverna*, 15-16 London St, W2 1HL (7262 4628); *Santorini Taverna*, 10-12 Moscow Rd, W2 4BT (7727 7112); *Tsiakkos & Charcoal*, 5 Marylands Rd, W9 2DU (7286 7896); *Xios*, 47 Moscow Rd, W2 4AH (7243 0606); *Zorba Greek Kebab Taverna*, 35-36 Leinster Terrace, W2 3ET (7262 5358).

SHOPS

Books *Greek Book Shop*, 57a Nether St, N12 7NP (8446 1985); *Greek Bookshop - Zeno Booksellers*, 6 Denmark St, WC2H (8882 1910); PO Box 28283, Palmers Green, N13 5ZG (8882 1910); *Hellenic Book Service*, 91 Fortess Rd, NW5 1AG (7267 9499).

Drinks *Dionysus Greek Wines & Spirits Ltd*, 156b Burnt Oak Broadway, Edgware HA8 0AX; *Greek Wine & Meze Ltd*, 283 Green Lanes, N13 4XS.

Food *Andreas Delicatessen*, 18 Lordship Lane, SE22 (8299 2214); *Andreas Michli & Son*, 405-11 St Ann's Rd, N15 (8802 0188); *Athenian Grocery*, 16a Moscow Rd, W2 (7229 6280); *Golden Harvest Bakery*, 447 Green Lanes, N4 (8348 2799); *Greek Deli*, 65 The Cut, SE1 8LL (7928 9424); *Greek Food*, 14 Tulse Hill, SW2 2TP (8671 0803); *Papamakris*, Burleigh Parade, Burleigh Gdns, N14 5AD (8886 1020).

General *Greek Shop*, 6 Newburgh St, W1V 1LH (7437 1197); *Greek Shop*, 20-28 Hatton Wall, EC1N 8JH (7831 5631).

Music *Trehantiri Greek & Arabic Music*, 365-367 Green Lanes, N4 1DY (8802 6530).

Tailors *Chris Georgiou*, 120 King's Cross Rd, WC1 (7278 5837); *Nicolas Georgiou*, 23 Goodge St, W1 (7580 2372).

Video *Greek City Video*, 31 Green Lanes, Palmers Green, N13 4TN (8889 0186).

SPECIAL *Alpha Catering Equipment (Greek) Ltd*, 416 Beulah Hill, SE19 3HE (8766 0086); *Greek Connection 2000 Ltd (Icons)*, 48 Morton Way, N14 7HP (8886 8135); *Greek Marble*, 224 Battersea Park Rd, SW11 4ND (7622 6661); *Greek Marble*, 5 Cheval Ct, 335 Upper Richmond Rd, Putney, SW15 6UA (8789 4456); *Greek Marble Centre Ltd*, 1 Connaught Av, Chingford, E4 7AE (8524 0100); *Greek Marble International Ltd*, 16-17 Arches, Miles St, SW8 1RZ (7622 6661); *Hellenic Centre*, 16-18 Paddington St, W1U 5AS (7487 5060).

TRANSLATION *A P Theodosiou Euro-Greek Translations Ltd*, 27 Lascotts Rd, Wood Green N22 4JG (8881 2482); *Greek Institute*, 34 Bush Hill Rd, Winchmore Hill, N21 2DS (8360 7968); *Greek Language Services*, 9 Sussex Ring, Woodside Park, North Finchley, N12 7HU (8445 5131); *Greek Translation and Typesetting*, Berkeley Square Ho, Berkeley Sq, W1X 5LE (7409 0953); *Greek Translations*, 64 Queen St, EC4R 1AD (7248 8707); *Greek Translations*, 31 Athenaeum Rd, N20 9AL (8445 3324); *Translations from or into Greek*, 48 Rockley Ct, Rockley Rd, W14 0DB (7603 6060).

TRAVEL *Best of Greece (Travel) Ltd*, 283 Green Lanes, N13 4XS (7255 2320); *Direct Greece*, Oxford Ho, 182 Upper Richmond Rd, SW15 2SH (8785 4000); *Greece Accommodation Direct*, 1 5 Fairbourne Rd, N17 6TP (8808 5500); *Greek Centre for Travel & Holidays*, 8a Moscow Rd, W2 4BT (7792 8888); *Greek Contacts Ltd*, 30 Woodberry Ave, N21 3LD (8351 0821); *Greek Flight & Holiday Centre Ltd*, 162 Regent St, W1R 5TB (7734 0734); *Greek Islands Club*, 7 Upper Sq, Isleworth, TW7 7BJ (8232 9780); *Greek National Tourist Organisation*, 4 Conduit St, W1S 2DJ (7734 5997); *Greek Options Ltd*, Abford Ho, 15 Wilton Rd, SW1V 1LT (7233 5233); *Greek Tourism Travel Ltd*, 630 Linen Hall, 162-168 Regent St, W1B 5TG (7437 0218); *Swan Hellenic Cruises*, 77 New Oxford St, WC1A 1PP (7800 2200).

WELFARE *Greek Animal Rescue*, 69 Great North Way, Hendon NW4 1PT (8203 1956); *Greek Animal Welfare Fund*, 1-2 Castle La, SW1E 6DR (7828 9736); *Greek & Cypriot Cultural Community Youth, Legal & Computer Centre, Arts & Media School*, Turle Rd, N4 3LS (7263 6445); *Greek and Greek Cypriot Community of Enfield*, c/o Mrs. Litsa Worrall, Community Ho, 311 Fore St, Edmonton N9 0PZ (8373 6299) [languages: **Greek**, English]; *Older People's Club*, St Demetrios Church Hall, Town Rd/Logan Rd, London N9 0LP (details: 8292 8753) [languages: **Greek**, English].

Greek Cypriot

ASSOCIATIONS *Greek Cypriot Brotherhood*, Britannia Centre, Britannia Rd, N12 9RU (8445 7070); *Greek and Cypriot Cultural Community, Youth, Legal & Computer Centre, Arts & Media School*, Turle Rd, N4 3LS (7263 6445); *Greek Cypriot Community Centre Islington*, 7b Elthorne Rd, N19 4AJ (7272 4444); *Greek Cypriot Community Trust*, Britannia Rd, N12 9RU (8445 7070); *Greek Cypriot Womens Organization*, 9 Denmark Rd, N8 0DZ (8348 9011); *Hackney Greek Cypriot Educational Association*, Flat 2 Beech Ho, Lordship Rd, N16 0PU; *Haringey Greek Cypriot Women's Organisation*, Denmark Rd, N8 0DZ (8348 9011); *National Federation of Greek Cypriots*, Britannia Centre, Britannia Rd, North Finchley, N12 9RU (8445 9999); *Syndesmos Atomon Me Eidikes Anagkes* (Association for Greek and Greek Cypriot People with Special Needs), Cypriot Community Centre, Earlham Grove, Wood Green, London N22 5HJ (contact Mr J Kyriakides 7229 2244 for details; languages: **Greek**, English].

EDUCATION See under **Greek**.

GOVERNMENT See under **Cypriot**.

MEDIA & INFORMATION *Parikiaki Greek Cypriot Newspaper*, 534A Holloway Rd, Holloway, N7 6JP (7272 6777).

RELIGION See under **Cypriot**.

RESTAURANTS

Haringey *Troodos Taverna*, 179 Priory Rd, N8 8NB (8342 9188).

Lambeth *Paphos Greek Taverna*, 1443 London Rd, Norbury, SW16 4AQ (8764 9431).

Waltham Forest *Cypriana Charcoal Brazier*, 662 Lea Bridge Rd, Leyton, E10 6AP (8539 3466).

WELFARE *Arachne Greek Cypriot Womans Group*, 15 Hercules St, N7 6AT (7263 6261); *Cypriot Elderly & Disabled Group Enfield*, contact: Mr Costas Efthymiou, c/o Cypriot Pensioners Association, The Portacabin, Knights La, Edmonton N9 0PG (8803 5513) [languages: **Greek**, English]; *Greek & Cypriot Cultural Community Youth, Legal & Computer Centre, Arts & Media School*, Turle Rd, N4 3LS (7263 6445); *Greek and Greek Cypriot Community of Enfield*, c/o Mrs. Litsa Worrall, Community Ho, 311 Fore St, Edmonton N9 0PZ (8373 6299) [languages: **Greek**, English].

Grenadian

GOVERNMENT *High Commission for Grenada,* 1 Collingham Gdns, Earl's Court, SW5 0HW (7373 5164/7809).

TRAVEL *Grenada Board of Tourism,* 1 Battersea Church Rd, SW11 3LY (7771 7016); *Grenada & Carriacou Travel,* 81a Askew Rd, W12 9AH (8743 4518/7949).

Guarani

Guarani is the name of a group of Tupic languages spoken in several South American countries. Although not mentioned in the *Multilingual Capital* (2000) survey, this has recently been reported among the languages spoken by schoolchildren in Kensington & Chelsea.

Guatemalan

ASSOCIATIONS *Guatemalan Accompaniment Group,* 1a Waterlow Rd, Archway, N19 5NJ (7281 4052); *Maya-Guatemalan Indian Centre,* 94a Wandsworth Bridge Rd, Fulham, SW6 2TF (7371 5291).

GOVERNMENT *Embassy of Guatemala,* 13 Fawcett St, SW10 9HN (7351 3042).

LANGUAGES *Spanish* is the official language but 40% of the population speak an **Amerindian** language (*Whitakers* 2000).

Guinean

GOVERNMENT *Consulate of the Republic of Guinea,* 20 Upper Grosvenor St, W1X 9PB (7409 3279).

LANGUAGES The most important indigenous languages of Guinea are **Fula** (40%), several **Manding** languages (collectively about 41%), and **Kisi** (6%; figures from Mann & Dalby 1987). The official language is French.

Guinea-Bissauan

GOVERNMENT *Consulate General of the Republic of Guinea Bissau,* 8 Palace Gate, Kensington W8 5NF (7589 5253).

LANGUAGES About 20 languages are spoken in Guinea-Bissau, of which only Balanta and **Fula** are the first languages of more than 20% of the population. However, Kriol **(Portuguese Creole)** is spoken as a second or additional language by almost everyone and **Portuguese** has official status.

Gujarati

ASSOCIATIONS *"Deep" Indian 50+ Club* [Enfield] (contact: Mrs G Merchant 8245 0724) [languages: Gujarati, Hindi, Punjabi; activities include reflexology, yoga and swimming]; *Gujarat Welfare Association,* 141 Plashet Rd, E13 0RA (8552 0525).

BUSINESS Many Gujarati-owner businesses are included under **Indian BUSINESS.**

EDUCATION More than 20 places in London provide mother tongue education for young children in *Gujarati* – visit <www.resourceunit.com> for full details.

Courses in *Gujarati* for adults are provided by several local education authorities in London (see <www.floodlight.co.uk> for details) and by *SOAS Language Centre* (7898 4888).

HEALTH & BEAUTY General information on cancer is available at *Asian Cancer Information Line* in Gujarati - freephone (08088 080000).

Leaflets on Caring for Dementia are available in Gujarati from the *Alzheimer's Disease Society,* Gordon Ho, 10 Greencoat Pl, SW1P 1PH (7306 0606).

Enfield Saheli, Community House, 311 Fore Street, Edmonton N9 0PZ [advice for Asian women on legal matters (8373 6218), mental health (8373 6220), general (8373 6219); languages: **Gujarati, Hindi, Punjabi, Urdu,** English].

LANGUAGE *Gujarati* is an **Indic** language spoken in the Indian state of Gujarat written in its own semi-syllabic script. In world terms, it ranks 27th with some 45m speakers. In London, *Gujarati* ranks 4th among schoolchildren as the language of 26,761 pupils (*Multilingual Capital* 2000). For details of the distribution of *Gujarati*-speaking pupils across London, see Map 15 at <www.global-london.com/gallery>.

LEGAL *Enfield Saheli,* Community House, 311 Fore Street, Edmonton N9 0PZ [advice for Asian women on legal matters (8373 6218), mental health (8373 6220), general (8373 6219); languages: **Gujarati, Hindi, Punjabi, Urdu,** English].

MEDIA & INFORMATION *Garavi Gujarat Newsweekly,* 1 Silex St, SE1 0DW (7928 1234); *Gujarat Samachar Publications Ltd,* 8 Coronet St, N1 6HD (7729 5453); *Gujarat Samachar Publications Ltd,* 14 Umberston St, E1 1PY (7488 0988); *Sunrise Radio Ltd,* Sunrise Ho, Sunrise Rd, Southall, UB2 4AU (8574 6666) [broadcasting in Gujarati 23.00 - 00.00 daily].

RELIGION *Darji Mitra Mandal of the UK,* The Darji Pavilion, Oakthorpe Road, Palmers Green N13 5HY (contact: Mr Raman V Tailor 8361 5981) [languages: **Gujarati, Hindi, Swahili,** English].

RESTAURANTS

Newham *Gujarat Tandoori Restaurant,* 215 Plashet Rd, Plaistow E13 0QU (8471 2133).

WELFARE *Asian Culture and Welfare Centre* [Enfield] (8363 5693) [languages used: **Gujarati, Hindi,** English]; *Enfield Asian Welfare Association,* 129-139 South St, Ponders End EN3 4RJ (8443 1197) [languages: **Bengali, Gujarati, Hindi, Punjabi, Urdu,** English]; *Enfield Saheli,* Community House, 311 Fore Street, Edmonton N9 0PZ [advice for Asian women on legal matters (8373 6218), mental health (8373 6220), general (8373 6219); languages: **Gujarati, Hindi, Punjabi, Urdu,** English]; *North London Muslim Welfare Association,* c/o Mr. Qureshi, 51 Northfield Rd, Enfield EN3 4BT (8804 1762) [phone for time of monthly meeting; languages: **Gujarati, Punjabi, Urdu,** English]; *Redbridge Gujarati Welfare Centre* within the

Methodist Church, Ilford La, Ilford IG1 2JZ (8270 2303); *Sangam Indian Elderly Ladies Group,* c/o Kamaljit Patti, Ruth Winston Activities and Resource Centre for Over 55s, 190 Green Lanes, Palmers Green N13 5UE (8886 5346) [Fridays 12.45 - 16.00; languages: *Gujarati,* Hindi, Punjabi].

Gulf

ACCOMMODATION *Al-Gulf,* 45 Queensway, W2 4QJ (7229 8945) [estate agents]; *Gulf Real Asset Management Ltd,* 140 Park La, W1Y 3AA (7499 9591).

BUSINESS *Anglo Gulf Agencies Ltd,* 72 Inverness Terrace, W2 3LB (7243 6181); *A S Gulf Services Ltd,* 10 Melrose Ave, SW16 4QU (8765 1105); *Gulf Consumer Goods Co Ltd,* Gulf Ho, Stephenson St, E16 4SA (7474 0177); *Gulf International Bank B S C,* 75 King William St, EC4N 7DX (7815 1000); *Gulf Oil (GB) Ltd,* Minoco Wharf, North Woolwich Rd, Canning Town E16 2BH (7473 9200).

EDUCATION *Gulf Centre for Strategic Studies Ltd,* 3rd & 4th fl, 5 Charterhouse Bldg, EC1M 7AN (7253 3805).

FREIGHT *Gulf Agencies,* 210 Edgware Rd, W2 (7724 6564); *Gulf Arab Express Ltd,* 280b Earls Court Rd, SW5 9AS (7912 0812); *Gulf Freight & Shipping,* 109 Gloucester Rd, SW7 4SS (7835 0566); *Yemen Gulf Line,* Prince Albert Ho, 2 Kingsmill Terrace, St John's Wood, NW8 6AA (7586 9571).

LEGAL *Gulf Legal Services Ltd,* 50 Victoria Embankment, EC4Y 0DX (7353 6304).

MEDIA & INFORMATION *Gulf Films International Ltd,* 73 Brook St, W1Y 1YE (7499 0636); *Gulf Media Services,* London Ho, 271-273 King St, Hammersmith W6 9LZ (8748 7014).

TRAVEL *Gulf Air,* 10 Albermarle St, W1S 4BL (7408 1717); *Gulf Travel,* 25 Henriques St, E1 1NB (7481 3166).

Gurenge

Gurenge (also called *Frafra*) is a Voltaic language spoken on the borders of Ghana and Burkina Faso. The *Multilingual Capital* (2000) survey noted the presence of one *Gurenge*-speaking schoolchild in Lambeth.

Gurkha

Gurkha refers to Nepalese recruits in the British Army. The word relates to their terms of employment and is not an ethnic term; Gurkhas come from various ethnic, linguistic and religious backgrounds within Nepal.

RESTAURANTS
West 1 *Gurkha Brasserie,* 23 Warren St, W1P 5DE (7383 4985).
Brent *Gurkha Village Nepalese T/A,* Empire Ho, Empire Way, Wembley HA9 0EW.
Croydon *Gurkha Spice,* 343 Brighton Rd, Croydon CR2 6EQ (8667 0711).

Ealing *Gurkha Nights,* 19 The Avenue, W13 8JR (8566 8591).
Hillingdon *Royal Gurkha Tandoori,* 7 Park La, Uxbridge UB9 6BJ (01895 825154).
Hounslow *Gurkha Tandoori,* 78 Bedfont La, Feltham TW14 9BP (8890 0099).
Wandsworth *Light of Gurkha T/A,* 88 Balham High Rd, Balham SW12 9AG (8673 4160).
WELFARE *Gurkha Welfare Trust,* PO Box 18215, 2nd fl, 1 Old St, EC1V 9XB (7251 5234).

Gurma

Gurma is a Voltaic language spoken in Burkina Faso, Niger, Togo and Benin. Four *Gurma*-speaking London schoolchildren were reported by the *Multilingual Capital* (2000) survey.

Guyanese

GOVERNMENT *Guyana High Commission,* 3 Palace Ct, W2 4LP (7229 7684)
RESTAURANTS *Guyanese & West Indian T/A,* 148 Plumstead Rd, SE18 7DY (8854 5115).

Gypsy

See under *Romani.*

H

Hahon

Hahon is a Solomonic language spoken in Papua New Guinea. One Hahon-speaking pupil in London (Brent) was identified by the *Multilingual Capital* (2000) survey.

Hainanese

Hainanese relates to the people, culture and language of Hainan, the large island off the coast of southern China.

LANGUAGE **Hainanese** is a variety of Chinese closely related to **Min-nan.**
RESTAURANTS
Barnet *Hainanese*, 63 Golders Green Rd, NW11 8EL (8455 0704).

Haitian

LANGUAGES The principal language is Haitian Creole, a **French Creole**. **French** is the first language of a minority of the population.
WELFARE *Haiti Support Group*, P O Box 29623, E9 7LX (8525 0456).

Hakka

Hakka is a Sinitic language with 35m speakers, mainly in China. It is written in the Chinese logographic script. Six London school-children were identified as speakers of **Hakka** in the *Multilingual Capital* (2000) survey.

Halal

Restaurants and shops specializing in Halal food are listed under **Muslim.**

Harari

Harari is a Semitic language spoken in and around Harar in Ethiopia. The *Multilingual Capital* (2000) survey reported that there were two **Harari**-speaking London school-children in Camden.

Hausa

EDUCATION Mother tongue education in **Hausa** is available for young children in four places in London – visit <www.resourceunit.com> for full details. Courses in **Hausa** for adults are available at *SOAS Language Centre* (7898 4888).

LANGUAGE *Hausa* is a Bauchic language spoken mainly in northern Nigeria (but also in Niger, Ghana, Benin, Cameroon, Chad and Sudan). The presence of 242 **Hausa**-speaking pupils in London was reported by the *Multilingual Capital* (2000) survey, of whom 94 were living in Ealing. The distribution of **Hausa**-speaking schoolchildren across London can be seen at <www.global-london.com/gallery> on Map 16.

Hawaiian

BUSINESS *Hawaii Exchange Co,* 6 Queensway, W2 3RX (7221 1585); *Hawaiian Pomade Company. Ltd,* Unit 1 Abercorn Trading Estate, Manor Farm Rd, Wembley HA0 1AN (8902 8924).
GOVERNMENT Hawaii is governed as one of the 50 states of the USA.
LANGUAGES Hawaiian is a Trans-Pacific language. The *Multilingual Capital* (2000) survey reported the presence of just one Hawaiian-speaking pupil in London (Ealing).
RESTAURANTS
Kingston *Blue Hawaii*, 2 Richmond Rd, Kingston Upon Thames KT2 5EB (8549 6989).
Lewisham *Hawaii Pizza Company*, 52 Bell Green, SE26 4PZ (8659 0999).
SPECIAL *Hawaiian Centre*, 42 Upper Berkeley St, W1H 7PL (7304 5730).
TRAVEL *Aloha Airlines of Hawaii,* 200 Buckingham Palace Rd, SW1W 9TA (7707 4584); *Hawaiian Dream Holidays,* Station Chambers, High St North, E6 1JE (8470 1181); *Hawaii Visitors Bureau*, PO Box 208, Sunbury on Thames TW16 5RJ (8941 4009).

Hebrew

EDUCATION Mother tongue education for young children in Modern **Hebrew** is available in Hackney – visit <www.resourceunit.com> for details. Courses in Modern Hebrew for adults are available at *SOAS Language Centre* (7898 4888) and are also provided by several London boroughs – see <www.floodlight.co.uk> for details. Details of courses in Biblical Hebrew can also be found at the same website.
Friends of the Hebrew University, 126 Albert St, NW1 7NE (7691 1500).
LANGUAGE **Hebrew** is a **Semitic** language with official status in Israel, written in its own consonantal script. The *Multilingual Capital* (2000) survey reported that there were 660 London schoolchildren from Hebrew-speaking homes, the great majority of whom live in the boroughs of Barnet and Hackney. (A map – Map 4 – showing the distribution of these children across London can be viewed at <www.global-london.com/gallery>) However, this survey relied mainly on figures from local authority schools and thus excluded **Hebrew**-speakers attending private schools.

MEDIA & INFORMATION *Haaretz,* 28a Park Hall Rd, N2 9PU (8883 9999) [dailly newspaper in *Hebrew* and English].

RELIGION *Union of Orthodox Hebrew Congregations,* 140 Stamford Hill, N16 6QT (8802 6226); *Waltham Forest Hebrew Congregation,* 140 Boundary Rd, E17 8LA (8509 0775).

SHOPS **Books:** *Aisenthal,* 11 Ashbourne Parade, Finchley Rd, NW11 0AD (8455 0501); *Emel Books,* 5-6 Star Mews, 52a Windus Rd, N16 6UP (8806 9970, fax 8806 9848); *Hebrew Books and Gifts,* 24 Amhurst Parade, Amhurst Park, N16 5AA (8802 0609, fax 8802 4567); *Jerusalem the Golden,* 146-148 Golders Green Rd, NW11 8HE (8455 4960) [Hebrew books, music, and videos]; *Jewish Memorial Council Bookshop,* 25-26 Enford St, W1H 2DD (7724 7778, fax 7706 1710); *Manor House Books,* 80 East End Rd, Finchley N3 2SY (8349 9484, fax 8346 7430); *Mesoiroh Seforim Bookshop,* 61 Oldhill St, N16 6LU (8809 4310).

SPECIAL *Hebrew National,* 1 Layton Rd, Brentford TW8 0PS (8847 5250).

TRANSLATION *Acuda Ltd,* 42-44 Carter La, EC4V 5EA (7236 3377); *Associated Translators,* 96 Kensington High St, W8 4SG (7937 7733); *Key Languages,* 16-18 Douglas St, SW1P 4PB (7630 6113).

Herero

Herero is a Bantuic language of Namibia (and also parts of Angola and Botswana). The *Multilingual Capital* (2000) survey reported the presence of two *Herero*-speaking schoolchildren in London.

Hesperonesic

The *Hesperonesic* languages, spoken mainly in Malaysia, Indonesia and the Philippines, include Tagalog among London's top 40 languages. A map – Map 17 – showing the distribution of the various *Hesperonesic* languages collectively across London can be viewed at <www.global-london.com/gallery>. Speakers of these languages are concentrated in the boroughs of Kensington & Chelsea and Westminster.

Hiligaynon

Hiligaynon (also known as *Ilonggo*) is a *Hesperonesic* language of the Philippines. The *Multilingual Capital* (2000) survey reported the presence of two *Hiligaynon*-speakers in Lewisham.

Hindi

ASSOCIATIONS *Darji Mitra Mandal of the UK,* The Darji Pavilion, Oakthorpe Road, Palmers Green N13 5HY (contact: Mr Raman V Tailor 8361 5981) [languages: *Gujarati, Hindi, Swahili,* English]; *"Deep" Indian 50+ Club* [Enfield] (contact: Mrs G Merchant 8245 0724) [languages: *Gujarati, Hindi, Punjabi;* activities include reflexology, yoga and swimming]; *Sangam Indian Elderly Ladies Group,* c/o Kamaljit Patti, Ruth Winston Activities and Resource Centre for Over 55s, 190 Green Lanes, Palmers Green N13 5UE (8886 5346) [Fridays 12.45 – 16.00; languages: *Gujarati, Hindi, Punjabi*].

EDUCATION Several places in London offer mother tongue education in *Hindi* for young children – visit <www.resourceunit.com> for details. Courses in Hindi for adults are available in London at a wide range of levels – see <www.floodlight.co.uk> for details.

HEALTH & BEAUTY Information on cancer in Hindi is available at *Asian Cancer Information Line* (08088 080000). An information leaflet in Hindi on breast cancer is available from the *Women's Nationwide Cancer Control Campaign,* 1st fl, Charity Ho, 14-15 Perseverence Works, EC2 8BD (7729 4688, fax 7613 0771).

Quitline, for help in stopping smoking, is available in Hindi at (0800 002 266).

Leaflets on Caring for Dementia are available in Hindi from the *Alzheimer's Disease Society,* Gordon Ho, 10 Greencoat Pl, SW1P 1PH (7306 0606).

LANGUAGE In slightly oversimplified terms, *Hindi* and *Urdu* can be considered varieties of a single *spoken* language, belonging to the *Indic* family, but as two separate *written* languages.

Hindi and *Urdu* – the latter is spoken in both India and Pakistan – are virtually indistinguishable in ordinary conversation, sharing the same basic vocabulary and grammar. However, the further one moves from ordinary conversation towards literary and scientific usage, the greater becomes the distinction between the two. *Hindi* draws on *Sanskrit* for such vocabulary whereas *Urdu* makes extensive use of *Arabic* and *Persian* words. As written languages, *Hindi* and *Urdu* are sharply distinguished by the fact that Hindi employs the Devanagari script while Urdu is written in an adaptation of the Arabic script.

Considered as a single *spoken* language, Hindi/Urdu ranks third in the world (after only Mandarin Chinese and English) with some 900m speakers in all, of whom this is the first language of about 550m (Dalby 1999-2000).

Although every local education authority in London records separate figures for Hindi and Urdu, the *Multilingual Capital* (2000) survey was primarily interested in *spoken* languages and thus combined these figures. Taken together, *Hindi* and *Urdu* emerged at the 5th most important language in London, spoken by 2.91% of pupils (26,122). It should, however, be added that the number of children reported for *Urdu* was almost ten times as many as that for *Hindi.* A map showing the distribution of *Hindi/Urdu*-speaking children across London can be viewed at <www.global-london.com/gallery> (Map 18).

MEDIA & INFORMATION *Amardeep Hindi Weekly,* 36 Trent Ave, W5 4TL (8840 3534); *Hindi Picture Ltd,* 19 Albany Rd, N4 4RR (8374 4333); *Spectrum Radio,* International Radio Centre, 4 Ingate Pl, SW8

3NS (7627 4433) [broadcasting in Hindi/Urdu 04.00 - 13.00 weekdays and 07.00 -12.00 Sat-Sun]; *Sunrise Radio Ltd*, Sunrise Ho,Sunrise Rd,Southall, UB2-4AU (8574-6666) [broadcasting in *Hindi/Urdu* from 01.00 - 21.00 daily].

RELIGION *Krishna Yoga Mandir*, c/o Pandit K C Krishnatreya, 61 Churchbury Rd, Enfield EN1 3HP (8363 9187) [*Hindi, Punjabi*, Sanskrit, English].

TRANSLATION *Way With Words Translation Services,* 4 Highwood Ct, 975 High Rd, N12 8QS (0800 917 4962, 8445 7911).

WELFARE *Asian Culture and Welfare Centre* [Enfield] (8363 5693) [languages: *Gujarati, Hindi,* English]; *Community Aid (Asian Project),* c/o Rina Choudhury, Ponders End Area Housing Office, Curlew Ho, 4 Napier Rd, Enfield EN3 4QW (8443 4361) [languages: *Bengali, Hindi, Urdu*, English]; *Enfield Asian Welfare Association,* 129-139 South St, Ponders End EN3 4RJ (8443 1197) [languages: *Bengali, Gujarati, Hindi, Punjabi, Urdu,* English]; *Enfield Saheli,* Community House, 311 Fore Street, Edmonton N9 0PZ [advice for Asian women on legal matters (8373 6218), mental health (8373 6220), general (8373 6219); languages: *Gujarati, Hindi, Punjabi, Urdu,* English].

Hindu

ASSOCIATIONS *Caribbean Hindu Society,* 16 Ostade Rd, SW2 2BB (8674 0755); *Hindu Cultural Society,* 321 Colney Hatch La, N11 3DH (8361 4484).

RELIGION *Greenwich Hindu Temple,* 63-67 Bannockburn Rd, Plumstead SE18 1ER (8854 4566); *Hindu Centre,* 7 Cedars Rd, E15 4NE (8534 8879); *Hindu Temple,* 22 King St, Southall UB2 4DA (8574 5276); *Hindu Temple Trust,* 17 Elmfield Rd, Southall UB2 5AJ (8813 8429); *Krishna Yoga Mandir,* c/o Pandit K C Krishnatreya, 61 Churchbury Rd, Enfield EN1 3HP (8363 9187) [*Hindi, Punjabi*, Sanskrit, English]; *London Sri Murugan Temple,* 78 Church Rd, Manor Park E12 6AF (8478 8433); *Mahalakshi Temple,* 272 High Street North, Manor Park E12 6SA (8552 5082); *Murugan Temple,* 200a Archway Rd, Highgate N6 5BA (8340 8582); *Overseas Bengali Association,* c/o Mr. Sukumar Mazumdar, 20 Orchard Ave, Southgate, N14 4ND (8886 4231) [*Hindu* religious matters; languages: *Bengali,* English]; *Radha Krishana Temple,* Iskon Centre, 10 Soho St W1V 5DA (7437 3662); *Radha Krishna Temple,* 33 Balham High Rd, SW12 9AL (8673 6437); *Shree Kutch Satsung Swaminarayan Temple,* Westfield La, Harrow HA3 9EA (8909 9899); *Shree Nathji Sanatan Hindu Mandir (Temple),* 159 Whipps Cross Rd, E11 1NP (8989 7539); *Shree Swaminarayan Temple,* 220-222 Willesden La, Cricklewood NW2 5RG (8459 4506); *S K S Swaminarayan Temple,* 22-24 Shaftesbury Rd, Forest Gate E7 8PF (8470 9375); *South East Hindu Association (Temple),* 5 Anglesea Ave, SE18 6EH (8854 4906); *Yagya Bhoomi Hindu Religious Services,* 179 Forest La, E7 9BB (8555 3539).

Hokkien

For *Hokkien,* see under **Min-nan.**

Honduran

GOVERNMENT *Honduras Consulate and Embassy of Honduras*,115 Gloucester Pl, W1U 6JZ (7486 4880).

LANGUAGES The principal language of Honduras is *Spanish.*

Hong Kong Chinese

ACCOMMODATION *Hong Kong International* [letting agents], Unit 6, Kentish Town Business Park, Regis Rd, NW5 3EW (7485 0517).

EDUCATION See under *Cantonese.*

GOVERNMENT Since 1997 Hong Kong has been governed as a Special Administrative Region of China.

LANGUAGE The principal language of Hong Kong is *Cantonese.*

RESTAURANTS *Oriental Hong Kong T/A,* 23a Ashfield Parade, Southgate N14 5EH.

TRAVEL *Hong Kong Tourist Association,* 6 Grafton St, W1X 3LB (7533 7100).

Horn of Africa

The *Horn of Africa* is a geographical term covering Eritrea, Ethiopia, Djibouti, and Somalia.

ASSOCIATIONS *Horn of Africa Community Group,* 190 Shepherds Bush Rd, Hammersmith W6 7NL (7371 6244).

RESTAURANTS
Brent *Horn of Africa,* 307 High Rd, NW10 2JT (8459 3868).

Tower Hamlets *Horn of Africa,* 114 Mile End Rd, E1 4UN (7790 1274).

WELFARE *Horn of Africa* [community centre], St Pauls Ct, Hammersmith & West London College, Gliddon Rd, West Kensington W14 9BL (8741 1119); *Horn of Africa Advice Centre,* Mount Park Rd, W5 2RS (8998 7634).

Hunanese

Hunanese relates to the province of Hunan in the south central part of China.

LANGUAGE *Hunanese* (also known as *Xiang*) is a Chinese language with some 45m speakers. Although this was not reported in the *Multilingual Capital* (2000) survey, the existence of the restaurant listed below suggests that there may be a few speakers of this in London.

RESTAURANTS
South West 1 *Hunan,* 51 Pimlico Rd, SW1 (7730 5712).

Hungarian

ASSOCIATIONS *Hungarian Senior Club Ltd,* 45-47 Cornhill, EC3V 3RH.

BUSINESS *Hungarian International Finance Ltd,* 9 King St, EC2V 8EA (7606 4107).

EDUCATION Mother tongue education in *Hungarian* is available at one place in London – visit <www.resourceunit.com> for details. Courses in Hungarian for adults are available at *SSEES* (7862 8561) and the *University of Westminster* (7911 5000) as well as by *Hungarian Language Services,* 11 Beverley Rd, Chiswick W4 2LL (8994 0517) and the *Russian Hungarian Language School,* 7 St Kilda's Rd, Harrow HA1 1QD (8930 9090).

GOVERNMENT *Embassy of the Republic of Hungary,* 35 Eaton Pl, SW1X 8BY (7235 5218) and 46 Eaton Pl, SW1X 8AW (7235 8767).

HEALTH & BEAUTY *Eva Magyar Health & Beauty Clinic,* 266 Hale La, Edgware HA8 8NP (8958 8351).

LANGUAGE *Hungarian* is a *Uralic* language with official status in Hungary. It is also spoken by minorities in neighbouring states and there are about 15m speakers in all. The *Multilingual Capital* (2000) survey reported that there were 384 *Hungarian*-speaking pupils in London of whom about 40% lived in Harrow.

RELIGION *Hungarian Reformed Church in the UK,* 17 St Dunstan's Rd, Hammersmith W6 8RD (8748 8858);

RESTAURANTS

West 1 *Gay Hussar,* 2 Greek St, W1V 5LA (7437 0973).

Barnet *The Old Europeans,* 106 High Rd, N2 (8883 3964).

SHOPS *Hungarian Food Centre,* 430 Finchley Rd, NW2 2HY (7431 8205); *Romis Hungarian Sandwich Shop,* 5 Turnham Green Terrace, Chiswick W4 1RG (8747 4001).

SPECIAL *Hungarian Cultural Centre,* 10 Maiden La, Covent Garden WC2E 7NA (7240 8448).

TRANSLATION *Hungarian Language Link,* 142 Wimbledon Park Rd, SW18 5UG (8871 4882); *Hungarian Language Services,* 11 Beverley Rd, W4 2LL (8994 0517); *Tramont Translation Management,* 57 Upper Park Rd, NW3 2UL (7692 6319; fax 7504 8638).

TRAVEL *Hungarian Air Tours,* Kent Ho, 87 Regent St W1R 7HF (7813 4973); *Hungarian National Tourist Offfice,* 46 Eaton Pl, SW1X 8AL (7823 1032); *Malev Hungarian Airlines plc,* 1st fl, 22-25a Sackville St, W1S 3DR *and* 10 Vigo St, W1X 1AJ (7439 0577); *Hungarian Travel Centre,* 145 Oxford St, W1R 1TB (7287 4939).

I

Iberian

Spain and Portugal together comprise the *Iberian* peninsula. See *Spanish* and *Portuguese,* respectively, for entries relating specifically to either of these languages and nationalities.

ACCOMMODATION *Iberian International Ltd* [overseas property], Riverbank Ho, Putney Bridge Approach, SW6 3JD (7384 1999).

BUSINESS *Iberian Carpets Ltd* [wholesale], Suite 32/34, Morley Ho, W1R5AB (7636 3326); *Iberian Link Engineering Services,* 35 Burrows Rd, NW10 5SL (8960 1459).

TRAVEL *Frantour Iberian Service Ltd,* 54 Wilton Rd, SW1V 1DE (7233 8660). [For the Spanish national airline called *Iberia,* see under *Spanish.*]

Ibibio

Ibibio is a Benuic language of Nigeria which is very closely related to *Efik.* The 2000 *Multilingual Capital* survey published combined figures for London schoolchildren speaking Efik or Ibibio – see *Efik* for details.

Icelandic

EDUCATION Courses in Icelandic are available at the *University College London Language Centre* (7679 7722).

GOVERMENT *Embassy of Iceland,* 2a Hans St, SW1X 0NJ (7259 3999).

LANGUAGE *Icelandic* is a *Germanic* language with official status in Iceland. It is related to Norwegian and other Scandinavian languages. The *Multilingual Capital* (2000) survey identified 14 *Icelandic*-speaking pupils in London.

TRANSLATION *Tramont Translation Management,* 57 Upper Park Rd, NW3 2UL (7692 6319; fax 7504 8638).

TRAVEL *Iceland Tourist Information Bureau,* 172 Tottenham Court Rd, W1P 0LY (7388 7550).

Idoma

Idoma is a Benuic language of Nigeria. The *Multilingual Capital* (2000) survey reported the presence of 32 *Idoma*-speaking pupils in London schools.

Idon

Idon is a Benuic language of Nigeria. Although no speakers of this were found in the *Multilingual Capital* (2000) survey, a few have been reported in some London boroughs within the past decade.

Igala

Igala is a Benuic language of Nigeria which is closely related to *Yoruba*. The presence of five *Igala*-speaking pupils in Ealing was reported in the *Multilingual Capital* (2000) survey.

Igbira

Igbira is an alternative name for **Ebira**; see under the latter spelling for further information.

Igbo

EDUCATION Mother tongue education in *Igbo* for young children is available in several places in London – visit <www.resourceunit.com> for full details. Courses in *Igbo* for adults are provided by *SOAS Language Centre* (7898 4888).

Igbo Tutorial School, 91 Brownlow Rd, Friern Barnet N11 2BN.

LANGUAGE *Igbo* is a **Benuic** language of Nigeria where it is spoken by some 19m people. A total of 1 993 *Igbo*-speaking pupils in London schools was reported by the *Multilingual Capital* (2000) survey, of whom the largest number (343) lived in Lewisham.

WELFARE *Afro - Care Umbrella,* c/o Andy Hammond, 45 North Sq, Edmonton Green N9 0HY (8372 5528) [languages: **French, Igbo, Swahili,** English]; *Igbo Cultural & Support Network,* Level 4, 73 Peckham Rd, SE5 8UH (7703 3743).

Igede

Igede is a Benuic language of Nigeria, spoken in London by nine schoolchildren according to the *Multilingual Capital* (2000) survey.

Ijo

Ijo is a Deltic language of Nigeria. The *Multilingual Capital* (2000) survey reported that this was spoken by 33 schoolchildren in London.

Ikwere

Ikwere is a Benuic language of Nigeria, closely related to *Igbo*. In the *Multilingual Capital* (2000) survey, the presence of *Ikwere*-speaking schoolchildren was reported only in Southwark.

Ilocano

Ilocano is a Hesperonesic language spoken in the Philippines (Luzon island). The presence of 32 *Ilocano*-speaking London schoolchildren was reported by the *Multilingual Capital* (2000) survey.

Ilonggo

Ilonggo is an alternative name for **Hiligaynon** – see under the latter name for details.

Indian

ACCOMMODATION *Raj Bed & Breakfast,* 67 Highgate High St, N6 5JX (8348 8760); *Raj E Rajan* [estate agents], 55a The Broadway, Greenford UB6 9PN (8813 0793); *Raj Properties Ltd,* 12 Green St, Forest Gate, E7 8BZ (8472 6869); *Taj Hotels, Resorts & Palaces,* 45-51 Buckingham Gate, SW1E 6AF (7834 6655); *YMCA Indian Student Hostel,* 41 Fitzroy Sq, W1T 6AQ (7387 0411).

ARTS *Aarti Live Indian Musical Band,* 277 Ealing Rd, Wembley HA0 1EU (8998 3712); *Arthur Millner Ltd* [Indian & Islamic artists], 2 Campden St, W8 7EP (7229 3268); *Dostana Indian Videos,* 63a Plumstead High St, SE18 1SB (8854 2684); *Indian Music Promotions,* 88 Kingsfield Ave, Harrow HA2 6AS (8427 3530); *Kiranpal Singh* [classical Indian musician], 16 Meadow Rd, Southall UB1 2JE (07951 601236); *Surtaal School of Indian Music,* 30 Chalfont Green, Edmonton N9 9RF (8803 7536).

ASSOCIATIONS: *Association of Indian Banks in the UK,* 30b Commercial Rd, E1 1LN (7481 3823); *Brent Indian Association,* 116 Ealing Rd, Wembley HA0 4TH (8903 3019); *"Deep" Indian 50+ Club* [Enfield] (contact: Mrs G Merchant 8245 0724) [languages: **Gujarati, Hindi, Punjabi**; activities include reflexology, yoga and swimming]; *Indian Workers' Association,* 112a The Green, Southall, UB2 4BQ (8574 7283); *Indo Pakistan Cultural Centre,* 16-18 Hornsey Rd, N7 7BP (7609 4484) [counselling, advice]; *Institute of Indian Culture,* 4a Castletown Rd, W14 9HE (7381 3086).

BARS & NIGHT-CLUBS *Akbar,* 77 Dean St, W1 (7437 2525).

BUSINESS *Confederation of Indian Industry,* Centre Point, 103 New Oxford St, WC1A 1DU (7836 4121).

Finance *Bank of Baroda,* 31-32 King St, EC2V 8EN (7457 1524); *Bank of India,* Park Ho, 16 Finsbury Circus, EC2M 7UL (7628 3165); *Canara Bank,* Longbow Ho, 14-20 Chiswell St, EC1Y 4TW (7628 2187); *Kotak Mahindra (UK) Ltd* [securities brokers], 6th fl, Portsoken Ho, 155-157 Minories EC3N 1LS (7505 3950); *State Bank of India,* 630 Finchley Rd, Golder's Green, NW11 (8458 3856); *State Bank of India,* 15 King St, EC2V 8EA (7600 6444); *State Bank of India,* State Bank Ho, 1 Milk St, EC2P 2JP (7600 4535).

Insurance *Life Insurance Corporation of India,* York Ho, Empire Way, Wembley HA9 0PX (8902 5294); *New India Assurance Co Ltd,* 14 Fenchurch Ave, EC3M 5BS (7480 6626).

Information Technology *Apar Infotech,* 1000, Great West Rd, Brentford TWX 9HH (8261 4488); *BFL Software,* 220 Kingsley Rd, Hounslow TW3 4AR (8263 2701); *Binatone Telecom plc,* Unit 1, Ponders End Industrial Estate, East Duck Lees La,

Enfield EN3 7SP (8344 8888); *BIPS Infotech Limited*, 25 Continental Ho, 497 Sunsleigh Rd, Alperton HA0 4LY (8733 8268); *Birla Technologies Limited*, 3 fl, Hygeia Bldg, 66-68 College Rd, Harrow HA1 1BE (8324 1236); *Blue Star Infotech (UK) Limited*, 3rd fl, Station Ho, Masons Ave, Wealdstone HA3 5AH (8863 6888); *Bluestone Web Services Ltd*, 159 High St, Harrow HA3 5DX (8427 5339); *BPL Systems Europe Ltd*, Middlesex Ho, 130 College Rd, Harrow HA1 1BQ (8424 0764); *Business Development Systems Europe Incorporated Ltd*, 4th fl, Linen Hall, 162-168 Regent St, W1R 5TE (7663 9718); *CCS Technologies (UK) Ltd*, Canada Ho, Vancouver Suite, 272 Field End Rd, Eastcote HA4 9NA (8582 0261); *Chenab Information Technologies Pvt. Ltd*, The Point Business Centre, Wembley Point, 1 Harrow Rd, Wembley HA9 6DE (8900 5600); *Choice Solutions (UK) Ltd*, 140 The Broadway, Link Ho, Surbiton KT6 7JE (8338 6183); *CMC Informatics* UK (8847 1713); *Cognizant Technology Solutions*, Fulton Ho, Fulton Rd, Wembley HA9 0TF (8902 8998); *Contech Software Ltd*, Provident Ho, Burrell Row, High St, Beckenham, BR3 1AT (8249 6528); *Danford Solutions Ltd*, 26-34 Old St, EC1V 9QR (7251 9314); *Digital India*, Enterprise Ho, 4th fl, 190 High Holborn (7412 6331); *DSL Technologies plc*, Suite 258, 2 Lansdowne Row, Berkeley Sq, W1J 6HL (7413 9167); *E-Pro Info Systems Ltd*, Unit 7, Concord Business Centre, Concord Rd, Acton W3 0TJ (8992 3127); *ENG Software Private Ltd*, 117 The Chandlery, 50 Westminster Bridge Rd, SE1 7QY (7721 8781); *Eurolink Software Ltd*, 5 Dunraven St, W1Y 3FG (7491 3591); *GDI Soft (UK) Ltd*, 23 Clayton Rd, Hayes UB3 1AN (8817 1038); *Gem Group*, 9 Grove Wood Ct, 14 The Grove, Isleworth TW7 4JZ (8568 4392); *ICICI Infotech Service Ltd*, Suite G01, 118 Piccadilly, W1J 7NW (7569 6838); *Indusa Infotech UK Ltd*, 258 Belsize Rd, NW6 4BT (7316 1879); *Infosys Technologies Ltd*, 7-15 Emerald Ho, Lansdowne Rd, Croydon CR0 2BX (8774 3345); *Iridium Interactive (Europe) Ltd*, 30 Parklands Ct, Great West Rd, Hounslow TW5 9AU (8737 3904); *Kaashyap Radiant Systems Ltd*, Pentax Ho, South Hill Ave, Northolt Rd, HA2 0DU (8938 4651); *L&T Information Technology Ltd*, 11 Berkeley St, Mayfair W1X 6BU (7355 5011); *Majoris Systems P Ltd*, 52 Channel Cl, Heston, TW5 0PJ (8572 6339 / 8577 6299); *Megasoft Consultants Ltd*, 3 Clifford St, W1X 1RA (7440 2640); *Melstar UK Ltd* and *Melstar Information Technologies Ltd*, Fielden Ho, 28 London Bridge St, SE1 9SG (7357 6005); *Newgen Software Technologies Ltd*, 68 Lombard St, EC3V 9LJ (7868 1736); *Nucleus Software Offshore UK Ltd*, Suite 13, Continental Ho, 497 Sunleigh Rd, Alperton HA0 4LY (8733 8242); *Orient Information Technology Ltd*, Pentax Ho, Southhill Ave, HA2 0DU (8938 4691); *Patni Computer Systems (UK) Ltd*, Vistacentre, 50 Salisbury Rd, Hounslow TW4 6JQ (8538 0120); *Pentafour Software (UK) Ltd*, 15 Cambridge Ct, 210 Shepherd's Bush Rd, Hammersmith W6 7NJ (7602

9295); *Pipal Software Solutions Ltd*, 8 The Square, Stockley Park UB11 1FW (8610 6011); *Polaris Software Lab Ltd*, Osprey Ho, 20-24 Goodmayes Rd, Ilford IG3 9UN (8599 4441); *Ramco Systems*, 2 Gayton Rd, Harrow HA1 2XU (8901 4075); *Servion Global Solutions Ltd*, 2 Gayton Rd, Harrow HA1 2XU (8901 4010/7327); *Sonata Software Ltd*, 202 Pentax Ho, South Hill Ave, South Harrow HA2 0DU (8938 4611); *SQL Star International*, 1 Beckett's Wharf, Lower Teddington Rd, Hampton Wick, KT1 4ER (8977 3778); *SRA Systems Ltd*, 63 Worton Way, Isleworth TW7 4AY (8847 2604); *Starsearch Technologies Ltd*, Suite 69, Grosvenor Gdns Ho, SW1W 0BS (7233 6070); *Synergy Log-In Systems Ltd*, Suite 106, 102-116, Windmill Rd, Croydon CR0 2XQ (8665 4252); *Technology Promotion Ltd*, 117 The Chandley, 50 Westminster Bridge Rd, SE1 7QY (7721 8781/8783); *Trigent Software Ltd*, 107 Fleet St, EC4A 2AB (7936 9034); *Usha Beltron Ltd*, 47 St John's Wood High St, NW8 7NJ (7722 0225/5252); *Vajcom International*, 4 4 Golden Manor Drive, NW11 9HT (87319932); *Wipro Infotech Software Services*, 137 Euston Rd, NW1 2AA (7387 0606); *WorldTel Ltd*, Charles Ho, 5 Regent St, SW1Y 4LR (7389 0500).

Other *Apeejay Surrendra Group* [shipping and tea], 35 Portland Pl, W1N 3AG (7580 4656); *Bhagat Associates*, 17 Kenton Ct, 356 Kensington High St, W14 8NN (7602 9638); *Bharat Heavy Electrical Ltd*, 213A Station Rd, HA1 2TP (8424 0522); *BPL Eurotrade Ltd*, Middlesex Ho, 130 College Rd, Harrow HA1 1BQ (8426 0779); *Cobra Beer Ltd*, 21 The Coda Centre, 189 Munster Rd, Fulham SW6 6AW (7385 5300); *East Indian Produce Co.Ltd*, 53 Grosvenor St, W1K 3HU (7499 7311); *Hero Cycles Ltd*, 427 Great West Rd, Hounslow TW5 0BY (8572 6363); *Hindustan Aeronautics Ltd*, India Ho, Aldwych WC2B 4NA (7497 2360); *Indian Tea Co*, 111 Hampden Way, N14 5AU (8361 2388); *Mahindra Consulting*, Fulton Ho, Fulton Rd, Wembley HA9 0TF (0870 736 8880); *Mazagon Dock Ltd – Indian Frigate Project Office*, 602 India Ho, Aldwych WC2B 4NA (7836 7275); *Mukand International Ltd*, Suite 26, 88/90 Hatton Garden, EC1N 8PN (7405 1940); *Oberoi Group*, 1 Thames Pl, Lower Richmond Rd, SW15 1HF (8788 2070); *Ranbaxy (UK) Ltd* [pharmaceuticals], 6th fl, CP Ho, 97-107 Uxbridge Rd, Ealing W5 5TL (8280 1600); *Reliance Europe Ltd*, 20th fl, Tower 42, 25 Old Broad St, EC2N 1HQ (7256 8567); *Shipping Corporation of India*, 4th fl, Bel Court Ho, 11 Blomfield St, EC2M 7AY (7628 8988); *Sietal Ltd*, Cooper Ho, 316 Regents Park Rd, N3 2JX (8343 0099); *Siemiens*, Siemiens Ho, Windmill Rd, Sunbury on Thames TW16 7HS (01932 752993); *State Trading Corporation of India*, Rooms 255-256, Linen Hall, 162-168 Regent St, W1R 5TB (7734 9974); *Tata Ltd*, 18 Grosvenor Pl, SW1X 7HS (7235 8285); *Tea Board of India*, India Ho, Aldwych, WC2B 4NA (7240 2394); *Technoimpex (Agencies) Ltd*, 36 Preston Rd, E11 1NN (8989 9994); *Titan International Marketing Ltd*, 18 Grosvenor Pl, SW1X

7HS (7235 4291); *UTI International Ltd,* 15 King St, EC2V 8EA (7454 0415).

EDUCATION Courses in all the major languages of India are available in London at a wide range of levels – see under individual language names for details.

FREIGHT *TKM Overseas Transport Ltd,* 7 Chester Close, SW1X 7BE (7235 5965, 7245 6053).

GOVERNMENT *Indian High Commission,* India Ho, Aldwych, WC2B 4NA (7836 8484).

HEALTH & BEAUTY

Ayurvedic services *A M I Ayurvedic and Unani Health,* 1468 London Rd, Streatham SW16 4BU (8406 4440); *Ayurvedic Co of Great Britain,* 81 Wimpole St, W1G 9RF (7224 6070); *Ayurvedic Medical Association UK Ltd,* 2 Richborough Rd, Cricklewood NW2 3LU; *Kusal Ayurvedic Wellness Clinic,* 38 Store St, WC1E 7DB (7580 5193); *Mistry's Health Food Store* [Ayurvedic medicines], 16-18 Station Parade, NW2 4NH (7450 7002).

Hair *Bombay Gents Hair Stylists,* 15 The Arcade, Kingsbury Rd, NW9 9HL (8206 2303); *Bollywood Hair,* 58 Plumstead High St, SE18 (8317 3256); *Raj Hair Studio,* 432 Lady Margaret Rd, Southall UB1 2NN (8813 0368); *Raj Hair Studio,* Unit 7, Southall Broadway, UB1 1QB (8843 1812); *Yaseen Hairdressers,* 277 Bethnal Green Rd, E2 (7729 7526); *Yasin Hairdressers,* 209 Boundary Rd, E13 (8470 7455).

Massage *Indian Head Massage,* 115f Charlton Rd, Blackheath SE3 8TL (8293 5991); *M Adolphine Reiki & Indian Massage,* 84 Greatfields Drive, Uxbridge UB8 3QW (01895 850730).

Other *Aermid Health Care,* 78 Apsley Ho, 23-29 Finchley Rd, St John's Wood NW8 0NZ (7586 0435); *Naz Project* [information on sexually transmitted infections and discussion of other sexual health matters], Pallingswick Ho, 241 King St, W6 9LP (8741 1879); *Raj Nursing Home,* 31-35 Osterley Park Rd, Southall UB2 4BN (8574 1795); *Qualb Centre,* 17 Forest Drive West, E11 1JX (8558 6241) [counselling and complementary therapy for Asian people with mental health problems in Waltham Forest]; *Vijay Vithani Dental Practice,* 12 Joyce Dawson Way, Thamesmead SE28 8RA (8311 9400); *Vishvas Project* (Women's Mental Health), Confederation of Indian Organisations (UK), 5 Westminster Bridge Rd, SE1 7XW (7928 9889); *Women's Health and Family Services Outreach Guidance,* Room F6, The Brady Centre, 192 -196 Hanbury St, E1 5JX (7377 8725).

LANGUAGES *Hindi* and *English* have official status and more than a dozen other languages have official status within particular states. These include *Bengali, Gujarati, Kannada, Konkani, Malayalam, Marathi, Oriya, Punjabi, Tamil, Telugu,* and *Urdu*– see individual entries for these.

LEGAL *ALMT Legal (Indian Legal Consultants),* 15 Cambridge Ct, 210 Shepherds Bush Rd, Hammersmith, W6 7NJ (7610 4421); *Rajah* [solicitors], 502 High Rd, Wembley HA9 7BH (8903 5793); *Singhania & Co,* 24 Buckingham Gate, SW1E 6LB (7233 5511); *Yoga Rajah & Co* [solicitors], 168 Greenford Rd, Harrow HA1 3QZ (8423 4007); *Yoga Rajah & Co* [solicitors], 41 Lee High Rd, Lewisham, SE13 5NS (8852 9962); *Yoga Rajah & Co* [solicitors], 125b Mitcham Rd, TootingSW17 9PE (8672 1811); *Raj & Pillai* [solicitors], 86a High St, Southall UB1 3DB (8843 2240).

MEDIA & INFORMATION There are five television channels available in London by cable: *Asianet, B4U* (8963 8400)*, Star TV, Sony,* and *Zee TV. Sunrise Radio* broadcasts in *Hindi* and other Indian languages.

There are three weekly newspapers with a largely Indian, Pakistani, Bangladeshi and Sri Lankan readership. Each of these includes news items, sports, films, music, fashion, advertisements for jobs, and a lonely hearts column. These newspapers are (i) *Asian Express,* 302a Bow House, 153-159 Bow Rd, E3 2SE (8981 6333, fax 8981 6444); (ii) *Eastern Eye,* Ethnic Media Group, Unit 2, 65 Whitechapel Rd E1 1DU (7650 2000, fax 7650 2001); (iii) *India Weekly,* Ashoka Publications, 105 St John St. EC1M 4AS (7251 3290) <newsdesk@indiaweekly.co.uk>.

Niwala Indian, 182 Broadhurst Gdns, NW6 3AY [internet services] (7372 6075).

MOTORING *Raj Chohan* [motor vehicle repairs and modification], rear of 127-133 Station Rd, West Drayton UB7 7ND (01895 422560); *Raj School of Motoring,* 153 Lady Margaret Rd, Southall UB1 2PS (8571 1079).

RELIGION More than 80% of Indians are *Hindu* while more than 10% are *Muslim.* The remainder are *Christian, Sikh, Buddhist,* and *Jain.*

For Hindu temples, see under *Hindu*. For mosques, see under *Islamic.*

Indian Muslim Federation UK, The Hall, Trinity Close, E11 4RP (8558 6399); *St Gregorio's Indian Orthodox Church,* The Vicarage, 44 Newbury Rd, Ilford IG2 7HD (8599 3836).

RESTAURANTS (see also *Bengali, Goan, Gujarati, Kerala, Punjabi, South Indian*)

East Central *Bayleaf Indian Brasserie,* 33 Old Bailey, EC4M 7HS (7236 2440); *Bengal Tiger,* 62-66 Carter La, EC4V 5EA (7248 6361); *Bombay Break,* 505 Central Markets, Farringdon Rd, EC1A 9NL (7253 3094); *Cafe Lazeez,* 88 St John St, EC1M 4EH (7253 2224); *City Spice,* 4 New Bridge St, EC4V 6AA (7583 4673); *Eastcheap Tandoori,* 13 Eastcheap, EC3M 1BU (7626 1920); *Great Eastern Tandoori,* 107-109 Great Eastern St, EC2A 3JD (7336 0661); *Guardian Tandoori,* 50 Exmouth

Market, Clerkenwell EC1R 4QE (7833 3587); *Gulshan Tandoori,* 15 Exmouth Market, EC1R 4QD (7837 7437); *Haweli,* 19-21 Old St, EC1V 9HL (7490 2055); *India Raj,* 105a Minories, EC3N 1LA (7481 1022); *Lever Street Tandoori,* 1 Lever St, Clerkenwell EC1V 3QU (7253 3398); *Massala,* 5 Clerkenwell Rd, EC1M 5PA (7490 4468); *Matab's,* 76 Aldgate High St, EC3N 1BD (7481 4010); *Passage to India,* 107 Great Eastern St, EC2A 3JD (7336 0661); *Philpot Tandoori,* 9 Philpot La, EC3M 8AA (7283 6291); *Planters Inn,* 25 Great Tower St, EC3R 5AQ (7621 1214); *Rajasthan,* 49 Monument St, EC3R 8BU (7626 1920); *Raj Mahal,* 65 Farringdon Rd, EC1M 3JB (7405 7311); *Raj Tandoori,* 52 Cowcross St, Clerkenwell, EC1M 6BX (7253 3847); *Regency,* 96 Old St, EC1V 9AY (7336 8696); *Shimla Pinks,* 7-8 Bishopsgate Churchyard, EC2M 3TJ (7628 7888); *Smithfield Tandoori,* 4 Lindsey St, EC1A 9HP (7606 1652).

South East 1 *Bridge Tandoori,* 214 Tower Bridge Rd, Southwark, SE1 2UP (7357 7826); *Castle Tandoori,* Unit 200-201 Shopping Centre, Elephant & Castle SE1 6TE (7703 9130); *Grange T/A,* 129 Grange Rd, SE1 3AL (7231 1215); *Imperial Tandoori,* 48 Kennington Rd, SE1 7BL (7928 4153); *Indian Summer T/A,* 132 Weston St, SE1 4XE (7407 7474); *Ivory Arch Tandoori* [vegetarian], 80-82 Walworth Rd, SE1 6SW (7703 0182); *London Bridge Tandoori,* 14 Borough High St, Southwark, SE1 9QG (7407 2605); *Mayur Tandoori,* 225 Old Kent Rd, Southwark SE1 5LU (7394 1913); *Morley Tandoori,* 69 Morley St, SE1 7QZ (7401 8685); *Shahi Tandoori T/A,* 77 Grange Rd, Southwark, SE1 3BW (7231 5015); *Shakti,* 41 Tower Bridge Rd, Southwark, SE1 4TL (7403 5387); *Simply Indian,* 25 Tabard St, SE1 4LA (7407 5005); *Southbank Tandoori,* 39 The Cut, Southwark, SE1 8LF (7928 6127); *Thames Tandoori,* 79 Waterloo Rd, SE1 8UD (7928 3856); *Tower Tandoori,* 74-76 Tower Bridge Rd, Southwark SE1 4TP (7237 2247).

South West 1 *Bombay Curry,* 25 Churton St, SW1V 2LY (7821 8320); *Cinnamon Club,* Old Westminster Library, 30 Great Smith St, SW1 (7222 2555); *Great Eastern Tandoori,* 30 Winchester St, Pimlico SW1V 4NE (7828 3366); *Great India Tandoori,* 79 Lower Sloane St, Westminster SW1W 8DA (7730 5638); *Indian Diner,* 54 Rochester Row, SW1P 1JU (7834 5468); *Jomuna,* 74, Wilton Rd, SW1V 1DE (7828 7509); *Kundan,* 3 Horseferry Rd, SW1P 2AN (7834 3434); *Pimlico Tandoori,* 38 Moreton St, SW1V 2PB (7834 3375); *Standard Tandoori,* 54 Rochester Row SW1P 1JU (7834 5468); *Taste of Raj,* 278 Vauxhall Bridge Rd, SW1V 1BB (7828 9845); *Woodlands* [vegetarian], 37 Panton St, SW1Y 4EA (7839 7258).

West 1 *Amjadia Pak-Indian,* 15 Picton Pl, W1U 1BS (7935 0885); *Anjums,* 72, Shaftesbury Ave, W1D 6NA (7437 9171); *Delhi Brasserie,* 44 Frith St, W1V 5TE (7437 8261); *Golden Orient,* 61 Berwick St, W1V 3PA (7437 1817); *Govinda's* [vegetarian], 9-10 Soho St, W1D 3DL (7437 4928); *Indian Brasserie,* 18 Rupert St, W1D 6DF (7437 0344); *Lal Qila Tandoori,* 117 Tottenham Court Rd, W1P 9HL (7387 4570); *Lords,* 161 Whitfield St, W1T 5ER (7383 3010); *Maharaja Tandoori,* 14 Denman St, W1V 7RE (7437 4478); *Maharani,* 77 Berwick St, W1F 8TQ (7437 8568); *Mumbai Spice,* 4 Blenheim St, W1Y 9LB (7409 0300); *Neel Kamal,* 160 New Cavendish St, W1W 6YP (7580 6125); *New Great Indian Tandoori,* 22a Seymour Pl, W1H 5WH (7723 5166); *Piccadilly Tandoori,* 2 Denman St, W1V 7RH (7437 5350); *Porte des Indes,* 32 Bryanston St, W1 (7224 1144); *Raj Tandoori,* 72 Berwick St, W1V 3PE (7439 0035); *Red Fort,* 77 Dean St, W1 (7437 2115); *Regent Tandoori,* 10 Denman St, W1V 7RF (7434 1134); *Romna Indian Tandoori,* 123 Seymour Pl, W1H 5DJ (7723 7387); *Soho Curry,* 61 Rupert St, W1V 7HN (7734 2230); *Tagore Tandoori,* 2 White Horse St, W1Y 7LA (7493 0024); *Taj Mahal,* 25 New Quebec St, W1H 7DE (7723 2228); *Veeraswamy,* Victory Ho, 99-101 Regent St, W1R 8RS (7734 1401); *Yatra,* Dover St, W1 (7493 0200).

West Central *Akash,* 14-15 Irving St, WC2H 7AU (7930 0744); *Bhatti,* 37 Great Queen St, WC2 (7831 0817); *Chutney Raj,* 137 Grays Inn Rd, WC1X 8TZ (7831 1149); *Depa,* 4 Leigh St, WC1H 9EW (7387 0613); *Empress of India,* 15-18 Great Newport St, WC2H 7JE (7379 6330); *Euro Tandoori,* 325 Grays Inn Rd, Kings Cross WC1X 8PX (7833 4795); *Grand,* 6 New Row, WC2N 4LH (7240 0785); *Grand II,* 31 Villiers St, WC2N 6ND (7930 7663); *Hot Chilli,* 52 Tavistock Pl, WC1 (7713 0903); *Humaira,* 112 Judd St, WC1 (7278 6183); *Kings Cross Tandoori,* 341, Grays Inn Rd, WC1X 8PX (7278 0506); *Last Days of the Raj,* 22 Drury La, WC2B 5RH (7836 5705); *Mandeer* [vegetarian], 8 Bloomsbury Way, WC1 (7242 6202); *Maharaja of India,* 19a Charing Cross Rd, WC2H 0ES (7930 3044); *Mela,* 152 Shaftesbury Ave, WC2H 8HL (7836 8635); *Motijeel,* 53a Marchmont St, WC1N 1AP (7837 1038); *New Taj Mahal,* 119 Kings Cross Rd, WC1X 9NH (7713 1725); *Sitar,* 149 The Strand, WC2R 1JA (7836 3730); *Strand Tandoori,* 45 Bedford St, WC2E 9HA (7240 1333); *Taj Mahal,* 25 New Quebec St, W1H 7DE (7723 2228); *Tale of India,* 19 New Row, WC2N 4LA (7240 5348); *Tandoori King,* 25-27 Theobalds Rd, WC1X 8SP (7404 4486); *Tandoori Nights,* 35 Great Queen St, WC2B 5AA (7831 2558); *Taste of India,* 25 Catherine St, Covent Garden WC2B 5JS (7836 2538); *Woburn Tandoori,* 16 Woburn Walk, WC1H 0JL (7383 7957).

Barking & Dagenham *Farjhana T/A,* 62a Longbridge Rd, Barking IG11 8RT (8220 6770);

Junakee T/A, 23 London Rd, Barking IG11 8AA (8591 9661); Sonali T/A, 94 Longbridge Rd, Barking, IG11 8SF (8594 5522).

Barnet Agra Tandoori Ltd T/A, 96 Audley Rd, Hendon NW4 3HG; Ahmed Tandoori T/A, 153 Hale La, Edgware HA8 9QW (8959 0519); Avon Tandoori, 96 Audley Rd, Hendon NW4 3HG; Balti Tandoori, 120 Ballards La, Finchley Central N3 2DN (8343 2062); Chilli Raj T/A, 200 Brent St, Hendon NW4 1BE; Cove Tandoori, 96 Audley Rd, Hendon NW4 3HG; Curry Garden, 96 Audley Rd, Hendon NW4 3HG; Deena Tandoori, 97 Colney Hatch La, Muswell Hill N10 1LR (8444 5025); Delhi Brasserie, 96 Audley Rd, NW4 3HG; East End Tandoori, 138 East End Rd, East Finchley N2 0RZ (8442 1948); Khana, 241 Regents Park Rd, N3 3LA (8343 4999); Kipling's Tandoori, 13 Finchley La, Hendon NW4 1BN (8203 5396); Mill Hill Tandoori, 2 The Broadway, Mill Hill NW7 3LL (8959 1384); New Balti Tandoori, 22 North End Rd, Golders Green NW11 7PT (8458 3480); Palace Tandoori, 40 Grants Cl, Mill Hill NW7 1DD; Quality Tandoori, 138 High Rd East Finchley N2 9ED (8883 1557); Raj Balti, 7 Sheaveshill Parade, Sheaveshill Ave, Colindale NW9 6RS (8205 4549); Rajdoot T/A, 96 Audley Rd, Hendon NW4 3HG; Raj Mahal, 295a Hale Lane, Edgware, HA8 7AX; Raj Mahal, 224 Regents Park Rd, N3 3HP (8349 1615); Rani Vegetarian, 7 Long La, Finchley N3 2PR (8349 4386); Sitar Tandoori, 105 Brent St, Hendon NW4 2DX (8202 2783); Tandoori Club T/A, 433 Oakleigh Rd North, Whetstone, Totteridge N20 0RU (8361 7991); Taj Mahal T/A, 649c Watford Way, Apex Corner, Mill Hill, NW7 3JR (8906 2800); Tandoori Club T/A, 4a Broadfield Parade, Glengall Rd, Edgware HA8 8TD (8905 3233); Village Tandoori, 40 Grants Close, Mill Hill, NW7 1DD; Woodhouse Tandoori T/A, 219 Woodhouse Rd, North Finchley N12 9BD (8361 6878).

Bexley Taj Mahal, 6 Wilton Rd, SE2 9RH (8312 2646).

Brent Bonani Tandoori, 371-373 High Rd, Willesden NW10 2JR (8459 0923); Brent Tandoori, 24 High Rd, Willesden NW10 2QD (8459 0649); Chetnas Bhel Poori House, 420-422 High Rd, Wembley, HA9 6AH (8900 1466); Crescent Tandoori, 47 Cricklewood Broadway, Cricklewood, NW2 3JX (8450 1116); Dollis Hill Tandoori, 1c Humber Rd, Cricklewood NW2 6EG (82081145); Ganges, 769 Harrow Rd, Wembley HA0 2LW (8904 0011); Golden Crown Tandoori, 314 Preston Rd, HA3 0QH (8385 1001); Kasturi, 231 Kenton Rd, Kenton HA3 0HD (8907 7151); Khas Tandoori, 39 Chamberlayne Rd, NW10 3NB (8969 2537); Lahoria, 274 Kingsbury Rd, NW9 0BY (8206 1129); Kismet Tandoori, 26 Station Parade, Willesden Green NW2 4NH (8208 2232); Neasden Tandoori & T/A, 286 Neasden La, Willesden NW10 0AD (8830 9400); Palace Tandoori T/A, 42 Craven Park Rd, Harlesden NW10 4AE (8965 8244); Panshi Tandoori, 31 Malvern Rd, Kilburn NW6 5PS (7328 1509); Raj, 37 Chamberlayne Rd, Willesden NW10

3NB (8969 2543); Raj, 146 High St Harlesden, NW10 4SP (8965 6036); Raj Mahal T/A, 295a Hale La, HA8 7AX; Rickshaw T/A, 8 Chamberlayne Rd, Kensal Green, NW10 3JD (8969 3286); Ruhit's Indian Cuisine, 4 Sidmouth Parade, NW2 5HG (8830 4222); Satyam Sweet Mart T/A [vegetarian], 24 Queensbury Station Parade, HA8 (8952 3947); Spice of India Tandoori, 119 Wembley Park Drive, HA9 8HG (8902 1213); Surma Valley, 19 Wembley Hill Rd, Wembley HA9 8AF (8902 4337); Tandoori Express T/A, 16 Station Terrace, NW10 5RX (8960 5274); Tandoori Kitchen T/A, 104 Windermere Ave, Wembley HA9 8RB (8385 0801); Wembley Tandoori, 133 Wembley Park Drive, HA9 8HQ (8902 2243).

Bromley Balti Tandoori T/A, 85a Penge Rd, SE20 7UN (8676 8090); Belash Tandoori, 205 High St, Penge SE20 7PF (8778 6155); Eastern Eye Tandoori, 75 High St, Penge SE20 7HW (8776 8080); Mogul Tandoori, 17 Penge La, Penge SE20 7DU (8778 0757); Moonlight Tandoori & T/A, 49 Maple Rd, Penge SE20 8LA (8776 9594); Rajdoot, 75 High St, SE20 7HW (8776 8080).

Camden Aroma Spice, 98, Fleet Rd, NW3 2QX (7267 0444); Balti Tandoori, 299 Finchley Rd, Hampstead NW3 6DT (7794 8344); Belsize Tandoori, 58 Belsize La, Hampstead NW3 5AR (7794 0717); Bharat Tandoori, 23 Camden High St, NW1 7JE (7388 4553); Cafe Mumbai, 96 Cricklewood Broadway, NW2 3EL (8452 1211); Camden Tandoori, 114 Camden Rd, NW1 9EE (7485 6196); Chetna, 56 Chetwynd Rd, NW5 1DJ (7482 2833); Chutneys [vegetarian], 124 Drummond St, NW1 (7388 0604); Cinnamon Spice, 12-14 Glenworth St, NW1 5PG (7935 0212); Classic Tandoori, 218 Belsize Rd, Kilburn NW6 4DJ (7372 8828); Deedar Tandoori, 18 Haverstock Hill, Hampstead NW3 2BL (7485 7200); Diwana Bhel Poori House [vegetarian], 121-123 Drummond St, NW1 (7387 5556); Fleet Tandoori, 104 Fleet Rd, Hampstead NW3 2QX (7485 6402); Fortess Tandoori, 131 Fortess Rd, Kentish Town NW5 2HR (7267 0045); Grove Tandoori, 162 Agar Grove, NW1 9TY (7284 3198); Haandi Tandoori, 161 Drummond St, NW1 2PB (7383 4557); Khana, 68 Cricklewood Broadway, NW2 3EP (8452 4789); Maharani, 109 Camden High St, NW1 7JN (7387 6551); New Delhi, 13 New College Parade, NW3 5EP (7722 9976); Ravi Shankar, 133 Drummond St, NW1 (7388 6458) [vegetarian]; Shah Tandoori, 159 Drummond St, NW1 2PB (7383 5677); Shahbag Tandoori, 70 Rosslyn Hill, Hampstead NW3 1ND (7794 9959); Shiva, 81 Kentish Town Rd, NW1 8NY (7284 2061); Spice Plaza, 212 West End La, NW6 1UU (7794 0228); Surya [vegetarian], 59-61 Fortune Green Rd, West Hampstead NW6 1DR (7435 7486); Taj Mahal, 46 Rosslyn Hill, NW3 1NH (7435 1473); Tamanna Balti House, 161 Fortess Rd, NW5 2HR (7482 2700); Vhujon, 90 Fortune Green Rd, West Hampstead, NW6 1DS (7431 4802).

Croydon Akbar Tandoori, 1480b London Rd, Streatham SW16 4BT (8679 6234); British Raj

Tandoori, 1534 London Rd, Streatham SW16 4EU (8679 7700); *Kismet Tandoori*, 1 Commercial Bldgs, High St, South Norwood SE25 6EE (8771 7092); *Mirch Masala*, 1416 London Rd, Norbury SW16 4BZ (8679 1828); *Mumbai*, 226 Bensham Manor Rd, Thornton Heath, CR7 7AW (8683 1114); *Penge Tandoori*, 53 Penge Rd, South Norwood SE25 4EJ (8776 6428); *Rajah T/A*, 291 Northborough Rd, SW16 4TR (8764 5060); *Sali Tandoori T/A*, 25 Woodside Green, South Norwood SE25 5EY (8654 4100); *Santok Maa's*, 848 London Rd, Thornton Heath CR7 7PA (8665 0626); *Shahee Bhel Poori* [vegetarian], 1547 London Rd, Norbury SW16 4AD (8679 6275); *Shish Mahal*, 36 Westow Hill, SE19 1RX (8761 1154); *Sitar*, 4 Portland Rd, South Norwood, SE25 4PF (8654 4291).

Ealing *A1 Sweet Centre*, 29 King St, Southall UB1 (8571 2857); *Acton Tandoori*, 138 Churchfield Rd, W3 6BS (8992 4964/4583); *Agrabad*, 47 High St, W3 6ND (8992 9689); *Asian Tandoori*, 114-116 The Green, Southall UB2 4BQ (8574 2597); *Babu Tandoori Centre*, 156 The Broadway, Southall UB1 1NN (8574 5281); *Bhai Jan's Baltis*, 57 New Broadway, W5 5AH (8567 5577); *Balti & Tandoori World*, 185-187 The Broadway, Southall (8867 9991); *Chandni*, 131 Uxbridge Rd, W13 9AU (8840 6170); *Chandni*, 131 Uxbridge Rd, West Ealing, W13 9AU (8840 6170); *Clay Oven*, 13 The Mall, W5 2PJ (8840 0313); *Ealing Balti House*, 150 Broadway, W13 0TL (8810 0320); *Ealing Cottage*, 76 Uxbridge Rd, W13 8RA (8567 5550); *Gangadin*, 28 Western Ave, W3 7TZ (8749 6625); *Gitanjli Mayfair*, 18-19 The Mall, W5 2PJ (8810 0006); *Golden Tandoori*, 122 Churchfield Rd, W3 6AH (8993 4532); *Greenford Tandoori*, 311 Ruislip Rd East, Greenford UB6 9BH (8578 5984); *Haweli*, 129 Uxbridge Rd, West Ealing W13 9AU (8579 1973); *Jubraj*, 7 Park Parade, Gunnersbury Ave, Ealing W3 9BD (8993 8884); *Laguna*, 123 Uxbridge Rd, W13 9NB (8579 9992); *L'Orient*, 9 Hanger Green, W5 3EL (8991 1966); *Meghna Tandoori*, 2 Abbey Parade, W5 1EE (8991 2122); *Monty's*, 54 Northfield Ave, W13 9RR (8567 6281); *Monty's*, 224 South Ealing Rd, W5 4RP (8568 3162); *Monty's*, 1 The Mall, W5 2PJ (8567 5802); *Moti-Mahal*, 94 The Broadway, Southall, UB1 1QF (8571 9443); *Northolt Indian T/A*, 260 Church Rd, Northolt UB5 5AW (8841 0013); *Omar Khayam*, 1 Grosvenor Parade, Uxbridge Rd, W5 3NN (8993 8491); *Pinner Tandoori T/A*, 2a Odeon Parade, Sudbury Heights Ave, Greenford UB6 0NA; *Poonam Tandoori*, 78 Western Rd, Southall UB2 5DZ (8571 4934); *Royal Tandoori*, 23 Boston Parade, Boston Rd, W7 2DG (8840 1226); *Sakonis* [vegetarian], 127-129 Ealing Rd, HA0 4BP (8903 9601); *Samrat*, 52 Pitshanger La, Ealing W5 1QY (8991 0300); *Shahee Tandoori*, 241 The Broadway, Southall UB1 1ND (8574 9203); *Shapla*, 44 Bilton Rd, Greenford, UB6 7DH (8997 3635); *Shapla*, 2 Abbey Parade, Hanger Lane, Ealing W5 1EE (8991 2125); *Sitar Tandoori*, 104 South Ealing Rd, W5 4QJ (8567 9146); *Spice*, 79 New Broadway, W5 5AL (8840 0202); *Spicy*

King, 10 Castlehill Parade, The Avenue, W13 8JP (8810 7171); *Standard Tandoori*, 231 High St, W3 9BY (8992 7345); *Sundarban Tandoori*, 3 Odeon Parade, Sudbury Heights Ave, Greenford UB6 0NA (8902 4706); *Taj Mahal Tandoori*, 12 Station Parade, W5 3LD (8992 2874); *Tandoori Centre*, 15 Churchfield Rd, Acton W3 6BD (8992 4418); *Tandoori Delight*, 158 South Ealing Rd, W5 4QL (8560 4455); *Tandoori Dial A Curry T/A*, 39 Greenford Ave, Hanwell W7 1LP (8292 1813); *Tandoori Express*, 93 The Broadway, Southall UB1 1LN (8571 6782); *Tandoori Kebab Centre T/A*, 161-163 The Broadway, Southall UB1 1LR (8571 2223); *Usha Tandoori*, 10 Queens Parade, W5 3HU (8997 8419); *Zayka Indian Cuisine*, 8 South Ealing Rd, W5 4QA (8579 7278).

Enfield *Albany Tandoori*, 569 Hertford Rd, Enfield EN3 5UL (8292 8100); *Enfield Tandoori*, 14 London Rd, Enfield EN2 6EB (8363 0424); *Epping Tandoori Ltd*, 4 Bursland Rd, Enfield EN3 7ET; *Friends*, 38-40 Aldermans Hill, N13 4PN (8882 5002); *Gordon Hill Tandoori*, Station Bldg, Lavender Hill, Enfield EN2 0QJ (8342 0483); *Grange Park Tandoori*, 21 The Grangeway, Winchmore Hill N21 2HD (8360 2127); *Jonaki T/A*, 824 Green Lanes, Winchmore Hill, N21 2RT (8364 1807); *Moonlight Tandoori*, 106 Crown La, Southgate N14 5EN (8886 1124); *Moynamoti Tandoori*, 229-231 Fore St, Upper Edmonton N18 2TZ (8807 4069); *Nirala Tandoori*, 11 Angel Corner Parade, Fore St, Edmonton N18 2QH (8807 3866); *Ponders End Curry Mahal*, 112 High St, Enfield, EN3 4ES (8804 1942); *Romna Gate Tandoori*, 14 The Broadway, Southgate N14 6PH (8882 6700); *Roshan Tandoori*, 373 Fore St, Lower Edmonton N9 0NR (8807 5185); *Royal Tandoori*, 57 Church St, Enfield EN2 6AN (8366 0025); *Shah Tandoori*, 121 Silver St, Edmonton N18 1RG (8345 5331); *Shamiana*, 392 Green Lanes, Palmers Green, N13 5PD (8882 6616); *Tandoori House*, 73 Windmill Hill, Enfield, EN2 7AF (8363 0685); *Tandoori Hut T/A*, 42 Fore St, Upper Edmonton, N18 2SS (8245 4400); *Taste of Raj*, 76 Aldermans Hill, Palmers Green N13 4PP (8886 8773); *Taste of Raj T/A*, 407 Green Lanes, Palmers Green N13 4JD; *Zaman Tandoori*, 101a St Marks Rd, Enfield, EN1 1BJ (8366 3464).

Greenwich *Ababil T/A*, 242 Green La, New Eltham, SE9 3TL (8857 4509); *Abbeywood Tandoori*, 13 Wickham La, Abbey Wood SE2 0XJ (8310 3534); *Blackheath Tandoori*, 128 Rochester Way, SE3 8AR (8319 8199); *Charlton Indian T/A*, 3 Wellington Gdns, SE7 7PN (8305 1621); *Crown Tandoori T/A*, 7 Lingfield Crescent, Eltham SE9 2RL (8294 1313); *Curry Royal Tandoori*, 9 Woolwich Rd, Greenwich SE10 0RA (8858 1384); *Dil Tandoori*, 17 Beaconsfield Parade, Beaconsfield Rd, Mottingham, Eltham SE9 4EA (8851 7428); *Greenwich Tandoori*, 106 Blackheath Rd, Greenwich SE10 8DA (8694 2396); *Gulshan T/A*, 746 Sidcup Rd, SE9 3NS (8857 0075); *Halal Tandoori*, 14 Conway Rd, SE18 1AH (0800 085 1831); *Indian Chef*, 100 Harrow Manor Way, SE2 9SA (8311 1000); *Kaltona*

Tandoori, 52 Eltham High St, Eltham SE9 1BT (8850 6578); *Mahathma Tandoori,* 156 Bexley Rd, Eltham SE9 2PH (8859 7954); *Meghna Tandoori,* 297 Plumstead High St, Woolwich SE18 1JX (8312 2091); *Millennium Balti House,* 17 Colomb St, SE10 9HA (8293 5464); *Mogul Tandoori,* 10 Greenwich Church St, Greenwich SE10 9BJ (8858 1500); *Old Delhi,* 31 Shooters Hill, SE18 3RL (8856 8377); *Papadam Tandoori,* 99 Plumstead High St, Woolwich SE18 1SB (8855 9370); *Plumstead Tandoori,* 52 Plumstead High St, Woolwich SE18 1SL (8855 4945); *Raja Sahid Tandoori,* 13-15 Herbert Rd, Woolwich SE18 3TB (8855 0863); *Raj T/A,* 69 Well Hall Rd, Eltham SE9 6SZ (8294 2494); *Ruchita Tandoori T/A,* 31 Avery Hill Rd, New Eltham SE9 2BD (8850 8536); *Standard Indian Tandoori,* 160 Trafalgar Rd, Greenwich SE10 9TZ (8858 0227); *Taj Mahal,* 6 Wilton Rd, Abbey Wood SE2 9RH (8312 2646); *Taste of Raj,* 10 The Village, Charlton SE7 8UD(8319 3439); *Spices,* 51 Mottingham Rd, SE9 4QZ (8851 8386); *Wild East Indian T/A,* 14 Conway Rd, SE18 1AH (08000 851831).

Hackney *Abiruchi South Indian Seafood & Vegetarian Restaurant* 42, Stoke Newington Church St, N16 0LU (7923 4564); *Anglo-Asian Tandoori,* Stoke Newington N16 0NB (7254 3633); *Eva Tandoori 3,* 277 Hackney Rd, Bethnal Green E2 8NA (7613 2613); *Ganges Tandoori,* 78 Dalston La, Hackney E8 3AH (7923 3308); *Massala T/A,* 208 Stoke Newington High St, N16 7HU (7249 0600); *Medina T/A,* 4 Brooke Rd, N16 7LS (7923 9752); *Rahima T/A,* 105 Morning La, E9 6ND (8985 1012); *Rasa* [vegetarian], 55 Stoke Newington Church St, N16 0AR (7249 0344); *Shahi T/A,* 181, Blackstock Rd, N5 2LL (7226 8312); *Shimul Tandoori,* 28 Clarence Rd, Clapton, E5 8HB (8985 0970); *Stoke Newington Tandoori ,* 15 Rectory Rd, Stoke Newington N16 7QL (7249 0203); *Victoria Tandoori,* 231 Victoria Park Rd, Hackney E9 7HD (8985 9077).

Hammersmith & Fulham *Ajanta Tandoori,* 10-12 Goldhawk Rd, W12 8DH (8743 5191); *Akash Tandoori,* 177 King St, W6 9JT (8748 4567); *Anarkali,* 303 King St, W6 9NH (8748 6911); *Dawaat,* 291-293 King St, W6 9NH (8748 7345); *Farooq Balti House,* 3 Charleville Rd, W14 9JL (7610 2020); *Gandhi,* 116 King St, W6 0QP (8748 1826); *Haweli,* 357 King St, W6 9NH (8741 4812); *Jeffrey's Tandoori,* 220 Uxbridge Rd, W12 7JD (8354 2324); *Karim,* 323 King St, W6 9NH (8748 4025); *Lily Tandoori,* 86c Lillie Rd, Fulham SW6 1TL (7385 1922); *LM Tandoori,* 242 Goldhawk Rd, W12 9PE (8740 5825); *Minar,* 323 King St, W6 9NH (8741 2380); *Nayaab,* 309 New King's Rd, SW6 4RF (7731 6993); *New Maharaja,* 10 Greyhound Rd, W6 8NX (7385 8421); *North End Tandoori,* 297 North End Rd, W14 9NS (7381 0299); *Olympia Tandoori,* 73 Hammersmith Rd, W14 8UZ (7603 3629); *Pyasa Tandoori,* 100 Goldhawk Rd, W12 8HD (8740 0676); *Raj,* 277 New Kings Rd, Fulham SW6 4RD (7736 4412); *Raj of India,* 46 Shepherds Bush Rd, W6 7PJ (7602 9930); *Rajput,* 144 Goldhawk Rd, W12 8HH (8740 9036); *Shaheer Karahi,* 33 Uxbridge Rd, W12 8LH (8743 3885); *Tandoori Garden,* 98 Lillie Rd, Fulham SW6 7SR (7381 1069); *Tandoori Nights,* 319-321 King St, W6 9NH (8741 5321); *Villa Bombay,* 255 Munster Rd, SW6 6BW (7381 8191).

Haringey *Akbar Tandoori,* 13 Salisbury Rd, Wood Green N22 6NL (8365 8509); *Anuraag Tandoori,* 773 High Rd, Tottenham N17 8AH (8808 5895); *Asia Spice,* 1 Queens Parade, Green Lanes, N8 0RD (8340 4797); *Bejoy Tandoori,* 78 Bounds Green Rd, N11 2EU (8888 1268); *Bombay,* 50 Topsfield Parade, Tottenham La, N8 8PT (8347 6070); *Crouch End Tandoori,* 33 Broadway Parade, Hornsey N8 9DB (8341 6264); *Curry Club T/A,* 127 Tottenham La, N8 9BJ (8342 9016); *Eva Tandoori,* 329-331 Alexandra Park Rd, Wood Green N22 4BP (07956 381490); *Fortis Green Tandoori,* 176-178 Fortis Green Rd, Muswell Hill N10 3DU (8442 1320); *Golden Tandoori,* 94 Stroud Green Rd, Finsbury Park N4 3EN (7272 6180); *Indian Ace,* Crossway Parade, The Crossway, N22 5QX (8889 4356); *Jai Krishna,* 161 Stroud Green Rd, N4 3PJ (7272 1680); *Jashan,* 19 Turnpike La, N8 0EP (8340 9880); *Kipling's,* 2 North Hill, N6 4PU (8340 1719); *Mossalla Tandoori,* 230 Archway Rd, Highgate N6 5AX (8340 7781); *Paramount,* 216 High Rd, Wood Green N22 8HH, (8888 6255); *Rajma Tandoori,* 346 Muswell Hill Broadway, N10 1DJ (8883 8252); *Tandoori Express Fast Food Delivery,* 87 Tottenham La, Hornsey N8 9BE (8292 1813); *Tandoori Grill,* 110 Myddleton Rd, Wood Green N22 8NQ (8365 7570); *Wood Green Tandoori,* 236 High Rd, Wood Green, N22 4HH (8889 3671); *Yasmin Tandoori,* 501 Green Lanes, Finsbury Park, N4 1AL (8348 6500).

Harrow *Agra Tandoori,* 33 Stanmore Hill, Stanmore HA7 3DS (8954 4784); *Ajanta Tandoori,* 410 Uxbridge Rd, Pinner HA5 4HP (8421 0489); *Balti House Golden Orient Tandoori,* 47 Burnt Oak Broadway, HA8 5JZ (8205 2700); *Charcoal Kebab Tandoori Centre,* 242 Streatfield Rd, Harrow HA3 9BX (8204 4503); *Connoisseur,* 37-39 High St, Harrow HA1 3HT (8423 0523); *Curry Mahal,* 372 Northolt Rd, Harrow, HA2 8ES (8422 7976); *Eastern Night Tandoori,* 6 Blackhorse Parade, High Rd, Pinner HA5 2EN (8429 4848); *Harrow Tandoori,* 57 Station Rd, Harrow HA2 7SR (8863 3159); *Hatch End Tandoori,* 282 Uxbridge Rd, Pinner HA5 4HS (8428 9781); *Kingfisher T/A,* 426b Rayners La, Pinner HA5 5DX; *Kunzan Tandoori T/A,* 60a High Street, Harrow, HA1 3LL; *Natraj,* 341 Northolt Rd, South Harrow HA2 8JB (8426 8903); *New Harrow Tandoori,* 237 Long Elmes, Harrow HA3 6LE (8421 0150); *Pinner Tandoori,* 141 Marsh Rd, Pinner HA5 5PB (8866 5474); *Rayners Tandoori,* 383 Alexandra Ave, Harrow HA2 9EF (8868 4317); *Red Rose Tandoori,* 238 Streatfield Rd, Harrow HA3 9BX (8732 2623); *Saathi,* 145 Greenford Rd, Harrow HA1 3QN (8423 4505); *South Harrow Tandoori T/A,* 399 Northolt Rd, Harrow HA2 8JE (8422 6360);

Standard, 302 Eastcote La, Harrow HA2 9AH (8422 3540); Taj Mahal , 196 Kenton Rd, Harrow HA3 8BX (8907 3569); Titash Indian & Nepalese Cuisine, 52 Bridge St, Pinner, HA5 3JF (8866 1555); Wealdstone Tandoori, 30 Headstone Drive, Harrow, HA3 5QH (8427 8044).

Hillingdon Amanat Dial-A-Tandoori, 29 High Rd, Uxbridge UB8 2HL (01895 850888); Anarkali Tandoor, 107 Station Rd, West Drayton UB7 7LT (01895 420172); AnikasT/A, 12 Hercies Rd, Hillingdon UB10 9NA (01895 270543); Asha Tandoori, 60 Station Rd, Hayes UB3 4DF (8573 4717); Bayleaf Tandoori, 6 Broadway, North Orbital Rd, Uxbridge UB9 5HB (01895 835581); Bilash Tandoori, 1290 Uxbridge Rd, Hayes UB4 8JG (8813 7440); Chambeli Tandoori, 1-2 Broadway E, North Orbital Rd, Uxbridge UB9 5HB (01895 832487); Concord Tandoori, 47-49 Green La, Northwood HA6 3AE; Darjeeling Tandoori, 89 High Rd, Uxbridge UB10 8LH (01895 679300); Eastcote Tandoori, 134 Field End Rd, HA5 1RJ (8866 8020); Eastern Promise, 19 The Broadway, Joel St, Northwood HA6 1NU (01923 841818); Grapes Tandoori, 524 Uxbridge Rd, Hayes, UB4 0SA (8569 1911); Golden Curry Tandoori, 81 High St, West Drayton, UB7 7QH (01895 443435); Harefield Tandoori, 40 High St, Uxbridge UB9 6BU (01895 825844); Harlington Tandoori, 318 High St, Hayes UB3 5DU (8754 1414); Hayes Tandoori, 93-95 Station Rd, Hayes UB3 4BH (8573 4949); Hillingdon Tandoori, 6 Byron Parade, Uxbridge Rd, Uxbridge UB10 0LZ (8561 7055); Husainabad Tandoori, 630-634 Uxbridge Rd, Hayes UB4 0RY (8561 8311); Jenny Tandoori, 14 Station App, Northwood, HA6 2XN (01923 840202); Lucky Tandoori Curry Centre, 116 Cowley Rd, Uxbridge UB8 2LX (01895 274455); Palace Tandoori, 113 Station Rd, West Drayton UB7 7LT (01895 431193); Persad Tandoori, 36 High St, Ruislip HA4 7AN (01895 630102); Rajdoot Tandoori, 59 Windmill Hill, Ruislip HA4 8PU (01895 634656); Raj Tandoori, 40 Windsor St, Uxbridge UB8 1AB (01895 238197); Red Rose Tandoori T/A, 996 Uxbridge Rd, Hayes UB4 0RL (8813 7020); Ruislip Tandoori, 115 High St, Ruislip HA4 8JN (01895 674890); Saffron, 746 Uxbridge Rd, Hayes UB4 0RU (8848 0005); Swan Tandoori T/A, 62 Swan Rd, West Drayton UB7 7JZ; Taj Mahal Tandoori, 4 Willow Tree La, Hayes, UB4 9BB (8845 7708); Tandoori Nite T/A, 5 Westbourne Parade, Uxbridge Rd, Uxbridge, UB10 0NY (8569 3861); Taste of Tandoori, 2 New Broadway, Uxbridge Rd, Uxbridge, UB10 0LH (01895 234679); Yiewsley Tandoori, 150 High St, West Drayton, UB7 7BD (01895 441642).

Hounslow Brentford Tandoori, 211 High St, Brentford, TW8 8AH (8560 4394); Bunny's Tandoori, 248 Hanworth Rd, Hounslow TW3 3TY (8572 8036); East & West T/A, 202 Hampton Rd West, Feltham TW13 6BG (8898 3624); Geetanjali, 470 Chiswick High Rd, W4 5TT (8994 0702); Golden Oriental, 43 Kingsley Rd, Hounslow TW3 1PA (8570 4279); Haweli Tandoori, 1 Parkfield

Parade, High St, Feltham TW13 4HJ (8751 0716); Heathrow Tandoori, 482 Great West Rd, Hounslow TW5 0BY (8572 1772); Hounslow Karahi & Tandoori, 64 Staines Rd, Hounslow TW3 3LF (8570 2611); Indian Palace, 414 Staines Rd, Bedfont TW14 8BT (8751 5822); Indian Rendezvous, 274 Bath Rd, Hounslow, TW4 7DF (8570 3055); Jubraj Indian Cuisine, 7 Park Parade, Gunnersbury Ave, W3 9BD (8993 8884); Kingsway, 270 Bath Rd, Hounslow West TW4 7DF (8572 0635); Monty's Tandoori & T/A, 46 Syon La, Isleworth TW7 5NQ; Priyas Tandoori, 624 Bath Rd, Hounslow TW5 9TL (8759 3768); Sharma Tandoori, 758 Bath Rd, Hounslow TW5 9TY (8759 0424); Taj, 482 Chiswick High Rd, W4 5TT (8994 3695); Taj Mahal, 8 Cavendish Terrace, High St, Feltham, TW13 4HE (8890 2347); Tandoori & Balti Palace, 9a Devonshire Rd, W4 2EU (8994 8030); Tandoori Express T/A, 4 York Parade, Great West Rd, Brentford TW8 9AA (8568 9055); Tandoori Fish Bar T/A, 176 Brabazon Rd, Hounslow TW5 9LP (8759 6374); Tandoori Nights, 232 Uxbridge Rd, Feltham TW13 5DL (8844 0364); Xera T/A, 6 Holly Parade, High St, Feltham, TW13 4HT (8893 2001); Zachary's Tandoori, 369 Hanworth Rd, Hounslow TW4 5LF (8570 8743); Zarin T/A, 100 Harlington Rd West, Feltham, TW14 0JJ (8831 9016).

Islington Balti House Tandoori, 130 Essex Rd, N1 8LX (7359 8999); Bangalore Brasserie, 1 Brecknock Rd, N7 0BL (7482 4458); Black Cobra Thai Indian Cuisine, 10 Brecknock Rd, Holloway N7 0DD (7700 1292); Curry in a hurry, 147 Junction Rd, N19 (7272 2007); Desh, 78 Highbury Park, N5 2XE (7359 3444); Didar Tandoori, 347 Caledonian Rd, Islington N1 1DW (7700 3496); Dilshad T/A, 55 Newington Green Rd, N1 4QU (7226 6746); Eva Tandoori, 604 Holloway Rd, Archway N19 3PH (7561 1107); Hillmarton Tandoori, 3 Hillmarton Terrace, Hillmarton Rd, Holloway N7 9JR (7700 2515); Indian Ocean, 359 Holloway Rd, N7 0RN (7607 0801); Indian Vegetarian Bhelpoori House, 92-93 Chapel Market, N1 9EX (7837 4607); Islington Tandoori, 201 Holloway Rd, Holloway N7 8DJ (7609 9166); Khas Tandoori, 41 Newington Green Rd, Islington N1 4QT (7704 2279); Lucknow Tandoori, 43 Newington Green Rd, IslingtonN1 4QT (7354 1078); Parveen, 6 Theberton St, Islington N1 0QX (7226 0504); Quality Tandoori, 55 Newington Green Rd, Islington N1 4QU (72261999); Raj Moni T/A, 279 Upper St, Islington N1 2TZ (7354 1270); Red Rose Tandoori, 597 Holloway Rd, Archway

N19 4DJ (7272 6655); *Royal Tandoori T/A*, 6 Chapel Market, N1 9EZ (7833 0900); *Sema T/A*, 141 Whitecross St, EC1Y 8JL (7253 2927); *Shahi Tandoori*, 181 Blackstock Rd, N5 2LL (7226 8312); *Shahnaz Tandoori*, 70-72 Liverpool Rd, Islington N1 0QD (7226 1475); *Sitara*, 784 Holloway Rd, N19 3JH (7281 0649); *Sunerbon Tandoori*, 50 Blackstock Rd, Finsbury Park N4 2DW (7359 9243).

Kensington & Chelsea *Al Basha*, 222 Kensington High St, W8 7RG (7937 1030); *Best Tandoori Khana*, 90 Golborne Rd, W10 5PS (8960 0407); *Bombay Brasserie*, Courtfield Close, Courtfield Rd, SW7 4BY (7370 4040); *Chelsea Spice & Grill*, 126 Bramley Rd, W10 6TJ (8960 7876); *Chutney Mary* [Anglo-Indian], 535 King's Rd, Chelsea, SW10 (7351 3113); *Curry Inn*, 41 Earls Court Rd, W8 6ED (7937 2985); *Delhi Brasserie*, 134 Cromwell Rd, SW7 4HA (7370 7617); *Earls Court Tandoori*, 275 Old Brompton Rd, Earl's Court SW5 9JA (7370 3366); *Kensington Tandoori*, 1 Abingdon Rd, W8 6AH (7937 6182); *Kwality Tandoori*, 38 Thurloe Pl, South Kensington SW7 2HP (7589 3663); *Modhubon*, 29 Pembridge Rd, W11 3HG (7243 1778); *Moti Mahal*, 3 Glendower Pl, SW7 3DU (7584 8428); *Nightime Tandoori*, 207-209 Portobello Rd, W11 1LU (7792 8766); *North Kensington Tandoori*, 148 Ladbroke Grove, W10 5NE (8969 1611); *Royal Tandoori*, 184 Holland Park Ave, W11 4UJ (7603 4778); *Saffron*, 306b Fulham Rd, SW10 9ER (7565 8183); *Star of Bombay*, 157 Westbourne Grove, W11 2RS (7229 6096); *Tandoori of Chelsea*, 153 Fulham Rd, Chelsea, SW3 6SN (7589 7617); *Vama - The Indian Room*, 438 Kings Rd, Chelsea SW10 0LJ (7351 4118); *Zaika*, 257-259 Fulham Rd, SW3 (7351 7823).

Kingston *Chillies*, 276 Burlington Rd, New Malden KT3 4NL (8949 7476); *Guru Express T/A*, 57 Brighton Rd, Surbiton KT6 5LR (8390 8642); *New Hawali*, 134 London Rd, Kingston KT2 6QJ (8547 3345); *Shikara*, 24 Coombe Rd, New Malden KT3 4QE (8336 0385).

Lambeth *Bombay Bicycle Club*, 95 Nightingale La, SW12 8NX (8673 6217); *Bombay Brasserie*, 220 Brixton Hill, SW2 1HE (8674 4736); *British Raj Tandoori*, 1534 London Rd, Streatham SW16 4EU (8679 7700); *Bombay Cuisine*, 15 The Pavement, Clapham Common SW4 0HY (7622 0494); *Bombay Spices T/A*, 218 Coldharbour La, SW9 8SA (7733 7877); *Dawn of Raj*, 99 Brixton Hill, SW2 1AA (8671 4216); *Gousia Tandoori*,12 Norwood Rd, Herne Hill SE24 9BH (8674 7641); *Indian Post*, 79a Gipsy Hill, SE19 1QL (8670 5079); *Ivory Arch Tandoori*, 5 Clapham High St, Clapham, SW4 7TS (7622 4003);*Kennington Tandoori*, 313 Kennington Rd, Lambeth SE11 4QE (7735 9247); *Khan Tandoori*, 24 Brixton Water La, Brixton SW2 1PE (7326 4460); *Khyber*, 346 South Lambeth Rd, SW8 1UQ (7622 3541); *Lal Baag Tandoori*, 8 Knights Hill, Tulse Hill SE27 0HY (8670 0909); *Maharani*, 117 Clapham High St, SW4 7TB (7622 2530); *Manzil Tandoori*, 101 Rosendale Rd, West Dulwich SE21 8EZ (8761 2031); *Old Calcutta*, 64a Brixton Rd, Brixton SW9

6BP (7582 1415); *Oval Tandoori*, 46 Brixton Rd, Brixton SW9 6BT (7735 7413); *Parbin Tandoori*, 151 South Lambeth Rd, SW8 1XN (7735 6979); *Passage To India*, 232 Gipsy Rd, West Dulwich SE27 9RB (8670 7602); *Prince of India Tandoori*, 49-51 Norwood Rd, Herne Hill SE24 9AA (8671 5876); *Pukka Indian Brasserie*, 89 Streatham Hill, SW2 4UD (8671 1171); *Raj Bilash T/A*, 44 Sunnyhill Rd, Streatham SW16 2UH (8677 8074); *Rajpoot*, 67 Streatham Hill, SW2 4TX (8674 9151); *Royal Tandoori*, 66 Brixton Rd, Brixton SW9 6BP (7582 6986); *Rufies T/A*, 15 Clapham High St, SW4 7TS (7720 0633); *Seema Tandoori T/A*, 6 Sanders Parade, Greyhound La, Streatham SW16 5NL (8677 2747); *Shazan Tandoori*, 4 Crown Point Parade, Upper Norwood SE19 3NG (8761 2511); *Shelina Tandoori* , 62 Church Rd, Upper Norwood, SE19 2EZ (8771 7900);*Simla T/A*, 95 Hambalt Rd, Clapham, SW4 9EQ (8675 2337); *Spice Balti Tandoori*, 54 Kennington Park Rd, SE11 4RS (7735 0300); *Spice Cottage*, 78 Streatham High Rd, SW16 1BS (8677 1719); *Tandoori Express T/A*, 62 Knights Hill, West Norwood SE27 0JD (8761 4318); *Village Tandoori T/A*, 50 Abbeville Rd, Clapham, SW4 9NF (8673 5043).

Lewisham *Babur Brasserie*, 119 Brockley Rise, SE23 1JP (8291 2400); *Babur T/A*, 443 Brockley Rd, SE4 2PJ (8291 4314); *Balti King Tandoori*, 176 Dartmouth Rd, Sydenham SE26 4QZ (8291 6554); *Bombay Spice T/A*, 118 Bromley Rd, Catford SE6 2UN (8695 8877); *Darjeeling*, 134, Lee High Rd, SE13 5PR (8473 8222); *Curry Garden Tandoori*, 133 Burnt Ash Rd, Grove Park SE12 8RA (8318 0113); *Curry Garden Tandoori*, 72 Tranquil Vale, Blackheath SE3 0BN (8852 3267); *Dewaniam*, 133-135 Stanstead Rd, Forest Hill, SE23 1HH (8291 5270); *Dilraj (Bangladeshi & Indian) T/A*, 33 Staplehurst Rd, SE13 5ND (8297 8989); *Gurshan Tandoori*, 206 Lower Rd, Deptford SE8 5DJ (7237 5932); *Himalaya Tandoori*, 393 Lewisham High St, SE13 6NZ (8690 2863); *Indian Summer*, 1 Burnt Ash Hill, SE12 0AA (8851 7730); *Khans*, 28 Montpelier Vale, SE3 0TA (8852 7091); *Ladywell Tandoori*, 81 Ladywell Rd, Lewisham SE13 7JA (8690 1047); *Lee High Indian T/A*, 78 Lee High Rd, SE13 5PT (8852 7199); *Lee Raj Tandoori T/A*, 55 Baring Rd, Grove Park SE12 0JS (8857 9003); *Mugal Tandoori & T/A*, 78 Brockley Rise, Forest Hill SE23 1LN (8314 1394); *Papadam Tandoori*, 275 Brownhill Rd, Catford SE6 1AE (8461 4114); *Rahana Tandoori*, 124 Hither Green La, Lewisham SE13 6QA (8852 1055); *Raj Balti House*, 16-18 Sunderland Rd, Forest Hill SE23 2PR (8291 0870); *Redrose Tandoori T/A*, 172 New Cross Rd, New Cross SE14 5AA (7732 8331); *Royal Tandoori T/A*, 387 Brockley Rd, Brockley SE4 2PH (8692 7260); *Shapla T/A*, 357 Brockley Rd, SE4 2AG (8691 1828); *Sonali Tandoori*, 315a Baring Rd, Grove Park ,SE12 0DZ (8851 4916); *Sopna Tandoori*, 39 Tranquil Vale, Blackheath SE3 0BU (8852 7872); *Spice of Life*, 260, Lee High Rd, SE13 5PL (8244 4770); *Tandoori Delight T/A*, 98 Sydenham Rd,

SE26 5JX (8659 4702); *Tandoori Night T/A,* 1 Sanford St, New Cross SE14 6NA (8692 4922); *Taste of Raj,* 9 Royal Parade, Blackheath Village SE3 0TL (8244 2823); *Tripti Tandoori,* 318 Lee High Rd, SE13 5PJ (8852 9891).

Merton *Ahmed Tandoori,* 2 The Broadway, Wimbledon SW19 1RF (8946 6214); *Bombay Bicycle Club T/A,* 302a Kingston Rd, SW20 8LR (8540 9997); *Bombay Express,* 340 Kingston Rd, Wimbledon Chase London SW20 8LR (8543 0494); *Bombay Massala,* 27 Leopold Rd, Wimbledon SW19 7BB (8944 0121); *Broadway Tandoori,* 250 The Broadway, Wimbledon SW19 1SB (8542 7697); *Colliers Wood Tandoori,* 29 High St, Wimbledon SW19 2JE (8715 9407); *Curry Mahal,* 403 Durnsford Rd, SW19 8EE (8946 7954); *Godhulee Tandoori,* 1 Kingston Rd, South Wimbledon SW19 1JX (8542 0243); *Golden Tandoori,* 57 Hartfield Rd, Wimbledon SW19 3SG (8542 0287); *K 2 Indian T/A,* 440 Durnsford Rd, Wimbledon SW19 8DZ (8944 8123); *Karahi Mahal,* 5 Kingston Rd, SW19 1JX (8542 0949); *Lal-Qila Tandoori,* 9 Approach Rd, Raynes Pk, SW20 8BA (8542 3843); *Momshad T/A,* 100 Merton High St, SW19 1BD (8543 8763); *Oasis,* 9 Approach Rd, Raynes Park SW20 8BA (8540 3250); *Oasis,* 9 Approach Rd, Raynes Park, SW20 8BA (8540 3250); *Organic Indian,* 27 Leopold Rd, Wimbledon, SW19 7BB (0800 0350380); *Raj Doot,* 72 High St, Wimbledon SW19 5EE (8947 5054); *Red Rose,* 554 Kingston Rd, Raynes Park, SW20 8DR (8542 1608); *R K Indian T/A,* 296 Haydons Rd, SW19 8JZ (8543 4008); *Wimbledon Tandoori,* 26 The Ridgway, SW19 4QW (8946 1797); *Zayka,* 281 Kingston Rd, Wimbledon, SW20 8LB (8543 9484).

Newham *Cafe Raj T/A,* 128 Shakespeare Crescent, Manor Park E12 6LP; *City Nights Tandoori,* 13 Freemasons Rd, Canning Town E16 3AR (7474 9694); *Eastern Eye,* 269 High Street South, East Ham E6 3PG (8470 8078); *Empress,* 729 Romford Rd, Manor Park E12 5AW (8478 2500); *Kalpona Tandoori,* 369 Prince Regent La, Canning Town E16 3JP (7511 0966); *Kanchans Rasoi,* 807 Romford Rd, E12 5AN (8478 7600); *Laltilla T/A,* 62 Hermit Rd, E16 4LF (7474 0400); *Lipa Indian T/A,* 517 Barking Rd, E6 2LN (8470 6214); *Mobeen,* 222-224 Green St, Forest Gate, E7 (8470 2419); *Parvez T/A,* 532 Barking Rd, E13 8QE (8470 8155); *Pier Garden Tandoori,* 9 Pier Rd, Canning Town E16 2JJ (7473 2000); *Raj Chaat House,* 328 Green St, Plaistow, E13 9AP (8471 5045); *Sabina Tandoori,* 261 Barking Rd, Plaistow E13 8EQ (7511 0982); *Sagor,* 538 High St North, E12 6QN, (8514 5825); *Samrat Tandoori,* 320 Barking Rd, Plaistow E13 8HL (7473 4333); *Sheezan Tandoori,* 297 Barking Rd, East Ham E6 1LB (8472 1370); *Shirin's Tandoori ,* 712 Romford Rd, Manor Park, E12 6BT (8514 7381); *Shujon Tandoori,* 308 Barking Rd, East Ham E6 3BA (8472 7048); *Sinbad Tandoori ,* 280 Barking Rd, Plaistow E13 8HR (7476 7691); *Sindu Mahal,* 274 Barking Rd, E6 3BA (8471 6226);*Spice,* 293, Barking Rd, E13 8EQ (7511 7760).

Redbridge *Chutney,* 362 High Rd, Woodford Green, IG8 0XQ (8559 2449); *Gaylord Tandoori T/A,* 1 The Shrubberies, George La, South Woodford E18 1BD; *Hot Spice T/A,* 36 Woodford Ave, Ilford IG2 6XQ (8551 6144); *Namostay T/A,* 19 Grays Corner, Ley St, Ilford IG2 7RQ (8518 3633); *Rajdoot Tandoori,* 147 High St, Wanstead E11 2RL (8989 6302); *Purbani Tandoori,* 153 High St, Wanstead E11 2RL (8989 4174).

Richmond *Akash Tandoori,* 27 High St, Twickenham TW2 7LB (8894 1010); *Bilas Tandoori,* 4 Broad St, Teddington TW11 8RF (8977 1529); *Delhi Durbar,* 21 Church St, Twickenham, TW1 3NJ (8892 5908); *Hampton Tandoori,* 59 Oldfield Rd, Hampton TW12 2HP (8941 4425); *Indian Style,* 113 Kew Rd, Richmond, TW9 2PN (8940 4308); *K 2 Indian T/A,* 199 Upper Richmond Rd W, East Sheen, SW14 8QT (8876 1992); *Jolly Indian,* 2 Hounslow Rd, Whitton TW2 7EX (8894 3122); *Minar Tandoori,* 195 High St, Hampton TW12 1NL (8979 0642); *Modern Tandoori,* 196-198 Stanley Rd, Teddington TW11 8UE (8977 8679); *Monzil Tandoori,* 88 Church Rd, Barnes, SW13 0DQ (8748 3809); *Riverside Indian Cuisine,* 2-4, High St, Hampton, TW12 2SJ (8979 4935); *Shanwaj Tandoori T/A Balti House,* 14 Staines Rd, Twickenham TW2 5AH (8893 4881); *Sheesh Mahal,* 21 London Rd, Twickenham, TW1 3SX (8892 5471); *Sopna Tandoori,* 175 High St, Hampton TW12 1NL (8979 2977); *Strawberry Hill Indian Cuisine,* Strawberry Hill Station, Tower Rd, Twickenham, TW1 4PP (8607 9656); *Taste of Raj T/A,* 109 Nelson Rd, Twickenham TW2 7AZ (8898 3419); *Taste of Raj 2,* 86 The Green, Twickenham TW2 5AG (8893 4720); *Taste of Raj in East Sheen,* 130 Upper Richmond Rd West, Mortlake, SW14 8DS (8876 8271); *Teddington Tandoori T/A,* 176 High St, Teddington, TW11 8HU (8977 5593); *Twickenham Tandoori,* 33 Church St, TW1 3NR (8892 6973); *Yeti Tandoori,* 429 Upper Richmond Rd West, Mortlake, SW14 7PJ (8392 2517); *Zaranj,* 279 Sandycombe Rd, Kew, TW9 3LU (8332 0754).

Southwark *Al Amin Tandoori,* 104b Forest Hill Rd, East Dulwich SE22 0RS (8299 3962); *Anwara Tandoori,* 57 Fenham Rd, Peckham SE15 1AB (7639 8478); *Bermondsey Tandoori Balti House,* 206 Jamaica Rd, Sth Bermondsey, SE16 4RT (7237 0833); *Denmark Hill Tandoori,* 117a Grove La, Camberwell SE5 8BG (7274 2359); *Dial an Indian,* 22a Camberwell Church St, SE5 8QU (7701 6004); *Eastern Eye,* 44 Lordship La, East Dulwich SE22 8HJ (8693 7584); *Mirash Tandoori,* 94 Grove Vale, East Dulwich SE22 8DT (8299 4610); *Mogul,* 2 Gwent Ct, Rotherhithe St, SE16 5SW (7394 0003); *Nogar Tandoori,* 59 Denmark Hill, Camberwell SE5 8RS (7252 4846); *Rajah T/A,* 342 East St, SE17 2SX (7701 1076); *Sagor Tandoori T/A,* 7 Barry Parade, Barry Rd, East Dulwich SE22 0JA (8299 1601); *Surrey Quays Tandoori,* 30-32 Albion St, South Bermondsey, SE16 7JQ (7237 1876); *Tandoori Nights of Dulwich,* 73 Lordship Lane, East Dulwich SE22 8EP (8299 4077); *Village Tandoori*

T/A, 71 East Dulwich Grove, SE22 8PR (8693 4915).

Tower Hamlets *Akash Tandoori, 176* Brick La, E1 6RU (7247 4287); *Bhaji Indian T/A,* 6 Chapel House St, E14 3AS (7531 6166); *Bombay Cuisine,* 102 Brick La, E1 6RL (7247 6222); *Bow Tandoori T/A,* 30 Stroudley Walk, Bow E3 3EW (8983 4511); *Café Spice Namaste,* 16 Prescot St, E1 (7488 9242); *Dilchad Indo-Bangla Resturant,* 24 Widegate St, E1 7HP (7247 8930); *Dockcorner Tandoori,* 540 Commercial Rd, Whitechapel E1 0HY (7790 6070); *Dockmaster's Ho,* West India Dock Gate, Hertsmere Rd, E14 (7345 0345); *Eastern Spice,* 12a Artillery Passage, E1 7LJ (7247 0772); *Eastern Tandoori,* 332 Burdett Rd, E14 7DL (7537 9550); *Globe Town Indian Cuisine,* 1 St James Ave, E2 9JD (8983 6816); *Halal Balti Express T/A,* 4a Grove Rd, Bow E3 5AX (8981 9771); *Indiana Tandoori, 129* Salmon La, Poplar E14 7PG (7987 2576); *Le Taj,* 134 Brick La, E1 (7247 4210); *Mala,* 2 Marble Quay, E1W 1UH (7480 6356); *Mem Saheb on Thames,* 65 Amsterdam Rd, E14 (7538 3008); *Muhib,* 73 Brick La, E1 6QL (7247 7122); *Mumbai Blues,* 104 Shoreditch High St, E1 6JN (7613 1003); *New Clifton Tandoori,* 75-79 Wentworth St, Whitechapel E1 7TD (7377 9402); *New Tayyab,* 83 Fieldgate St, Whitechapel, E1 (7247 9543); *Rajboy Curry Tandoori,* 564 Commercial Rd, Poplar E14 7JD (7791 3535); *Raj Moni T/A,* 203 Mile End Rd, E1 4AA; *Rajputh Tandoori T/A,* 252 Bethnal Green Rd, Bethnal Green E2 0AD; *Shah Noor Tandoori,* 123 Roman Rd, Bethnal Green E2 0QN (8980 0368); *Salique's Tandoori,* 32 Hanbury St, Whitechapel E1 6QR (7377 5232); *Sheba Tandoori,* 136 Brick Lane, Whitechapel E1 6RU (7247 7824); *Shish Mahal,* 208 Mile End Rd, E1 4LJ (7791 0434); *Sima Tandoori,* 295 Bethnal Green Rd, E2 6AH (7729 1641); *Sima Tandoori,* 239 Mile End Rd, E1 4AA; *Sonar Gaon Tandoori,* 161 Brick La, Whitechapel E1 6SB (7729 7835); *Tabla,* Dockmaster's Ho, West India Dock Gate, Hertsmere Rd, E14 (7345 0345); *Taj Mahal T/A,* 512 Commercial Rd, Tower Hamlets, E1 0HY (7780 9147); *Taj Mahal T/A,* 65 New Rd, E1 1HH; *Tandoori Nights T/A,* 3 West India Dock Rd, Poplar E14 8EZ (7515 6048); *Tiffin,* 165 Cannon Street Rd, E1 2LX (7702 3832).

Waltham Forest *Balti Raj T/A,* 215 Wood St, E17 3NT (8509 3700); *Baltisan,* 102 Station Rd, E4 7BA (8524 3333); *Dil Tandoori,* 21 Kirkdale Rd, E11 1HP (8539 3239); *Forest Tandoori,* 102 Wood St, Walthamstow E17 3HX (8520 6085); *Gandhi Tandoori,* 267 Hoe St, Walthamstow E17 9PT (8520 0769); *Golden Curry Tandoori,* 734 High Rd, Leytonstone, E11 3AW (8539 5429); *Mohuna T/A,* 65a Old Church Rd, E4 6ST (8523 9799); *Purbani Tandoori T/A,* 34 The Avenue, Highams Park, Chingford E4 9LD (8531 9450); *Raja Tandoori,* 224 High St, Walthamstow E17 7JH (8520 2927); *Raj Brasserie,* 322 Lea Bridge Rd, Leyton E10 7LD (8539 8504); *Razmin Tandoori Indian T/A,* 22 Hoe St, Walthamstow E17 3HN (8521 0963); *Redfort Tandoori T/A,* 151 Wadham Rd, Walthamstow E17

4HU (8531 1300); *Roti,* 44 Hatch La, Chingford E4 6LQ (8524 8750); *Royal Tandoori T/A,* 48 Wood St, Walthamstow E17 3HT (8520 1702); *Ruchita Tandoori T/A,* 7a Cherrydown Ave, Chingford E4 8DP (8529 4749); *Samrat Tandoori,* 78 Chingford Mount Rd, Chingford E4 9AA (8527 5320); *Shanti Tandoori Halal Balti Express,* 206 Francis Rd, Leyton E10 6PR (8558 5727); *Shish Mahal,* 815 High Rd Leyton, E10 7AA (8556 6717); *Tandoori Cottage T/A,* 68 Chingford Mount Rd, Chingford E4 9AA (8531 9547); *Tandoori Express T/A,* 215 Wood St, Walthamstow E17 3NT (8509 0893); *Tandoori Village T/A,* 16 Burnside Ave, Chingford E4 8YJ (8531 3835); *Vujon T/A,* 43b Hatch La, E4 6LP (8529 0666).

Wandsworth *Akash Tandoori,* 70 Northcote Rd, Battersea SW11 6QL(7228 6434); *Akash Tandoori,* 9 Granville Rd, Southfield, Wandsworth SW18 5SB (8875 0860); *Azmir T/A,* 72 Brookwood Rd, SW18 5BY (8874 4183); *Balham Tandoori,* 76 Bedford Hill, Balham SW12 9HR (8675 8088); *Balti House,* 76 Northcote Rd, SW11 6QL (7924 2347); *Balti Kitchen T/A,* 63 Falcon Rd, SW11 2PG (7738 9657); *Bombay Bicycle Club T/A,* 18 Trinity Rd, SW17 7RE (8672 0088); *Bombay Bicycle Club T/A,* 28 Queenstown Rd, SW8 3RX (7720 0500); *Bombay Bicycle Club T/A,* 232 Upper Richmond Rd, SW15 6TG (8785 1188); *Gandhi Tandoori,* 8 Plumstead High St, Woolwich SW18 1SN (8855 5179); *Ganges Indian Cuisine,* 205 Lower Richmond Rd, Putney SW15 1HJ (8789 0798); *Gaylord Tandoori,* 44 Battersea Rise SW11 1EE (7228 3981); *Indian Diner,* 286 Battersea Park Rd, SW11 3BT (7738 0404); *Indian Ocean,* 216 Trinity Rd, Wandsworth Common, SW17 7HP (8672 7740); *Kastoori* [vegetarian], 188 Upper Tooting Rd, SW17 7EJ (8767 7027); *Minar Tandoori & T/A,* 24 Roehampton High St, Putney SW15 4HJ (8788 4438); *Mithali,* 139 Lavender Hill, SW11 5QJ (7228 6438); *Munal Tandoori,* 393 Upper Richmond Rd, Putney SW15 5QL (8876 3083); *Nazmin Tandoori Inn,* 398 Garratt La, Wandsworth SW18 4HP (8946 2219); *Nematkadah,* 225 Upper Tooting Rd, SW17 7TG (8672 6647); *Nilima Tandoori,* 175 Replingham Rd, Wandsworth SW18 5LY (8871 2078); *Panahar Tandoori,* 184 Lavender Hill, Battersea SW11 5TQ (7228 8947); *Paradise of Bengal,* 187-189 Queensway, W2 5HL (7229 1640); *Peacock Tandoori,* 242 Upper Tooting Rd, Tooting SW17 7EX (8672 8770); *Putney Tandoori,* 137 Lower Richmond Rd, Putney SW15 1EZ (8788 4891); *Raja Tandoori,* 169 Upper Tooting Rd, Tooting SW17 7TJ (8767 4425); *Red Rose Tandoori,* 286 Upper Richmond Rd, Putney, SW15 6IH (8780 2074); *Roehampton Tandoori T/A,* 19 Roehampton High St, Putney SW15 4HL (8780 9815); *Samrat,* 18 Lacy Rd, SW15 1NL (8788 9110); *Samrat Tandoori ,* 309 Mitcham Rd, Tooting SW17 9JQ (8672 6560); *Sarkhel's,* 199 Replingham Rd, Southfields, SW18 5LY (8870 1483); *Shanaz,* 102, Tooting High St, SW17 0RR (8767 5012);

Shapla Tandoori T/A, 96 Lower Richmond Rd, Putney, SW15 1LN (8788 3923); *Shoihee Shonah Tandoori,* 206 Trinity Rd, Tooting SW17 7HP (8767 8728); *Standard Tandoori,* 5 West Hill, Wandsworth SW18 1RB (8874 3424); *Tabaq,* 47 Balham Hl, SW12 (8673 7820); *Taj Mahal,* 150 Upper Richmond Rd, SW15 2SW (8788 5941); *Tandoori Cottage T/A,* 368 Garratt La, Wandsworth SW18 4ES (8879 1674); *Tanim's T/A,* 232 Earlsfield Rd, SW18 3DX (8877 1990); *Tariq's Tandoori T/A,* 220 York Rd, Battersea SW11 3SD (7738 0893).

Westminster *Akash,* 500a Edgware Rd, W2 1EJ (7706 1788); *Al Dar,* 61-63 Edgware Rd, W2 2HZ (7402 2541); *Anam Tandoori Home Delivery,* 413 Harrow Rd, W9 3QJ (8960 5552); *Bombay Palace,* 50 Connaught St, London W2 2AA (7723 8855); *Cafe Bombay,* 370 Harrow Rd, W9 2HU (7289 2023); *Deedar,* 12a Bathurst St, W2 2SD (7262 5603); *Durbar,* 24 Hereford Rd, W2 4AA (7727 1947); *Everest,* 41 Craven Rd, W2 3BX (7262 3853); *Ganges,* 101 Praed St, W2 1NT (7723 4096); *Golden Shalimar,* 6 Spring St, W2 3RA (7262 3763); *Indian Connoisseur,* 8 Norfolk Pl, W2 1QL (7402 3299); *Jewel of Siam,* 39 Hereford Rd, W2 4AB (7229 4363); *Karahi,* 27-29 Westbourne Grove, W2 4UA (7727 2556); *Khan's,* 13-15 Westbourne Grove, W2 4UA (7727 5420); *Khyber Tandoori,* 56 Westbourne Grove, W2 5SH (7727 4385); *Mahal,* 138 Edgware Rd, W2 2DZ (7723 7731); *Maharaja,* 50 Queensway, W2 3RY (7727 1135); *Maida Vale Tandoori,* 49 Chippenham Rd, W9 2AH (7266 4616); *Meghna Grill,* 113 Boundary Rd, NW8 0RG (7624 2595); *Meshwar,* 128 Edgware Rd, W2 2DZ (7262 8304); *Mughal's,* 11, London St, W2 1HL (7262 9090); *Old Delhi,* 48 Kendal St, W2 2BP (7723 3335); *One Nation Tandoori ExpressT/A,* 322 Kilburn La, Maida Vale W9 3EF (8969 8034); *Passion,* 119 Shirland Rd, W9 2EW (7289 5667); *Raj Brasserie,* 536 Harrow Rd, W9 3QF (8960 4978); *Standard,* 23 Westbourne Grove, W2 4UA (7229 0600); *Sultan Tandoori Buffet,* 57 Westbourne Grove, W2 4UA (7792 2565); *Taj,* 143 Edgware Rd, W2 2HR (7262 9906); *Tandoori Nights II,* 119 Shirland Rd, W9 2EW (7289 6228); *Taste of Balti,* 107 Westbourne Grove, W2 4UW (7229 3868).

SHOPS There are three main areas for Indian shops: (a) Ealing Rd in Wembley; (b) Southall, Ealing; and (c) Green St, West Ham. In all three areas one can buy Indian clothes (traditional and modern), groceries (especially fresh fruit and spices), jewelery, music and video cassettes, religious pictures and statues, sweetmeats, as well as *beedies,* joss sticks and *pan* (betel nut). All three areas also have many Indian restaurants and snack bars. Nevertheless, each area has its own special characteristics.

(a) Ealing Rd consists of two shopping areas separated by about 200m of private residences. The northern part close to Wembley Central station includes some of the more expensive shops selling clothing and jewelry. In the southern part around Alperton Post Office there is more emphasis on groceries, inexpensive clothing, and hardware but jewelry is also well represented. The main ethnic influence is Gujarati but other groups from the Indian subcontinent do have shops and restaurants there including Sri Lankans.

(b) Most of the Indian shops in Southall are in the Broadway, High St, and South Rd. They offer a very wide range of goods. the dominant ethnic influence is Punjabi (Sikh).

(c) The shops in Green St stretch for about 3 km north of West Ham station. Bangladeshi and Pakistani shops are found here as well those belonging to all the main Indian groups. The range of goods and services available is perhaps even wider here than in the other two areas and there is greater emphasis on low prices.

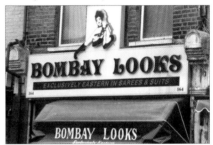

Clothing *Bombay Looks,* 164 Green St, E7 8JT (8471 2444); *Bombay Saree House,* 265-267 Whitechapel Rd, E1 1BY (7247 3365); *East,* 105 King's Rd, Chelsea, SW3 4PA (7376 3161) and 4 The Square, Richmond TW9 1DZ (8948 3302); *Orissa Fashion,* 47 Erskine Rd, Sutton SM1 3AT (8641 1310); *Raj Fashions* [ladieswear], 96 Western Rd, Southall UB2 5DZ (8574 3061); *Raj Fashions & Handicrafts,* 68 Plumstead High St, SE18 1SL (8317 4992); *Rangoli* [women's clothing], 144 Ealing Rd, Wembley HA0 (8903 3500); *Sapna Sarees,* 101 Ealing Rd, Wembley HA0 (8903 4924).

Food *Alauddin Sweetmeat,* 72 Brick Lane, E1 (7377 0896); *Ambala Sweet Centre* [Indian and Pakistani sweets], 112 Drummond St, NW1 2HN (7387 3521); *Ambala Sweets,* 48 Upper Tooting Rd, SW17 7PD (8767 1747); *Ambrosia,* 19 Queens Market, Green St, E7 (8472 6660); *Artillery Wines & Food,* 5 Artillery Passage, E1 (7247 7181); *Bangla Superstore,* 17-19 Brick Lane, E1 (7247 1009); *Deepak Cash & Carry,* 953-59 Garratt Lane, SW17 (8767 7819); *D M K Raj* [greengrocer], 1 Terrace Rd, Plaistow E13 0LP (8472 4991); *Dokal & Sons,* 133 The Broadway, Southall, UB1 (8574 1647); *Gifto Cash & Carry,* 115-119 The Broadway, Southall, UB1 (8574 8602); *Green Street Fresh Fish,* 3 Station Parade, Green St, E7 (8742 8918);

Gupta, 100 Drummond St, NW1 (7380 1590); *Halal Meat*, 232 Ealing Rd, Wembley, HA0 (8902 8282); *Indian Food Fair*, 90 The Broadway, Southall UB1 1QF (8574 1579); *Indian Food Stores*, 68a The Broadway, Southall, UB1 1QD (8574 1592); *Indian Ocean Trading Centre* [groceries], 228a Seven Sisters Rd, N4 3NX (7561 9061); *London Oriental Foods*, 122 Drummond St, NW1 (7387 3740); *Mahavir Sweet Mart*, 127c High Rd, N2 8AJ (8883 4595); *Naklank Sweet Mart*, 50b Ealing Rd, Wembley HA0 4TQ (8902 8008); *Organic India Ltd*, 30 Queen's Ct, Kenton La, HA3 8RL (8907 3727); *Pooja* [Gujarati & Punjabi], 278 Green St, E7 (8552 6757); *Prashad Sweets*, 222 Ealing Rd, Wembley, HA0 (8902 1704); *Quality Foods*, 47-61 South Rd, Southall, UB1 (8917 9188); *Raj* [convenience store] 48 James La, Leyton E10 6HZ (8539 7908); *Raj N Raja Enterprises* [supermarket], 1a Babington Rd, Streatham, SW16 6AP (8677 4947); *Raj Superstore*, 7 Russell Parade, Golders Green NW11 9NN (8458 1064); *Royal Sweets*, 280 Ealing Rd, Wembley, HA0 (8903 9359); *Savera Bakery*, 129 Drummond St, NW1 (7380 0290); *Royal Sweets*, 92 The Broadway, Southall, UB1 (8574 0832); *Sira Cash & Carry* [herbs], 128 The Broadway, Southall, UB1 (8574 2280); *Supreme Sweets*, 706 Kenton Rd, Kenton HA3 9QX (8206 2212); *Tana Mana* [fabrics and clothing from India], 150-152 Stoke Newington Church St, N16 0JX (7249 5656); *Tea & Coffee Plant* [Darjeeling organic tea], 170 Portobello Rd, W11 2EB (7221 8137);*VB & Sons*, 147 Ealing Rd, Wembley, HA0 (8795 0387); *Wembley Exotics*, 133-135 Ealing Rd, Wembley, HA0 (8900 2607).

Other *Bollywood* [music and money transfer], St Stephen's Parade, Green St, E7 (8472 0754); *Bombay Incense Co*, PO Box 2015, E11 1TJ (8989 8773) [New Age shop]; *Good Morning Panwalla* [pan (betel nut) suppliers], 107 Green St, E7 (8472 0960); *Indian Record House*, 41 The Broadway, Southall UB1 1JY (8574 4739);

Jaipur Designs, 13 Goodge St, W1 (7636 5560); *Raj Centre* [newsagent], 11 Kilburn High Rd, NW6 5SB (7624 4418); *Raj Enterprises*, 393 Bethnal Green Rd, E2 0AN (7613 4378); *Raj Gifts*, 117 Burnt Oak Broadway, HA8 5EN (8952 2937); *Raj News* [newsagent], 36 Sterling Way, Upper Edmonton N18 2XZ (8803 9067); *T Raj* [off licence], 1 Terrace Rd, Plaistow E13 0LP (8472 5660); *Taj Mahal Carpets & Furniture*, Railway Arches, Malcolm Pl, E2 0EU (8981 6487).

SPECIAL *Asian Funeral Directors*, 198 Ealing Rd, Wembley (8900 9252). *Indian Funeral Service*, Alexander Ho, Lower Park Rd, N11 1ST (8361 6151); *David Edmonds Indian Furniture*, 1 Prince of Wales Terrace, W4 2EY (8742 1920).

TRANSLATION *Indo Lingua Services Ltd*, Newcom Ho, 125 Poplar High St, E14 0AE (7515 3987). For translation into or from particular Indian languages, see entries under the names of these languages in the general alphabetical list.

TRAVEL *Air India*, 1st fl, Great West Ho, Great West Rd, Brentford TW8 9DF (8754 1010); *Brightways Travels*, 94 The Green, Southall UB2 4BG (8574 2622); *Government of India Tourist Office*, 7 Cork St, W1X 2LN (7437 3677); *Jet Airways India Ltd*, 188 Hammersmith Rd, W6 7DJ (8970 1555); *Taj Tours*, 87 Ealing Rd, Wembley HA0 4PY (8900 1986, fax 8903 0120);

WELFARE *Anglo-Indian Circle Ltd*, 28a Sancroft Rd, Harrow HA3 7NS (8427 0659); *Confederation of Indian Organisations (UK)*, 5 Westminster Bridge Rd, SE1 7XW (7928 9889); *Indo Pakistan Cultural Centre*, 16-18 Hornsey Rd, N7 7BP (7609 4484); *Man Sangathan Southall Community Centre*, 20 Merrick Rd, UB2 4AU (8843 9153); *Sangam Indian Elderly Ladies Group*, c/o Kamaljit Patti, Ruth Winston Activities and Resource Centre for Over 55s, 190 Green Lanes, Palmers Green N13 5UE (8886 5346) [Fridays 12.45 - 16.00; languages: *Gujarati, Hindi, Punjabi*]; *Vishvas Project* (Women's Mental Health), Confederation of Indian Organisations (UK), 5 Westminster Bridge Rd, SE1 7XW (7928 9889); *Women's Health and Family Services Outreach Guidance*, Room F6, The Brady Centre, 192 -196 Hanbury St, E1 5JX (7377 8725).

Indo-Chinese
====

EDUCATION *Lewisham Indo Chinese Community and School*, 33 Clyde St, SE8 5LW (8692 2772).

Indonesian

See also **Balinese** and **Javanese**.

ARTS *Indonesian & Balinese Art Ltd,* 3 Blore Ct, W1V 3RG (7494 9666).

BUSINESS *Arabian Indonesian Corporation,* 37 Marylebone High St, W1M 3AB (7486 7577).

EDUCATION Courses in *Indonesian* are available at *SOAS Language Centre* (7898 4888).

GOVERNMENT *Indonesian Embassy,* 38 Grosvenor Sq, W1X 9AD (7499 7661).

LANGUAGES *Bahasa Indonesian* is the main and the only official language but many other – for the most part related – languages are also spoken. *Bahasa Indonesian* is largely inter-intelligible with *Malay* and these two were treated as a single language in the *Multilingual Capital* (2000) survey. See *Malay* for further information.

RELIGION *Whitaker's Almanack* (2002) states that 87% of the *Indonesian* population is Muslim, and that the remainder of the population is made up of Christians, Buddhists, Hindus, and Animists.

RESTAURANTS

South East 1 *Indonesian & Malaysian,* 98 Bermondsey St, Southwark SE1 3UB ((7407 0329).

West 1 *Rasa Sumadra,* 5 Charlotte St, Fitzrovia, W1 (7637 0222) [seafood].

Barnet *Melati,* 21 Great Windmill St, NW11 (7437 2745).

Lambeth *Satay Bar,* 447 Coldharbour La, Brixton SW9 (7326 5001).

Wandsworth *Nancy Lam's Enak Enak Indonesian & Far Eastern Cuisine,* 56 Lavender Hill, SW11 5RQ (7924 3148).

TRAVEL *Garuda Indonesian Airlines,* 35 Duke St, W1M 5DF (7486 3011).

International

ACCOMMODATION *Youth Hostel Association (International),* 79 Euston Rd, NW1 (7388 9998).

ASSOCIATIONS *United Nations Association of Great Britain & Northern Ireland,* 3 Whitehall Ct, SW1A 2EL (7930 2931); *United Nations Association – London Region,* 23 New Quebec St, W1H 8DH (7402 9029).

BARS & NIGHT-CLUBS *Julie's Wine Bar,* 135-137 Portland Rd, Holland Pk, W11 (7727 7985).

EDUCATION *International Institute for Strategic Studies,* 13-15 Arundel St, WC2R 3DX (7379 7676); *International School of London,* 139 Gunnersbury Ave, W3 8LG (8992 5823); *Royal Institute of International Affairs,* Chatham Ho, 10 St James Sq, SW1Y 4LE (7957 5737).

GOVERNMENT *United Nations High Commissioner for Refugees,* Millbank Tower, 21-24 Millbank, SW1P 4QP (7828 9191).

LEGAL *Amnesty International Ltd,* 1 Easton St, WC1X 8DJ (7413 5500); *Amnesty International - United Kingdom Section,* 99-119 Rosebery Ave, Clerkenwell EC1R 4RE (7814 6200); *Denton Wilde Sapte,* 5 Chancery La, Clifford's Inn, EC4A 1BU (7320 6000) [international law]; *Freshfields,* 65 Fleet St, EC4Y 1HS (7936 4000) [international law].

MEDIA & INFORMATION *United Nations Information Centre,* 21st fl, Millbank Tower, 21-24 Millbank, SW1P 4QH (7630 1981).

RESTAURANTS

East Central *Bridge Brasserie,* 1 St Paul's Walk, EC4 (7236 0000); *Futures,* 2 Exchange Sq, EC2 (7638 6341) [vegetarian]; *Saints',* 1 Clerkenwell Rd, EC1 (7490 4199).

South East 1 *Delfina Studio Café,* 50 Bermondsey St, SE1 (7357 0244); *Laughing Gravy,* 54 Blackfriars Rd, Southwark, SE1 (7721 7055).

South West 1 *Che,* 23 St James's St, SW1 (7747 9380); *Conservatory at the Lanesborough,* 1 Lanesborough Pl, Hyde Park Cnr, SW1 (7259 5599); *Mulberry,* 20 Chesham Pl, SW1 (7201 1905).

West 1 *a k a bar & restaurant,* 18 west Central St, WC1 (7836 0110); *Blues Bistro & Bar,* 42-43 Dean St, W1 (7494 1966); *Cafe Emm,* 17 Frith St, W1V (7437 0723); *Cafe Heal's,* Level 1, Heal's, 196 Tottenham Ct Rd, W1 (7636 1666); *Garlic & Shots,* 14 Frith St, W1 (7734 9505); *Kettner's,* 29 Romilly St, W1 (7734 6112); *Mildred's,* 58 Greek St, W1 (7494 1634); *Randall & Aubin,* 16 Brewer St, W1 (7287 4447).

West Central *Coffee Gallery,* Courtauld Institute, Somerset House, Strand, WC2 (7848 2527); *Detroit,* 35 Earlham St, WC2 (7240 2662).

Brent *Astons,* Regent St, off Kilburn La, NW10 (8969 2184).

Camden *Cafe International,* 15 Frognal Parade, NW3 5HH (7435 7049); *Cucina,* 45a South End Rd, NW3 (7435 7814); *Giraffe,* 46 Rosslyn Hill, NW3 (7435 0343).

Ealing *English and International T/A,* 50 South Ealing Rd, W5 4QY (8451 4883).

Hackney *International Café,* 85 Green Lanes, Stoke Newington N16 9BX (7354 9517); *International Cuisine T/A,* 13 Chatsworth Rd, Clapton E5 0LH (8533 1116).

Islington *Duke of Cambridge,* 30 St Peter's St, N1 (7359 3066).

Kensington & Chelsea *Balans West,* 239 Old Brompton Rd, SW5 (7244 8838); *Bali Sugar,* 33a All Saints Rd, Westbourne Park, W11 (7221 4477); *Pelham Street,* 93 Pelham St, SW7 (7584 4788); *Wiz,* 123a Clarendon Rd, W11 (7229 1500).

Lambeth *Bah Humbug,* The Crypt, St Matthew's Church Peace Garden, SW2 (7738 3184); *Belle Vue,* 1a Clapham Common South Side,

SW4 (7498 9473); *Helter Skelter*, 50 Atlantic Rd, SW9 (7274 8600); *Sun and Doves*, 61-63 Coldharbour La, Camberwell, SE5 (7733 1525).

Newham *International Café*, 355 Barking Rd, Plaistow E13 8EE (7474 6717).

Tower Hamlets *First Edition*, 25 Cabot Sq, E14 (7513 0300); *Tsunami*, International Ho, 1 St Katherine's Walk, E1 (7481 0972).

SHOPS *International Cash & Carry*, 160 Railway Approach, Shepherd's Bush Market, W12 8DF (8743 2313); *International Supermarket*, 7-17 High St, Walthamstow E17 7AD (8509 9557); *LCL International Booksellers Ltd*, 104 Judd St, WC1 (7837 0486).

LCL **INTERNATIONAL** LTD
BOOKSELLERS
EDUCATIONAL BOOKSELLERS · LANGUAGE CONSULTANTS
TEL:0171 837 0487 ·FAX:0171· 833 9452

WELFARE *Anti-Slavery International*, Thomas Clarkson Ho, The Stableyard, Broomgrove Rd, SW9 9TL (7501 8920).

Iranian

ARTS & CULTURE *Iran Heritage Foundation*, P O Box 2256, London W1A 1YS (7493 4766).

ASSOCIATION *Iran Society*, 2 Belgrave Sq, SW1X 8PJ (7235 5122); *Society for Contemporary Iranian Studies*, SOAS, Thornhaugh St, Russell Sq, WC1H 0XG (7730 7025).

BUSINESS *Bank Melli Iran*, 98a Kensington High St, W8 4SG (7937 9815); *Bank Melli Iran*, 4 Moorgate, EC2R 6AL (7600 3636); *Bank Saderat Iran*, 5 Lothbury, EC2R 7HD (7606 0951); *Bank Sepah Iran*, 5-7 Eastcheap, EC3M 1JT (7623 1371); *Iran Overseas Investment Bank Ltd*, 120 Moorgate, EC2M 6TS (7638 4831).

FREIGHT *Islamic Republic of Iran Shipping Lines*, 134-138 Borough High St, SE1 1LB (7378 7121).

GOVERNMENT *Embassy of the Islamic Republic of Iran*, 16 Prince's Gate, SW7 1PT (7225 3000); *Embassy of the Islamic Republic of Iran – Consular Section*, 50 Kensington Ct, W8 5DD (7937 5225).

LANGUAGES **Farsi (Persian)** is the official language and the first language of 60% or more of the population. Significant minorities speak **Azeri** or **Kurdish** and several other languages are spoken by small minorities.

MEDIA & INFORMATION *Iranfile*, P O Box 326, London SW15 3NN [month;y publication].

RELIGION The population is overwhelmingly Muslim (mainly Shia but with a significant Sunni minority). There are very small Christian, Jewish, and Zoroastrian minorities.

RESTAURANTS See also entries under **Persian.**

West 1 *Patogh*, 8 Crawford Pl, W1 (7262 4015); *Safa*, 22 Nutford Pl, W1H 5YH (7723 8331).

Camden *Hafez II*, 559 Finchley Rd, NW3 7BJ (7431 4546).

Hammersmith & Fulham *Yas*, 7 Hammersmith Rd, Olympia, W14 (7603 9148).

Kensington & Chelsea *Alounak II*, 10 Russell Gdns, W14 (7603 7645); *Apadana*, 351 Kensington High St, W8 6NW (7603 3696); *Mohsen*,152 Warwick Rd, W14 (7602 9888).

Westminster *Alounak Kebab*, 44 Westbourne Gr, W2 5SH (7229 0416); *Hafez*, 5 Hereford Rd, W2 4AB (7229 9398); *Iran*, 59 Edgware Rd, W2 (7723 1344).

SPECIAL *Forum Iran*, Suite 221, 235 Earls Court Rd, SW5 9FE (7801 3013).

TRANSLATION *Caspian Iranian-Arabic Interpreting Services*, 14 Haven Green, Ealing W5 2UU (8998 8236). See also entry for **Farsi.**

TRAVEL *Iran Airline*, 73 Piccadilly, W1V 0QX (7491 3656; 7409 1360); *Iranian Travel Service*, Suite 23, KBC Ho, 7-11 High St Kensington, W8 5NP (7937 2288).

Iraqi

EDUCATION *British School of Archaeology in Iraq*, c/o Institute of Archaeology, 31-34 Gordon Sq, WC1H 0PY (7733 8912).

GOVERNMENT *Iraqi Embassy*, 21 Queens Gate, SW7 5JE (7584 7141).

LANGUAGES **Arabic** is the principal language and has official status but other languages spoken by significant minorities include **Kurdish** and **Aramaic.**

Irish

ACCOMMODATION *An Teach Irish Housing Association Ltd*, Haringey Irish Cultural Centre, Pretoria Rd, N17 8DX (8365 1751); *Irish Centre Hostels Ltd*, Conway House 20/22, Quex Rd, NW6 4PG (7624 2918); *Irish Centre Hostels Ltd*, 33 Medway St, SW1P 2BE (7222 2071); *Irish Centre Housing Ltd*, 52 Camden Sq, NW1 9XB (7485 8889); *Irish Nationwide Building Society*, 252 Westminster Bridge Rd, SE1 7PD (7928 9285).

ARTS *Brady's Irish Music Agency*, 18 Cypress Gdns, SE4 2FB (8699 1544); *Celtic Association* [Irish dancing], 41 Hertfoed Rd, Barnet EN4 9BH (8449 6291).

ASSOCIATIONS *British & Irish Ombudsman Association*, 24 Paget Gdns, Chislehurst BR7 5RX (8467 7455); *Cara Irish Housing Association*, 140 Amhurst Rd, E8 2AG (7923 1844); *Croydon Irish Association*, Broadcoombe Monks Hill East, South Croydon CR2 8HX (8657 1099); *Federation of Irish Societies*, 52 Camden Sq, NW1 9XB (7916 2725); *Hillingdon Irish Society*, Royal La, Hillingdon UB8 3QP (01895 448229); *Honourable Irish Society*, 74-

75 Watling St, EC4M 9BJ (7489 7777); *Irish Club,* 82 Eaton Sq, SW1W 9AJ (7235 4164); *South London Irish Association Centre,* 138-140 Hartfield Rd, SW19 3TG (8543 0608).

BARS & NIGHT-CLUBS

East Central *O'Neill's Irish Bar,* Cannon St, EC4N 5AA (7653 9951); *O'Neill's Irish Bar,* 31 Houndsditch, EC3A 7DB (7397 9841); *O'Neill's Irish Bar,* 64 London Wall, EC2M 5TP (7786 9231); *Ryan's Bar,* 56 Carter La, EC4 (7329 1100); *Seamus O'Donnell,* Old Bailey, EC4; *Tipperary,* 66 Fleet St, EC4 (7583 6470).

West 1 *O'Neill's Irish Bar,* 4 Conway St, W1T 6BA (7307 9941); *O'Neill's Irish Bar,* 22 Woodstock St, W1C 2AP (7647 8931); *Ryan's Bar,* 52 Wells St, W1 (7636 5121); *The Toucan,* 19 Carlisle St, W1 (7437 4123).

West Central *O'Neill's Irish Bar,* 14 New Row, Covent Garden, WC2N 4LF (7557 9831).

Brent *Barretts Free House,* Cricklewood Broadway, NW2.

Bromley *O'Neill's Irish Bar,* 9 High St, Beckenham BR3 1AZ (8663 1001).

Camden *O'Neill's Irish Bar,* 73-77, Euston Rd, NW1 2QS (7255 9861).

Croydon *O'Neill's Irish Bar,* 96 Church Rd, SE19 2EZ (8768 1001).

Ealing *Joices Irish Bar,* Western Ave, W5 3BQ (8997 4349); *Lavin's Irish Bar,* Uxbridge Rd, Hanwell, W7.

Haringey *O'Neill's Irish Bar,* 87 Muswell Hill Broadway, N10 3HA (8883 7382).

Islington *McLoughlin's,* 427 Caledonian Rd, N7 (7607 1098).

Kensington & Chelsea *O'Neill's Irish Bar,* 326 Earl's Court Rd, SW5 9BQ (7244 5921).

Kingston *O'Neill's Irish Bar,* 3 Eden St, Kingston KT1 1BQ (8481 0131).

Merton *O'Neill's Irish Bar,* 66 The Broadway, Wimbledon SW19 1RQ (8545 9931).

Redbridge *Maguires Irish Bar,* 19-21, Chapel Rd, Ilford Essex IG1 2AF (8478 2161); *O'Neill's Irish Bar,* 109 Station Rd, Ilford IG1 4DW (8514 9930).

Southwark *O'Neill's Irish Bar,* Windsor Walk, SE5 8BB (7701 8282).

BUSINESS
Banking

East Central *Allied Irish Bank (GB),* 12 Old Jewry, EC2R 8DP (7606 4900); *Anglo Irish Bank Corporation,* 10 Old Jewry, EC2R 8DN (7710 7000); *Bank of Ireland Securities Services Ltd,* 36 Queen St, EC4R 1HJ (7248 0919).

West 1 *Allied Irish Bank (GB),* Berkeley Square Branch, 10 Berkeley Sq, W1J 6AA (7629 8881); *Allied Irish Bank (GB) Private Banking,* Berkeley Square Ho, Berkeley Sq, W1J 6DB (7499 7848); *Bank of Ireland,* 20 Berkeley Sq, W1J 6LL (7409 2740).

Barnet *Allied Irish Bank (GB),* 1136 High Rd, N20 0RA (8492 0504); *Bank of Ireland,* 727-729 High Rd, Finchley N12 0BJ (8446 4481).

Brent *Allied Irish Bank (GB),* 103 Kilburn High Rd, Kilburn NW6 6JH (7328 3487).

Croydon *Allied Irish Bank (GB),* 77 High St, Croydon CR0 1QE (8680 8634).

Ealing *Allied Irish Bank (GB),* 62 The Mall, Ealing W5 3TA (8579 5157).

Hammersmith & Fulham *Bank of Ireland,* 30-32 Shepherds Bush Green, W12 8RE (8749 2891).

Hillingdon *Allied Irish Bank (GB),* 51 Belmont Rd, Uxbridge UB8 1SA (01895 272222, 01895 272448).

Islington *Allied Irish Bank (GB),* 629-635 Holloway Rd, Archway, N19 5SU (7272 0404); *Allied Irish Banks Independent Financial Services Ltd,* 629-635 Holloway Rd, N19 5SU (7281 9881); *Bank of Ireland,* 43-45 Seven Sisters Rd, Holloway N7 6BH (7263 7365).

Kensington & Chelsea *Bank of Ireland,* 17-19 Old Brompton Rd, South Kensington SW7 3HZ (7589 1295).

Lewisham *Allied Irish Bank (GB),* 209-211, Lewisham High St, Lewisham, SE13 6LY (8318 1322).

Merton *Allied Irish Bank (GB),* 201-203 The Broadway, Wimbledon SW19 1NL (8540 9400).

Redbridge *Allied Irish Bank (GB),* 241-243 High Rd, Ilford IG1 1NE (8553 3746).

Wandsworth *Allied Irish Bank (GB),* 47 Upper Tooting Rd, SW17 7TR (8767 3611); *Bank of Ireland,* 178 Balham High Rd, Balham SW12 9DQ (8673 5633).

Other *CST Irish Imports Ltd,* Unit 2, Waterside Trading Centre, Hanwell W7 2QD (8574 7377); *Enterprise Ireland,* 150 New Bond St, W1S 2AQ

(7491 3660); *Irish Food Board,* 2 Tavistock Pl, WC1H 9RA (7833 1251); *Irish Heliculture,* 33 Keyes Rd, NW2 3XB (8357 0050); *Irish Linen Co,* 35 Burlington Arcade, W1J 0PS (7493 8949); *Irish Permanent,* 141 King St, W6 9JG (8748 0258); *National Association of British & Irish Millers Ltd,* 21 Arlington St, SW1A 1RN (7493 2521).

FREIGHT *Ireland Overnite Ltd,* Unit 14, Chelsea Fields Industrial Estate, 278 Western Rd SW19 2QA (8646 6195); *Irish Removal Specialist,* 184-186 Oakleigh Rd North, N20 0UA (8361 7493).

GOVERNMENT *Irish Embassy,* 17 Grosvenor Pl, SW1X 7HR (7235 2171).

LANGUAGES *irish Gaelic* and *English* have official status.

LEGAL *British Irish Rights Watch,* 20-21 Tooks Ct, EC4A 1LB (7405 6415);

MEDIA & INFORMATION *Irish Post Ltd,* Cambridge House, Cambridge Grove, W6 0LE (8741 0649); *Irish World Newspaper,* 934 North Circular Rd, NW2 7JR (8453 7800); *Spectrum Radio,* International Radio Centre, 4 Ingate Pl, SW8 3NS (7627 4433) [broadcasting for *Irish* listeners (in English) 00.00 - 01.00 Mon, 13.00 - 14.00 Sat].

RECREATION *Celtic Association* [Irish dancing], 41 Hertfoed Rd, Barnet EN4 9BH (8449 6291); *Irish Dance Network,* Victor Ho, Marlborough Gdns, Whetstone N20 0SH (8361 0678); *London Irish Rugby Football Club,* The Avenue, Sunbury-on-Thames TW16 5EQ (01932 783034).

RELIGION About 87% of the population is Roman Catholic and the remainder are mainly Christians of other denominations.

RESTAURANTS

East Central *O'Briens Irish Sandwich Bar,* 101 Fleet St, EC4Y 1DE (7583 4360); *O'Briens Irish Sandwich Bar,* 57-58 Houndsditch, EC3A 7BE (7621 1655).

West 1 *Ard Ri Dining Room,* Level 1, The O'Conor Don, 88 Marylebone La, W1 (7935 9311); *Mulligans of Mayfair,* 13-14 Cork St, W1 (7409 1370); *O'Briens Irish Sandwich Bar,* 70 Tottenham Court Rd, W1T 2HE (7636 7094).

West Central *O'Briens Irish Sandwich Bar,* Charing Cross Station, Strand, WC2N 5HS (7930 3511); *O'Briens Irish Sandwich Bar,* 16, George St, Croydon CR0 1PA (8680 0001); *Porterhouse Stout & Oyster Bar,* 20-22 Maiden La, WC2 (7379 7917); *The Toucan,* 19 Carlisle St, W1 (7437 4123).

Brent *Stables Irish Restaurant,* 869 Harrow Rd, NW10 5NG (8969 7333).

Westminster *The Cow,* 89 Westbourne Park Rd, W2 5QH (7221 0021).

SHOPS *An Siopa Eire,* 70 Uxbridge Rd, W7 3SU (8567 1022); *Four Provinces Bookshop,* 244 Grays Inn Rd, WC1X (7833 3022) [not Mon.]; *Green Ink Bookshop,* 8 Archway Rd, N19 5RG (7263 4748); *Ireland in London,* 5 Montpelier St, SW7 1EX (7589 4455); *Irish Bookshop,* 8 Archway Mall, N19 5RG (7263 4748); *Irish Meat Market,* 72 Goldhawk Rd, W12 8HA (8762 9689); *The Irish Shop,* 14 King St, WC2E 8HN (7379 3625); *Mandy's Irish Shop*

[recorded music], 830 Garratt La, SW17 0NA (8767 9942); *O'Flanagan's Irish Bookshop,* 81 Westbourne Park Rd, W2 5QH (7229 3626) <www.oflanagans.com>.

TRAVEL *Irish Golf Tours,* 260 Kilburn High Rd, NW6 2BY (7625 7969); *Irish Tourist Board,* 150 New Bond St, W1S 2AQ (0800 0397000).

WELFARE *BIAS Irish Travellers Project,* 90 High St, Harrow on the Hill, HA1 3LP (8422 3541); *Hammersmith & Fulham Irish Centre,* Blacks Rd, W6 9DT (8563 8232); *Haringey Irish Centre Advice Service,* Pretoria Rd, N17 8DX (8365 1125); *Haringey Irish Community Care Centre,* 72 Stroud Green Rd, N4 3ER (7272 9230); *Haringey Irish Cultural & Community Centre,* Pretoria Rd, Tottenham N17 8DX (8885 3490); *Irish in Greenwich,* 24-24a Greens End, SE18 6JY (8854 4466); *Irish Youth Foundation (UK) Ltd,* Irish Centre, Blacks Rd, Hammersmith W6 9DT (8748 9640); *Lewisham Irish Community Centre,* 2a Davenport Rd, SE6 2AZ (8695 6264); *London Irish Centre,* 50-52 Camden Sq, NW1 9XB (7916 7300); *London Irish Womens Centre,* 59 Stoke Newington Church St, Hackney N16 0AR (7249 7318); *Southwark Irish Forum,* 116a Lordship La, SE22 8HD (8299 9940); *Southwark Irish Pensioners,* 19 Spa Rd, SE16 3QP (7232 1004).

Irish Gaelic

See under **Gaelic.**

Ishan

For the **Ishan** language, see under the variant spelling **Esan.**

Islamic

Many related entries can be found under **Muslim. Islamic** sects with separate entries include **Ahmadiyya** and **Ismaili.**

ARTS & CULTURE *Ahuan Islamic Art,* 1 7 Eccleston St, SW1 (7730 9382); *Arabesque Islamic Art,* 3/250 Kings Rd, SW3 5UE (7460 2235); *Arabesque Islamic Art,* 151 Sydney St, Chelsea SW3 6NT (7460 2235); *Arthur Millner Ltd* [Indian & Islamic artists], 2 Campden St, W8 7EP (7229 3268); *Arts and the Islamic World (UK) Ltd,* 16 Grosvenor Crescent, SW1X 7EP (7245 9898); *Hadji Baba Ancient Art,* 34a Davies St, W1Y 1LG (7499

9363); *Islamic Art*, 58 Davies St, W1Y 2LP (7491 3001); *Islamic Arts Foundation,* 144-146 Kings Cross Rd, WC1X 9DH (7833 8275); *Islamic Art Circle,* c/o dept of Oriental Antiquities, British Museum, Great Russell St, WC1B 3DG (8374 2391); *Islamic Art Society,* 1-11 Hay Hill, W1J 6DH (7499 4551); *Islamic Cultural Centre (Wembley),* 72 Harrow Rd, Wembley, HA9 6PL (8903 3760); *Islamic Culture & Education Centre,* 75 Falcon Rd, SW11 1NZ (7228 4267); *Islamic Education & Cultural Society of Hayes,* Hayes Civic Hall, Pump Lane, Hayes, UB3 3NB (8561 4654); *John Addis Islamic Gallery,* Dept of Oriental Antiquities, British Museum, Great Russell St, WC1B 3DG (7323 8259); *Kufa Gallery,* 26 Westbourne Grove, W2 5RH (7229 1928); *Oasis Ancient & Islamic Arts,* Stand E14 Grays Mews Antique Market, 1-7 Davies Mews, W1Y 1AR (7493 1202); *Rau (Islamic Turkestani Antiques),* 36 Islington Green, N1 8DU (7359 5337); *Visual Islamic & Traditional Art Programme,* Unit 6A, 19-22 Charlotte Rd, EC2A 3SG (7613 8500); *Yazdani Ancient & Islamic Art Ltd,* 128 Mount St, W1Y 5HA (7491 2789).

ASSOCIATIONS *Chingford Islamic Society,* 92 Chingford Mount Rd, E4 9AA (8523 5826); *Islamic Medical Association Kosova,* 19 Chatsworth Rd, E5 0LH (8986 5444); *Islamic Social Association,* 384 Uxbridge Rd, W12 7LL (8762 9909); *Islamic Society for Promotion of Religious Tolerance,* 121 Harley St, W1N 1DH (7935 3330); *Islamic Universal Association,* Old MDS Bldg, St James Gdns, W11 4RF (7602 5273); *London Islamic Cultural Society Community Centre,* 385 Wightman Rd, N8 0NA (8348 0353); *London Islamic Turkish Association,* 16 Green Lanes, N16 9ND (7249 5417); *Madina Masjid Islamic Association,* 225 High Street North, East Ham, E6 1JG (8472 3069); *Newham North Islamic Association,* 88 Green St, E7 8JG (8472 6887); *Sisters in Islam (Muslim Girls Club),* c/o Mrs. Rahana Hassan, Ponders End Youth Centre, 129 South St, Ponders End EN3 4PX (8804 5908) [languages: **Bengali, Urdu,** English]; *Society for the Revival of Islamic Heritage,* 23 Crawford St, W1H 1PJ (7486 5215); *Sri Lanka Islamic Association,* Broadway Bldg, Boston Rd, W7 3TT (8840 3270); *Stratford Islamic Association,* 3 Brydges Rd, E15 1NA (8519 6367); *Sydea R Islam Women's Association,* 6 Whites Row, E1 7NF (7247 9278); *Waltham Forest Islamic Association,* 451 Leabridge Rd, E10 7DY (8292 8111); *World Ahlul Bayt Islamic League,* 19a Chelmsford Sq, NW10 3AP / 17a Phillimore Gardens, Willesden, NW10 3LL (8459 8475).

BUSINESS *Institute of Islamic Banking & Insurance,* 16 Grosvenor Crescent, SW1X 7EP (7245 0404); *Institute of Islamic Banking & Insurance,* 144-146 Kings Cross Rd, WC1X 9DH (7713 0308); *Islamic Halal Meat Company,* 118 Edgware Rd, W2 2DZ (7723 2248); *Islamic Investment House Ltd,* 36 Edinburgh Rd, Plaistow, E13 9HS; *Islamic Priory Management Co Ltd,* 78 Harley Street, W1N 1AE.

EDUCATION *Al-Muntada Islamic School,* 7 Bridges Pl, Fulham, SW6 4HW (7371 7308); *Amina Hatun Islamic School Ltd,* 6 Sydney Rd, Muswell Hill, N10 2LP; *Amina Hatun Islamic School Ltd,* The Annexe, Suffolk Rd Entrance, 277a St Anns Rd, Seven Sisters, N15 5RG (8880 1771); *Amina Hatun Islamic School Ltd,* 6 Sydney Rd, Muswell Hill N10 2LP; *Centre of Islamic Studies,* SOAS, Thornhaugh St, Russell Sq, WC1H 0XG (7898 4380); *Hifzul Quran and Islamic Education Centre,* 15 Barnardo Gdns, Barnardo St, E1 0LN; *Institute of Islamic Banking & Insurance,* 16 Grosvenor Crescent, SW1X 7EP (7245 0404); *International Colleges of Islamic Science,* Crusader Ho, 289 Cricklewood Broadway, NW2 6NX (8450 8383); *Islamia Schools Trust,* 129 Salusbury Rd, NW6 6PE (7372 2171); *Islamic Academy of London,* 44 Plashet Rd, E13 0PU (8586 7660); *Islamic Culture & Education Centre,* 75 Falcon Rd, Battersea SW11 2PF (7228 4267); *Islamic Education & Cultural Society of Hayes,* Hayes Civic Hall, Pump La, Hayes UB3 3NB (8561 4654); *Islamic University,* 153 Lenine Ho, Kilburn La, W10 4BQ (8964 3307); *London School of Islamic Psychotherapy,* 63 Margery Park Rd, Forest Gate, E7 9LD (8555 2733); *Markaz Centre for Arabic & Islamic Studies,* 365 Old Kent Rd, SE1 5JH (7231 9540).

HEALTH & BEAUTY *International Islamic Dawah Centre,* 57 Park Rd, NW1 6XU (7724 8099); *Islamic Medical Association Kosova,* 19 Chatsworth Rd, E5 0LH (8986 5444).

LEGAL *Centre of Islamic & Middle Eastern Law,* SOAS, Thornhaugh St, Russell Sq, WC1H 0XG (7419 7632); *Centre of Islamic Studies,* SOAS, Thornhaugh St, Russell Sq, WC1H 0XG (7898 4380); *Islamic Human Rights Commission,* PO Box 598, Wembley HA9 7QG (8902 0888); *Pakistan Islamic Law Chambers,* 1 Brady St, E1 5DG (7247 6560).

MEDIA & INFORMATION *Al-Anssar Islamic Information Centre Ltd,* 226 Coldharbour La, SW9 8SD (7326 0500); *Al Saqi Publishers,* 26 Westbourne Grove, W2 5RH (7221 9347); *Iqra Trust,* 24 Culcross St, W1Y 3HE (7491 1572) [information]; *Islam 21,* P O Box 21272, London W9 3YN (0870 0130286) [bi-monthly publication]; *Islamic Computing Centre,* 73 St Thomas's Rd, Finsbury Park N4 2QJ (7359 6233); *Islamic Information Centre,* 209 Cricklewood Broadway, NW2 3HS (8208 1770); *Islamic Information Centre,* Brownlow Ho, Brownlow Rd, W13 0SQ (8840 4140); *Islamic Information Centre,* 15 Station Rd, Harrow, HA1 2UF (8427 2822); *Islamic Information Centre,* 346 High Rd, Wembley, HA9 6AZ (8795 1359); *Islamic Information Centre,* 31 Featherstone Rd, Southall, UB2 5AB (8843 9927); *Islamic Mission Information Centre,* Brownlow House, Brownlow Rd, West Ealing, W13 0SQ (8840 4140); *Islamic Republic News Agency,* Imperial Life Ho, High Rd, Wembley HA9 6AS (8903 5531); *International Islamic Dawah* [TV, video & film], 57 Park Rd, Camden NW1 6XU (7724 8099); *Mujaddidi*

Publications (Ibn ul Waqt), 1579 London Rd, Norbury SW16 4AA (8240 8888); *Spectrum Radio,* International Radio Centre, 4 Ingate Pl, SW8 3NS (7627 4433) [Islamic programme broadcast in English 15.00 - 17.00 daily]; *World Islamic Information Centre,* 99 Uxbridge Rd, W12 8NL (8749 3877).

MOTORING *Islamic School of Motoring Ltd,* Flat A, Block 1, Fieldgate Mansions, Myrdle St, E1 1EY.

RELIGION

Islamic centres

West 1 *Mayfair Islamic Centre,* 19 Hertford St, W1Y 7DB.

Brent *B & H Islamic Centre,* 129 Cricklewood Broadway, NW2 3JG (8450 5392); *Imam Khoei Islamic Centre,* Stone Hall, Chevening Rd, NW6 6TN (8960 6378); *Islamic Centre,* Brent View Rd, NW9 7EL (8201 5904); *Islamic Centre of Brent,* Chichele Rd, NW2 3AT (8450 1986); *Islamic Centre of Brent,* 33a Howard Rd, Cricklewood, NW2 6DS (8450 1986); *Islamic Centre of England,* 8 Alexander Av, NW10 3QS (8830 3906); *Islamic Cultural Centre (Wembley),* 72 Harrow Rd, Wembley HA9 6PL (8903 3760).

Croydon *Croydon Mosque Islamic Centre,* 525 London Rd, Thornton Heath CR4 6AR (8684 7512).

Enfield *Edmonton Islamic Centre,* 198 Fore St, Upper Edmonton, N18 2JE (8807 5151).

Greenwich *Greenwich Islamic Centre,* 131 Plumstead Rd, SE18 7DW (8855 0786).

Hackney *UK Turkish Islamic Cultural Centre,* 1 Clissold Rd, N16 9EX (7275 9001).

Hammersmith & Fulham *Al-Noor Islamic Centre,* 352 North End Rd, Fulham, SW6 1NB (7381 9493).

Haringey *London Islamic Cultural Society Community Centre,* 385 Wightman Rd, N8 0NA (8348 0353); *UK Turkish Islamic Cultural Centre,* 10 Caxton Rd, N22 6TB (8352 1435).

Hounslow *Jamia Masjid New Islamic Centre,* Wellington Rd South, Hounslow TW4 5JH (8570 0938).

Lambeth *Ahl Ul Bayt Islamic Centre,* 11 Edgeley Road, SW4 6HE (7720 8470); *Peckham Islamic Centre,* 12 Choumert Grove, Peckham, SE15 4PD (7277 8500); *Peckham Islamic Centre (Mosque Trust),* 92 Rye La, SE15 4RZ (7277 8500); *South London Islamic Centre,* 8 Mitcham La, SW16 6NN (8677 0588).

Merton *Morden Islamic Centre,* 2a Crown La, Morden SM4 5BL (8540 1185).

Newham *Islamic Centre (East London),* 295 Barking Rd, E6 1LB (8471 9355); *Islamic Centre (Upton Park),* 72 Selwyn Park, E13 0PY (8472 2745); *Manor Park Islamic Cultural Centre,* 724 Romford Rd, E12 6BT (8514 7772); *Newham North Islamic Association,* 88 Green St, Forest Gate, E7 8JG (8472 6887).

Redbridge *Ilford Islamic Centre,* 56 Albert Rd, IG1 1HW (8553 5739).

Southwark *Dulwich Islamic Centre Trust,* 23 North Cross Rd, SE22 9ET (8299 1046); *Peckham Islamic Centre,* 12 Choumert Grove, SE15 (7277 8500).

Sutton *Sutton Islamic Centre,* 62 Oakhill Rd, Sutton SM1 3AG (8641 6869).

Wandsworth *Tooting Islamic Centre,* 145 Upper Tooting Rd, SW17 7TJ (8767 2344).

Westminster *International Islamic Dawah Centre,* 57 Park Rd, NW1 6XU(783 6633); *Islamic Centre England,* P O Box 8148, W2 1GD (8830 4011); *Islamic Centre England (London),* 140 Maida Vale, W9 1QB (7604 5500); *Islamic Cultural Centre (Regent's Park) / London Central Islamic Cultural Centre,* 146 Park Rd, Regent's Park NW8 7RG (7724 3363); *Mayfair Islamic Centre,* 19 Hertford St, W1Y 7DB.

Mission *Islamic Mission Information Centre,* Brownlow Ho, Brownlow Rd, West Ealing W13 0SQ (8840 4140); *UK Islamic Mission,* Masjid Bilal & Islamic Centre, 295 Barking Rd, East Ham E6 1LB (8471 9355); *UK Islamic Mission,* 202 North Gower St, NW1 1LY (7380 0465).

Mosques

Brent *Brent Mosque,* Chichele Rd, NW2 3AT (8450 1986); *Mosque & Islamic Centre of Brent,* 33a Howard Rd, Cricklewood, NW2 6DS (8450 1986).

Greenwich *Woolwich Mosque,* 131 Plumstead Rd, Woolwich SE18 7DW (8855 0786).

Hackney *North London Mosque,* 70-72 Cazenove Rd, N16 6AA (8806 6540); *Sheikh Mazim Mosque,* 9-15 Shacklewell La, Hackney, E8 2DA (8471 9355); *Valide Sultan Mosque,* 1a Clissold Rd, N16 9EX (7275 9001).

Hounslow *Jamia Masjid,* Wellington Rd South, Hounslow TW4 5JH (8570 0938).

Kingston *Kingston Mosque,* 55 East Rd, KT2 6EJ (8549 5315).

Lambeth *Brixton Mosque,* 1 Gresham Rd, SW9 7PH (7326 4098); *Jamaat-Mosque,* 26 Estreham Rd, SW16Ê5PQ (8769 7553).

Merton *Wimbledon Mosque,* 264 Durnsford Rd, SW19 8DS (8946 3350).

Newham *Masjid Bilal & Islamic Centre,* 295 Barking Rd, East Ham, E6 1LB; *Muslim Cultural Centre and Madinah Mosque,* 225 High St North, E6 1JG (8472 3069).

Tower Hamlets *Bow Central Mosque,* 246 Bow Rd, Bow E3 3AP (8980 6622); *East London Mosque Trust Ltd,* 82-92, Whitechapel Rd, E1 1JQ (7247 1357); *Esha Atul Islam Mosque & Community Centre,* 16 Ford Sq, E1 2HS (7790 0693); *London Jamme Masjid Trust Ltd,* 59 Brick La, E1 6QL (7247 6052); *Shahporan Masjid and Islamic Centre Trust,* 444 Hackney Rd, Bethnal Green, E2 6QL.

Waltham Forest *Masjid-e-Umer,* 79 Queens Rd, E17 8QR (8520 2658); *Noor Ul Islam,* 715a High Rd, Leyton E10 5AB (8558 3014).

Wandsworth *Al-Muzzammil Mosque & Community Centre of Tooting,* Gatton Rd, SW17 0SQ (8767 7477); *Balham Mosque,* 47a Balham High Rd, SW12 9AW (8675 7912).

Westminster *London Central Mosque*, 146 Park Rd, Regent's Park NW8 7RG (7724 3363);.

SHOPS *Al-Barakah Islamic Shop*, 57 Brick La, E1 6PU (7375 3536); *Zam Zam* [Islamic gift items], 388 Green St, E13 9AB (8470 1300).

Bookshops *Al-Hoda Islamic Booksellers*, 76 Charing Cross Rd, WC2H 0BN (7240 8381); *Al-Hudaa Islamic Bookshop*, 73 Old Montague St, E1 5NL (7366 4691); *Al Istiqaamah Bookstore*, Catford Mews, Winslade Way SE6 4JU (8690 1622); *Al-Quran Islamic Book Centre*, 22 Chatsworth Rd, Clapton E5 0LP (8985 9437); *Al Saqi Books*, 26 Westbourne Grove, W2 5RH (7229 8543); *Call to Islam*, 29 Wakefield St, East Ham E6 1NG (8548 4888); *Dar Al Dawa*, 97 Westbourne Grove, W2 4UW (7221 6256); *Dar Al Taqwa*, 7a Melcombe St, NW1 6AE (7935 6385); *Hosain's Books & Antiques*, 25 Connaught St, W2 2AX (7262 7900); *House of Knowledge*, 23 Crawford St, W1 (7486 6992); *Islamic Book Centre*, 120 Drummond St, NW1 2HN (7209 0710); *Islamic Bookshop*, 22 Chatsworth Rd, E5 0LP (8985 9437); *Sub Rung Centre* [Islamic books], 113 Green St, E13.

SPECIAL *Al-Falah Islamic Foundation*, 1 Cowper Rd, SW19 1AA (8540 9662); *Al-Furqan Islamic Heritage Foundation*, Eagle Ho, High St, SW19 5EF (8944 1233); *Al Tajir World of Islam Trust*, 33 Thurloe Pl, SW7 2HQ (7581 3522); *International Forum for Islamic Dialogue Ltd*, 3rd Floor Premier Ho, 313 Kilburn La, W9 3EG (8964 2944); *Islamic Computing Centre*, 73 St Thomas's Rd, Finsbury Park, N4 2QJ (7359 6233); *Islamic Council of Europe*, 16 Grosvenor Cres, SW1X 7EP (7235 9832); *Islamic Forum Europe*, 169 Mile End Rd, E1 4AQ (7423 9766); *UK Turkish Islamic Funeral Services*, 203 Green Lanes, N16 9DJ (7359 1170).

TRAVEL *World Islamic Airways Ltd*, Flat 8 Northways, College Crescent, Hampstead, NW3 5DR.

WELFARE *Dawatul Islam UK & Eire*, 56 Bigland St, E1 2ND (7790 5166); *Heritage of Islam Trust*, International Radio Centre, 2204-2206 Queenstown Rd, SW8 3NR (7510 1062); *Islamic Community Centre*, 115 Clyde Rd, N15 4JZ (8809 2137); *Islamic Relief*, 151 Park Rd, NW8 7HT (0870 444 3135); *London Islamic Cultural Society Community Centre*, 389-395 Wightman Rd, Hornsey N8 0NA (8348 0353).

Ismaili

EDUCATION *Institute of Ismaili Studies*, 42-44 Grosvenor Gdns, Westminster SW1W 0EB (7881 6000).

RELIGION *Ismaili Centre*, 1 Cromwell Gdns, SW7 2SL (7589 2226); *Ismailia Council for the U K*, 1 Cromwell Gdns, SW7 2SL (7589 3235).

SPECIAL *Aga Khan Foundation*, 3 Cromwell Gdns, SW7 2HB (7591 6800).

Isoko

Isoko is a Benuic language spoken Nigeria. Three Isoko-speaking London schoolchildren were identified in the *Multilingual Capital* (2000) survey.

Israeli

ASSOCIATIONS *Anglo-Israel Archaeological Society*, 126 Albert St, NW1 7NE (7691 1467); *Anglo-Israel Association*, 9 Bentinck St, W1U 2EH (7486 2300); *Israeli Business Club London*, 1a Accommodation Rd, NW11 8ED (8905 5710); *Jewish Philanthropic Association for Israel & Middle East*, 741 High Rd, N12 0BQ (8446 1477); *Labour Friends of Israel*, 38 Great Smith St, SW1P 3BU (7222 4323).

BUSINESS *British-Israel Chamber of Commerce*, 79 Baker St, W1U 6RG (7224 3212); *Israel Discount Bank*, 65 Curzon St, W1J 8PE (7499 1444); *State of Israel Bonds*, Commonwealth Ho, 1-19 New Oxford St, WC1A 1NF (7405 6222); *Israel Estates Corporation*, 96 High St, Hornsey, N8 7NT (8347 5767); *State of Israel Bonds*, 6 Bloomsbury Sq, WC1A 2LP (7405 6222).

EDUCATION *Friends of Israel Education Trust*, 25 Lyndale Ave, NW2 2QB (7435 6803); *Tel Aviv University Trust*, 1 Bentinck St, W1M 5RN (7487 5280).

GOVERNMENT *Embassy of Israel*, 2 Palace Green, W8 4QB (7957 9500); *Embassy of Israel – Consular Section*, 15a Old Court Pl, W8 4QB (7957 9516).

LANGUAGES Both **Hebrew** and **Arabic** have official status in Israel.

RECREATION *Israel Folk Dance Institute*, 741 High Rd N12 0BQ (8446 6427).

RELIGION See **Jewish.**

SPECIAL *New Israel Fund of Great Britain*, 26 Enford St, W1H 1DG (7724 2266); *Jewish National Fund for Israel*, 58 Edgware Way, Edgware, HA8 8GQ (8421 7600).

TRAVEL *El Al Israel Airlines*, United Kingdom Ho, 180 Oxford St, W1D 1EL (7957 4100); *El-Al Israel Airlines Cargo*, The Cargo Terminal, 588 London Heathrow Airport, Hounslow TW6 3SQ (8897 5900); *Budget Israel*, Trafalgar Ho, Grenville Pl, NW7 3SA (8906 9909); *Israel Government Tourist Office*, UK Ho, 180 Oxford St, W1D 1NN (7299 1111).

WELFARE *British Israel World Federation*, Unit 8, Blades Ct, 121 Deodar Rd, SW15 2NU (8877 9010); *New Israel Fund of Great Britain*, 26 Enford St, W1H 2BH (7724 2266); *Peltours Ltd* [Israel bookings],

Sovereign Ho, 11 Ballards La, N3 1UX (8343 0590); *United Jewish Israel Appeal,* 741 High Rd, N12 0BQ (8446 1477).

Italian

ACCOMMODATION *C K Italian Property Partnership Ltd,* 788-790 Finchley Rd, Golders Green NW11 7TJ.

ARTS *Italia Conti Academy of Theatre Arts,* 23 Goswell Rd, EC1M 7AJ (7608 0047); *Italian Job* [music management], Winchester Wharf, Clink St, SE1 9DG (7403 2177); *Italian Job* [music publicity], 89 Borough High St, SE1 1NL (7403 2177); *Liaisons Abroad* [Italian opera specialists], 181 Kings Rd, SW3 5EB (7376 4020).

ASSOCIATIONS *British Italian Society,* 21-22 Grosvenor St, W1X 9FE (7495 5536); *Il Circolo - Italian Cultural Association Ltd,* 5 Cathcart Rd, West Brompton SW10 9NL; *Christian Association Of Italian Workers,* 134 Clerkenwell Rd, Clerkenwell, EC1R 5DL (7278 0069); *Missionary Fellowship,* 31 Earlsthorpe Rd, Sydenham, SE26 4PE (8778 7979); *St Peters Italian Catholic Social Club,* 4 Back Hill, Clerkenwell EC1R 5EN (7837 3476).

BARS & NIGHT-CLUBS *Bar Italia,* 22 Frith St, W1 (7437 4520); *Bar San Remo,* 4 Sutton Parade, Hendon NW4 1RR (8201 5317); *Il Vicolo,* 3/4 Crown Passage, SW1Y 6PP (7839 3960).

BUSINESS

Banks *Banca di Roma,* EC2V 7NQ (7726 4043); *Banca Antoniana Popolare Veneta,* 85 Gracechurch St, EC3V 0AR (7623 2773); *Banca Commerciale Italiana,* 90 Queen St, EC4R 1AB (7651 3000); *Banca di Roma*; 81-87 Gresham St, EC2V 7NQ (7726 4106); *Banco di Sicilia,* 25 Old Broad St, EC2N 1HT (7638 0201); *Banca d'Italia,* 39 King St, EC2V 8JJ (7606 4201); *Banca IMI,* Wren House, 15 Carter Lane, EC4V 5SP (7454 4800); *Banca March,* 30 Eastcheap, EC3M 1HD (7220 7488); *Banca Monte dei Paschi di Siena SPA (London),* 122 Leadenhall St, EC3V 4QH (7645 7800); *Banca Popolare di Milano,* 2 George Yard, Lombard St, EC3V 9DH (7283 7111); *Banca Popolare di Novara,* Bucklersbury House, Walbrook, EC4N 8EL (7489 0404); *Cardine Banca Spa,* 63 Queen Victoria St, EC4N 4UA (7815 4405); *UniCredito Italiano,* 17 Moorgate, EC2R 6PH (7606 9011).

Italian Chamber of Commerce for UK, 1 Princes St, W1R 8AY (7495 8191); *Italian Trade Centre,* 37 Sackville St, W1X 2DQ (7734 2412).

Diverse Italian businesses *Anglo-Italian Consulting Consular Services,* 48A Goldhawk Rd, Shepherd's Bush, W12 8QP (8749 8876); *Cedef Italian Financial Products Ltd,* 12-16 Gough Sq, EC4A 3DW; *Fine Italian Foods Ltd* [import & export], 3 Somers Pl, Upper Tulse Hill SW2 2AL (8671 6622); *Cooperative Italian London* [export & import agents], Unit D35-D36 New Covent Garden Market, Vauxhall SW8 5LL (7720 3253); *Fornitore Italiano Ltd* [import & export agents], Unit 20, Britannia Lofts, 16-26 Banner St, EC1Y 8QE (7490 0114); *French & Italian Cuisine Food* [import & export agents], 68 Wallingford Av, Ladbroke Grove, W10 6PY (8969 6034); *Inediti Verapress International Ltd,* 252 Pentonville Rd, N1 9JY (7278 9200); *Italian Business Consultants,* 26a Yeoman's Row, Chelsea SW3 2AH (7589 3008); *Italian Cake Co Ltd,* Northumberland Ho, Drake Ave, Staines TW18 2AP (01784 465655); *Italian Connections Catering Ltd,* 106 Goldhawk Rd, Shepherd's Bush W12 8HD (8743 9850); *Italian Engineering Ltd,* Standbrook Ho, 2-5 Old Bond St, W1X 3TB; *Italian Framing Co,* 18 Ingate Pl, South Lambeth SW8 3NS (7498 0777); *Italian Imports,* 3-4 Little Portland St, West End, W1N 5AG (7580 71 85); *talian Kitchen (Covent Garden) Ltd,* 2 Bloomsbury St, WC1B 3ST (7381 6636); *Italian Landscapes,* 52 Lavington Rd, West Ealing W13 9NN (8579 8880); *Italian Trademarks Promotions Ltd,* Bell Ho, 175 Regent St, W1R 7FB (7383 9836); *Italian Wine Company Ltd,* Falcon Park Industrial Estate, Neasden La, NW10 1RZ (8438 4607); *Italian Wine Cellar,* 195 Ferndale Rd, Brixton, SW9 *BA (7274 7170); *Maestro (Italian Systems) Ltd,* 78 Marylebone High St, W1M 4AP (7644 5000); *La Fornaia Ltd,* Unit 4H, McNichol Drive, NW10 7AW (8453 1818); *UniCredito Italiano,* 17 Moorgate, EC2R 6PH (7606 9011).

EDUCATION *Dante Alighieri Society Language Schools,* 4 Upper Tachbrook St, Westminster, SW1V 1SH (7828 9660); *Italia Conti Academy of Theatre Arts,* 23 Goswell Rd, EC1M 7AJ (7608 0047); *Italian Cultural Institute,* 39 Belgrave Sq, Westminster SW1X 8NT (7235 1461); *Italian Day Nursery,* 176 Clapham Rd, Brixton SW9 0LA (7735 3058); *Italian Language School Ltd,* Babmaes Ho, 2 Babmaes St, Westminster SW1Y 6NT; *Italian Language Services Ltd,* Italian Institute of Culture, 39 Belgrave Sq, WestminsterSW1X 8NX (7823 1887).

In addition to the above, mother tongue education in *Italian* for young children is available in at least two places in London – visit <www.resourceunit.com> for details. There are also more than 300 university and local authority courses in Italian for adults available in London – see <www.floodlight.co.uk> for details.

EMPLOYMENT *Felix Bureau* [Italian catering employment], 80 Shaftesbury Ave, W1V 7DG (7437 8513).

FREIGHT *F S Italian Railway Freight Forwarders,* 17 Linhope St, Camden, NW1 6HT (7724 0011); *Italian General Shipping Ltd,* St Clare Ho, 30-33 Minories, EC3N 1DD (7488 9821); *Italian General Shipping, 30-33 Minories, Monument, EC3N 1DD (7488 9821); Registro Italiano Navale,* 14 Waterloo Pl, SW1Y 4AR (7839 6099).

GOVERNMENT *Anglo-Italian Consulting Consular Services,* 48A Goldhawk Rd, Shepherd's Bush, W12 8QP (8749 8876); *Italian Consulate General,* 38 Eaton Pl, SW1X 8AN (7235 9371); *Italian Embassy,* 14 Three Kings Yard, W1Y 2EH (7312 2200).

HEALTH & BEAUTY *The Italian Hospital,* Queen Sq, WC1; *Marco's Hair Studio,* 56 Northcote Rd, Battersea, SW11 1PA (7228 0495); *Raffaele's Hair Stylists,* 618 Greenford Rd, Greenford, UB6 8QT (8578 3391).

LANGUAGE Italian is a **Romanic** language with official status in Italy and about 70m speakers in all. Italian was reported as the language of 2 501 London schoolchildren in the *Multilingual Capital* (2000) survey. Map 19 showing the distribution of these across London can be viewed at <www.global-london.com/gallery>.

LEGAL *Italian Legal Interpreter,* 78 Morshead Mansions, Maida Vale W9 1LG (7286 0665); *John Howell & Co* [solicitors], 17 Maiden La, Covent Garden, Holborn, WC2 7NL (7420 0400).

MEDIA & INFORMATION *Italian Post,* 182 Caledonian Rd, Islington N1 0SQ (7278 9200); *Spectrum Radio,* International Radio Centre, 4 Ingate Pl, SW8 3NS (7627 4433) [broadcasting in Italian 17.00 - 18.00 weekdays]; *Telecom Italia Spa,* Princes Ho, Jermyn St, SW1Y 6DN (7434 5550).

MOTORING *Anglo Italian Motor Service,* 3 Patshull Rd, NW5 2JX (7485 1613); *G G B (Italian Car Spares) Ltd,* 98 White Hart La, Wood Green N22 5SG (8889 4336); *Scuola Guida Italiana,*178 Clerkenwell Rd, EC1 (7837 9707).

RECREATION *London Italian Golf Society,* 9 Moor St W1V 5LJ (7439 1904); *The British Italian Sports Club,* 49 Hallam St, West End W1N 5JN (7580 6065).

RELIGION *Catholic Centre,* 197 Durants Rd, Enfield, EN3 7DE (8804 2307); *Clerkenwell Italian Church,* 4 Back Hl, Clerkenwell Rd, EC1R 5EN (7837 1528); *Italian Catholic Centre,* 197 Durants Rd, Enfield EN3 7DE (8804 2307); *Saint Peter's Italian Catholic Church,* 136 Clerkenwell Rd, EC1R 5DL (78371528); *Stockwell Italian Mission (RC),* 20 Brixton Rd, SW9 6BU (7735 8235).

RESTAURANTS

East Central *Actors Retreat,* 326 St John St, Clerkenwell, EC1V 4NT (7837 0722) ; *Alba,* 107 Whitecross St, Ec1 (7588 1798); *Andrea The Kitchen Garden,* 30C Great Sutton St, Clerkenwell, EC1V 0DU (7253 0130); *Barracca,* 2C Cherry Tree Walk, Whitecross St, Clerkenwell, EC1Y 8NX (7588 0710); *Café Milano,* 133 Central St, Ec1V 8AP (7250 1467); *Carlo's Trattoria,* 8-10 Exmouth Market, Clerkenwell, EC1R 4QA (7713 0820); *Bolton's,* 13 Cullum St, Monument, EC3M 7JJ) ; *Clerkenwell,* 73 Clerkenwell Rd, Clerkenwell, EC1R 5BU (7405 4173); *La Rochetta,* 40 Clerkenwell Green, Clerkenwell, EC1R 0DU (7253 8676); *Strada,* 8-10 Exmouth Market, Clerkenwell, EC1R 4QA (7278 0800); *Venezia,* 3-5 Goswell Rd, Clerkenwell, EC1M 7AH 97490 1715): *Gatti's ,* 1 Finsbury Av, Moorgate, EC2M 2PA (7247 1051); *G Franco's Pasta House,* 9 Luke St, Moorgate, EC2A 4PX (7613 4926); *Caravaggio Ltd,* Bankside Ho, 107-112 Leadenhall St, Monument, EC3A 4DP (7626 6206); *Cotriani,* 48 Leadenhall Market, Monument, EC3V 1LT 97621 0709); *Great Eastern Dining Room,* 54-56 Great Eastern St, Shoreditch, EC2 (7613 4545); *Lovats,* 31 Lovats La, Monument, EC3R 8EB (7220 7613); *Mangiare Ltd,* 145 Minories, EC3N 1LS (7481 3255): *San Nazzaro,* 57 Aldgate High St, Monument, EC3N 1AL (7480 7402); *Issimo Tratottoria,* 10 Lime St, Monument, EC3M 7AA (7623 3616); *Da Vinci,*42-44 Carter La, St. Paul's, EC4V 5EA 97236 3938); *Harry's Bar,* 15 Blackfriars La, St. Paul's, EC4V 6ER (7329 0240); *La Scala,* 74 Luke St, Moorgate, EC2A 4PY (7613 1230); *Peasant,* 240 St John Street, EC1 (7336 7726); *Perc%nto,* 28 Ludgate Hill, EC4 (7778 0010).

South East 1 *Bella Pasta,* 37 Tooley St, Southwark, SE1 2QF (7407 5267); *Blue Olive,* 56-

58 Tooley St, London Bridge, SE1 (7407 6001); *Cantina del Ponte,* Butler's Wharf Bldg, 36c Shad Thames, SE1 (7403 5403); *Caprini,* 77 Waterloo Rd, Souhwark, SE1 8UD (7928 66422); *La Barca Ristorante,* 81 Lower Marsh, Southwark, SE1 7AB (7261 9221); *La Dolce Vita,* 4-5 London Rd, Southwark, SE1 6JZ (7928 7138); *La Spezia,* 35 Railway Approach, Southwark, SE1 9SS (7407 0277); *Perdoni's,* 18-20 Kennington Rd, Southwark, SE1 7BL (7928 6846); *Piazza,* 65 The Cut, Southwark, SE1 8LL (7401 7492); *Pizzeria Castello,* 20 Walworth Rd, Elephant & Castle, SE1 (7703 2556); *Pizzeria Nettuno,* 222 Elephant & Castle Shopping Centre, Southwark, SE1 6TA (7701 9166); *Roma Coffee Bar,* 93 Snowsfields, SE1 3SS (7407 6002); *Sirena,* Southbank Ho, Black Prince Rd, Southwark, SE1 7SL (7587 0683); *The Our Cellar,* 47-49 Borough High St, Southwark, SE1 1NB.

South West 1 *L'Amico,* 44 Horseferry Rd, Westminster, SW1P 2AF (7222 4680); *L'appuntamento,* 23 Haymarket, Westminster, SW1Y 4DG (7930 7800); *L'arco,* 79 Buckingham Palace Rd, SW1W OQJ (7834 1151); *L'arco,* 79 Buckingham Palace Rd, Westminster, SW1W 0QJ (7834 1151); *Bella Pasta,* 152 Victoria St, Westminster, SW1E 5LB (7828 7664); *Bongusto,* 76 Buckingham Gate, Westminster, SW1E 6PD (7222 7185); *Cafe Europa,* 8-9 Grosvenor Pl, Westminster, SW1X 7SH (7245 0403): *La Campagnola,* 10 Lower Belgrave St, Westminster, SW1W OJL (7730 2057) ; *Caraffini,* 61, Lower Sloane St, Westminster, SW1W 8DH (7259 0235); *Como Lario,* 22 Holbein Pl, Westminster, SW1W 8NL (7730 2954); *Colombina,* 4 Duke of York St, Westminster, SW1Y 6LA (7930 8279); *Como Lario,* 22 Holbein Pl, Westminster, SW1W 8NL (7730 2954); *Crostino,* Fountain Sq, Buckingham Palce Rd, SW1W 9SH (7233 6606); *Dino & Gianna,* 34-38 Vauxhall Bridge Rd, Westminster, SW1V 2RY (7630 8400); *La Fontana,* 101 Pimlico Rd, Westminster, SW1 8PH (7730 6630) ; *Franco's,* 63, Jermyn St, Westminster, SW1Y 6LX (7493 3645); *Galileo's,* 69 Haymarket, Westminster, SW1Y 4RE (7839 3939); *Gran Paradiso,* 52 Wilton Rd, Westminster, SW1V 1DE (7828 5818); *Grissini-London,* 1st fl, 2 Cadogan Pl, SW1 (7858 7171); *Isola,* 145 Knightsbridge, SW1 (7838 1044); *L'Incontro,* 87 Pimlico Rd, Westminster, SW1W 8PH (7730 6327); *Marabel's,* 16 St Barnabas St, Westminster, SW1W 8PE (7730 5550); *Mimmo D'ischia Ltd,* 61 Elizabeth St, Westminster, SW1W 9PP (7730 5406); *Olivio,* 21 Eccleston St, Westminster, SW1W 9LX (7730 2505); *Oliveto,* 49 Elizabeth St, Westminster, SW1W 9PP (7730 0074); *O' sole Mio,* 39, Churton St, Westminster, Sw1V 2LT (7976 6887); *Pescatori,* 66 Haymarket, Westminster, SW1Y 4RF (8892 9875); *Pizza on the Park,* 11-13 Knightsbridge, Westminster, SW1X 7LY (7235 5273); *Quod,* 57 Haymarket, SW1 (7925 1234); *Ristorante De Palme Di Mimmo,* 65 Wilton Rd, Westminster, SW1V 1DE (7828 6908); *Sale E Pepe,* 9-15 Pavillion Rd,

Westminster, SW1X OHD (7235 0098): *Sorriso,* 10A Broadway, Westminster, SW1H 0BE (7222 3338); *Spaghetti House,* 3 Bressenden Pl, SW1 (7834 5650); *Spaghetti House,* 16-17 Jermyn St, Piccadilly, Westminster, Sw1Y 6LT (7629 6097); *Spaghetti House,* 77 Knightsbridge, Westminster, SW1X 7RB (7235 8141); *Spaghetti House,* 71 Haymarket, Westminster, SW14 4RF (7839 3939):*Uno,* 1 Denbigh St, Westminster, SW1V 2HF (7834 1001); *Stefano Cavallini,* 5-6 Halkin St, Westminster, SW1X 7DJ (7333 1234); *Santini,* 29 Ebury St, Westminster, SW1W ONZ (7730 4094): *Vicolo,* 3-4 Crown Pass, Westminster, SW1Y 6PP (7839 3960); *Zafferano* 15 Lowndes St SW1 (7235 5800).

West 1 *Alloro,* 19-20 Dover St, W1 (7495 4768); *Anacapri,* 10 Dorset St, W1H 3FG (7935 6441); *Amalfi,* 29-31 Old Compton St, W1V 5PL (7437 7284); *Aperitivo,* 41-45 Beak St, W1 (7287 2057); *L'Artista,* 10 Old Compton St, W1V 5PG (7439 2275); *Il Barbino,* 64 Seymour St, W1H 5AF (7402 6866); *Barocca Bar,* 13 Moor St, W1V 5LH (7437 2324); *Becchia Milano,* 74-77 Welbeck St, W1G 0AY (7935 2371); *Beppe,* 35 Paddington St, W1M 3RL (7224 0716); *Bella Pasta,* 61-63 Shaftesbury Ave, W1V 7AA (7494 0288); *Bella Pasta,* 25 Argyll St, W1V 1AA (7437 0992); *Bella Pasta,* 116 Baker St, W1M 1LB (7224 3334); *Bella Napole,* 101 Dean St, W1V 5RA (7437 9440); *Bertorelli's,* 19 Charlotte St, W1P 1HB (7636 4174); *Da Beppe,* 116 Tottenham Court Rd, W1P 9HL (7387 6324); *Biagi's,* 39 Upper Berkeley St, W1H 7PG (7723 0394); *Bonbonniere,* 12 Woodstock St, West End, W1R 1HJ (7408 0648); *Bonds,* 4 Blenheim St, West End, W1Y 9LB (7629 1875); *Il Boscaiolo,* 47 Bryanston St, W1H 7DN (7724 9615); *Bucci,* 62 Goodge St, W1P 1FP (7636 1956); *Cafe Roma,* 37 Berwick St, W1V 3RF (7437 1076); *Caffe Uno,* 26-28 Binney St, W1Y 1YN (7499 9312); *Caffe Uno,* 5 Argyll St, W1V 1AD (7437 6191); *Caffe Uno,* 100 Baker St, W1M 1LA (7486 8606); *Caffe Uno,* 64 Tottenham Court Rd, W1P 9PA (7636 3587); *Caffe Uno,* 26-28 Binney St, West End, W1Y 1YN (7499 9312); *Café Venezia,* 15-16 New Burlington St, West End, W1X 1FF (7439 2378); *Caldesi,* 15-17 Marylebone La, West End,W1M 5FF (7935 9226); *La Capannina,* 24 Romilly St, West End, *Capiteli Remo,* 20 Weighouse St, West End, W1Y 1YJ (7629 2224); W1V 5TG (4737 2473); *Capri,* 17 Air St, West End, W1R 5RL (7734 1992); *La Cavalleria Rusticana,* 124 Cleveland St, West End , W1P 5DN (7388 4032); *Cecconi's,* 5A Burlington Gardens, West End, W1X 1LE (7434 1509); *Centrale,* 16 Moor St, W1V 5LH (7437 5513); *Christi Ristorante,* 55 Berwick St, West End, W1V 3RA (7287 4052); *Christi Restauranti,* 32 James St, West End, W1M 5HS (7935 0416); *Condotti,* 4 Mill St, W1 (7499 1308); *Da Corradi,* 22 Shepherd Market, W1Y 7HU (7499 1742); *La Cucina,* 30 Rupert St, West End, W1V 7FR (7388 4032); *Eating House,* 47-51 Bryanston St, West End, W1H 7DN (7262 4113); *Il Cucciolo,* 12 Denman St, West End, W1V 7RE

(7437 0302); *Il Faro*, 10 Charlotte St, West End, W1P 1HE (7636 2889); *Diverso*, 85 Piccadilly, West End, W1V 9HD (7491 2222); *Gianini Pasta Bar*, 162 New Cavendish St, West End, W1M 7FR (7580 4673); *Graffiti*, 163-165 Wardour St, West End, W1V 3TA (7439 4668); *Harry's Bar*, 26 South Audley St, West End, W1Y 5DJ (74080844); *Ibla*, 89 Marylebone High St, West End, W1M 3DF (7224 3799); *Il Panino Italiano*, 3 Winnett St, W1V 7HS (7437 5045); *Il Sorriso*, 95 Charlotte St, W1P 1LB (7636 3144).

Indigo, 75 Beak St, West End, W1R 3LF (7287 1840); *Italia Uno*, 91 Charlotte St, W1P 1LB (7637 5326); *Krusts* [Italian & French], 13 Seymour Pl, W1H 5AN (7724 3446); *La Genova*, 32 North Audley St, West End, W1Y 1WG (7629 5916); *La Locanda*, 35-37 Heddon St, West End, W1R 7LL (7734 6689); *La Rosa*, 1 Green's Ct, W1R 3FT (7734 6917); *La Spighetta*, 43 Blandford St, West End, W1H 3AE (7486 7340); *Linda's Pasta Bar*, 24 Poland St, W1V 3DD (7437 5596); *Little Cabin*, 14 Burlington St, W1X 1RL (7734 6167); *Little Italy*, 21 Frith St, W1V 5TS (7734 4737); *Little Venice*, 9 Portman Sq, W1A 3AL (7837 9397); *Locanda Locatelli*, Churchill Intercontinental, Seymour St, W1 (7935 9088); *Luigi's*, 136 Wardour St, W1V 3AU (7437 8845); *Maria Bella*, 3 Great Titchfield St, W1P 7FA (7636 7310); *Monte Bello*, 84 Great Titchfield St, W1P 7AF (7636 3772); *Papa Picolino*, 12 Great Castle St, W1N 7AD (7636 6560); *Pasta Fino*, 27 Frith St, W1V 5TR (7439 8900); *La Perla*, 28 Brewer St, W1R 3FW (7437 2060); *La Perugina*, 196-198 Great Portland St, W1N 5TB (7436 2547); *Da Paolo*, 3 Charlotte Pl, W1P 1AQ (7580 0021); *Passione*, 10 Charlotte St, W1 (7636 2833); *Piccadilly*, 31 Great Windmill St, W1V 7PG (7734 4956); *Pescatori*, 11 Dover St, W1X 3PH (7493 2652); *Picolo Diavolo*, 8 Old Compton St, W1V 5PG (7437 1024); *Pizza & Pasta*, 56-60 Wigmore St, W1H 9DG (7224 3438); *Il Porcellino*, 10 Blenheim St, W1Y 9LE (7629 9894); *Pollo*, 20 Old Compton St, W1 (7734 5917); *Pulcinella*, 37 Old Compton St, W1V 5PL (7287 3920); *Ristorante Italiano*, 54 Curzon St, W1Y 7PF (7629 2747); *Sack*, 49 Greek St, W1V 5LQ (7439 4159); *Serafino*, 8 Mount St, W1Y 5AD (7629 05544); *Sergio's*, 84A Great Titchfield St, W1P 7AF (7436 7301); *Signor Grilli*, 40 Goodge St, W1P 1HF (7637 7405); *Sirena*, 44 James St, W1M 5HS (7637 7405); *Il Siciliano*, 33 Dean St, West End, W1V 5AP (7437 6024); *Spaghetti House*, 74-76 Duke St, Mayfair, W1M

5DS (7629 6097); *Spaghetti House*, 15-17 Goodge St, W1P 1FE (7636 6582).

Spiga, 84-86 Wardour St, W1V 3LF (7734 3444); *Strada*, 15-16 New Burlington St, London, W1S 3BJ (7287 5967); *Topo Gigio*, 46 Brewer St, West End, W1R 3HN (7437 8516); *Trattoria Montebianco*, 86 Cleveland St, W1P 5DR (7387 2375); *Trattoria Mondella*, 36 Goodge St, W1P 1HF (7637 9037); *Vasco & Piero's Pavillion Restaurant*, 15 Poland St, W1 (7437 8774); *Vecchio Alpino*, 42 Marylebone High St, W1M 3AD (7935 4640); *Venice*, 65 Great Tichfield St, W1 (7636 5618); *Verbanella*, 15 Blandford St, W1H 3AD (7935 8896); *Il Vicolo*, 114 Crawford St, W1H 2JF (7224 2048); *Vjetti*, 42 Marylebone High St, W1M 3AD (7486 3753); *Zilli Fish*, 36-40 Brewer St, W1 (7734 8649).

West Central *Bella Pasta*, 22 Leicester Sq, Holborn, WC2H 7LE (7321 0016); *Bella Pasta*, 10 Irving St, Holborn, WC2H 7AT (7839 5509); *Bella Pasta*, 30 Henrietta St, Holborn, WC2E 8NA (7836 8396); *Bella Pasta*, 70 St. Martins La, Holborn, Wc2N 4JS (7836 0484); *Bella Pasta*, 1 Cranbourn St, Holborn, WC2H 7AJ (7734 1246); *Biagio*, *Trattoria Italiano*, 15-17 Villiers St, Holborn, WC2N 6ND (7839 3633); *Caffe Uno*, 24 Charing Cross Rd, WC2H 0HX (7240 2524); *Caffe Uno*, 37 St Martins La, WC2N 4ER (7836 5837); *Caffe Uno*, 20-21 Leicester Square, Holborn, WC2H 7LE (7747 5100); *Casa Mamma*, 339 Grays Inn Rd, Bloomsbury, WC1X 8PX (7837 6370); *Il Castelletto*, 17 Bury Pl, Bloomsbury, WC1A 2JB (7405 2232); *Ciao Bella*, 86-90 Lambs Conduit St, Bloomsbury, WC1N 3LZ (7242 4119); *Ciao Bella*, 86-90 Lambs Conduit St,

121

Bloomsbury, WC1N 3LZ (7242 4119); *Conca D'Oro*, 54 Red Lion St, Bloomsbury, WC1R 4PD (7242 6964); *Da Mario*, 63 Endell St, Holborn, WC2H 9AJ (7240 3632); *Il Fornello*, 150 Southampton Row, Bloomsbury, WC1B 5AL (7837 4584); *Franco & Johnies*, 23 Villiers St, Holborn, Wc2N 6ND (7321 0137); *Gigi's*, 31 Catherine St, Holborn, WC2B 5JS (7836 3609); *Giotto*, 50-54 New Oxford St, Bloomsbury, WC1A 1ES (7323 0891); *Giovanni's*, 10 Goodwin's Ct, 55 St. Martin's La, Covent Garden, WC2 (7240 2877); *Isolabella*, 45-46 Red Lion St, Bloomsbury, WC1R 4PF (7405 6830); *Italian*, 27 Wellington St, Covent Garden, WC2 (7240 5269); *Italian Kitchen*, 43 Newark St, Holborn, WC2E 7PA (7379 9696); *Italian Kitchen*, 43 New Oxford St, Bloomsbury, WC1A 1BH (7836 1011); *Italian Kitchen T/A*, 2 Bloomsbury St, Bloomsbury, WC1B 3ST (7381 6636); *It's Pizza & Pasta*, 74 Southampton Row, Bloomsbury, WC1B 4AR (7405 2876);

La Bardigiana, 77 Marchmont St, WC1 (7837 5983); *La Padella*, 2 Exeter St, Holborn, WC2E 7DS (7836 1413); *Luna Nuova*, 22 Shorts Gardens, Holborn, WC2H 9AU (7836 4110); *Lugger*, 147 Strand, Holborn, WC2R 1JA (7836 8282); *Luigi's*, 15 Taviststock St, Holborn, WC2E 7PA (7240 1789); *Maggiore's Italian Kitchen*, 17-21 Tavistock St, Covent Garden, WC2 (7379 9696); *Mediterraneo*, 112 King's Cross Rd, Bloomsbury, WC1X 9DS (7636 7310); *Neal Street*, 26 Neal St, Holborn, WC2H 9PS (7836 8368); *Orso*, 27 Wellington St, Holborn, WC2E 7DA (7240 5269); *Paradiso & Inferno*, 389 Strand, Holborn, WC2R OLT (7836 7491); *Il Passetto*, 230 Shaftesbury Av, Holborn, WC2H 8EG (7379 7962); *Pasta Browns*, 32 Bedford St, Holborn, WC2E 9ED (7836 7486); *Pasta House*, 368 Grays Inn Rd, Bloomsbury, WC1X 8BB (7833 0544); *La Piazza*, 35 Cranbourn St, Holborn, WC2H 7AD (7379 6867); *Pizza & Pasta Bardigiana*, 77 Marchmont St, WC1N 1AP (7837 5983);

La Quercia D'Oro, 16A Endell St, Holborn, WC2H 9BD (7379 5108); *San Francesco*, 19 Catherine St, Holborn, WC2B 5JS (7836 6354); *Saraceno*, 182 Grays Inn Rd, WC1X 8EW (7837 9281); *La Scala*, 35 Southampton St, Holborn, WC2E 7HE (7240 1030); *Spaghetti House*, 24 Cranbourn St, Holborn, WC2N 4ER (7836 8168); *Spaghetti House*, 30 St Martins La, Holborn, WC2N 4ER (7836 1626); *Spaghetti House*, 20 Sicilian Ave, Bloomsbury, WC1A 2QD (7405 5215); *Strada*, 6 Great Queen St, Holborn, WC2B 5DH (7405 6293); *Trattoria Bardigiani*, 4-5 Bernard St, Bloomsbury, WC1N 1LJ (7837 8744); *Villa Stefano*, 227 High Holborn, WC1V 7DA (7831 7318); *Zilli*, Great Queen St, WC2 (7240 0011) [fish]; *Zucchino*, 43 Theobalds Rd, WC1X 8SP (7405 9494).

Barnet *Al Fresco*, 1327 High Rd, Totteridge, N20 9Hu (8445 8808); *Café Uno*, 1288-1290 High Rd, Whetstone, Totteridge, N20 9HJ (8445 5462); *Capriccio*, 20 Temple Fortune Parade, NW11 0QS (8455 4432); *Da Franco Ristorante*, 30 Queens Parade, Friern Barnet Rd, Friern Barnet, N11 3DA (8368 6224); *Frankie and Benny's*, Finchley Leisure Development, Lesisure Way, North Finchley, N12 OQZ (8445 2895); *L'Artista*, 917 Finchley Rd, Golders Green, NW11 7PE (8731 7501); *Mulino*, 92-94 The Broadway, Mill Hill, NW7 3TB (8959 3898); *Papa Pino*, 843 High Rd, North Finchley, N12 8TP (8343 9545); *Picolo*, 8 Princes Parade, Golders Green Rd, Golders Green, NW11 9PS (8459 9483); *La Potenza*, 46 Market Place, Golders Green, NW11 6JP (8458 7305); *Regatta*, 10-12 The green, Winchmore Hill, N21 1AY (8886 5471); *San Remo*, 4 Sutton Parade, Hendon, NW4 1RR (8201 5317); *La Scala*, 308 Ballards La, North Finchley N12 OEY (8445 6742); *Sfizio*, 1031 Finchley Rd, Golders Green, NW11 7ES (8455 4884); *Trattoria Trevi*, 119 Ballards La, Finchley Central, N3 1LJ (8346 0252); *Valentino's*, 266 Watford Way, Hendon, NW4 4UJ (8203 1164).

Bexley *Al Dente*, 176 Broadway, Bexleyheath DA6 7BT (8303 9426).

Brent *Italia Romantica Ltd*, 29 Cavendish Rd, NW6 7XR (8830 2090); *Italian Express T/A*, 311 West End La, Kilburn, NW6 1RD (7435 3939); *Mezzaluna*, 424 Finchley Rd, Cricklewood, NW2 2HY (7794 0452); *Small & Beautiful*, 351 Kilburn High Rd, Kilburn, NW6 7QB (7328 2637).

Bromley *Bibioteca*, 51 High St, Beckenham BR3 1AW (8663 6789); *Caffe Uno*, 95-97 High St,

BR7 5AG (8295 4565); *Ferrari's Italian Brasserie,* International Ho, East St, Bromley BR1 1PP (8464 8877); *Gino's,* 20 Bromley Hill, Bromley BR1 4JX (8464 4782); *La Pasta,* 60 High St, Bromley BR1 1EG (8466 6898); *Mia Venezia,* 2 Plaistow La, Bromley BR1 4DS (8466 1160); *O Sole Mio,* 199 High St, Beckenham BR3 1AH (8650 4848).

Camden *Artigiano,* 12a Belsize Terrace, NW3 (7794 4288); *Brizzi,* 131 Drummond St, Camden, NW1 2HL (7387 2156); *Caffe Uno,* 4 South Grove, N6 6BS (8342 8662); *Caffe Uno,* 40-42 Parkway, Camden, NW1 7AH (7428 9124);*Decorum,* Chalk Farm Road, Camden, NW1 8AN (7916 0653); *Fragio,* 144 Finchley Rd, Hampstead, NW3 5HS (7794 9924); *Fratelli,* Plaza Parade, Kilburn, NW6 5RP (7543 2543); *Luna,* 48 Chalk Farm Rd, Camden, NW1 8AJ (7482 4667); *Hampstead Boulevard,* 311 West End La, NW6 1RD (7435 5040); *Hampstead Osteria,* 152 Haverstock Hill, Hampstead, NW3 2AY (7722 5047); *La Brocca,* 273 West End La, (7433 1989); *Olive Garden,* 108 Heath Rd, Hampstead, NW3 1QG (8429 0323); *Il Pappatore,* 235 Euston Rd, Camden, NW1 2BU (7387 3216); *Pane Vino,* 323 Kentish Town Rd, NW5 (7267 3879); *Pasta Habit,* 103 Highgate Rd, Kentish Town, NW5 1TR (7267 9239); *Pasta Plus,* 62 Eversholt St, Camden, NW1 1DA (7383 4943); *Pellicano Espresso,* 19 Hampstead High St, Hampstead, NW3 1PX (7433 3404); *Pizza & Pasta,* 197 Baker St, Camden, NW1 6UY (7486 6027); *Rigoletto,* 98 West End La, Kilburn, NW6 2LU (7328 3308); *Rose & Jack's,* 53 Camden High St, Camden, NW1 7JH (7388 3380); *La Sopresa,* 3 Heath St, Hampstead, NW3 6TP (7435 0024); *Trattoria Fiorentina,* 42 Camden High St, Camden, NW1 0JH (7419 7163); *Vegia Zena,* 17 Princess Rd, Camden, NW1 8JR (7483 0192); *Versilia,* 250 Finchley Rd, Hampstead, NW3 6DN (7794 7640).

Croydon *Caterino's,* 1540 London Rd, SW16 4EU (8764 6022); *Café Palazzo,* 18 Westow Hill, Upper Norwood, SE19 1RX (8670 8900).

Ealing *L'Amico Pizzeria,,* 221 Northfield Av, West Ealing, W13 9QU (8566 4050); *Bella Pasta,* 36 New Broadway, Ealing, W5 2XA (8579 7089); *Bellini,* 69 Hangar La, Ealing, W5 1DP (8997 0145); *Caffe Bianco,* 29 Bond St, Ealing, W5 5AS (8566 4141); *Caffe Uno,* 24 New Broadway, Ealing, W5 2XA (8567 9093); *Il Gusto,* 58 Pitshanger La, Ealing, W5 178 Uxbridge Rd, West Ealing, W13 8RA (8566 5815); QY (8933 2211); *Leon D'Oro,* 51 Steyne Rd, Acton, W3 9NU (89992 1703); *Mamma Amalfi,* 45 The Mall, Ealing, W5 3TJ (8840 5888); *Paolo's,* 7 Hanger Green, Ealing, W5 3EL (8997 8560); *Ragazzi,* 78 Uxbridge Rd, West Ealing, W13 8RA (8566 5815).

Enfield *Bella Pasta,* 36 New Broadway, Ealing, W5 2XA (8579 7089); *Bella Pasta,* 2 The Town, Enfield, EN2 6LE (8367 7514); *Bellini,* 69 Hangar La, Ealing, W5 1DP (8997 0145); *Caffe Uno,* 15 Silver St, Enfield, EN1 3EF (8367 03337); *Casa Verde,* 13 Wades Hill, Winchmore Hill, N21 1BD (8882 5051); *La Caverna,* 169 Chase Side,

Enfield, EN2 OPT (8367 2845); *Enzo's,* 88-90 Chase Side, Enfield, EN2 6NX (8363 6974); *Gorgonzola,* 60 Chase Side, Southgate, N14 5PA (8886 4884); *Punto,* 838 Green Lanes, Winchmore Hill, N21 2RT (8360 0158); *Regatta Ristorant Italiano,* 10-12 The Green, Winchmore Hill N21 1AY (8886 5471); *Romantica,* 24 Hampden Sq, Southgate, N14 5JR (8368 7201); *La Ruota,* 130 High St, Enfield, EN3 4ET (8804 0286).

Greenwich *Bella Vista,* 3-5 Montpelier Vale, Blackheath, SE3 OTA (8318 1143); *Caffe Italia,* 107 Humber Rd, Black heath, SE3 7LW (8858 7577); *Electriq Café,* 183 Eltham High St, Eltham, SE9 1TS (8859 4095); *Gorgonzola,* 60 Chase Side, Southgate, N14 5PA (8886 4884); *Il Pinguino,* 62 Brixton Rd, Eltham, SE9 6BS (7735 3822); *Il Traghetto,* 123 Woolwich High St, Woolwich, SE18 6DS (8854 8710).

Hammersmith & Fulham *Ask,* 345 Fulham Palace Rd, Fulham, SW6 6TD (7371 0392); *Avellino,* 127A Hammersmith Rd, West Kensington, W14 OQL (7603 5187); *L'arco,* 222 North End Rd, West Kensington, W14 9NU (7381 8905); *Bambinos The Second, 107 Dawes Rd, Fulham, SW6 7DU (7385 9538);* *Barbarella,* 428 Fulham Rd, Fulham SW6 1DU (7385 9434); *Bistro Benito,* 166 Earls Cort Rd, Earl's Court, SW5 9QQ (7370 4857); *Cafe Roma,* 22 Shepherds Bush Green, W12 8PH (8743 7800); *Café Uno,* 804 Fulham Rd, Fulham, SW6 5HE (7731 0990); *Capri,* 2A Holcombe St, Hammersmith, W6 9JR (8748 5000); *Capricciosa,* 160 Cromwell Rd, Earl's Court, SW5 OTL (7244 6444); *Casa Carlo,* 32 Vanston Pl, Fulham, SW6 1AX (7381 3782); *De Cecco,* 189 New Kings Rd, Fulham, SW6 4SW (7736 1145); *Cibo,* 3 Russell Gardens, West Kensington, W14 8EZ (7371 2085);*Gioia Mia,* 270 Uxbridge Rd, W12 7JA (8743 5500); *La Picolo Pizzeria,* 243 King St, Hammersmithy, W6 9LP (8563 7360); *Il Pagliaccio,* 184 Wandsworth Bridge Rd, Fulham, SW6 2UF (7371 5253); *New York Diner,* 157 King St, Hammersmith, W6 9JT (8748 2898); *River Cafe,* Thames Wharf, Rainville Rd, W6 (7381 8824); *Strada,* 175 King's Rd, Parson's Green, Fulham, SW6 4SW (7731 6404); *Villa Bianca,* 30 Fulham Palace Rd, Hammersmith, W6 9PH (8846 9792).

Haringey *Caffe Uno,* 348 Muswell Hill Broadway, N10 1DJ (8883 4463); *Capri,* 256 Archway Rd, Highgate, N6 5AX (8341 7327); *Il Cavaliere,* 81 Blackstock Rd, Finsbury Pk, N4 2JW (7226 7678); *Florians,* 4 Topsfield Parade, Middle La, Hornsey, N8 8PR (8348 8348); *La Porchetta,* 147 Stroud Green Rd, N4 (7281 2892); *Pizzeria Pappagone,* 131 Stroud Green St, Finsbury Pk, N4 3PX (7263 2114); *San Carlo,* 2 Highgate High St, Highgate, N6 5JL (8341 9589); *La Sosta Ltd,* 14 Middle La, N8 8PL (8340 1303).

Harrow *Bar Tonino,* 10 Station Approach, Pinner, HA5 5LZ (8868 6099); *Caffe Uno,* 15-17 High St, Pinner, HA5 5PJ (8429 3239); *Caffe Uno, 20 High St, Teddington, TW11 8EW (8943 5488); Canaletto,* 302 Uxbridge Rd, Pinner, HA5 4HR

(8428 4232); *Its,* St Georges Centre, Hill Crescent, Harrow, HA1 2PW (8427 0962); *Ortenzi,* 105 Field End Rd, Pinner HA5 1QG (8429 0323); *Pasta Bowl,* 381 Station Rd, Harrow, HA1 2AW (8427 1555); *Sorrentina,* 6 Manor Parade, Sheepcote Rd, Harrow, HA1 2JN (8427 9411).

Hillingdon *Arvino,* 67 Station Rd, West Drayton, UB7 7LR (01895 445825); *Bella Pasta,* 25 Bakers Rd, Uxbridge, UB8 1RG (01895 811911) *Carinello,* 8 The Broadway, Joel St, Northwood, HA6 1PF (01923 822364); *Da Remo,* Village Rd, Uxbridge, UB9 5BE (01895 832 425); *Giovanni's,* Denham Lodge, Oxford Rd, Uxbridge, UB9 4AA (01895 231 568); *Nonna Rosa,* 119 High St, Uxbridge, UB8 1JT (01895 233 570); *Mezzaluna,* 148 High St, Ruislip, HA4 8LT (0189 567 342).

Hounslow *Il Buongustaio,* 208 Great West Rd, Hounslow, TW5 9AW (8570 50 34); *Caffe Uno,* 163-165 Chiswick High Rd, W4 2DT (8742 1942); *Frankie & Benny's,* Browells La, Feltham, TW13 7EQ (8844 1424); *ITS,* 404-406 Chiswick High Rd, Chiswick, W4 5TF (8995 3636); *Grano,*162 Thames Rd, Chiswick, W4 (8995 0120); *La Mirage,* 809 Chiswick High Rd, Chiswick, W4 4HH (8994 1661); *Palatino,* 6 Turnham Green Terrace, Chiswick, W14 1QP (8994 0086).

Islington *Belmondo,* 47 Cross St, Islington, N1 2BB (7704 0383); *Caffe Uno,* 62 Upper St, N1 0NY (7226 7988); *Cantina Italia,* 19 Canonbury La, N1 2AS (7226 9791); *Casale Franco,* 134-137 Upper St, Islington, N1 1QP (7226 8994); San Daniele Delfriuli, 72 Highbury Pk, Highbury, N5 2XE (7359 0341); *La Forchetta,* 73 Upper St, N1 0NY (7226 6879); *Galiano's,* 104 Highbury Pk, Highbury, N5 2XE (7359 9042); *Maremma,* 11 Theberton St, Islington, N1 OQY (7226 3923); *Metrogusto,* 14 Theberton St, N1 (7226 9400); *Portofino,* 39 Camden Passage, Islington, N1 8EA (7226 0884); *Venezia,* 3-5 Goswell Rd, Clerkenwell, EC1M 7AH (7490 1715); *Puppys,* 63 Newington Green Rd, Islington, N1 4QU (7704 0325); *Stingray,* 36 Highbury Pk, Highbury, N5 2AA (7354 9309); *Strada,* 105-106 Upper St, Islington, N1 1QN (7226 9742); *Toni Brocolli,* 305-307 Upper St, Islington, N1 2TU (7359 7487); *Trattoria Aquillino,* 31 Camden Passage, Islington, N1 8EA (7226 5454).

Kensington & Chelsea *L'Altro,* 210 Kensington Park Rd, Notting Hill, W11 1NR (7792 1066); *Arlecchino,* 143 Edgware Rd, Bayswater, W2 2HR (7724 4309); *De Amicis,* 14 Notting Hill Gate, Notting Hill, W11 3JE (7229 8205); *Beccofino,* 100 Draycott Av, Chelsea, SW3 3AD (7584 3600); *Bella Pasta,* 155 Earls Court Rd, Earl's Court, SW5 9RQ (7244 8320); *Bella Pasta,* 60 Old Brompton Rd, South Kensington, SW7 3DY (7584 4028); *La Bersagliere,* 372 Kings Rd, Chelsea, SW3 5UZ (7352 5959); *Bertorelli,* 17 Notting Hill Gate, Notting Hill, W11 3JQ (7727 7604); *Bistro Benito,* 166 Earls Court Rd, Earl's Court, Sw5 9QQ (7370 6029); *Bucci,* 386 Kings Rd, Chelsea, SW3 5UZ (7351 9997); *Buona Sera at the Jam,* 289A Kings Rd, Chelsea, SW3 5EW (7351 9997); *Café 206,* 206

Westbourne Gro, Notting Hill, W11 2RH (7221 1535); *Caffe Uno,* 804 Fulham Rd, Fulham, SW6 5HE (7731 0990); *Caffe Uno,* 9 Kensington High St, W8 5NP (7937 7830); *Capricciosa,* 160 Cromwell Rd, SW5 0TL (72446444); *Cibo,* 3, Russell Gdns, W14 8EZ (7371 6271); *Il Carretto,* 20 Hillgate St, Kensington, W8 7SR (7229 5040); *El Blu,* 3 2 Kensington Church St, Kensington, W8 4HA (7937 8752); *Il Covo,* 30 Old Brompton Rd, South Kensington, SW7 3DL (7225 3358); *Dall'artista,* 243 Old Brompton Rd, Earl's Court, SW5 9HP (7373 1659); *Daphne's,* 112 Draycott Ave, SW3 (7589 425); *Dino's,* 117 Gloucester Rd, South Kensington, SW7 4ST (7373 3678); *Dino's,* 242 Earls Court Rd, Earl's Court, SW5 9AA (7373 3767); *Dino's,* 1-3 Pelham St, South Kensington, SW7 2ND(7589 3511); *Dino's,* 16 Kensington Chirch St, Kensington, W8 4LF (7937 3896); *Dino's,* 127 Kings Rd, Che;sea, SW3 4PW (7352 4921); *Diva,* 43 Thurloe St, South Kensington, SW7 2LQ (7584 2000); *Elistano,* 25-27 Elystan St, Chelsea, SW3 3NT (7584 5248); *Enigma,* 249 Fulham Rd, West Brompton, SW10 9EW (7795 0048); *Il Falconiere,* 84 Old Brompton St, South Kensington, SW7 3LQ (7589 2401); *La Famiglia,* 7 Langton St, West Brompton, SW10 OJL (7351 076 1); *La Femiche,* 148 Holland Pk Av, Notting Hill, W11 3RH (7221 6090); *Floriana,* 15 Beachamp Pl,Chelsea, SW3 1NQ (7838 1500); *Formula Veneta,* 14 Hollywood Rd, West Brompton, SW10 9HY (7352 7612); *Frantoio,* 397 King's Rd, SW10 0LR (7352 4146); *Il Goloso,* 204 Fulham Rd, West Brompton , SW10 9PJ (7352 9827); *Lorenzo's,* 138A Cromwell Rd, South Kensington, SW7 4HA (7373 2883); *Made in Italy,* 249 King's Rd, Chelsea, SW3 (7352 1880): *Montpeliano,* !3 Montpelier St, South Kensington, SW1 1HQ (7589 0032); *Olio & Farina,* 4 Sydney St, Chelsea, SW3 6PP (7352 3433); *Orsino,* 119 Portland Rd, Holland Park, W11 (7221 3299); *Osteria Basilico,* 29 Kensington Park Rd, Notting Hill, W11 2EU (7727 9372); *Osteria Le Fate,* 5 Draycott Av, 3 Bray Pl, Chelsea, SW3 3LL (7591 0071); *Il Pagliaccio,* 184 Wandsworth Bridge Rd, Fulham, SW6 2UF (7371 5253); *Palio,* 1 7 5 Westbourne Gro, Notting Hill, W11 2SB (7221 6624); *Paparazzi Café,* 58 Fulham Rd, Chelsea, SW3 6HH (7589 0876); *Papa Luigi's,* 2 Castletown Rd, West Kensington, W14 9HE (7610 3974); *Pasta Paridiso,* 143 Goldhawk Rd, Shephard's Bush, W12 8EN (8740 0844); *Pasta Prego,* 1A Beauchamp Pl, Chelsea, Sw1 1NG (7225 1064); *La Perla,* 6 2 Fulham Rd, Chelsea, SW3 6HH (7584 8375); *Pizzeria Venezia,* 12 Kenway Rd, Earl's Court, SW5 ORR (7370 5958); *Il Portico,* 277 Kensington High St, Kensington, W8 6NA (7602 6262); *Sabatino,* 1 Palace Gate, Kensington, W8 5LS (7589 9992); *San Martino,* 101-105 Walton St, Chelsea, SW3 2HP (7589 1356); *Sandrini,* 260 Brompton Rd, Chelsea, SW3 2AS (7584 1074); *San Frediano,* 62 Fulham Rd, SW3 6HH (7589 2232); *San Lorenzo,* 2 2 Beauchamp Pl, Chelsea, SW3 1NH (7584 1074); *Sambuca,* 62 Lower Symons St, Chelsea, SW3 2TJ

(7730 6571); *Scalini,* 1-3 Walton St, Chelsea, SW3 2JD (7225 2301); *Scoff's,* 267 Kensington High St, Kensington, W8 6NA (7602 6777); *Sockhen,* 9 Old Brompton Rd, South Kensington, SW7 3HZ (7584 0132); *Spago 2,* 45 Kensington High St, Kensington, W8 5ED (7937 6471); *Srantoio,* 397 Kings Rd, West Brompton, SW10 OLR (7352 4146); *Toto's,* Walton Ho, Walton St, Chelsea, SW3 2JH (75892062); *The Ripe Tomato,* 7 All Saint's Rd, Notting Hill, W11 1HA (7565 0525); *Thirteen & a half,* 13 Beauchamp Pl, Chelsea, SW3 1NQ (7584 4810); *Toto's,* Walton St, Chelsea, SW3 2JH (7589 2062); *Tusc,* 256 Old Brompton Rd, Earl's Court, SW5 9HR (7373 9082); *Tuscan,* 116 Princedale Rd, Notting Hill, W11 4NH (7792 9302); *Vecchia Riccione,* 350 Old Brompton Rd, Earl's Court, SW5 9JU (7370 1888); *Zafferano,* 15-16 Lowndes St, SW1 (7235 5800); *Zucca,* 188 Westbourne Gro, Notting Hill W11 2HR (7727 0060).

Lambeth *Al Italia Pizza,* 445 Streatham High Rd, SW16 3PH (8679 3800); *Il Bello,* 161 Battersea Park Rd, South Lambeth, SW8 4BU (7498 8659); *Da Franco,* 27 Streatham High Rd, SW16 1DS (8769 6081); *Eco,* 162 Clapham High St, Clapham, SW4 7UG (7978 1108); *Eco,* 4 Market Row, Electric La, Brixton, SW9 (7738 3021); *Italian Job,* 196 Norwood Rd, SE27 9AU (8671 4477); *Lorenzo's,* 122 Streatham High Rd, Streatham, SW16 1BW (8664 6033); *Pangaea,* 15 Atlantic Rd, Brixton, SW9 8HX (7737 6777); *La Pergola,* 66 Streatham High Rd, Streatham, SW16 1DA (8769 2601*Sandro,* 129 Queenstown Rd, South Lambeth, SW8 3RH (7498 1692); *La Vineria,* 84 Clapham Park Rd, Clapham, SW4 7BX (7720 1515).

Lewisham *Gino's,* 5 Bromley Rd, SE6 2TS (8698 2769); *La Lanterna,* 179 Brockley Rd, Brockley, SE4 2RS (8692 3804); *Montecassino,* 94 Sydenham Rd, Sydenham, SE26 5JX (8778 6262); *La Rondinella,* 62 Baring Rd, SE12 0PS (8851 4565).

Merton *Alforno,* 2A Kings Rd, Wimbledon, SW19 8QN (8540 5710); *Bella Pasta,* 18 High St, Wimbledon, SW19 5DX (8944 1909); *Caffe Uno,* 21 High St, SW19 5DX (8946 0544); *Dolce Vita,* 44 The Broadway, Wimbledon, SW19 1RH (8543 5444); *Luigi's,* 129 Gipsy Hill, Upper Norwood, SE19 1QS (8670 1843); *Il Padrino,* 136 Merton Rd, Merton, Wimbledon, SW19 1EH (8543 9174); *San Lorenzo Fuorporta,* 38 Wimbledon High Rd, Wimbledon, SW19 7PA (8946 8436); *Villaggio Italiano,* 25 High Street Wimbledon, SW19 5DX (8946 7779).

Newham *La Vigna,* 250 Barking Rd, East Ham, E6 3BB (8472 8799).

Redbridge *Gotico,* 62 High St, Wanstead, E11 2RJ (8530 4245); *Nino's,* 18 Electric Parade, George La, South Woodford, E18 2LY (89896912); *Trattoria Parmigiana,* 715 High Rd, Leytonstone, Wanstead, E 11 4RD (8539 1700);

Richmond *Bellini's,* 2-3 Rocks La, Barnes, SW13 ODB (8255 9922); *Caffe Uno,* The Watermans Arms, Lonsdale Rd, SW13 9PY (8876

3414); *Caffe Uno,* 20 High St, Teddington, TW11 8EW (8943 5488); *Caffe Uno,* 375 Lonsdale Rd, Barnes, SW13 9PY (8876 3414); *La Fortuna,* 109 Sheen La, Mortlake, SW14 8AE (8876 9414); *Georgios,* 105 Sheen La, Mortlake, SW14 8AE (8876 1799); *Italian Place,* 38 High St, Teddington, TW11 8EW (8943w 2433); *Italian Place,* 40 High St, Teddington TW11 8EW (8943 9200); *Mamma Mia,* 459 Upper Richmond Road West, SW14 7PR (8878 6725); *Osteria Pulcinella,* 36 Church St, Twickenham, TW1 3NR (8892 5854); *Pasta Paridso,* 22 High St, Hampton, TW12 1PD (8943 1160); *Piasta,* 128-130 Porto Venere, 3 Odean Parade, London Rd, Isleworth, TW7 4DE (8560 6900); *Sanremo,* 195 Castlenau, Barnes, SW13 9ER (8741 5909); *Trattoria Sorrento,* 132 High St, Teddington, TW11 8JB (8977 4745).

Southwark *Arancia,* 52 Southwark Park Rd, SE16 (7394 1751); *Bella Pasta,* 96-98 Dulwich Village, Dulwich, SE21 7AQ (8693 3969); *O' Sole Mio,* 7 Croxted Rd, Dulwich, SE21 8SZ (8670 4444).

Tower Hamlets: *Amerigo Vespucci,* 25 Cabot Sq, Canary Wharf, E14 (7513 0288); *Corvino,* 71 Middlesex St, Whitechapel, E1 7DA (7247 7710); *La Forchetta,* 464 Bethnal Green Rd, E2 (7739 9467); *La Gondola,* 253 Globe Rd, Bethnal Green, E2 (8980 8776); *Parco's,* Aldgate Barrs, Marsh Centre, 1 Whitechapel High St, E1 (7488 2817); *Pascali,* 89 Roman Rd, Bethnal Green, E2 OQN (8981 7991); *Piazzaffiri,* 5 White Kennet St, Whitechapel, E1 7BS (7247 4629).

Wandsworth: *Antipasto & Pasta,* 5 1 1 Battersea Park Rd, SW11 (7223 9765); *Buono Sera,* 22-24 Northcote Rd, Battersea, SW11 1NX (7228 9925); *Cantinetta Venetazzu,* 32 Battersea Sq, SW11 3RA (7978 5395); *Cantuccio,* 143 St John's Hill, SW11 (7350 2564); *Ciao,* 196 Lavender Hill, Battersea, SW11 1JA (7801 0342); *Capolito Roma,* 31 St. Johns Rd, SW11 1QN (7228 6113); *Carnevale's,* 558 Garratt La, SW18 4DX (8944 9351); *Conservatory,* 218 Trinity Rd, Tooting, SW17 7HP (8767 5810); *Enoteca,* 28 Putney High St, Putney, SW15 1SQ (8785 4449); *Da Franco,* 238 Upper Richmond Rd, Putney, SW15 6TG (8788 3457); *L'Inizo,* 51A South Lambeth Rd, South Lambeth, SW8 1RH (7582 1218); *Ferrari's Italian Brasserie,* 225 Balham High Rd, SW17 7BQ (8682 3553); *Metrogusto,* 153 Battersea Park Rd, Battersea, SW8 (7720 0204); *Milano Pizza,* 12 Upton Rd, N18 2LJ (8807 9041); *Pepe Nero,* 133 Lavender Hill, Battersea, SW11 5QJ (7978 4863); *San Gennaro,* 22 Battersea Park Rd, Battersea, SW11 4HY (7622 0475); *San Pietro Pizzeria,* 189 Garratt La, SW18 4DR (8871 9464); *Sandro,* 129 Queenstown Rd, South Lambeth, SW8 3RH (7498 1692); *Vito's,* 175 Northcote La, SW11 6QF (7228 7673).

Waltham Forest *Il Toscano,* 25 Orford Rd, Walthamstow, E17 9NL (8503 6831); *Trattoria La Ruga,* 59 Orford Rd, Walthamstowe, E17 9NJ (8520 5008); *Uffizzi,* 753-755 Lea Bridge Rd, E17 (8509 2259).

Wandsworth *Buona Sera,* 22-24 Nortcote Rd, Battersea, SW11 1NX (7228 9925); *Cantinetta,* 31-32 Battersea Sq, Battersea, SW11 3JB (7978 5395); *Ciao Italia,* 196 Lavender Hill, Battersea, SW11 1JA (7801 0342); *Da Franco,* 238 Upper Richmond Rd, Putney, SW15 6TG (8788 3457); *Enoteca,* 28 Putney High St, Putney, SW15 1SQ (8785 4449); *Osteria Antica Bologna,* 23 Northcote Rd, SW11 (7978 4771); *Pepe Unero,* 133 Lavender Hill, Battersea, SW11 5QJ (7978 4863); *Salvo Jure,* 48 Brushfield St, Whitechapel, E1 6AG (7247 7676); *Strada,* 11-13 Battersea Rise, Battersea, SW11 1HG (7801 0794).

Westminster *Assaggi,* 39 Chepstow Pl, W2 (7792 5501); *Avanti,* 143 Edgware Rd, Bayswater, W2 2HR (7724 4309); *Bella Pasta,* 108-110 Queensway, Bayswater, W2 3RR (7229 2439); *Bella Pasta,* 55-57 Queensway, Bayswater, W2 4QH (7792 2880); *Bizzarro,* 18-22 Craven Rd, Bayswater, W2 3PX (7723 6029); *El Mino,* 25 Sale Pl, Bayswater, W2 1PU (7402 7722); *Caffe Uno,* 11 Edgware Rd, Bayswater, W2 2ER (7723 4898); *Caffe Uno,* 122 High St, NW8 7SG (7722 0400); *Caffe Uno,* 106 Queensway, Bayswater, W2 3RR (7229 8470); *Caffe Uno,* 122 St John's Wood High St, NW8 7SG (7722 0400); *Concordia Notte,* 29-31 Craven Rd, Bayswater, W2 3BX (7723 3725); *Casa Frattini,* 104A Chepstow Rd, Bayswater, W2 5QS (7221 1821); *Its,* 17 Kendal St, Bayswater, W2 2AW (7724 4637); *L'Accento,* 16 Garway Rd, W2 4NH (7243 2201); *La Lupa,* 23 Connaught St, Bayswater, W2 2AY (7723 0540); *Mamma Am34 Spring St, Bayswater, W2 1JA (7723 0319); alfi,* Unit 110, Whiteleys Shopping Centre, Queensway, Bayswater, W2 4SB (7792 9992); *Mister Frascati, San Marco,* 10 London Rd, Bayswater, W2 1HL (7724 3672); *Taomina,* 19 Craven Terrace, Bayswater, W2 3QH (7262 2090); *Valentino,* 179-181 Edgware Rd, Bayswater, W2 1ET (7262 4127); *Villa Rosa,* 9 Craven Rd, Bayswater, W2 3BP (7723 7318).

SHOPS

Books *Italian Bookshop,* 7 Cecil Ct, Charing Cross Rd, WC2N 4EZ (7240 1634, fax 7240 1635).

Drinks *Italian Fine Wines Ltd,* 343 City Rd, Clerkenwell EC1V 1LR; *Italian Wine Cellar,* 195 Ferndale Rd, Brixton SW9 8BA (7274 7170).

Fashion *Da Vinci menswear,* 8 The Arcade, Liverpool St, EC2M 7PN (7929 1209); *Florence Italian Fashion Ltd,* 131A Salusbury Rd, Kilburn, NW6 6RG; *Florence Italian Fashions,* 18 Dollis Hill Estate, Brook Rd, Cricklewood NW2 7BZ (8450 2522); *Green Apple Italian Fashion Shoes,* 145 Shoreditch High St, Whitechapel E1 6JE (7613 0902); *Henry Ltd,* 81 Piccadilly, W1V 0HL (7499 1789); *Il Piacere Donna Ltd,* 185 Westbourne Grove, W11 2SB (7467 0778); *Italian Emporium Ltd,* Unit 1, Towers Business Park, Carey Way, Wembley HA9 0LQ (8795 2230); *Italian Imports,* 3-4 Little Portland St, W1N 5AG (7580 7185); *Italian Menswear,* 3 Berkeley St, West End, W1X 6NE (7491 3202); *Italian Signature,* 118 Great Portland St, W1N 5PG (7436 9639); *Italian Suit Shop Ltd,* 3 Berkeley St, W1X 6NE (7491 3202); *Italian Suit Trading Ltd,* 40 Bowling Green La, Clerkenwell EC1R 0NE (7713 5322); *Luna Italian Shoes,* 94 High St, Walthamstow, E17 7JY (8520 8561); *Il Piacere Donna Ltd,* 185 Westbourne Grove, W11 2SB (7467 0778); *Magazzino Italiano Ltd* [clothing], 4-5 Hazlitt Mews, West Kensington W14 0JZ; *Moda Italiana,* 68 Uxbridge Rd, Shepherd's Bush, W12 (8749 7437).

Food & drink *Angelo's Italian Delicatessen,* 14 College Rd, Willesden NW10 5EP (8969 0040); *Carluccio's,* 28a Neal St, WC2 (7240 1487); *Cooperative Italian London Ltd,* Fruit & Veg Market, New Covent Gdn Market, SW8 5JL (7720 3252); *Connections Catering,* 106 Goldhawk Rd, Shepherd's Bush W12 8HD (8743 9850); *Delizie d'Italia,* 70 Lupus St, SW1V 3EJ (7834 1471); *Di Lieto Bakery & Delicatessen,* 175 South Lambeth Rd, SW8 (7735 1997); *Dolce Italia,* 111 High Rd, N2 8AG (8444 5666); *Fratelli Arrigo,* 260 West Hendon Broadway, NW9 6AG (8202 0582); *Gastronomia Italia,* 8 Upper Tachbrook St, SW1V 1SH (7834 2767); *G Gazzano & Son,* 167-169 Farringdon Rd, EC1R 3AL (7837 1586); *Giuliano,* 1a Lacy Rd, SW15 1NH (8785 1741); *Grangelato Italian Ice Cream,* 104 Long Acre, WC2E 9NT (7240 8831); *Gran Sasso,* 44-46 Caledonian Rd, N1 (7837 4080); *I Camisa & Son,* 61 Old Compton St, W1 (7437 7610); *I Sapori di Stefano Cavallini,* 146 Northcote Rd, SW11 6RD (7228 2017); *Italian Fine Wines Ltd,* 343 City Rd, Clerkenwell EC1V 1LR; *Italian Fruit Ltd,* 423 King's Rd, West Brompton SW10 0LR (7351 5841); *Italian Ice Creams,* 133a High Rd, Wood Green N22 6BB (8881 7913); *Italian Place,* 40 High St, Teddington TW11 8EW (8943 9200);

Italian Wine Cellar, 195 Ferndale Rd, Brixton SW9 8BA (7274 7170); *I Tre Colori,* 350 Bowes Rd, N11 1AN (8368 9660); *La Gastronomia,* 86 Park Hall Rd, SE21 8BW (8766 0494); *La Gastronomia Delicatessen,* 135 Half Moon La, SE24 9JY (7274 1034); *L Terroni & Sons,* 138-140 Clerkenwell Rd, EC1 (7837 1712); *Lina Stores,* 18 Brewer St, W1 (7437 6482); *Luigi's Delicatessen,* 349 Fulham Rd, SW10 (7352 7739); *M Policelli Delicatessen,* 6A Thackery St, Kensington, W8 5ET (7937 0191); *Montes,* 23 Canonbury Lane, N1 (7354 4335); *Olga Stores,* 30 Penton St, N1 (7837 5223/5467); *Panino d'Oro,* 47 Marchmont St, WC1 (7837 4819); *Speck,* 2 Holland Park Terrace, Portland Rd, W11 (7229 7005).

Footwear *Da Vinci,* 107 Sheen La, SW14 8AE (8876 8023); *Donelli,* 102 Dean St, W1V 5RA (7437 2533); *Due Passi,* 27 James St, W1M 5HY (7224 1921);

Furniture *Casa Bella,* 29 George St, W1H 5PE (7224 2430); *Dickens Furniture Ltd,* 85 Monier Rd, E3 2PS (8533 0801); *Italian Collection,* 80 West Green Rd, Tottenham N15 5NS (8802 2517); *Italian Connection Ltd,* 27-31 Hampstead Rd, NW1 3JA (7388 8383); *Italian Furniture Retail Ltd,* 9 Ainsdale Crescent, Pinner HA5 5SF; *Italian Furniture Store,* 319 Kilburn High Rd, NW6 (7372 2250); *Italian Interiors,* 8 Redcliffe St, West Brompton SW10 9DS (7370 1642).

TRANSLATION *Anglo-Italian Consulting,* 128 Darwin Rd, W5 4BH (8560 9437); *French & Italian Legal Translator,* 39 Northumberland Pl, Bayswater W2 5AS (7229 4967); *French Italian Translations,* 77 Hotham Rd, SW15 1QW (8788 5011); *Italian Legal Interpreter,* 78 Morshead Mansions, Maida Vale W9 1LG (7286 0665); *Italian Teaching* (translators & interpreters), 8 Parliament Hill, Hampstead NW3 2SY (7431 4121); *Italian Translations,* PO Box 717, Ealing W5 3EY (8998 3024); *Italian Translating Service,* 26 Arran Rd, Catford SE6 2NL (8695 6751); *Italian Translation Services,* 7 Dingwall Gdns, Golders Green NW11 7ET (8458 4019); *Italian Translation Services,* 134 Townmead Rd, Fulham SW6 2SR (7371 8511); *Italtext,* 13 Belsize Park Gdns, NW3 4JG (7586 8705); *Spanish & Italian Translation Services,* Flat 1 !09 Kings Av, Clapham, SW4 8EN (8671 0447); *S Sulis Translations,* 42 Sybil Phoenix Cl, Deptford, SE8 5BA (7237 4934).

TRAVEL *Alitalia Italian Airlines* (8745 8200); *Italian Affair Ltd,* 5-7 Humbolt Rd, Hammersmith W6 8QH (7381 6636); *Italian Connection (London) Ltd,* 1st fl, 252-254 Pentonville Rd, N1 9JY (7520 0470); *Italian Connections Travel,* 28 Manchester St, W1M 5PF (7935 5352); *Italian Department,* 6 Port Ho, Plantation Wharf, Battersea SW11 3TY (7801 9807); *Italian Escapades,* 227 Shepherds Bush Rd, Hammersmith, W6 7AS (8748 2661); *Italia nel Mondo Travel Services Ltd,* 6 Palace St, SW1E 5HY (7834 7651); *Italian Escapades,* 227 Shepherds Bush Rd, Hammersmith W6 7AS (8748 2661); *Italian Impressions Holidays Ltd,* Morley Ho, 314-320 Regent St, W1R 5AB (7436 3393); *Italian Cookery Weeks Ltd* [travel agents], 5 Cullingworth Rd, Willesden NW10 1HN (8208 0112); *Italian Travel,* 74 Cleveland St, W1P 5DS (7636 6311); *Italian Travel Club Ltd,* 247-249 Gray's Inn Rd, WC1X 8QZ (01825890202); *Italian Travel Club,* 247 249 Gray's Inn Rd, Bloomsbury, WC1X 8QZ (01825 890 202); *Liaisons Abroad* [Italian opera specialists], 181 Kings Rd, SW3 5EB (7376 4020).

WELFARE *Advice Agency for Italians,* 124 Canonbury Rd, Islington N1 2UT (7359 3701); *Christian Association of Italian Workers,* 134 Clerkenwell Rd, Clerkenwell EC1R 5DL (7278 0069); *INAS Italian Welfare Service (Ufficio Pensioni),* 248 Vauxhall Bridge Rd, SW1V 1AU (7630 7933 / 7834 2157); *INCA-CGIL* [Italian welfare], 124 Canonbury Rd, N1 2UT (7354 5488); *Italian Day Nursery,* 176 Clapham Rd, Brixton, SW9 OLA (7735 3058); *Italian Hospital Fund,* 54 Wilton Rd, Westminster SW1V 1DE (7233 6675); *Italian Missionary Fellowship,* 31 Earlsthorpe Rd, Sydenham SE26 4PE (8778 7979).

Itigo

Itigo is a Transirianic language of Indonesia (Irian Jaya). This was reported as the language of two London schoolchildren in the *Multilingual Capital* (2000) survey.

Itsekiri

Itsekiri, a Benuic language of Nigeria, is closely related to *Yoruba* and is sometimes considered a variety of the latter. In the *Multilingual Capital* (2000), this was reported as the language of six London schoolchildren.

Ivoirien

ASSOCIATIONS *Association des Ivoiriens en Grande Bretagne*, 2 Upper Belgrave St, SW1X 8BJ (8692 7245).

GOVERNMENT Embassy of the Republic of Côte d'Ivoire, 2 Upper Belgrave St, SW1X 8BJ (7235 6991).

LANGUAGES A large number and wide range of African languages is spoken in the Ivory Coast. The most important of these is **Baule**, the language of about 24%, but twelve others are spoken by between 1% and 11% of the population (Mann, Dalby, et al 1987). **French** has official status.

J

Jain

ASSOCIATIONS *Digambar Jain Association of UK,* 12 Clonard Way, Hatch End HA4 5BU (8965 9990); *Digambar Jain Visa Mewada Association of UK,* 10 St Johns Villas, Friern Barnet Rd, N11 3BU (8368 7202); *Federation of Jain Associations in UK,* 11 Lindsay Drive. Kenton HA3 0TA (8204 2871); *Jain Association of UK,* 74 Wensleydale Ave, Clayhall, Ilford 1G5 0NB (8560 7110); *Jain Social Group,* 48 Hillcrest Ave, Edgware HA8 8PA; *Jain Social Group – South London,* Hill Side, Bishop's Walk, Croydon CR0 5BA (8655 1499); *National Council of Vanik Association,* 37 Howberry Rd. Edgware HA8 6SS (8357 2269); *Navnat Vanik Association,* Navnat Bhavan, 36 Masons Ave, Wealdstone, HA3 5AR (8861 5825); *Vanik Association of UK,* 71 Pretoria Rd. Streatham SW16 6RL (8677 0774); *Young Indian Vegetarians,* 226 London Rd, West Croydon CRO 2TF (8684 3792); *Young Jains,* 2 Lynford Gdns, Edgware HA8 8UG (8958 6578).

EDUCATION *Institute of Jainology,* 23 Randor Pl, W2 2TG (7262 3329).

RELIGION *Atul K Shah,* 199 Kenton La, Harrow HA3 8TK; *Bhakti Mandal,* 41 Bethecar Rd, Harrow HA 1 (8863 3877); *International Mahavir Jain Mission (UK),* 25 Sunny Gdns, Hendon NW4 (8459 0775); *Jain Sangh - East London & Essex,* 167 Eastern Ave, Redbridge (8551 4749); *Jain Vishva Bhakti,* 148 Hendon Way, NW2 2NE (8458-5653); *Navyug Jain Pragati Mandal,* 31 Winworth Hill, Wembley HA9 9SF (8904 5650); *Shree Mahavir Swami Digamber Jin Mandir,* Broadway (via Montrose Rd), off Locket Rd, Harrow Weald HA3 7EH (8428 8676/3005).

SPECIAL *Veerayatan UK,* Pitteullen, Pinner Hill, Pinner HA5 3XU (8866 2828).

WELFARE *Mahavir Foundation,* 11 Lindsay Drive, Kenton HA3 0TA (8204 2871).

Jamaican

ACCOMMODATION *Jamaica Real Estate Ltd,* 9 Stroud Green Rd, Finsbury Park N4 2DQ.

ASSOCIATIONS *Jamaican Reunion Club Ltd,* 43 Credenhill St, Streatham SW16 6PP (8677 6967).

BARS *Jamaica Wine House,* St Michaels Alley, Cornhill EC3V 9DS (7626 9496).

BUSINESS *Jamaica National Building Society,* 234 Elephant & Castle Shopping Centre, SE1 6TE (7708 2443); *Jamaica National Overseas (UK) Ltd,* Unit 223, Elephant & Castle Shopping Centre, SE1 6TE (7708 2443); *Jamaica Trade Commission,* 1 Prince Consort Rd, SW7 2BZ (7584 8894); *National Commercial Bank Jamaica Ltd,* 42 Manchester St, W1M 5PE (7935 5873).

GOVERNMENT *Jamaican High Commission,* 1 Prince Consort Rd, SW7 2BA (7823 9911).

RESTAURANTS

Camden *Port Royal Jamaican Patties,* 19 Kentish Town Rd, NW1.

Islington *Jamaican Joint T/A,* 150a Seven Sisters Rd, Holloway N7 7PL (7263 5763).

Lambeth *Fresh Jamaican Cuisine T/A,* 336 Coldharbour La, Brixton SW9 8QH (7737 4162); *Jamaican Barbeque Centre,* 38 Norwood High St, Tulse Hill SE27 9NR (8766 7669).

SHOPS *Jamaica Blue Mountain Coffee Shops Ltd,* 18a Maddox St, W1R 9PL (7408 2272); *Jamaican Patties Ltd,* Trojan Business Centre, Cobbold Rd, NW10 9ST (8451 6166).

TRAVEL *Air Jamaica* [reservations], Central Ho, Lampton Rd, Hounslow TW3 1HY (8570 7999); *Jamaica Tourist Board,* 1-2 Prince Consort Rd, SW7 2BZ (7224 0505; for brochures only, call free on 0800 445 533).

WELFARE *Friends of the Heart Foundation of Jamaica,* 205 Mitcham La, Streatham SW16 6PW (8769 1436); *Jamaica Hospital League of Friends,* 107 Leander Rd, Thornton Heath CR7 6JZ (8665 9471).

Japanese

ACCOMMODATION *Japan Homes,* 32 North End Rd, NW11 7PT (8455 9656) and 114 Finchley Rd, NW3 5HT (7431 7755); *Japan Hotel Coupon System,* 162 Regent St, W1R 5TB (7437 1247); *Japan Letting Agency,* 177 High St, Acton W3 9DJ (8993 6100); *Japan Properties Ltd,* 656 Finchley Rd, NW11 7NT (8209 1400); *Japan Services,* 2 Queens Drive, W3 0HA (8752 0445); *Japan UK Property,* 92 High St, Wimbledon SW19 5EG (8947 3111); *Kyo Service* [Central Office], 17 Lower Merton Rise, Adelaide Rd, NW3 3RA (7722 2721, fax 7483 2146); *Kyo Service* [Head Office], 280 Preston Rd, Harrow, HA3 0QA (8908 1135, fax: 8908 1860); *London and Tokyo Property Services,* 62 Queens Grove, NW8 6ER (7722 8700); *London Japanese Estate Services,* 206 Worple Rd, Raynes Park SW20 8PN (8942 8288); *London-Japanese Estates Ltd,* 6-14 Underwood St, Islington N1 7JQ; *London Tokyo Property Services Ltd,* (residential letting agents), 214 Baker St, NW1 5RT (7486 4256); *London Tokyo Property Services Ltd,* 219a Finchley Rd, NW3 6LP (7372 7341); *London Tokyo Property Services Ltd,* 8 North End Rd, NW11 7PH (8731 8314); *London Tokyo Property Services Ltd,* 176 Putney High St, SW15 1RS (8780 1101);

London Tokyo Property Services Ltd, 351b Regents Park Rd, N3 1DH (8343 2306); *London Tokyo Property Services Ltd* Station Parade, Noel Rd, W3 0DS (8752 1906); *Nippon Property,* 75b George St, Croydon CR0 1LD (8686 2433); *Shogun Realty,* 21 Pratt St, Camden Town NW1 0BG (7916 5500, fax 7916 5620); *Tokyo Agency Ltd,* 108 Ballards La, N3 2DN (8349 0536); *Tokyo Leasing (UK) Ltd,* 4-10 Heneage La, EC3A 5DQ (7283 6100); *Wakoma & Co* (Letting). Gateway Ho, 318-320 Regents Park Rd, N3 2LN (8343 2115, fax: 8343 2303).

ARTS *Hanga Ten Contemporary Japanese Print,* Hurlingham Studios, 1a Ranelagh Gdns, SW6 3PA (7371 9677); *Japanese Gallery,* 66d Kensington Church St, W8 4BY (7229 2934); *Japan Print Gallery,* 43 Pembridge Rd, W11 3HG (7221 0927).

ASSOCIATIONS *Daiwa Anglo Japanese Foundation,* Japan Ho, 13-14 Cornwall Terrace, NW1 4QP (7486 4348) [charity]; *Japan Association for Preventing Marine Accidents,* Dexter Ho, Royal Mint St, EC3N 4JR (7488 3168); *Japanese Shipowners Association,* Dexter Ho, Royal Mint Ct, EC3N 4JR (7488 0899); 51 Greencoat Pl, SW1P 1DS (7630 5563); *Japan Foundation,* 17 Old Park La, W1Y 3LG (7499 4726); *Japan Society for the Promotion of Science,* 12 Berkeley St, W1J 8DT (7629 3577); *Nippon Club,* Samuel Ho, 6 St. Albans St, SW1Y 4SQ (7930 2004).

BARS & NIGHT-CLUBS *Bar Japan,* 251a Old Brompton Rd, SW5 9HP (7370 2323); *Bar Kaz,* Basement, 16 Hanway St, W1P 9DD [with karaoke] (7637 1410); *Club 29,* 29 Maddox St, W1R 9LD (7629 4101) [with karaoke]; *Elbow Room Pool Bar,* 103 Westbourne Grove, W2 4UW (7221 5211); *Ginza,* 42 Albemarle St, W1X 3FE (7499 0718); *Kaede,* 27 Romilly St, W1V 5TQ (7287 6264); *Le Club Polo,* 56 St Giles' High St, WC2H 8LH (7836 7484); *Reve,* 18 Thayer St, W1M 5LD (7486 6906); *Rokudenashi,* 15 Kingly St, W1R 5LD (7287 1221).

BUSINESS

General *Anglo-Japan Business Bureau,* Hammers La, NW7 4DD (8959 3211); *Anglo Japanese Economic Institute,* Morley Ho, 314-322 Regent St, W1R 5AD (7637 7872); *Japanese Chamber of Commerce and Industry,* Salisbury Ho, 29 Finsbury Circus, EC2M 7DT (7628 0069); *Japan Europe Business Support (Jebs) Ltd,* The Kestrel Suite, Broadway Ho, The Broadway, Wimbledon SW19 1RL (8543 9365).

Banks *Bank of Japan,* Basildon Ho, 7-11 Moorgate, EC2R 6AD (7606 2454); *Bank of Tokyo,* 6 Broadgate, EC2M 2SX (7667 8869); *Bank Of Tokyo Mitsubishi Ltd,* 12 Finsbury Circus, EC2M 7BT (7588 1111); *Bank of Yokohama,* 40 Basinghall St, EC2V 5BE (7628 9973); *Development Bank of Japan,* City Tower, 40 Basinghall St, EC2V 5DE (7638 6210); *Fuji Bank,* River Plate Ho, 7-11 Finsbury Circus, EC2M 7DH (7588 2211); *Hokkaido Takushoku Bank Ltd,* 3 Cissbury Ring North, North Finchley, N12 7AL; *Industrial Bank of Japan Ltd,* 1 Friday St, EC4M 9BT (7248 1111); *Mitsubishi Bank,*

Finsbury Circus Ho, 12-15 Finsbury Circus, EC2M 2BT (7577 1140); *Mitsubishi Trust & Banking Corporation,* 24 Lombard St, EC3V 9AJ (7929 2323); *Mizuho International plc,* 1 Friday St, EC4 (7236 1090); *Nomura International plc,* Nomura Ho, 1 St Martins Le Grand, Clerkenwell EC1A 4NP (7521 2000).

Other Financial Services *Japan Center for International Finance(JCIF),* Bracken Ho, Friday St, EC4M 9JA (7236 1502); *Japan International Asset Management Ltd,* Glen Ho, Stag Pl, SW1E 5AG (7828 9517); *Nikkei Europe,* Bush Ho, Aldwych, WC2 (7379 4994); *Mitsubishi Corporation Finance plc,* Bow Bells Ho, Bread St, EC4M 9BQ (7246 2600); *NEC Industries (UK) plc,* 9-13 St Andrew St, EC4A 3AE (7853 6800); *Nippon Credit International Ltd,* 40 Basinghall St, EC2V 5DE (7825 2000); *Tokyo Mitsubishi International,* 6 Broadgate, EC2M 2AA (7628 5555).

Electricity / Gas / Oil *Japan National Oil Corporation,* Egyptian Ho, 170 Piccadilly, W1V 9DD (7629 4821); *Japan Petroleum Exploration Company. Ltd,* Nash Ho, St George St, W1 (7495 5044); *Mitsubishi Electric BV,* 18th fl, Centre Point, WC1A 1EB (7379 7160); *Nippon Oil Exploration and Production UK Ltd,* 38 Finsbury Sq, EC2A 1PX (7256 2405); *Nippon Oil (UK) plc,* Pollen Ho, 10 Cork St, W1S 3LL (7439 1377); *Osaka Gas Europe plc,* Nash Ho, St. George St, W1R 9DE (7753 8642); *Tokyo Electric Power Co Inc,* Berkeley Square Ho, Berkeley Sq, W1J 6BR (7629 5271) and Norfolk Ho, 31 St.James's Sq, SW1Y 4JJ (7973 9703).

Food *Japan Vintners,* Flat 4 36, Halsey St, SW3 2PT (7584 9199); *Nippon Meat Packers UK Ltd,* 1 St. Katharines Way, E1 9UN (7481 4180); *Tokyo Foods Ltd,* Unit 10, Industrial Estate, Artesian Close, NW10 8RW (8830 1942);

Industry *Kobe Steel Europe Ltd,* Marlborough Ct, 14-18 Holborne, Clerkenwell EC1N 2NE (74 04 2401); *Metal Mining Agency of Japan,* Chancery Ho, 53 Chancery La, WC2A 1QS (7404 0608); *Mitsubishi Heavy Industries Ltd,* Bow Bells Ho, Bread St, EC4M 9BQ (7634 5111); *Mitsubishi Materials Corporation,* Bow Bells Ho, Bread St, EC4M 9BQ (7236 0130); *Nippon Steel Corporation,* 128 Queen Victoria St, EC4V 4BJ (7248 8646).

Insurance *Japan England Insurance Brokers Ltd,* 66 Mark La, EC3R 7HS (7480 6226); *Nippon Life Insurance,* 4th fl, 20 Little Britain, EC1A 7DH (7600 2804, 7726 0190); *Nippon Insurance Co of Europe Ltd,* 50 Mark La, EC3R 7QH (7488 9899).

Marketing *Europe Japan Centre,* Mutual Ho, 70 Conduit St, W1S 2GF (7287 8605); *Euro Japan Marketing Ltd,* 55 Bryanston St, W1H 7AA (7868 8510); *Euro Japan Marketing Ltd,* 150 Regent St, W1R 5FA (7432 0355); *Swiss Japan Marketing Ltd,* 64 Middlesex St. E1 7EZ (7247 3549).

Shipping *I T C (Japan) UK Ltd* [marine spares], 1 Coventry Rd, Ilford IG1 4QR (8518 3927); *Japan Ship Centre (JETRO),* Leconfield Ho, Curzon St, W1Y 8LQ (7470 4700) and 9 Marshalsea Rd, SE1 1EP (7403 1666); *Japan Ship Owners Mutual Protection & Indemnity Association,* 78 Fenchurch St, EC2M 4BT (7702 1638); *Nippon Steel Shipping Ltd,* 11 Telfords Way, E1 9BQ (7702 1051).

Unclassified *Adesco Tokyo Ltd,* 309 Brompton Rd, SW3 2DT (7823 7309); *Dai Nippon Printing (UK) Ltd,* 27 Throgmorton St, EC2N 2AN (7588 2088); *Japan Centre Group Ltd,* 212 Picadilly, W1V 9LD (7917 9539); *Japan Eurotex Ltd,* 77 South Audley St, W1Y 5TA (7518 9940); *Japan Office Equipment,* 26 Danbury St, N1 8JU (7704 0748); *Japan Office Service (UK) Ltd,* 52 Upper St, N1 0QH (7288 1000); *Michiko Koshino Japan Company Ltd,* Unit 8, Alice Owen Tech Centre, Goswell Rd, EC1V 7JQ(7837 9794); *Nihon Inter Service Ltd,* Trafalgar Ho, Grenville Pl, NW7 3SA (8906 9650); *Nihon Nohyaku,* 8 Cork St, W1X 1PB (7434 0033); *Nihon Shika Group,* Salisbury Ho, Finsbury Circus, EC2M 7AU (7638 9696); *Nippon Kaiji Kyokai Class NK,* 12 Finsbury Circus, EC2M 7EB (7621 0963); *Nippon Paint Europe Ltd,* 40 Basinghall St, EC2M 5TU (7628 4667); *Nippon Shinpan Company Ltd - European Regional Office,* Bow Bell Ho, Bread St, EC4M 9BQ (7822 1718); *Osaka Cultured Pearl Co,* 12 Greville St, EC1N 8SB (7242 3954); *Tokyo-Mitsubishi International plc,* 6 Broadgate, EC2M 2RQ (7628 5555); *Tokyo Washin Co,* 54 Regent St, W1R 5PJ (7287 5901); *Trans-Nippon,* Townmead Business Centre, William Morris Way, SW6 2SZ (7384 1888);

EDUCATION Mother tongue classes for Japanese-speaking children are available at Croydon High School for Girls, the Japanese School in London, and Shingakusha - see below for addresses and telephone numbers. In addition to the following organizations, there are many local education authorities and several universities within London which offer a steadily increasing number of courses in Japanese, currently running at about 100, at a wide range of levels - see *Floodlight* <www.floodlight.co.uk> for details.

Alpha Japanese Language Institute, 3-5 Neal St, Covent Garden WC2H 9PU (7240 8761) <alpha@alpha.ac.jp>; *Anglo-Japanese Academic Centre Ltd,* 23 Wakehams Hill, Pinner HA5 3AQ; *Anglo-Japanese History Project,* Morley Ho, Regent St, W1B 3BE (7580 1799); *Asahi Culture Centre - London,* 10-11 Charterhouse Sq, EC1M 6DT (7334 0388, fax 7334 0301); *Hinoki International School London,* 1f Lawford Ho, Albert Pl, Finchley N3 1QA (8343 4332, fax: 8343 4359); *Institute of International Education in London,* Regent's College, Inner Circle, Regent's Park, NW1 4NS (7487 7678, fax: 7487 7679); *Japanese Education Teacher's Society* (JETS), 92 Vallance Rd, N22 4UG (8365 8454, fax 8889 8072); *Japan Festival Education Trust,* 59 Buckingham Gate, SW1E 6AJ (7630 8696); *Japanese Tuition,* 230 Bishopsgate, EC2M 4QH (7375 3111); *Japanese School in London,* 87 Creffield Rd, Acton, W3 9PU (8993 7145, fax: 8992 1224); *Japan Festival Education Trust,* Swire Ho, 59 Buckingham Gate, SW1E 6AJ

(7630 8696); *Japan Foundation,* 17 Old Park La, W1K 1QT (7499 4726); *Japan Foundation London Language Centre,* 27 Knightsbridge, SW1X 7LY (7838 9955); *Kumon Educational UK,* 5f The Grange, 100 High St, Southgate, N14 6ES (8447 9010, fax: 8447 9030); *London Bunka Yochien* [Kindergarten], Church of the Holy Family, Vale La, Acton, W3 0DY (8992 9822, fax: 8992 4209); *Maeda Gakuen - Finchley Branch,* 6 Hendon Ave, Finchley, N3 1UE (8343 2191, fax 8343 1747); *Maeda Gakuen - Acton Branch,* Queens Drive Playing Field, Queens Drive, Acton, W3 0HT (8896 9696, fax 8896 1687); *Preparation For Japanese Schools / Universities (ENA),* 296 High St, W3 9BJ (8992 2030, fax: 8992 2025) and 2 Cyprus Rd, N3 3RY (8343-0088, fax: 8343 3818); *Shingakusha (UK) Co Ltd,* Unit 4, Acton Hill Mews, 310-328 Uxbridge Rd, W3 9QN (8993 7624, fax 8993 7620); *Student Exchange* (7839 1101); *University Consultants (Japan) Ltd,* 7 Gower St, WC1E 6HA (7323 4284).

Cookery *Cordon Bleu* [French cooking in Japanese], 114 Marylebone La, W1M 6HH (7935 3503, fax 7935 7621).

Flower Arrangement (Ikebana) *Igirisu-Ya / Constance Spry Flower School,* Mimosa Ho, 12 Princes St, W1R 7RP (7408 1020 fax 7491 8401); *Ikenobo Ikebana Society-UK London Chapter,* 9 Ravenscroft Ave, HA9 9TJ (8904 6599, fax: 8904 6599); *Ikebana International,* 44 Norlands Crescent, Chislehurst, BR7 5RN (8467 9933); *Kenneth Turner Flower School,* 1st fl, 58 South Molton St, W1Y 5HH (7409 2560, fax: 7409 3132); *Konomi Floral Design,* 141 Albert Rd, N22 7AG (8881 1822); *Ohara School of Ikebana-England, Chapter ,* 26 West Sq, SE11 4SP (7735 3116, fax 7587 1681).

EMPLOYMENT *Active Recruitment,* 3 Westminster Palace Gdns, Artillery Row, SW1P 1RL (7976 7551); *Ashford Associates Recruitment Consultants,* 4th fl, 1 Royal Exchange Ave, EC3V 3LT (7626 4592); *Cannon Persona,* Ground Fl, 12 Nicholas La, EC4N 7BN (7621 0055); *Centre People,* 1-6 Lombard St, EC3V 9JT (7929 5551); *Euro London Appointments,* Three Kings Ct, 150 Fleet St, EC4A 2DQ (7583 0180); *Jac Recruitment,* 12th fl, Cannon Centre, 78 Cannon St, EC4M 6HH (7623 9900); *People First,* 46 Moorgate, EC2R 6EH (7256 9050).

FREIGHT *Cargo Creative Service Ltd (Endo Unyu),* Unit 5 & 6, Goose Green Trading Estate, 47 East Dulwich Rd, SE22 9BN (8693-0084, 8299 1447); *Japan Airlines Company.Ltd,* Export Cargo Building 551, Shoreham Road East, Heathrow Airport, TW6 3SB (8759 2629); *Japan Links Ltd,* 1 Maycroft, Pinner, HA5 3UB (8429 4450); *Koyanagi Worldwide,* 8-9 Crystal Way, Harrow HA1 2HP (8427 6355); *Kuwahara Ltd,* 6 Mcnicol Drive, Park Royal, NW10 7AW (8963 1100); *Nippon Express (UK) Ltd,* c/o Oriental City, 399 Edgware Rd, Colindale, NW9 0JJ (8205 1578); *Nippon Express (UK) Ltd,* Six Bridges Trading Estate, Marlborough Grove, SE1 5JT (7252 1388); *Nippon Express (UK)*

Ltd, Unit 7 Parkway Trading Estate, Cranford La, Hounslow TW5 9QA (8737 4000); *Nippon Cargo Airlines,* 549 Shoreham Road East, Heathrow Airport, TW6X 6AU (8990 9339); *Nippon Interdean (Europe),* Central Way, NW10 7XW (8961 1132); *Nippon Trans Euro,* Drury Way, Brent Park NW10 0JN (8784 0288). *Tokyo Air Service Co Ltd,* Swallowfield Way, Hayes UB3 1DQ (8561 2050).

GOVERNMENT *Japanese Embassy and Consulate General,* 101-104 Piccadilly W1J 7NJ (7465 6500) www.embjapan.org.uk; *Japan Information & Cultural Centre,*101-104 Piccadilly, W1V 9FN (7465 6500, fax 7491 9347); *Japan International Cooperation Agency,* 45 Old Bond St, W1X 4HS (7493 0045, fax 7493 0042); *Japan Local Government Centre,* 15 Whitehall, SW1A 2DD (7839 8500); *Nagoya Representative Office,* c/o JETRO, 5th fl, Leconfield Ho, Curzon St, W1Y 8LQ (7470 4700).

HEALTH & BEAUTY
Clinics and Hospitals *Anglo Japanese Health Care,* 234-236, Hendon Way, NW4 3NE (8202 7272); *Barbican Health Clinic,* 2-6 Austin Friars, EC2N 2HE (7638 4988, 7638 5008); *International Angels,* 101 Selkirk Rd, SW17 0EW (8488 1686); *Japan Green Medical Centre* (City Centre) 205-207 City Rd, EC1V 1JN (7253 2323) and (Acton Clinic) Unit 7, Acton Hill Mews, 310-328 Uxbridge Rd, W3 9QN (8896 1424); *Japan Natural Ltd* [acupuncture], 59 Brewer St, W1F 9UN (7287 3466); *London Iryo Centre,* 234-236 Hendon Way, NW4 3NE (8202 7272); *Nippon Club Medical Clinics* [north], Hospital of St John & St Elizabeth, Brampton Ho, 60 Grove End Rd, St John's Wood NW8 9NH (7266 1121) and [south] The Lodge, Parkside Hospital, 53 Parkside, Wimbledon, W19 5NX (8971 8008).

Dental Care *Arthur & Yoriko Cooper,* Dental Surgeons, 2 Haslemere Gdns, Finchley N3 3EA (8349 9162); *Nihon Shika Group,* Salisbury Ho Suite 1, EC2M 5QQ (7638 9696); *Keith Cohen Dental Surgery,* 23 Harley St, W1N 1DA (7436-2328); *Ko Dental* (Head Clinic) 66 Wimpole St, W1M 7DE (7935 5983, 7486 2412) and (Hendon Clinic) 25 Queens Rd, Hendon, London NW4 2TL (8202 3762); *Shaftebury Clinic,* 1st fl, Wingate Ho, 93-107 Shaftesbury Ave, W1V 8BT (7437 6002); *S S Kay Dental Surgery,* Apartment 6, 103-105 Harley St, W1N 1HD (7486 1059);

Hair & Beauty Salons *Anglo Japanese Hair Salon,* 56 London Wall, EC2 (7588 0335); *Baron Yoshimoto Hair-Art Studio,* Hermitage Lodge, The Hermitage, Richmond, TW10 6SH (8948-4841); *Baron Yoshimoto (Raymond Altback),* 82 St John's Wood High St, NW8 7NH (7722 1225, 7586 2486); *Be-Be Hair & Beauty,* 2 Oxford Rd, NW6 5SL (7328 0908); *B:Zar,* 68 Berwick St, W1 (7494 0426); *Camiyui,* 14 Station Parade, Ealing Common, W5 3LD (8992 2988/9947) and 25 Oxendon St, SW1 (7930 5112/5113); *Capa,* 31 Berkeley St, W1 5FA (7499 5245); *Cosmic Hair Salon,* 254 Pentonville Rd, N1 8JY (7833-2606/2557); *Cosmic Hair Salon,* 71 The Grove, Ealing Broadway, W5 5LL (8566

5600, 8567 9642); *Cosmic Hair Salon,* 2 Sunnyside Terr, Edgware Rd, Colindale, NW9 5DL (8201 3373, 8201 3383); *G South,* 115 Ballards La, Finchley N3 (8346 5506); *Igreque Ono,* 78 Marylebone La, W1M 5FF (7486 3440); *Iwaya Beauty Shop,* 7 Hendon La, N3 1RT (8343 2283); *Kyoko Hair Studio,* 46 Maddox St, W1R 9PB (7629 2753, 7629 4892); *Moriyama,* 58 Upper Montague St, W1H 1FP (7724 8860); *Mega Mix,* 64 Blandford St, W1H 3HE (7486 2030); *Moga Hair And Make-Up Salon,* 1st fl, 33 Brook St, W1Y 1AJ (7491 7761, 7499 3885); *M Salon,* 30 Avery Row, W1X 9HD (7499 0565); *Sanrizz Japanese Salon,* 5 Cheval Pl, SW7 1EW (7823 8731); *Sanrizz Salon,* 134 Brompton Rd, SW3 1HY (7589 4531); *Shiroma Hairdressing Salon* 6-7 Exchange Arcade, Broadgate, EC2M 3WA (7638-1616); *S K Hair & Beauty Unisex Salon,* 40 James St, W1M 5HS (7935 0096, 7486 2953); *Ticro Hair,* 67 Endell St, WC2 (7836 5030); *W International,* 23 Bute St, South Kensington, SW7 3EY (7225 1717, 7225 2727); *Yamamoto,* 18b Eldon St, EC2M 7LA (7628 6923); *Yoshi Hair Studio,* 9 Russell Parade, Golders Green Rd, NW11 9NN (8455 5765, 8455 5717); *Yuko System,* Unit 2, 1 Curzin St, W1Y 7FN (7629 7555).

LANGUAGE Japanese is the first language of more than 98% of the population of Japan. The remaining minorities speak Ryukyuan languages (in the Ryukyu islands), Korean, or Ainu (Hokkaido island).

Mother tongue education in Japanese is available for young children is several places in London; visit <www.resourceunit.com> for details.

Japanese is a language of the **East-Asia** geozone (Dalby 1999-2000). It is ranked 10th in the world with 130m speakers (of whom it is the first language of 120m) and is the official language of Japan. It is written in (combinations of) several different scripts – see <WRITING SYSTEMS> for more information.

Multilingual Capital (2000) reported that Japanese was the first language of 793 London schoolchildren. Map 20, showing the areas of London where the largest numbers of Japanese-speakers live, can be viewed at <www.global-london.com/gallery>.

LEGAL *Japanese Immigration Centre*, 75 Cannon St, EC4N 5BN (7556 7112); *Japanese Immigration Centre*, Unit 3, The Leather Market, Weston St, Southwark SE1 3ER (7582 7490).

MEDIA & INFORMATION *Japan Media Services Ltd,* Studio 1a, Highgate Business Centre, 3 Greenwood Pl, NW5 1LB (7485 0253).

Audiovisual *Fuji International Productions Ltd,* 29 Princes St, W1R 7RG (7734 8888); *Japan Satellite TV (Europe) Ltd,* 3rd floor, Quick Ho, 65 Clifton St, EC2A 4JE (7426 7330); *Nexus Japan Ltd,* 47 Poland St, W1F 7NB (7434 9243) [film makers]; *NHK Japan Broadcasting Corporation,* 4 Millbank, SW1P 3JA (7393 8100); *Nippon TV Network Corporation,* 66 Newman St, W1T 3EQ (7636 0002); **Japan** Satellite TV (Europe) Ltd, Quick Ho, 65 Clifton St, EC2A 4JE (7426 7330); *Tokyo*

Broadcasting System (TBS) London, Bowater Ho, Knightsbridge, SW1X 7LT (7225 2552); *TV Tokyo,* 66 Newman St, W1P 3LA (7323 5505).

Information Technology *Japan Centre Plaza,* 213 Piccadilly, W1J 9HF (7734 4043) [information]; *Japanese European Internet Link Services,* 94 Highgate Rd, NW5 1PB (7482 4494).

Print [*shimbun* = 'newspaper'] *Asahi Shimbun Ltd* (7336 7963), *Asahi Shimbun European Bureau,* (7490 4923), and *Asahi Shimbun International Ltd* (7334 0909, fax 7334 0906), Welken Ho, 10-11 Charterhouse Sq, EC1M 6DN; *Hokkaido Shimbun,* 1 Hay Hill, W1X 7LF (7355 2566); *Insight Japan,* 6 Hugh St, SW1V 1RP (7821 7980); *Japanese Newspaper London Bureau,* International Press Centre, 75-76 Shoe La, EC4A 3JB (7353 6952); *Japan Journals Ltd,* 52 Haymarket, SW1Y 4RP (7973 8401) and 93 Newman St, W1T 3EZ (7255 3838); *Japan Press,* 148 Curtain Rd, EC2A 3AR (7739 4666); *LondonZok* [arts and fashion magazine], Unit 2, 2 relay Rd, W12 7SJ (8740 8746); *Nihon Keizai Shimbun Europe Ltd,* Bush Ho, Aldwych, WC2B 4PX (7379 4994, fax: 7497 2754); *Nikkei Business Publications,* 23 Fleet St, EC4 (7936 2855); *Sankei Shimbun,* 29 Princes St, W1 (7439 4383); *Yomiuri Europe Ltd,* Unit 19, Industrial Park, Carpenter Rd, E15 2DZ (8986 0707, fax: 8986 0729). *Yomiuri Shimbun,* 76 Shoe La, EC4A 3JB (7353 6952).

Telecom *Japan Telecom Co Ltd,* 1 Love La, EC2V 7JN (7600 0041); *Nippon Telecom Ltd,* 7 Castle Close, SW19 5NH (8296 9953); 29 Princes St, W1R 7RG (7439 4383).

MOTORING *Camel Japan Co. Ltd,* Unit 6, Goose Green Trading Estate, 47 East Dulwich Rd, SE22 9BN (8693 8445); *E15 Japanese Cars,* 265 Carpenters Rd, Stratford, E15 2DU (8522 0005); *Five Star Japanese Auto Spares,* 44 Waterloo Rd, Cowley, Uxbridge UB8 2QX (01895 850104); *Heathrow Japanese Spares,* 212 Page Rd, Feltham TW14 8DN (8893 7033); *Hounslow Japanese Spares,* 191 Wellington Rd South, Hounslow TW4 5HA (8814 1234); *Japan and Europe Motors Ltd,* West Hendon Broadway, Edgware Rd, NW9 7AR (8202 2522); *Japanese Auto Spares,* Unit 4, 263 Carpenters Rd, E15 2DU (8555 6661); *Japanese Auto Spares,* 52 Mortham St, E15 3LS (8555 6661); *Japanese Auto Spares,* 44 Waterloo Rd, Uxbridge UB8 2QX (01895 850104); *Japanese Car Parts,* 240 Brownhill Rd, SE6 1AU (8461 5556); *Japanese Car Spare Centre,* Beaconsfield Rd, Hayes UB4 0SL (8573 6676); *Japanese Car Spare Centre,* 461 Lady Margaret Rd, Southall UB1 2QD (8578 3323); *Japanese Import Cars,* 158 High Rd, N15 4NU (8800 6799); *Japanese Parts Centre,* 57 Warton Rd, Stratford E15 2JY (8503 0002); *Just Japanese* (breakers and dismantlers), 2-22 Well St, Stratford E15 1NP (8519 1661); *Japan Spare Parts,* 40 Vaughan Gdns, Ilford IG1 3NZ (8554 8014); *Jem Anet,* Oriental City, 399 Edgware Rd, Colindale NW9 0JJ (8358 2333) and The Hyde, Edgware Rd, NW9 6BH (8202 4408); *Just Japanese Car Spares,*

9 Stacey Ave, Upper Edmonton N18 3PP (8803 3777); *Just Japanese,* Unit 3, Pudding Mill La, E15 2PJ (8519 5522) [motor factors]; *Khitai Japanese Cars & Spares,* 86 High Rd, Leyton E15 2BP (8539 6421); *Kurumaya Auto,* Unit 12, London Business Park, 715 North Circular Rd, NW2 7AH (8450 0009); *Nihon Motor Spares*, 921 Romford Rd, E12 5JT (8514 6319); *Nihon Spares & Tyres,* 921 Romford Rd, E12 5JT (8514 4222); *Nippon Autocare,* 14, Liddell Rd, NW6 2EW (7328 6120); *Nippon 2000 Spares & Tyre Co Ltd,* Units A & B, Invicta Industrial Estate, Hunts La, E15 2QE (8519 5115); *Nippon Motors Ltd,* 26 South Ealing Rd, W5 4QA (8840 5886); *N R Japanese Spares*, 74 Rosebank Rd, E17 8NH (8988 0827); *Thames Cars,* 483 Green Lanes, Palmers Green, N13 4BS (8882 4744) <www.thamescars.f9.co.uk>; *Total Japanese Auto Spares*, 92 Carpenters Rd, Stratford E15 2DU (8221 0211); *Waltham Japanese Repairs*, 77 Rosebank Rd, Walthamstow E17 8NH (8532 8604); *Zulfi Japanese Auto Spares,* 2 9 Featherstone Rd, Southall UB2 5AB (8574 0887).

RECREATION *Japan Racing Association,* 27 Dover St, W1S 4LX (7495 4333); *Nippon Club Ltd,* Samuel Ho, St Albans St, SW1Y 4SQ (7930 2004).

Karaoke:- See bars (above) and restaurants (below) for an indication of those offering karaoke.

Martial Arts:- *Japan Martial Arts,* 112 Bellegrove Rd, Welling, DA16 3QD (8301 3415); *School of Japanese Karate and Self Defence,* Shotokan International, Chase School, Churchbury La, Enfield EN1 3HQ (8368 6249).

RELIGION *London Group of the International Zen Association UK (North)* [Japanese Soto], Highbury Roundhouse Community Centre, 71 Ronalds Rd, N7; *London Group of the International Zen Association UK (South)* [Japanese Soto], 4a Park St, off Stoney St, SE1; *London Group of the International Zen Association UK (West)* [Japanese Soto], Shiatsu College, Unit 62, Pall Mall Deposit, 126-128 Barlby Rd, W10; *London Soto Zen Group* [Japanese Soto], 23 Westbere Rd, NW2; *St Botolph Without Bishopsgate* [occasional services in Japanese], Bishopsgate, EC2 (7588 1053); *Zen Practice Centre* [Japanese Soto/Rinzai], 22 Nettlewood Rd, SW16 5DX (8679 5412).

RESTAURANTS

East Central *Aykoku-Kaku,* Bucklersbury Ho, 9 Walbrook, EC4N 8DQ (7236 9020); *Ginnan*, 1 Rosebery Ct, Rosebery Ave, Clerkenwell EC1R 5HP (7278 0008); *Hana,* 49 Bow La, EC4M 9DL (7236 6451); *Japanese Canteen,* 19 Exmouth Market, EC1R 4QD (7833 3521); *Japanese Canteen Ltd (T/A),* 9 Ludgate Broadway EC4V 6DU (7329 3555); *Japanese Canteen,* 394 St John St, Clerkenwell EC1V 4NJ (7833 3222); *Miyabi,* Liverpool St, EC2M 7QN (7618 7100); *Miyama,* 17 Godliman St, EC4V 5BD (7489 1937); *Moshi Moshi Sushi,* 7-8 Limeburner La, EC4M 7HY (7248 1808) and Liverpool Street Station, EC2M 7QH (7247 3227); *Noto,* 2-3 Bassishaw High Walk, Moorgate EC2V 5DS (7256 9433); *Noto Ramen House,* Bow

Bells Ho, Bread St, St Paul's EC4M 9BE (7329 8056); *Ribon,* 6 Holborn Viaduct, EC1A 2AE [with karaoke] (7329-3252); *Sushi & Souzai Aldgate,* 3 St Botolph St, EC3 (8573 1770); *Sushi & Souzai Broadgate,* 5 Broadgate Circle, EC2A 2BQ (7374 4224); *Sushi & Souzai Moorgate,* Moorgate Underground Stn, EC2Y 9AE (7638 3866); *Sushi & Souzai Queen Victoria,* 51a Queen Victoria St, EC4N 4SQ (7332 0108); *Tajima-Tei,* 9-15, Leather La, EC1N 7ST (7404 9665); *Tatsuso,* 32 Broadgate Circle, Broadgate, EC2M 2QS (7638 5863); *Tokyo City,* 46 Gresham St, EC2V 7EH (7726 0308); *Yo Sushi,* 95 Farringdon Rd, EC1 (7841 0777).

South East 1 *Feng Sushi,* 13 Stoney St, SE1 (7407 8744); *Shino's,* County Hall, Westminster Bridge Rd, SE1 (7401 6514); *Inshoku,* 24 Lower Marsh, SE1 (7928 2344); *Yo Sushi,* Unit 3b, Belvedere Rd, SE1 (7928 8871).

South West 1 *Café Sushi Bar,* 34 Jermyn St, SW1Y 6HS (7292 3409); *Ichiriki,* 17 Strutton Ground, SW1P 2HY (7233 1701); *Isohama T/A,* 312 Vauxhall Bridge Rd, SW1V 1AA (7834 2145); *Kura,* 3 Park Cl, SW1X 7PQ (7581 1820); *Matsuri,* 15 Bury St, SW1Y 6AL (7839 1101); *Mitsukoshi,* Dorland Ho, 14-20 Regent St, SW1Y 4PH (7930 0317); *Noto,* Harrod's, Brompton Rd, SW1 (7730 1234); *Suntory,* 72-73 St James's St, SW1A 1PH (7409 0201); *Yo Sushi,* Harvey Nichols, 5th fl, Knightbridge, SW1 (7235 5000).

West 1 *Bahia* [Thai/Malaysian/Japanese], 28 Frith St, W1V 5TL (7434 3881); *Benihana,* 37 Sackville St, W1X 2DQ (7494 2525, fax 7494 1456); *Cafe Plaza,* 7a Hanover St, W1R 9HH (7629 4361); *Cha Cha House,* 102 Baker St, W1M1LA (7935 4739); *Dai Chan,* 18 Frith St, W1V 5TS (7494 3878); *Defune,* 61 Blandford St, Marylebone, W1 (7935 8311); *Defune,* 34 George St, W1U 7DP (7486 2579); *Donzoko,* 15 Kingly St, W1R 5LD (7734 1974); *Furusato,* 43 South Molton St, W1Y 1HB (7499 3944); *Hokkai,* 61 Brewer St, W1R 3FB (7734 5826); *Ikeda,* 30 Brook St, W1K 5DH (7499 7145); *Ikkyu,* 67a Tottenham Court Rd, W1P 9PA (7436 6169, 7636 9280); *Japanese Canteen,* 5 Thayer St, W1U 3JF (7487 5505); *Jirocho,* 134

133

Wardour St, W1V 3AU (7437 3027); *Ju-Jiro*, 18 Frith St, W1V 5TS (7494 3878); *Kanzan*, 18 Thayer St, W1M 5LD (7486 6906); *Karaoke Box*, 18 Frith St, W1V 5TS (7494 3878, 7287 3682); *Karaoke Club Ginza*, 42 Albemarle St, W1X (7499 0648, 7499 0718); *Karaoke Kanariya*, 43 South Molton St, W1Y 1HB (7499 8780); *Kaz*, 59-61 Brewer St, W1R 3FB [with karaoke] (7734 5826); *Kiku*, 17 Half Moon St, W1Y 7RB (7499 4208); *Kikuchi*, 14 Hanway St, W1P 9DD [with karaoke] (7637 7720, 7436 9513); *Komatsu Sushi*, 40 Great Windmill St, W1 (7287 5298); *Kuru Kuru Sushi*, 76 Brewer St, W1R 3PH (7734 7316); *Misato*, 11 Wardour St, W1D 6PB (7734 0808); *Miyama*, 38 Clarges St, W1J 7ES (7493 3807); *Nakamura*, 31 Marylebone La, W1M 5FH (7935 2931); *Niko Niko*, 19 Percy St, W1T 1DY (7436 4139);

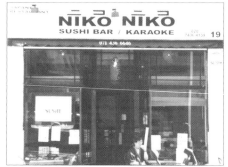

Nobu, 19 Old Park La, W1 (7447 4747); *Plaza Igirisuya*, 7a Hanover St, W1R 9HH (7629 4361); *Ramen Taro*, 61 Brewer St, W1R 3FB (7734 5826); *Rokudenashi*, 15 Kingly St, W1R [with karaoke] (7287 1221); *Ryo*, 84 Brewer St, W1R 3PF (7439 0785, 7287 1318); *Saga*, 43 South Molton St, W1K 5RW (7408 2236); *Saito-An*, 10 Greek St, W1V 5LE (7287 3713); *Sakana-tei*, 11 Maddox St, W1R 9LE (7629 3000); *Sakura*, 9 Hanover St, W1S 1YF (7629 2961); *Satsuma*, 56 Wardour St, Soho, W1 (7437 8338); *Seto*, 19 Kingly St, W1R 5LB (7434 0309); *Shieri Lounge*, 58-59 Great Marlborough St, W1 [with karaoke] (7287 5221); *Shiki*, 27 Davies St, W1Y 1LN (7409 0750); *Shogun*, Adams Row, W1K 2LA (7493 1255); *Simpson Sushi Bar*, 203 Piccadilly, W1A 2AF (7529 9806); *Skura*, 9 Hanover St, W1S 1YF (7629 2961); *Soba Noodle Bar*, 38 Poland St, W1V 3DA (7734 6400); *Sumosan*, Albemarle St, W1 (7495 5999); *Tententei*, 56 Brewer St, W1F 9TJ (7287 1738); *Ten Tokyo Joes*, 85 Piccadilly, W1V 9HD (7495 2595); *Tokyo Diner*, 2 Newport Pl, W1 (7287 8777); *Tomo*, 7a Hanover St, W1R 9HH (7629 4361); *Wagamama Noodle Bar*, 10a Lexington St, Soho W1R 3HS (7292 0990); *Wagamama*, 101a Wigmore St, W1 (7409 0111);*Yae*, Basement, 27 Romilly St, W1V 5TQ [with karaoke] (7287 6264); *Yanbaru*, 22 Harcourt St, W1H 4HE (7723 4110); *Yoisho*, 33 Goodge St, W1P 1FD (7323 0477); *Yoshino*, 3 Piccadilly Pl, W1V 9PD (7287 6622); *Yo Sushi*, 52 Poland St, W1V 3DF (7287 0443) and Selfridges,

400 Oxford St, W1 (7629 1234); *Yume*, 18b Thayer St, W1M 5LD (7935 3377); *Yumi*, 110 George St, W1H 5RL (7935 8320).

West Central *Abeno Okonomi-Yaki*, 47, Museum St, WC1A 1LY; *Aki*, 182 Gray's Inn Rd, WC1X 8EW (7837 9281); *Edokko*, 50 Red Lion St, Bloomsbury, WC1R 4PF (7242 3490); *Epoc*, 70 Brewer St, W1 [with karaoke] (7434 0571); *Gonbei*, 151-53 King's Cross Rd, WC1X 9BN [with karaoke] (7278 0619); *Ikkyu*, 7 Newport Pl, WC1H 4JR (7439 3554); *New Japan Express*, 171 Drury La, WC2B 5QA (7242 2950); *Kenta*, 56 St Giles High St, WC2H 8LH (7379 7381); *Ryo-Ta*, 13-15 West St, Holborn, WC2H 9NE (7240 0634); *Sushi & Souzai Chancery Lane*, 12 Chichester Rents, WC2 (7404 1161); *Tokyo Diner*, 2 Newport Pl, WC2H 7JP (7287 8777); *Tsukuba*, 51-53, Shelton St, WC2H 9HE (7240 0178); *Wagamama*, 4a Streatham St, Bloomsbury WC1A 1JB (7323 9223); *Yo Sushi*, Myhotel, 11-13 Bayley St, WC1 (7636 0076); *Zipangu*, 8 Little Newport St, WC2H 7JJ (7437 5042).

Barnet *Akasaka*, 10a Golders Green Rd, NW11 8LL (8455 0676); *Café Japan*, 626 Finchley Rd, NW11 7RR (8455 6854); *Daruma-San*, 356 Regents Park Rd, N3 2LJ (8343 2608); *Iroha*, 31 Vivian Ave, Hendon, NW4 3UX (8202 9005).

Brent *Abeno Otonomiyake*, Oriental City, 399 Edgware Rd, Colindale NW9 0JJ (8205 1131); *Dream Japan*, 89 Cricklewood La, NW2 1HR (8452 7490); *Murasaki*, 43 Chamberlayne Rd, NW10 (8964 3939); *Sushi Bar Noto*, Oriental City, 399 Edgware Rd, NW9 0JJ; *Sushi-say*, 33b Walm La, Cricklewood NW2 5SH (8459 2971); *Yakitori*, 626 Finchley Rd, Golders Green, NW11 7RR (8455 6854); *Yumenoya*, 89 Cricklewood La, NW2 (8452 7490).

Camden *Asakusa*, 265 Eversholt St, NW1 [with karaoke] (7388 8533, 7388 8399); *Asuka*, Berkeley Arcade, 209a Baker St, Regent's Park, NW1 6UY (7486 5026); *Benihana*, 100 Avenue Rd, NW3 3HF (7586 9508); *Jinkichi*, 73 Heath St, Hampstead, NW3 6UG (7794 6158); *Otafuku*, 75 Parkway, NW1 7PP (7482 2036); *Ribon T/A*, 82 Parkway, Camden Town NW1 7AN; *Sushi Gen*, 243 West End La, NW6 1XN (7431 4031); *Sushiwaka*, 75 Parkway, Camden Town, NW1 7PP (7482 2036); *Taro*, 293 Finchley Rd, NW3 (7794 0190); *Wagamama*, 11

Jamestown Rd, NW1 (7428 0800); *Wakaba,* 122a Finchley Rd, NW3 5HT (7586 7960); *Yakiniku Taro,* 293 Finchley Rd, NW3 6DT (7794 0190); *Yo Sushi,* O2 Centre, 255 Finchley Rd, NW3 (7431 4499).

Ealing *Momo,* 14 Queens Parade, Hanger La, North Ealing W5 3HU (8997 0206); *Musha Japanese Teppan Grill,* 133 Uxbridge Rd, West Ealing W13 9AU (8566 3788); *Sushi Hiro,* 1 Station Parade, Ealing Common, W5 3LD (8896 3175).

Hammersmith & Fulham *Onami,* 236 Blythe Rd, W14 0HJ (7603 7267); *Samurai Teppanyaki* 593-599, Fulham Rd London SW6Ê5UA (7386 7728); *Sumos,* 169 King St, Hammersmith, W6 9JT (8741 7916); *Yoshi Sushi,* 210 King St, Hammersmith W6 9JG (8748 5058).

Harrow *Kei's Lunch Service,* 67 Lincoln Rd, N Harrow, HA2 7RH (8868 0711).

Islington *Kam-Pai,* 26 Penton St, N1 9PS (7833 1380).

Kensington & Chelsea *Benihana,* 77 King's Rd, SW3 4NX (7376 7799, fax 7376 7377); *Hiroko of Kensington,* Hilton International Kensington, 179-199 Holland Park Ave, W11 4UL (7603-5003); *Itsu,* 118 Draycott Ave, SW3 (7584 5522); *Japanese Canteen,* 305 Portobello Rd, W10 5TD (8968 9988); *Kuru Kuru Sushi,* 39 Thurloe Pl, SW7 2HP (7589 2225); *Latitude Café,* 163-165 Draycott Ave, Chelsea, SW3 3AJ (7589 8464); *Little Japan,* 32 Thurloe St, SW7 2LT (7591 0207); *San Sui,* 10 Clarendon Rd, Notting Hill W11 3AA (7229 7136); *Wagamama,* 26 Kensington High St, W8 (7376 1717); *Zuma,* Raphael St, SW7 (7584 1010).

Kingston *Minami,* 74 Richmond Rd, Kingston KT2 5EL (8846 6691); *Sushi Express,* 91 Burlington Rd, New Malden KT3 4LR [not Mon.] (8949 4462).

Lambeth *Fujiyama Noodle Bar,* 7 Vining St, Brixton SW9 8QA (7737 2369); *Ichiban,* 58a Atlantic Rd, SW9 (7738 7006).

Lewisham *Sapporo Ichiban,* 13 Catford Broadway, SE6 4SP (8690 8487).

Merton *Noshi Noshi,* 80 Coombe La., Raynes Park SW20 [not Mon.] (8947 2219).

Wandsworth *Cho-San,* 292 Upper Richmond Rd, SW15 6TH (8788 9626); *Dan Dan,* 333 Putney Bridge Rd, SW15 2PG (8780 1953); *Tokiya Sushi Bar,* 74 Battersea Rise, SW11 (7223 5989).

Westminster *Asuka,* Berkeley Arc, 209a Baker St, NW1 6AB (7486 5026); *Inaho,* 4 Hereford Rd, Bayswater, W2 4AA (7221 8495); *Kashi No Ki,* Hilton International Regent's Park, 18 Lodge Road, NW8 7JT (7586-0911); *Nanbu Tei,* 209a Baker St, NW1 6AB (7486 5026); *Saki,* 82 Queensway, W2 3RL (7229 2234); *Yo Sushi,* Whiteleys, Unit 218, Queensway, W2 (7727 9392).

SHOPS

Antiques *Asahi Japanese Kimonos,* 110 Golborne Rd, W10 5PS (8960 7299); *Japanese Gallery,* 66d Kensington Church St, W8 4BY (7229 2934); *Japanese Gallery Ltd,* 23 Camden Passage N1 8EA (7226 3347).

Bakery *Wagashi Japanese Bakery,* Unit 1c, Connaught Business Centre, Malham Rd, SE23 1AG (8699 1393).

Books *Adanami Shobo,* 387 Edgware Rd, Colindale NW9 (8201 3499) and 70 Brewer St, W1R (7439 3844, fax 7734 7053); *Asahiya Shoten Ltd,* Oriental City, Unit 34, 399 Edgware Rd, Colindale NW9 0JJ (8200 0039, fax 8200 8872); *Books Nippon,* 64-66 St Paul's Churchyard, EC4M 8AA (7248 4956); *Japan Centre Group Ltd,* 3 Lombard St, EC3V 9AA (7623 4443); *Japan Centre Bookshop,* 212 Piccadilly, W1V 9LD (7439 8035, fax 7287 1082); *JP Books,* Basement, Dorland Ho, 14-20 Regent St, SW1Y 4PH (7839 4839, fax: 7925 0346); *OCS Japanese Books,* 2 Grosvenor Parade, Uxbridge Rd, Ealing W5 3NN (8992 6335).

Fashion *Asahi Japanese Kimonos,* 110 Golborne Rd, W10 5PS (8960 7299); *Miss Japan,* 18 Tregarvon Rd, SW11 5QE (7738 0666);

Florists *Japanese Floral & Garden Designs,* 21 Queens Gate Place Mews SW7 5BG (7584 7662).

Food & Drink *Arigato Japanese Supermarket,* 48-50 Brewer St, W1 (7287 1722); *Atari-Ya,* 595 High Rd, North Finchley, N12 0DY (8446 6669) and 7 Station Parade, Noel Rd, Acton, W3 0DS (8896-1524); *Clearspring Ltd* [organic Japanese food products], 19a Acton Park Estate, W3 7QE (8749 1781); *East-West Foods,* Shop 3, The Oaks Shopping Centre, High Street, Acton W3 (8992 7277); *Harro Service Ltd,* 20-22 Worple Rd., Wimbledon, London SW19 4DH (8944 1928); *JA Centre (Tazaki Foods Ltd),* Unit B, Eley Industrial Estate, Eley Rd., London N18 3BH (8803 8942); *Japan Centre (Natural House Foods),* 212 Piccadilly, W1V 9LD (7434 4218); *Mount Fuji International* (01743 741 169) <www.japanesegreentea.co.uk>; *Japan Natural Ltd,* 212 Piccadilly, W1V 9LD (7434 4218); *Marimo,* 350-356 Regents Park Rd, Finchley N3 2LJ (8346 1042); *Minamoto Kichoan,* 44 Piccadilly, W1V 9AJ (7437 3135); *Miura Foods* (Kingston Shop), 44 Coombe Rd, Kingston-upon-Thames KT2 7AF (8549 8076); *Miura Foods* (Sanderstead Shop), 5 Limpsfield Rd, Sanderstead, South Croydon CR2 9AA (8651 4498); *Natural House,* Japan Centre, 212 Piccadilly, W1 (7434 4218); *Ninjin Ltd,* 6-8 St Christophers Pl,

135

W1M 5HB (7486 9841) and at the Hilton Hotel Regents Park, 18 Lodge Rd, St John's Wood NW8 7JT (7586 0911); *Oriental City,* 399 Edgware Rd, Colindale , NW9 0JJ (8200 0009); *Rice Wine Shop,* 82 Brewer Street, Soho, W1A 3PF (7439 3705); *TK Trading,* Unit 7, The Chase Centre, 8 Chase Rd, NW10 6QD (8453 1743); *Yamazaki Bakery,* Unit 14, Oriental City, 399 Edgware Rd, Colindale NW9 0JJ (8205 5569); *Yoshino & Co. (UK) Ltd* [head office] 15-16 Monkville Parade, Temple Fortune, Finchley Rd, London NW11 0AL (8209 0966/7); *Yoshino & Co. (UK) Ltd. (Sakana no Yoshino),* Unit 10, Oriental City, 399 Edgware Rd, Colindale, London NW9 0JJ (8205 6500).

Music *Vinyl Japan (UK) Ltd,* 98 Camden Rd, NW1 9EA (7284 0359) [records].

SPECIAL *Europe Japan Centre,* Mutual Ho, Conduit St, W1R 9FD (7287 8605); *Mitsubishi Research Institute Inc,* Atlas Ho, 1-7 King St, EC2V 8AU (7315 3145); *Research Institute of Telecommunications and Economics Japan,* 12 Finsbury Circus, EC2M 7EB (7628 8818); *Terribroadgate Ltd,* 23 Whistlers Ave, Battersea SW11 3TS (7924 6766).

TRANSLATION *Anglo-Japan Business Bureau,* 53 Hammers La, NW7 4DD (8959 3211); *Anglo Japanese Translations Ltd,* 6 Manfred Ct, Manfred Rd, Putney SW15 2RT (8874 1075); *Centre for Japanese and East Asian Studies* (translators and interpreters), PO Box 427, Pinner HA5 3FX (8429 2839); *Japanese Business & Technical Translations*, 63 Abingdon Villas, W8 6XA (7565 0909); *Japanese / English Translations*, 21 Maitland Ct, Lancaster Terrace, W2 3PA (7402 0112); *Japanese For All,* 18 Ashen Grove, SW19 8BN (8241 8054); *Japanese Interpreting and Translation Services,* 15 Belsize Park Gdns, Hampstead NW3 4JG (7722 2494); *Japanese Language Services Ltd,* 11e Fawley Rd, Kilburn NW6 1SJ (7435 3160); *Japan Press,* 148 Curtain Rd, EC2A 3AT (7739 4666); *Kibo Japanese Translations and Marketing,* Suite 4, 83-84 Berwick St, W1F 8TS (7434 0422); *Japanese Translations Services (UK) Ltd,* 5 The Mall, W5 2PJ (01453 767033, 8840 9639); *TTC Japanese Language Service,* 20 St Mary's Rd, W5 5ES (8566 4626).

TRAVEL *All Nippon Airways (ANA),* 100 George St, W1H 5RH (7569 0900*)* and ANA Ho, Old Bond St, W1X 3TA (7915 3336); *ANA World Tours (Europe) Ltd,* 3rd fl, Nuffield Ho, 41-46 Piccadilly, W1X 9AJ (7478 1900); *AWL Travel Ltd,* 1 Artillery Row, SW1P 1RH (7222 6200); *Blue Sky Tours,* 1st fl, 9 Denmark St, WC2H 8LS (7240 1488); *Central Japan Railway Co,* Bow Bells Ho, Bread St, EC4M 9BQ (7822 1701); *Creative Tours Ltd,* 2nd fl, 1 Tenterden St, W1R 9AH (7495 1775); *Emerald Travel,* 1st fl, 15-16 New Burlington St, W1X 1FF (7312 1712); *Euro-Japan Holidays Ltd,* 93 Newman St, W1T 3EZ (7637 7000); *Gendai Travel Ltd,* 171 Drury La, WC2B 5QA (7404 5375); *His Travel,* 25-28 Old Burlington St, W1X 1RJ (7439 3311); *Imperial Hotel Tokyo* (reservations), 1 Tenterden St,

W1R 9AH (7355 1775); *Japan Airlines,* Hanover Ct, 5 Hanover Sq, W1S 1JR (0845 7747700); *Japan Business Travel (UK) Ltd,* 174 New Bond St, W1S 4RB (7629 8356); *Japan National Tourist Organisation,* Heathcoat Ho, 20 Savile Row, W1S 3PR (7734 9638); *Japan Travel Bureau (Europe) Ltd,* 95a Cromwell Rd, SW7 4JT (7663 6000); *Japan Travel Centre,* 212-213 Piccadilly, W1J 9HF (7255 8283); *Kippu-Ya,* 1 Artillery Row, SW1P 1RH (7976 8338); *Miki Travel Ltd,*18-20 Cannon St, EC4M 6XD (7398 5050); *M O Air International UK Ltd* (London City Office), Royex Ho, 5 Aldermanbury Sq, EC2V 7HR (7600 0110); *My Bus Centre,* 15 Lower Regent St, SW1Y 4LR (7976 1191); *Nippon Chauffeur Cars,* 187 Kings Cross Rd, WC1X 9DB (7833 3441); *Nippon Travel Agency (Europe) Ltd,* 3rd fl, Skyline Ho, 200 Union St, SE1 0LW (7902 2700); *Nissin Travel Service,* 4th fl, 23/25 Eastcastle St, W1N 7BP (7323 3938); *Sakura Travel,* Lower Ground Fl, 21 Woodstock St, W1R 1HS (7491 3360); *Thomas Cook Ltd (Japanese Travel Service),* 30 St James's St, SW1A 1HB, 7853 6400); *Tokyu Travel (Europe) Ltd,* 295 Regent St, W1R 7YA (7493 0468, 7493 2173); *Travel Topia Ltd,* 88b Belsize La, NW3 5BE (7794 6232).

WELFARE *Daiwa Anglo Japanese Foundation,* Japan Ho, 13-14 Cornwall Terrace, NW1 4QP (7486 4348); *Japan Animal Welfare Society,* 51 Greencoat Pl, SW1P 1DS (7630 5563).

Javanese

ACCOMMODATION *Java Properties International Ltd,* 45 Avenue Mansions, Finchley Rd, NW3 7BA.

BUSINESS *Java Cotton Company,* 52 Lonsdale Rd, W11 2DE (7229 3212); *Java Investments Ltd,* 34a Queensbury Station Parade, HA8 5NN.

RESTAURANTS

Waltham Forest *Java,* 885 High Rd Leytonstone, E11 1HR (8532 9020).

SHOPS *Java Java* [tea & coffee], 69 Endell St, WC2H 9AJ (7836 7260) *and* 26 Rupert St, W1V 7FN (7734 5821); *Java Jewellery Ltd,* 29 Hatton Gdn, EC1N 8DA (7404 3399).

Jewish

ARTS & CULTURE *Ben Uri Art Society,* Sceptre Ct, 40 Tower Hill, Ec2N 4DX (7482 1234); *Jewish Museum,* 129 Albert St, NW1 7NB (7284 1997); *Jewish Museum,* 80 East End Rd, N3 2SY (8349 1143); *Jewish Museum,* Sternberg Centre, 80 East End Rd, Finchley N3 2SY (8349 1143); *Jewish Music Institute,* PO Box 232, Harrow HA1 2NN (8909 2445); *Jewish Music Institute,* SOAS, University of London, Thornhaugh St, Russell Sq, WC1H 0XG (8909 2445); *London Jewish Cultural Centre,* The Old House, c/o King's College, Kidderpore Ave, NW3 7SZ (7431 0345).

ASSOCIATIONS *Anglo Jewish Association,* Commonwealth Ho, 1 New Oxford St, WC1A 1NU (7404 2111); *Association of Jewish Ex-Servicemen & Women,* Ajex Ho, East Bank, N16 5RT (8800 2844); *Association of Jewish Friendship Clubs,* 26

Enford St, W1H 1DG (7724 8203); *Association of Jewish Sixth Formers,* 1 Endsleigh St, WC1H 0DS (7387 3384); *Commonwealth Jewish Council,* Victoria Chambers, Strutton Ground, SW1P 2HX (7222 2120); *Institute for Jewish Policy Research,* 79 Wimpole St, W1G 9RR (7935 8266); *International Council of Jewish Women,* 24 Stephenson Way, NW1 2HD (7388 8311); *Jewish Association for Business Ethics Ltd,* PO Box 3840, The Hyde, NW9 6LG (8200 8007); *Jewish Council For Racial Equality,* 33 Seymour Pl, W1N 6AT (8455 0896); *Jewish Historical Society of England,* 33 Seymour Pl, W1H 6AT (7723 5852); *Jewish Lads and Girls Brigade,* 3 Beechcroft Rd, E18 1LA (8989 8990); *Licensed Kosher Caterers Associations Ltd,* 10 Perrins La, NW3 1QY; *Jewish National Fund for Israel,* 58 Edgware Way HA8 8JW, (8421 7600); *Jewish Refugees Committee World Jewish Relief,* The Forum, 78-80 Camden St, NW1 0EG (7691 1771); *Stepney Jewish (B'nai B'rith) Clubs and Settlemant and Meals on Wheels,* Head Office, 2 Beaumont Grove, E1 4NQ (7790 6841) Day Centre (77906819); *Jewish Vegetarian Society,* 855 Finchley Rd, NW11 8LX (8455 0692); *Jewish Women's Centre,* 19 Northfield Rd, N16 5RL (8800 9467); *League of Jewish Women,* 24 Stephenson Way, NW1 2HD (7387 7688); *Oxford & St George's North London Jewish Centre,* 120 Oakleigh Rd North, N20 9EZ (8446 3101); *Thirty-Fives Women's Campaign for Soviet Jewry - Jewish Aid Committee,* 779-781, Finchley Rd, NW11 8DN (8458 7147); *Jewish Youth Fund,* 10 Charterhouse Sq, EC1M 6LQ (7251 4434); *Union of Jewish Students,* 1 Endsleigh St, WC1H 0DS (7387 4644).

BUSINESS *Jewish Association for Business Ethics,* The Hyde, Silkfield Rd, NW9 (8200 8007);

Catering *Kosher Catering Hire,* 43a Oldhill St, Stoke Newington, N16 6LR (8806 4838).

Manufacturers & Distributors *Attaboy Ltd,* 235 Golders Green Rd, Golders Green, NW11 9ES (8455 1429); *Drumstick Products Co,* 10 Manor Rd, Stoke Newington N16 5SB (8802 7197); *E & M Kosher Foods,* 22 Seymour Ct, Cazenove Rd, Stoke Newington, N16 6UA (8806 2726); *Eliko Food Distributors Ltd,* Unit 1, 12-48 Northumberland Pk, Tottenham, N17 OTX (8801 9977); *Finchley Lunch Service,* 100 Bridge La, Golders Green Nw11 OER (8458 9039); *Fronwein's Ltd,* 1095 Finchley Rd, Golders Green, NW11 OQB (8455 9848); *Greenfields Kosher Foods,* Greenfield Ho, 10-12 Windus Rd, Stoke Newington N16 6UP (8806 3978), ; *Kauffman's Ltd,* 7 Coronation Rd, Willesden, NW10 7PQ (8965 6543); *Kenny Arfin Catering,* 88 South Lodge Circus Rd, St. John's Wood, NW8 9EU (7266 2393); *Kosher Cuisine,* Unit C Colindale Business Pk, Carlisle Rd, Colindale NW9 OHN (8905 6611); *Kosher Food Products,* 198 Preston Rd, Wembley, HA9 8PA (8904 7625); *L Botchin Ltd,* 423 Kingsbury Rd, Colindale, NW9 9DT (8204 2236); *Kosher Food Advisor,* 148 Gladesmore Rd, Seven Sisters N15 6TH (8809 5056); *Lunar Delights,* Unit 6, 158 Clapton

Common, Clapton, E5 9AG (8809 1134); *Premier Kedassia Meats,* 44 Glengall Rd, Edgware, Ha8 8SX (8905 4676); *S&J Sales Co,* 10 Timberwharf Rd, Stoke Newington, N16 6DB (8880 2585); *Schaverien UK Ltd,* Edgware Ho, 389 Burnt Oak Broadway, Edgware, HA8 5TX (8905 6611); *Sussers Ltd,* 15 Halleswelle Prd, Fichley Rd, Golders Green, NW11 ODL (8455 4336); *United Kosher Ltd,* 1st fl, Treasure Ho, 19-21 Hatton Garden, Clerkenwell EC1N 8LF.

EDUCATION *Agency For Jewish Education,* 44 Albert Rd, NW4 2SH (8457 9700); *Ben Gurion University Foundation,* 1st fl, 154 Fleet St, EC4A 2JD (7353 1395); *Centre for Jewish Education,* 21 Maple St, W1T 4BE and 109 Whitfield St, W1P 5RP (7580 0214); *Centre for Jewish Studies,* SOAS, Thornhaugh St, Russell Sq, WC1H 0XG (7898 4380); *Hasmonean Boys Grammar School,* Holders Hill Rd, NW4 1NA (8203 1411); *Hasmonean Primary School,* 10 Shirehall La, NW4 2PD (8202 7704); *Ilford Jewish Primary School,* Carlton Drive, Barkingside IG6 1LZ (8551 1431); *Independent Jewish Day School,* 46 Green La, NW4 2AH (8203 2299); *Institute for Jewish Policy Research,* 79 Wimpole St, W1G 9RY (7935 8266); *Institute of Jewish Studies,* UCL, Gower St, WC1E 6BT (7679 3520); *Jewish Free School,* 175 Camden Rd, NW1 9HD (7485 9416); *Jewish Learning Exchange,* 152 Golders Green Rd, NW11 8HE (8458 4588); *Jewish Prep School,* Andover Pl, NW6 5ED (7328 2802); *London School of Jewish Studies,* Schaller Ho, Albert Rd, NW4 2SJ (8203 6427); *Michael Sobell Sinai School, Jewish Studies Department,* Shakespeare Drive, Kenton HA3 9UD (8204 2030); *Leo Baeck College,* Sternberg Centre for Judaism, 80 East End Rd, N3 2SY (8349 5600); *London School of Jewish Studies,* Schaller Ho, 44 Albert Rd, NW4 2SJ (8203 6427); *Moriah Jewish Day School,* Cannon La, Pinner HA5 1JF (8868 2001); *North West London Jewish Day School,* 180 Willesden La, NW6 7PP (8459 3378); *Ohel Moshe Yeshivah (Jewish College),* 83 Bridge La, NW11 0EE (8458 5149); *Simon Marks Jewish Primary School,* 75 Cazenove Rd, N16 6PD (8806 6048); *Society for the Study of Ethiopian Jews (Falashas),* SOAS, Thornhaugh St, Russell Sq, WC1H 0XG (7898 4350); *Spiro Ark Jewish Education,* The Burroughs,NW4 4BT (8201 7172); *Union of Jewish Students,* 1-2, Endsleigh St, WC1H 0DS (7387 4644).

MEDIA & INFORMATION *European Jewish Publication Society,* PO Box 19948, N3 3ZL (8346 1668); *Jewish Central Enquiry Desk,* Commonwealth Ho, 1-19 New Oxford St, WC1A 1NF (7543 5421); *Jewish Chronicle,* 25 Furnival St, EC4A 1JT (7415 1500); *Jewish Information Bureau,* 37 Hallswelle Rd, NW11 0DH (8455 5586); *Jewish Music Distribution,* 13 Hurstwood Rd, NW11 0AS (01323 832863) / SOAS, University of London, Thornhaugh St, Russell Sq, WC1H 0XG (8909 3535); *Jewish Review,* 2b Golders Green Rd, NW11 8LH (8455 2243); *Jewish Quarterly,* PO Box 2078,

W1A 1JR (7629 5004); *Jewish Telegraph,* N3 1HJ (8349 9321); *Jewish Tribune,* 215 Golders Green Rd, NW11 9BY (8458 9988); *Jewish Tribune,* 97 Stamford Hill, N16 5DN (8800 6688); *London Jewish News,* 53 Highgate Rd, NW5 1TL (7692 6932).

RELIGION *Bevis Marks Synagogue,* Bevis Marks, EC3A 5DQ (7626 1274); *Bushey Jewish Cemetery,* Little Bushey La, Bushey WD2 3TP (8950 6299); *Central Synagogue,* 36-40 Hallam St, W1N 5LH (7580 1355); *Chelsea Synagogue,* Smith Terrace, SW3 4DL (7352 6046); *Hammersmith & West Kensington Synagogue,* 71 Brook Green, W6 7BE (7602 1405); *Jews for Jesus,* 174 Finchley Rd, Hampstead NW3 6BP (7431 9636); *Liberal Jewish Cemetery,* Lodge Pound La, NW10 2HG (8459 1635); *Liberal Jewish Synagogue,* 28 St Johns Wood Rd, NW8 7HA (7286 5181); *Maida Hill Spanish Portuguese Jewish Synagogue,* 2 Ashworth Rd, W9 1JY (7289 2573); *National Jewish Chaplaincy Board,* 21 Gloucester Gdns. NW11 9AB (8731 7471); *New West End Synagogue,* St Petersburgh Pl, W2 4JT (7229 2631); *Religious Articles of Stam,* 17 Cheyne Walk, NW4 3QH (8202 1898); *Saint John's Wood Synagogue,* 37 Grove End Rd, NW8 1AP (7286 3838); *Sandy's Row Synagogue,* Sandy's Row, Middlesex St, E1 7HW (7377 5854); *South Hampstead Synagogue,* 21-22 Eton Villas, NW3 4SP (7722 1807); *Spanish and Portuguese Jews Congregation,* 2 Ashworth Rd, W9 1JY (7289 2573); *Spanish and Portuguese Jews Congregation,* 9 Lauderdale Rd, W9 1LT (7286 2153); *Spanish and Portuguese Synagogue Communal Hall,* 8 St James Gdns, W11 4RB (7603 7961); *Union of Orthodox Hebrew Congregations,* 140 Stamford Hill, N16 6QT (8802 6226); *United Synagogue,* Adler Ho, 735 High Rd, N12 0US (8343 6301); *Waltham Forest Hebrew Congregation,* 140 Boundary Rd, E17 8LA (8509 0775); *West Central Liberal Synagogue,* 109 Whitfield St, W1P 5RP (7636 7627); *West End Great Synagogue,* 32 Great Cumberland Pl, W1H 7DJ (7724 8121); *West London Synagogue,* 33 Seymour Pl, W1H 6AT (7723 4404); *Willesden Jewish Cemetery,* United Synagogue, Beaconsfield Rd, NW10 2JE (8459 0394).

RESTAURANTS

East Central *DD's Kosher T/A,* 41 Greville St, EC1N 8PJ (7242 5487).

West 1 *Reuben's,* 79 Baker St, Marylebone, W1 (7486 0035); *Six-13,* 19 Wigmore St, W1 (7629 6133).

Barnet *Bloom's Restaurant,* 130 Golders Green Rd, Golders Green, NW11 8HB (8455 1338); *Cafe On The Green,* 122 Golders Green Rd, Golders Green, NW11 8HB (8209 0232); *Dizengoff Restaurant,* 118 Golders Green Rd, Golders Green, NW11 8HB (8458 7003); *Folman's Fish Restaurant,* 134 Brent St, Hendon NW4 2DR (8202 5592); *The White House,* T/A, 10 Bell La, Hendon, NW4 2AD (8203 2427); *Solly's,* 148A Golders Green Rd, NW11 (8455 2121).

Hackney *VIP Bagel Shop,* 105 Gore Rd, E9 (8986 6061).

Haringey *DD'S Sandwiches,* Mill Mead Rd, Tottenham, N17 9QU (8493 9033).

Tower Hamlets *Brick Lane Beigel Bake T/A,* 159 Brick La, E1 (7729 0616).

Westminster *Harry Morgan's,* 31 St John's Wood High St, NW8 7NH (7722 1869).

SHOPS

Bakeries *Brick Lane Beigel Bake,* 159 Brick Lane, E1 (7729 0616); *Carmelli Bakeries,* 128 Golders Green Rd, NW11 (8455 3063); *Hendon Bagel Bakery,* 55-57 Church Rd, NW4 (8203 6919).

Books & Gifts *Aisenthal,* 11 Ashbourne Parade, Finchley Rd, NW11 0AD (8455 0501); *Emel Books,* 5-6 Star Mews, 52a Windus Rd, N16 6UP (8806 9970, fax 8806 9848); *Jerusalem the Golden,* 146a Golders Green Rd, NW11 (8458 7011); *Jewish Memorial Council Bookshop,* 25-26 Enford St, W1H 2DD (7724 7778, fax 7706 1710); *Joseph's Bookshop,* 2 Ashbourne Parade, 1257 Finchley Rd, NW11 0AD (8731 7575); *Manor House Books,* 80 East End Rd, Finchley N3 2SY (8349 9484, fax 8346 7430); *Menorah Print and Gift Centre,* 16 Russell Parade, Golders Green NW11 9NN (8458 8289); *Steimatzky,* 46 Golders Green Rd, NW11 (8458 9774).

Fish & Meat *E&F Butchers,* 99 Upper Clapton Rd, Clapton, E5 9BU (8806 5360); *Greenspans Butcher,* 9-11 Littleton Rd, East Finchley, N2 ODW

138

(8455 7709); *Kelman's Kosher Products,* North End Rd, Wembley, HA9 0AT (8795 0300); *Leslie Mann Fishmongers,* 35 Vivian Ave, Hendon NW4 3UX (8202 8930); *Premier Meats,* 158, Clapton Common, Clapton E5 9AG (8809 4656).

Groceries *B Kosher Convenience Stores,* 91 Bell La, Hendon, NW4 2AS (8202 1711); *Country Market,* 7-9 Russell Parade, NW11 (8455 0134); *Golders Green Kosher Delicatessen & Butcher,* 12-13 Hallswelle Parade, Finchley Rd, NW11 (8381 4450); *Harry Morgan,* 31 St John's Wood High St, NW8 (7722 1869); *Kosher King Freezer Centre,* 235 Golders Green Rd, NW11 (8455 1429); *Kosher Net Greengrocers,* 158 Clapton Common, Clapton, E5 9AG (8800 8283); *Kosher Paradise,* 10 Ashbourne Parade, Finchley Rd, Golders Green, NW11 0AD (8455 2454); *M&D Grodzinski,* 223 Golders Green Rd, NW11 (8458 3654); *Platters,* 10 Hallswelle Parade, Finchley Rd, NW11 (8455 7345).

Other *Jewish Association for Mentally Ill (JAM) Charity Shop,* 88 Golders Green Rd, NW11 8EN (8201 8074); *Rumpler's Confectioners,* Unit 14, 38-40 Upper Clapton Rd, Clapton, E5 8BQ (8806 7065); *Taboon Bakery,* 17 Russell Parade, Golder Green Rd, NW11 9NN (8455 7451); *Steve's Kosher Kitchen* [delicatessen], 5 Canons Corner, Edgware, HA8 8AE (8958 9446).

SPECIAL *Connect Jewish Marriage Bureau,* 23 Ravenshurst Ave, NW4 4EE (8203 5207); *Jewish Agency for Israel,* Balfour Ho, 741 High Rd, N12 0BP (8446 8109/1144); *Jewish Memorial Council* and *Jewish Committee for HM Forces,* WIH2 DD (7724 7778); *Sharett* [kosher catering], Unit A306, Connaught Business Centre, Hyde Estate Rd, NW9 6JP (8200 1400);.

WELFARE *Association of Jewish Refugees,* 1 Hampstead Gate, 1a Frognal, NW3 6AL (7431 6161); *Barkingside Jewish Youth Centre,* Carlton Drive, Ilford IG6 1LZ (8551 0947); *Bernhard Baron St Georges Jewish Settlement,* 120 Oakleigh Rd Nth, N20 9EZ (8446 3101); *Central Council for Jewish Community Services,* 17 Highfield Rd, NW11 9LS (8458 1035); *East End Jewish Clothing Collection Fund,* Kerry Ho, Sidney St, E1 3EL (7790 4965); *Edgware & Harrow Jewish Day Centre,* 118 Stonegrove, Edgware HA8 8AB (8905 4737); *Federation of Jewish Relief Organisations,* 143-145 Brondesbury Park, NW2 5JL (8451 3425); *Hackney Jewish Family Services,* 85 Lordship Rd, N16 5HF (8880 2244); *Jewish AIDS Trust,* Walsingham Ho, 1331 High Rd, N20 9HR (8446 8228); *Jewish AIDS Trust - HIV/AIDS Education Unit,* 1331 High Rd, N20 9HZ (8446 8228); *Jewish Association for the Mentally Ill Ltd(JAMI) – Day Centre,* JAMI House, 131 Golders Green Rd, NW11 8HJ (8731 7319); *Jewish Council for Racial Equality,* 33 Seymour Pl, W1H 5AP (8455 0896); *Jewish Bereavement Counselling Service,* PO Box 6748, Finchley Synagogue, Kinloss Gardens, N3 3DU (8349 0839); *Jewish Blind & Disabled,* Care & Campaign Office, 164 East End Rd, N2 0RR (8883 1000); *Jewish*

Care Bereaved Partners Group, IG10 4ET (8502 7811);

Jewish Blind & Disabled, Redbridge Community Campaign Office, Hilary Dennis Ct, 34 Sylvan Rd, Wanstead E11 1QN (8532 2999); *Jewish Blind & Disabled,* Registered Office, 118 Seymour Pl, W1H 5DJ (7262 2003); *Jewish Blind & Disabled,* Sheltered Housing Projects, Milne Ct, 14 Churchfields, South Woodford E18 2QZ (8559 7529); *Jewish Blind and Disabled,* 14 Churchfields, South Woodford E18 2QZ (8505 6445); *Jewish Blind and Disabled,* Cherry Tree Ct, Boakes Close, Roe Green, NW9 9AZ (8204 1505); *Jewish Blind & Disabled (JBD), The Sheltered Housing Projects* Cecil Rosen Court, 327 East La, Wembley, HA0 3LB (8908 0302);

Jewish Care, Head Office, 221 Golders Green Rd, NW11 9DQ (8922 2000); Area Teams, Hackney Bearsted Centre, 85 Lordship Rd, N16 0QY (8880 2244); **community centres:** *Stamford Hill Community Centre,* 91 Stamford Hill, N16 5TP (8800 5672) and *Stepney Community Centre,* 2 Beaumont Grove, E1 4NQ (7790 6441); **group homes:** *Joel Emanual Almhouses,* Sir John & Lady Cohen Ct, 1 Rookwood Rd, N16 6SD (8800 5829); *Rela Goldhill Lodge,* 370 Finchley Rd, NW3 7AJ (7794 9574); *Rela Goldhill Lodge,* Limes Ave, NW11 9TJ (8905 5229); and also at 26 Caddington Rd, NW2 1RS (8450 4045), 6 Gillingham Rd, NW2 1RT (8452 7801), 165 Melrose Ave, NW2 4NA (8452 7589), 181 Melrose Ave, NW2 4NA (8452 3759), 17 Monpelier Rise, NW11 9SS (8209 1257), and 158 Station Rd, N3 2SG (8349 9632); **residential homes:** *Charles Clore House,* 170 Fortis Green, N10 3HN (8883 2965); *Ealon House,* 7b Mapesbury Rd, NW2 4HX (8459 2569); *Ella and Ridley Jacobs House,* 19-25 Church Rd, Hendon NW4 4EB (8203 5368); *Kay Court,* 368 Finchley Rd, NW3 7AJ (7435 8214); *Lady Sarah Cohen House,* Asher Loftus Way, Colney Hatch La, N11 3ND (8920 4400); *Rosetrees,* Asher Loftus Way, N11 3ND (8362 0789); *Rubens House,* 184 Ballards La, N3 2NB (8349 9879); *Vi & John Rubens House,* 5-27 Clarence Ave, Gants Hill IG2 6JH (8518 6599); *Waverley Manor,* 160 Great North Way, NW4 1EH (8203 1511); *Wolfson House,* 311-315 Green Lanes, N4 2ES (8802 9281); **special day care centres:** *Holocaust Survivors Centre,* Church Rd, NW4 1QA (8202 9844); *Sam Beckman,* 29 Babington Rd, NW4 4LD (8203 0521); *Thrift Shop,* 21a Walm La, N2 5SH (8459 3420); *Jewish Care's Shalvata,* Parson St, Hendon NW4 1QA (8203 9033); *Jewish Care, Special Day Care Centres:* Redbridge Sinclair House, Woodford Bridge Rd Ilford, (8551 0017) and Rectory House, Rectory La, Edgware HA8 7LF (8951 3739);

Jewish Child's Day, 707 High Rd, N12 0BT (8446 8804); *Jewish Counselling Service,* 23 Ravenshurst Ave, NW4 4EL (8203 6311); *Jewish Crisis Helpline (Miyad),* 23 Ravenhurst Ave, NW4 4EE (8203 6211); *Jewish Deaf Association,* Julis Newman Ho, Woodside Park Rd, N12 8RP (8446

0502, 8445 7975) / 118 Seymour Pl, W1H 1NP (7262 2003); *Jewish Home Network,* 1007 Finchley Rd, NW11 7HB (8458 5111) [educational services]; *Jewish Joint Burial Society,* North Western Reform Synagogue, Alyth Gdns,Finchley Rd, NW11 7EN (8455 8579); *Jewish Marriage Council,* 23 Ravenshurst Ave, NW4 4EL (8203 6311); *Jewish Memorial Council - Minister to Small Jewish Communities* and *Jewish Memorial Council Pension Funds,* 25 Enford St, W1H 2DD (7724 7778); *Jewish Rescue & Relief Committee,* 215 Golders Green Rd, NW11 9BY (8458 1710); *Jewish Women's Aid,* PO Box 2670, London N12 9ZE (8445 8060); *Jewish Women's Centre,* 19 Northfield Rd, N16 5RL (8800 9467); *Jewish Women's Network,* PO Box 89, Stanmore (8896 2050); *Lady Sarah Cohen House* [residential Jewish hospital], Colney Hatch La, N11 3ND (8920 4100); *London Jewish Family Centre,* 113b Golders Green Rd, NW11 (8209 1117); *Oxford & St. George's North London Jewish Centre (Office)* 120 Oakleigh Rd Nth, N20 9EZ (8446 3101);

Raphael Centre Jewish Counselling Service, Shalvata, Parson St, Hendon NW4 4EB (8203 9881); *Society of Friends of Jewish Refugees,* 741 High Rd, N12 0BQ (8446 1477); *Stepney Jewish (B'nai B'rith) Clubs & Settlement & Meals on Wheels,* 2 Beaumont Grove, E1 4NQ [Head Office] (7790 6841), [Day Centre] (7790 6819); *UK Jewish Aid,* 33 Seymour Pl, W1H 5AU (7723 3442); *United Jewish Israel Appeal,* 741 High Rd, N12 0BQ (8446 1477); *Woodside Park Jewish Day Centre,* Wiseman-Linden Hall, Woodside Park Rd, N12 8RZ (8446 8599).

Jingpho

Jingpho is a Kachinic language spoken in Burma, China (Yunnan) and India (Assam). Only one *Jingpho*-speaking pupil in London was identified by the *Multilingual Capital* (2000) survey.

Jonkha

Jonkha is a Tibetan language with official status in Bhutan. The *Multilingual Capital* (2000) survey identified only one *Jonkha*-speaking pupil in London.

Jordanian

ASSOCIATIONS *Anglo-Jordanian Society,* 311 Lillie Rd, SW6 7LL (7386 0045).

BUSINESS *Jordan International Bank,* 103 Mount St, W1Y 6AP (7493 7528).

GOVERNMENT *Embassy of the Hasamite Kingdom of Jordan,* 6 Upper Phillimore Gdns, W8 7HA (7937 3685).

MEDIA & INFORMATION *Jordan Information Bureau,* 6 Upper Phillimore Gdns, W8 7HB (7937 9499).

TRAVEL *Jordanian Tourist Office & Royal Jordanian Airlines,* 32 Brook St, W1Y 1AG (7878 6333).

K

Kachchhi

See under the alternative spelling **Katchi.**

Kahe

Kahe is a Bantuic language spoken in Tanzania. The presence of one **Kahe**-speaking London pupil was noted by the *Multilingual Capital* (2000) survey.

Kaje

Kaje is a Benuic language spoken in Nigeria. Two London schoolchildren who spoke this were located by the *Multilingual Capital* (2000) survey.

Kakwa

Kakwa is a Nilotic language spoken in Sudan, Congo (Kinshasa) and Uganda. One **Kakwa**-speaking pupil was located by the *Multilingual Capital* (2000) survey in Haringey.

Kalabari

See under the alternative spelling, *Calabari.*

Kalenjin

Kalenjin is the name of a group of Nilotic languages spoken in parts of Kenya and Uganda. Although not mentioned in the *Multilingual Capital* (2000) survey, the presence of some **Kalenjin**-speaking pupils has recently been reported in Hammersmith & Fulham.

Kamba

Kamba is a Bantuic language of Kenya. **Kamba**-speaking pupils have been reported in London within the past decade although none were found at the time of the *Multilingual Capital* (2000) survey.

Kannada

Kannada is a Dravidic language with official status in the Indian state of Karnataka. The presence of **Kannada**-speaking pupils in London has been recorded within the past decade although none were located at the time of the *Multilingual Capital* (2000) survey.

Karen

Karen is a collective name for the Karenic languages spoken on both sides of the Burma / Thailand border. The presence of **Karen**-speaking pupils has been recorded in London within the past decade but none were found at the time of the *Multilingual Capital* (2000) survey.

Kashmiri

HEALTH & BEAUTY *Kashmir Hairdressers,* 732 High Road Leyton, E10 6AA (8556 8397); *Kashmir Hairdressers,* 77 Palmerston Rd, E17 6PU (8521 8767).

LANGUAGE **Kashmiri** is an Indic language spoken in Kashmir. It is generally written in an adaptation of the Arabic consonantal script. *Multilingual Capital* (2000) reported that **Kashmiri** was the first language of six London schoolchildren.

LEGAL *Jammu & Kashmir Council For Human Rights,* 167 Sanderstead Rd, South Croydon CR2 0PH (8651 0600); *Jammu & Kashmir Council For Human Rights,* 3 Singleton Close, SW17 9JY (8640 8546).

MEDIA & INFORMATION *Kashmir Printers (London) Ltd,* 33 Granby St, E2 6DR (7729 2399).

RESTAURANTS

Ealing *Kashmir Tandoori & Sweet Centre,* 155-157 The Broadway, Southall UB1 1LP (8574 3505, 8574 2534).

Hackney *Kashmir Kebabish,* 5 Ridley Rd, E8 2NP (7249 7163); *Kashmir Tandoori,* 163 Mare St, E8 3RH (8985 1311).

Newham *Kashmir,* 18 Queens Market, E13 9BA (8471 7116).

Merton *Kashmir Curries,* 260 Church Rd, Mitcham CR4 3BW (8640 3824).

Wandsworth *Kashmir Curries,* 103 East Hill, SW18 2QB (8871 2868).

SHOPS

Kashmir Art & Craft, 2 Marylebone St, W1G 8JQ (7224 5699); *Kashmir Butcher,* 63 Stroud Green Rd, N4 3EG (7281 2079); *Kashmir Butchers,* 16 Lymington Ave, N22 6JA (8888 3935); *Kashmir Greengrocers,* 19 Electric Ave, SW9 8JP (7733 8866); *Kashmir Halal,* 120-122 Katherine Rd, East Ham E6 1ER (8472 8669); *Kashmir Halal Butcher,* 27 Electric Ave, SW9 8JP (7274 8358); *Kashmir Halal Butchers,* 153 Rye La, SE15 4TL (7277 6287); *Kashmir Halal Meats,* Dagenham Dock, Chequers La, Dagenham RM9 6PR (8595 9495); *Kashmir Halal Meats,* 71 Clarendon Gdns, Ilford IG1 3JW (8518 5886); *Kashmir Saree Centre,* 322 Bethnal Green Rd, E2 0AG (7739 6491); *Kashmir Store,* Kenway Rd, Earl's Ct; *Kashmir Super Foods,* 141 Ilford La, Ilford IG1 2RP (8478 5371); *Pak Kashmir* [groceries], 66 Ilford La, Ilford IG1 2JZ (8553 5152).

SPECIAL *Kashmir Centre,* Brownlow Ho, Brownlow Rd, W13 0SQ (8840 7999); *Kashmir Choice,* 104 Strand, WC2R 0AB (7836 3725).

WELFARE *Kashmir International Relief Fund,* 452 Hoe St, E17 9AH (8558 9050).

Katab

Katab is a Benuic language spoken in Nigeria. The *Multilingual Capital* (2000) survey noted the presence of one **Katab**-speaking pupil in Hammersmith & Fulham.

Katchi

Katchi (also written *Kachchhi* and *Kutchi*) is an Indic language, spoken in the Rann of Kutch in the Indian state of Gujarat, which is related to *Sindhi*. It is written in the Gujarati semi-syllabic script. The *Multilingual Capital* (2000) survey reported that **Katchi** was the first language of 341 London schoolchildren, of whom 99 lived in Harrow.

Kawa

See under the alternative spelling **Wa.**

Kazakh

BUSINESS *Kazakhstan Republic Trading House*, 91 Wimpole St, W1M 7DA (7629 2630).

EDUCATION Courses in **Kazakh** are available at *SOAS Language Centre* (7898 4888).

GOVERNMENT *Embassy of Kazakhstan*, 33 Thurloe Sq, SW7 2SD (7581 4646)

LANGUAGE **Kazakh** is a language of the **Trans-Asia** geozone spoken mainly in Kazakhstan and which is currently written in the Cyrillic alphabet. Only one **Kazakh**-speaking pupil in London was reported in the *Multilingual Capital* (2000) survey.

Kenyan

ASSOCIATIONS *Kenya Society*, 36 Buckingham Palace Rd, SW1 0RE (7828 5961).

GOVERNMENT *Kenya High Commission*, 45 Portland Pl, W1B 1AS (7636 2371).

LANGUAGES **Swahili** and **English** have official status but are known mainly as second or additional languages. The first languages each spoken by more than 10% of the population are Gikuyu (20%), Luo (14%), Luhya (13%), **Kamba** (11%), and **Kalenjin** (11%; figures from Mann & Dalby 1987).

MEDIA & INFORMATION *Kenya Times*, Ludgate Ho, 107 Fleet St, EC4 (7353 3144).

SHOPS *Kenya Halal Meat and Poultry*, Unit S56-57, Shepherds Bush Market, W12 8DG (8932 2444).

Keralite

The word **Keralite** is applied to the people of the South Indian state of Kerala.

LANGUAGE The principal language of Kerala is **Malayalam.**

RELIGION Although a majority of Keralites is Hindu, there are substantial Christian and Muslim minorities, See **Malayalam** for Christian services in the main Keralite language.

Kerala Bhavan, 16 London Rd, Croydon CR0 2TA (8688 6216).

RESTAURANTS

South West 1 *Quilon,* 41 Buckingham Gate, SW1E 6AF (7821 1899);

West 1 *Kerala,* 13 Gt Castle St, W1N 7AD (7580 2125, fax 7436 0715); *Rasa Samudra* [vegetarian], 5 Charlotte St, W1T 1HD (7637 0222).

Croydon *Curry Hut,* 222 Brigstock Rd, Thornton Heath, CR7 7JD (8684 1818).

TRAVEL *Kerala Travels Ltd,* 96 Katherine Rd, East Ham E6 1EN (8470 7329).

Khana

Khana is a Benuic language spoken in Nigeria which has been reported among London schoolchildren within the past decade although no speakers of this were noted at the time of the *Multilingual Capital* (2000) survey.

Khasi

Khasi is a language of the South-Asia geozone spoken in India and Bangladesh. A few speakers of this have been reported in London within the past decade but none were recorded by the *Multilingual Capital* (2000) survey.

Khmer

EDUCATION Mother tongue instruction for young children in Khmer is available in Tower Hamlets; visit <www.resourceunit.com> for details.

Courses in **Khmer** (*Cambodian*) for adults are available at *SOAS Language Centre* (7898 4888).

LANGUAGE **Khmer** (also known as *Cambodian*) is a language of the **South-Asia** geozone, spoken in Cambodia, which is written in its own semi-syllabic script. The *Multilingual Capital* (2000) survey reported that this was the first language of seven London schoolchildren.

Ki

In the *Multilingual Capital* (2000) survey, **Ki** was reported as the language of 11 schoolchildren in Greenwich. **Ki** probably refers to the Benuic language of this name spoken in Nigeria and Cameroon (but it might alternatively refer to a Bantuic language, *Ki*, also known as Ngoro, spoken in Cameroon.)

Kiga

See under the alternative name, **Chiga.**

Kikongo

See under **Kongo.**

Kikuyu

See under the alternative spelling, **Gikuyu.**

Kimbundu

Kimbundu is a Bantuic language of Angola. **Kimbundu** has recently been reported as one of the languages spoken by some pupils in Merton although no speakers of this were noted in the *Multilingual Capital* (2000) survey.

Kimeru

Kimeru is a Bantuic language spoken in Kenya which has been reported among London schoolchildren within the past decade although none were found at the time of the *Multilingual Capital* (2000) survey.

Kingwana

Kingwana (also known, without its prefix, as *Ngwana)* is a Bantuic language of Congo (Kinshasa) which is very closely related to Swahili and is often considered a variety of the latter. The *Multilingual Capital* (2000) survey reported that there were two **Kingwana**-speaking pupils in Lewisham.

Kirghiz

See under the alternative spelling, Kyrghyz.

Kirundi

Kirundi (also known, without its prefix, as *Rundi*) is a Bantuic language with official status in **Burundi**. The presence of several **Kirundi**-speaking London schoolchildren was reported in the *Multilingual Capital* **(2000) survey.**

Kisi

Kisi is a **Melic** language of Sierra Leone, Guinea and Liberia. The *Multilingual Capital* (2000) survey reported this as the language of one London schoolchild living in Barnet.

Kiswahili

See under the alternative spelling, **Swahili.**

Kiwi

Kiwi is a name popularly applied to New Zealanders and to things from New Zealand. See **New Zealander** for all entries.

Komi

The presence of two **Komi**-speaking schoolchildren in Barnet was reported by the *Multilingual Capital* (2000) survey. However, it is not clear to which of two languages of this name this refers: an **Uralic** language spoken in the Russian Federation and a Bantuic language spoken in Gabon.

Komoro

Komoro is among the languages which have been reported as being spoken by some pupils in London within the past decade although not were found at the time of the *Multilingual Capital* (2000) survey. This name is sometimes applied to the Bantuic languages spoken in the Comoro Islands, all of which are closely related to **Swahili**. See **Comoran.**

Kongo *(Kikongo)*

The word **Kongo** (full name, **Kikongo**) is applied to a number of closely related **Bantuic** languages spoken in parts of Gabon, Congo/Brazzaville, Congo/Kinshasa and Angola. Only one **Kongo**-speaking pupil in London was reported by the *Multilingual Capital* (2000) survey.

Konkani

Konkani is an Indic language spoken mainly in the Indian state of Goa where it has official status. It is the only Indic language written with the Roman alphabet. The presence of 77 Konkani-speaking pupils in London was reported in the *Multilingual Capital* (2000) survey, of whom 10 lived in Brent.

Kono

Kono is a Mandic language spoken in Sierra Leone. The presence of 7 Kono-speaking pupils in Greater London was reported in the *Multilingual Capital* (2000) survey, of whom 5 lived in Lambeth.

Korean

The Korean people are believed to have lived in and around the Korean Peninsula, and to have formed a distinct ethnic group, for at least 4,000 years. Although influenced and, at times, occupied by their Chinese and Japanese neighbours, the Koreans have always maintained their own independent culture and traditions. The present political division of the country into separate North and South administrations dates from the end of the Second World War in 1945.

The Korean community in London lives mainly in the adjoining boroughs of Kingston and Merton, and particularly in the vicinity of New Malden station.

ACCOMMODATION *Kim's Lettings*, Kings Avenue Ho., Kings Ave, New Malden KT3 4DY (8336 1179, fax 8336 1187); *Seoul Letting and Management*, 22 High St, New Malden.

ASSOCIATIONS *Anglo-Korean Cultural Institute*, 240 Burlington Rd, New Malden KT3 4NN (8241 0990); *Korean Residents' Society in the UK*, 164a Red Lion Business Centre, Tolworth KT6 7QY (8397 7061, fax 8408 1635).

BUSINESS   Details of many Korean-owned businesses in London and of the London offices of many businesses based in Korea can be found at <www.koreancommunity.org.uk>.

Banking and investment: *Bank of Korea,* 3rd fl., 1 Minster Ct, Mincing La, EC3R 7AA (7626 8321, fax 7626 7201); *Cho Hung Bank*, 1 Minster Ct, Mincing La, EC3R 7AA (7623-7791, fax 7283-8464); *Commercial Bank of Korea,* 27th fl, Centre Point, 103 New Oxford St., WC1A 1DD (7379 7835, fax 7379 4849); *Donghwa Bank,* Level 3, City Tower, 40 Basinghall St, EC2V 5DE (7628 7643, fax 7628 8933); *Export-Import Bank of Korea*, 3rd fl, Boston Ho, 63-64 New Broad St, EC2M 1JJ (7628 8384); *Hanvit Bank*, Ropemaker Pl, 25 Ropemaker St, EC2Y 9LB (7638 3981, fax 7374- 6531); *Housing and Commercial Bank Korea*, 7th fl, Princes Ct, 7 Princes St, EC2R 8AQ (7776 7300); *Industrial Bank of Korea Europe SA*, 7-11 Moorgate, EC2R 6AF (76007667); *KDB Bank UK Ltd,* 16th fl, 99 Bishopsgate, EC2M 3XD (7426 3550, fax 7426 0103); *Kexim Bank UK Ltd*, Moorgate Hall, 155 Moorgate, EC2M 6XB (7628-6464); *Kookmin Bank,* 4th fl., Creechurch Ho, 37-45 Creechurch La, EC3A 5DJ (7283 1818, fax 7283 0491); *Korea Exchange Bank,* 30 Old Jewry, EC2R 8EB (7606 0191, fax 7606 0383); *Korea First Bank*, 80 Cannon St, EC4; *Korea First Investment Ltd,* 3rd fl, 2 Throgmorton Ave, EC2N 2DL (7638 7217); *Korea Long Term Credit Bank International Ltd,* 7 Princes St, EC2R 8AQ (7710 8300); *Koram Bank*, 2nd fl, 30-40 Eastcheap, EC3M 1HD (7283-0833, fax 7626-8828); *Seoul Bank, London Branch,* 3 Finsbury Sq, EC2A 1AD (7588 6162, fax 7588 9655); *Shinhan Bank*, 3rd fl, 51-55 Gresham St, EC2V 7HB (7600-0606, fax 7600-1826).

Insurance: *Hyundai Marine & Fire Insurance Co Ltd*, 37 Eastcheap, EC3M 1DT (7929 3822); *Korea Insurance Brokers Ltd,* 66 Mark La EC3R 7HS (7481 0033).

Trade: The *Korea Trade Centre* (KOTRA), 5th Floor, 39 St James St, SW1A 1JD (7491 8057, fax 7491 7913). *The Association for Korean Businessmen in the UK* is also located at this address, telephone and fax numbers. *Korea Investment Management (Europe) Ltd*, 3rd fl, Fengate Ho, 14 Philpot La, EC3M 8AJ (7220 7336); *Daewoo (UK) Ltd* [export & import agents], Templar Ho, 82 Northolt Rd, Harrow HA2 0YJ (8423 7200); *Samsung Europe plc*, Great West Ho, Great West Rd, Brentford TW8 9DQ (8380 7000).

EDUCATION *London Korean School,* Chessington Community College, Garrison La,

Chessington KT9 2JS (8974 1156) [Saturday school]; *North London Korean School*, North Ealing Combined School, Pitshanger La, Ealing W5 1RP (8997 2653) [Saturday school]; *UK Korean Consortium Ltd (educational services)* Rm 207-208, 162-168 Regent St, W1R 5TB (7287 5661).

Courses for adults in **Korean** are available at *SOAS Language Centre* (7898 4888).

FREIGHT *ACI Express (UK) Ltd*, 33 Hopingwood Ave, New Malden, KT3 4JX (8949 0088, fax 8949 4848); *Direct Shipping*, Lombard Business Park, 8 Lombard Rd, SW19 3TZ (8241 2238/9, fax 8545 7464); *Fleet Shipping International Ltd,* Fleet Ho, 41-47 Blue Anchor La, SW16 3UL (7232 0777); *Haein*, Unit 11-12, Durnsford Estate, 55-59 Weir Rd, Wimbledon, SW19 8UG (8947 9811, fax 8947 5722); *Hankook Express*, Unit 8, The Courtyard, Dyan Drive, West Cross Centre, Great West Rd, Brentford TW8 9ER (8569 9900, fax 8569 8032); *Pacific Express (Shipping),* 63 High St, New Malden (8949 3261).

GOVERNMENT *Embassy of the Republic of Korea*, 60 Buckingham Gate, SW1E 6AJ (7227 5500, fax 7227 5503).

HEALTH & BEAUTY

Clinics *Joo's Clinic*, 70 Morden Rd, Morden SW19 3BP (8542 3287); *Koryo Hanpang / Seoul Acupucture Medical Clinic,* 15 The Broadway, Tolworth KT6 7DJ (8390 9591, fax 8339 9562); *Won* 56 Cambridge Rd, New Malden KT3 3QL (8767 3888). *Koryo Sooji Clinic*, 2b Alleyn Park, Southall UB2 5QT(8571 4536) [The above three are traditional Korean Chinese hospitals].

Hair *Park Jun Hair*, 9 Coombe Rd, New Malden (8949 0191); *Seshi Hair*, 236 Kingston Rd, New Malden KT3 3RN (8942 8868); *Sharon Hair,* 113 Burlington Rd, New Malden (8949 0722).

Other *Korean Red Ginseng Co Ltd*, PO Box 16018, London SW11 3WH (7585 0312).

LANGUAGE Korean is spoken in Korea and part of Siberia. It is ranked 17th among the world's languages with some 75m speakers.

In the *Multilingual Capital* survey (2000), the presence of 496 Korean-speaking pupils in Greater London was reported, of whom 167 lived in Kingston.

Korean is written in a conceptually unique script called Hangul which is simultaneously syllabic and alphabetic. Note that there is more than one way of writing of transcribing Korean in Roman letters which results in variation between p and b, t and d, ch and j, and g and k. For example, the name of the Hangul script is also written Hankul. Korean also has a series of ejective consonants normally written in Roman script as pp, tt, and kk - as in the name of the Kkachine restaurant.

MEDIA & INFORMATION *Channel Sun* is a Korean language television service available in the UK by cable. *Euro Journal* is a newspaper for Koreans in London and, apart from the title, is printed entirely in Korean. *Euro Times* is similarly a magazine almost entirely in Korean (8337 5388, fax 8337 8878). The *Korea Times* London Office is at 171 High St, New Malden KT3 4BH (8949 5976, fax 8949 7681). *Korea Telecom,* 228 Merton Rd SW19 1EQ (8543 2288); *Euro Net (Internet Cafe),* 195 High St, New Malden KT3 4BH (8942 4692).

MOTORING *Ace Motors*, 4 Park Rd, New Malden, KT3 5AF (8949 2772, fax 8949 2772); *Daewoo Car Centre (Car Dealers),* Shirley Ho, 27 Camden Rd, NW1 9LL (7284 2255); *Hankook International Motors Ltd,* 86 Burlington Rd, New Malden KT3 4NT; *Hyundai Car (UK) Ltd,* Lex Ho, 17 Connaught Pl, W2 2EL (01494 428600); *Korea Motors*, 136 Manor Drive North, New Malden, KT3 5PB (8335 0755, fax 8335 0755).

RELIGION Religious services in Korean are held at the *Lotus Temple*, Buddhist-Korean Society, 5 Water La, Kingston KT6 7QY (8397 7061) and at the following Christian churches, listed by location. **City**: *Cole Abbey*, 114 Queen Victoria St, EC4; **Harrow:** *Harrow Baptist Church*, College Rd, Harrow; **Kingston:** *Emmanuel Church,* 1 Grand Ave, Surbiton KT5; *Grace Korean Church,* Kingston Rd, New Malden KT3; *Oakland Baptist Church,* 6 Langley Rd, Surbiton; *Saint Paul Church,* Kingston Hall, Queen's Rd, Kingston KT2; *Saint Peter's Church,* Cambridge Rd, Norbiton; *Surbiton Baptist Church,* Balaclava Rd, Surbiton KT6; **Merton:** *Elim Church,* Montague Rd, Wimbledon SW19; **Richmond:** *Saint Richard's Church,* Ashburnham Rd, Richmond TW10; **Tower Hamlets:** *East London Baptist Church,* Burdett Rd, E3; **Westminster:** *St Cyprian's Church,* Glentworth St, NW1; *Welsh Baptist Church,* 30 Eastcastle St, W1.

London Zen Group [Korean Chogye], 13 Rodney Pl, SW19 2LQ (8542 5826); *Zen London* [Korean Zen], 11 Dorchester Ct, Leigham Court Rd, SW16 2PH (8696-7601).

RECREATION **Martial Arts:** *British Tae Kwon-Do Council*, 58 Wiltshire La, Pinner HA5 2LU (8429 0878); *International Tae Kwon-Do Federation Dojang,* Cannons Swimming Pool, North London Collegiate School, Stanmore HA7 4RJ (8958 9344); *Tae Kwon-Do,* 63 The Vale, Hounslow TW5 9HS (8572 7106); *World Tae Kwon Do Club,* 89 Sandringham Rd, Worcester Park KT4 8UH (8395 7881).

RESTAURANTS
East Central *Arana,* 116 Newgate St, EC1 [not Sat or Sun] (7600 1134); *New Seoul,* 164 Clerkenwell Rd, EC1 [not Sat or Sun] (7278 8674); *Youngbin-Kwan* 3 St Alphage, Highwalk Barbican, EC2 [not Sat or Sun] (7638 9151, 7628 0492).

South West 1 *Kaya,* 42 Albemarle St, SW1 (7499 0622).

West 1 *Arirang,* 31-32 Poland St, Soho W1 (7437 6633); *Cho Won,* 27 Romily St, Soho W1 [not Sun] (7437 2262); *Han Kang,* 16 Hanway St, W1 [not Sun] (7637 1985): *Jin,* 16 Bateman St, W1V 5TB (7734 0908); *Myung Ka,* 1 Kingly St, W1 (7734 8220); *Shilla,* 58-60 Gt Marlborough St, W1 (7434 1650).

West Central *Nam Tae Mun*, 56 St Giles High St, WC2 [not Sun] (7836 7235).

Barnet *Yijo,* 1 Station Rd, N3 2SB (8343 3960).

Brent *Han Kook Ok,* Yaohan Oriental Shopping Centre, 399 Edgware Rd, NW9 (8200 1338).

Camden *Taro,* 293 Finchley Rd, Hampstead NW3 [not Mon.] (7794 0190).

Ealing *Mozori,* 41 Churchfield Rd, Acton W3 [not Sun] (8896 0202).

Hammersmith & Fulham *Yoshi Sushi,* 210 King St, W6 (8748 5058).

Hounslow *Cheong Sol,* 775 London Rd, Hounslow TW3 [not Sun] (8572 3102).

Islington *Bu San (Pusan),* 41-43 Holloway Rd, N7 8JP (7607 8264).

Kensington & Chelsea *Sansui,* 10 Clarendon Rd, W11 [not Sun.] (7229 7136).

Kingston *Asadal,* 180 High St, New Malden KT3 4ES (8942 2334); *Biwon,* Apex Tower, High St, New Malden KT3 4DQ [not Sun.] (8949 8809); *Hamjibak,* 169 High St, New Malden (8942 9588); *Ire,* 169 High St, New Malden KT3 4BH [not Sun] (8949 0049); *Jang Won,* 272 Burlington Rd, New Malden KT3 4NL (8949 2506); *Jissine,* 74 Burlington Rd, New Malden KT3 4NU [not Mon] (8942 0682); *Korea Garden,* 73 Kingston Rd, New Malden KT3 3PB (8336 1208); *Maypole,* 149 Merton Rd, Wimbledon SW19 [not Mon] (8543 3646); *Miga,* 79-81 Kingston Rd, New Malden KT3 3PB (8942 1811); *Yumi Hwoikwan,* 96 Burlington Rd, New Malden KT3 4NT (8715 1079); **Merton:** *Kkachine,* 34 Durham Rd, Raynes Park SW20 (8947 1081).

Richmond: *Kangnam,* 178 Upper Richmond Rd West, Mortlake SW14 8AW (8876 9063).

Westminster *Yun-Kyung Seoul,* 113-115 Praed St, W2 1RL (7723 9550).

SHOPS

Groceries *Jinmi Super,* 127 Kingston Rd, New Malden, KT3 3NX (8336 1882); *Kobau Super,* 87 Kingston Rd, New Malden, KT3 3PA (8942 9952); *Lotte Shopping,* 126 Malden Rd, New Malden KT3 6DD (8942 9552); *Nak Won* (Korean traditional rice cake shop), 89 Kingston Rd, New Malden, KT3 3PA (8949 6474); *Songane Super,* 96 Burlington Rd, New Malden, KT3 4NT (8715 1079). Many other Korean shops, selling *kimchi* (pickled cabbage), rice cakes, Korean groceries, music- and video-cassettes, etc., are located in Kingston, particularly in the New Malden area.

Others *Daewoon Food,* 416 Alexandra Ave, Rayners Lane, Harrow (8868 6372); *Damoa Bakery,* 11 Station Building, Coombe La, Raynes Park SW2 0NE (8946 4420).

SPECIAL **Computing:** *Bluenet Computer Ltd,* 298 Ewell Rd, Surbiton, KT6 7AQ (8390 8003, fax 8390 0748); *Entec,* 27 Coombe Rd, New Malden (8942 7404), *LDC-Net Ltd,* LDC Ho, 298 Ewell Rd, Surbiton, KT6 7AQ (8390 8003, fax 8399 4944, 8390 0748); *Sekyee Company Ltd,* 3 Castle Rd, NW1 8PR (7419 9563, fax 8482 4986); *Seohoon Computer Co, Ltd,* Excel Ho, 6 Pepys Rd, Raynes Park SW20 8NH (8947 9313/5952, fax 8879 3958); *Skim Company,* 10 The Green, Ewell, Epsom, KT17 3JN (8393 1388, fax 8394 2522).

TRANSLATION *Korean Technical Translations,* Nightingale Centre, 8 Balham Hill, SW12 9EA (8673 0865).

TRAVEL *Bora Travel,* 65 Sheephouse Way, New Malden, KT3 5PF (8241 7987, fax 8335 3020); *Cie France Tour,* 73 Kingston Rd, New Malden KT3 3PB (8288 0750, fax 8241 2417); *Coworld Tour,* N 201, 1 Durham St, SE11 (7582 2822); *Crown Travel Agency Ltd,* 15 Leyfield, Worcester Park KT4 7LS (8337 7041, fax 8337 7042); *Daeyoung Travel,* 38 High St., New Malden, KT3 4EH (8336 0733, fax 8336 0744*); Grand Tour Europe Ltd,* 39 High St., New Malden, KT3 4TT (07967 407817, fax (8337 7042); *Hanyound Tours Ltd,* 16 Hanway St., W1P 9DD (7916 3010, fax 7916 3011); *Hyojin High Tour,* 44 Eton Ave, New Malden, KT3 5AZ (8942 4560); *KJK Travel Ltd,* 60 High St., New Malden, KT3 4EZ (8949 5969, fax 8942 7998); *Korean Air,* 67 Piccadilly, W1 (admin. 7495 2299). *Korea National Tourism Corporation,* New Zealand Ho, Haymarket W1 (7321 2535) <kntotb@dircom.co.uk>; *Park Travel,* 243-247 Pavilion Rd., SW1X 0BP (7730 3355, fax 7824 8205); *Korea Travel,* 318b Kennington La, SE11 (7587 5220, fax 7587 1833); *KST / Korean Travel Services,* 171 High St., New Malden, KT3 4BH (8949 1177, fax 8949 7998*); Samho Travel,* 334 Kennington La, Kennington SE11 (7735 1770, fax 7735 3339); *Sapphire Travel,* Track Ho, 34 Francis Grove, Wimbledon SW19 4DT (8228 4868; fax 8228 4889); *Seoul Overseas Tour & Travel (UK) Ltd,* 1st fl. 60 High St., New Malden, KT3 4EZ (8942 4778; fax 8942 4779); *Sunny Tours,*

26 Cranleig Ho, West Barnes La, SW29 9BE (8879 7744); *Unimaster Travel,* 117 Praed St, W2 1RL (7402 0077, fax 7402 1511).

Korku

The *Multilingual Capital* (2000) survey mentioned the presence of just one **Korku**-speaking London schoolchild in Barnet. **Korku** is a language of the **South-Asia** geozone spoken in India.

Kosher

Restaurants and shops specializing in Kosher food are listed under **Jewish**.

Kosova / Kosovo *(Kosovar, Kosovan)*

The province called Kosovo by Serbs and Kosova by Albanians is under UN administration. Until 1989 this area had autonomous status within the former Yugoslavia. About 90% of the population are ethnically Albanians, often termed Kosovar Albanians.

ASSOCIATIONS *Islamic Medical Association Kosova,* 19 Chatsworth Rd, E5 0LH (8986 5444).

LANGUAGES About 90% of the population speak a distinctive variety of **Albanian.** (In London *only,* this is sometimes termed *Kosovan.*) The rest of the population speak **Serbian.**

MEDIA **&** INFORMATION *Kosova Information Centre,* 132 Buckingham Palace Rd, SW1W 9SA (7730 1050); *Kosova Information Centre,* 173 Castelnau, SW13 9ER (8741 1141).

TRANSLATION *Albanian & Kosovan Interpreting,* 29 Castle Ave, West Drayton UB7 8LG (07956 322095).

WELFARE *Hospital Kosovo Aid Appeal,* 15 Dafforne Rd, Tooting SW17 8TY (8682 1300); *Kosova Aid,* 50 Great Portland St, W1N 5AH (7580 5540); *London Kosovo Aid Appeal,* London SW17 8II (0800 028 2140).

Kpelle

Kpelle is a *Mandic* language spoken in Liberia and Guinea. Although generally written in the Roman alphabet, **Kpelle** also has its own syllabic script. The *Multilingual Capital* (2000) survey noted the presence of one **Kpelle**-speaking pupil in Islington.

Kposo

Kposo is an *Aframic* language of Ghana and Togo which has been reported as being spoken by a few London schoolchildren within the past decade although none were found at the time of the *Multilingual Capital* (2000) survey.

Krio

Krio is an *English Creole* spoken in Sierra Leone (and also in the Gambia, where it is known as *Aku*). The *Multilingual Capital* (2000) survey reported that this was the first language of 321 schoolchildren of whom a quarter lived in Lambeth.

Krobo

Krobo is an Aframic language of Ghana which has been reported as being spoken by a few London schoolchildren within the past decade although none were found at the time of the *Multilingual Capital* (2000) survey.

Kru

The word *Kru* is applied collectively to all the **Kruic** languages spoken in Liberia and the Ivory Coast, as well as to one particular language of this group located in Liberia. In the *Multilingual Capital* (2000) survey, *Kru* was reported as the first language of five London schoolchildren.

Kurdish

The **Kurdish** people form the great majority of the population in the extreme south eastern part of Turkey and in an area extending across the northern half of the Iraq – Iran border.

ACCOMMODATION *Halkevi Kurdish & Turkish Community Centre,* 92-100 Stoke Newington Rd, N16 (7249 6980); *Kurdish Community Centre,* Selby Centre, Selby Rd, Tottenham N17 8JL (8885 4988); *Kurdish Housing Association,* Selby Centre, Selby Rd, Tottenham N17 8JL (8808 9954).

ASSOCIATION *Kurdish Association,* 241 King St, Hammersmith W6 9LP (8563 7918); *Kurdish Cultural Centre,* 14 Stannary St, Lambeth SE11 4AA (7735 0918); *Kurdistan Community Centre,* Fairfax Hall, 11 Portland Gdns, N4 1HU (8211 7662); *Kurdistan Workers Association,* Fairfax Hall, 11 Portland Gdns, N4 1HU (8880 1804); *Western Kurdistan Association,* Palingswick Ho, 241 King St, Hammersmith W6 9LP (8748 7874).

EDUCATION Mother tongue education for young children is available in **Kurdish** (**Sorani**) is available is several centres in London; visit <www.resourceunit.com> for details.

Courses for adults in Kurdish are available at *SOAS Language Centre* (7898 4888) and perhaps elsewhere in London – check with <www.floodlight.co.uk>.

Kurdish Refugee Training Project, 11 Portland Gdns, Finsbury Park N4 1HU (8211 7662); *Kurdish Studies Forum,* c/o CNMES, SOAS, Thornhaugh St, Russell Sq, WC1H 0XG (8518 8032); *Kurdistan Education and Business Development Ltd,* 117 Leadale Rd, N15 6BJ.

HEALTH & BEAUTY *Turkish-Kurdish Health, Advocacy, and Counselling Services,* The Lawson Practice, St Leonards, Nuttall St, Islington N1 5LZ (7613 5944).

LANGUAGE *Kurdish* is the name given to a group of related **Iranic** languages spoken in Iraq, Turkey, Syria and Iran, of which there are several distinctive varieties including *Kurmanji* and *Sorani*. *Kurdish* is generally written in an adaptation of the **Arabic** script in which all vowels are represented in all circumstances. The *Multilingual Capital* (2000) survey reported the presence of 1 405 *Kurdish*-speaking London schoolchildren of whom almost one third lived in Haringey. Map 21 showing the areas of London where the largest numbers of *Kurdish*-speaking children live, can be viewed at <www.global-london.com/gallery>.

LEGAL *Kurdish Human Rights Project,* 319 Linen Hall, 162-168 Regent St, W1R 5TB (7287 2772); *Turkish-Kurdish Health, Advocacy, and Counselling Services,* The Lawson Practice, St Leonards, Nuttall St, Islington N1 5LZ (7613 5944).

MEDIA & INFORMATION *Islington Kurdish Information Centre,* 129 St Johns Way, N19 3RQ (7272 9499); *Kurdistan Information Centre,* 10 Glasshouse Yard, EC1A 4JN (7250 1315).

TRANSLATION *Associated Translators,* Macmillan Ho, 96 Kensington High St, W8 4SG (7937 7733).

WELFARE *Greenwich Kurdish Community,* 16 Leslie Smith Sq, SE18 4DW (8855 3357); *Kurdish Advice Centre,* St. Marys Community Centre, Birkbeck Rd, N8 7PF (8347 8657); *Kurdish Charitable Association,* Horwood Ho, Paveley St, NW8 8TH (7724 0582); *Kurdish Charitable Association,* Holwood Ho, Nan Clarks La, Mill Hill NW7 4HH (7724 0582); *Kurdish Community Centre,* Selby Centre, Selby Rd, Tottenham N17 8JL (8885 4988); *Kurdish Community Centre,* 11 Portland Gdns, N4 1HU (8809 0743); *Kurdish Cultural Centre,* 14 Stannary St, Lambeth SE11 4AA (7735 0918); *Kurdish Disability Organisation* (fax 7281 3842); *Kurdish Project (Turkish Spoken),* 73 London Rd, Croydon CR0 2RF (8688 7271); *Turkish and Kurdish Community Centre,* 92-100 Stoke Newington Rd, N16 7XB (7249 6980); *Turkish-Kurdish Health, Advocacy, and Counselling Services,* The Lawson Practice, St Leonards, Nuttall St, Islington N1 5LZ (7613 5944).

Kurmanji

Kurmanji is one of the major *Kurdish* languages (see entry for this), spoken mainly in Turkey and Iraq. *Kurmanji* is among the languages which have been reported as being spoken by some London schoolchildren in the recent past although none were recorded at the time of the *Multilingual Capital* (2000) survey.

Kusaie

Kusaie is a **West-Pacific** language spoken on Kosrae which now forms part of the Federated States of Micronesia. In the *Multilingual Capital* (2000) survey, *Kusaie* was reported at the first language of one pupil in Ealing.

Kutchi

See entry under *Katchi.*

Kuwaiti

ASSOCIATIONS *National Union of Kuwaiti Students,* 41 Porchester Terrace, W2 3TS (7706 2535).

BUSINESS

Banks *National Bank of Kuwait (International) plc,* N B K Ho, 13 George St W1H 5PB (7224 2277); *National Bank of Kuwait SAK,* Portman Sq, W1H 9PR (7224 2277); *National Bank of Kuwait SAK,* 69 Edgware Rd, W2 2HZ (7224 2277); *United Bank of Kuwait plc,* 15 Baker St, W1M 2EB (7487 6500).

Petroleum *Independent Petroleum Group of Kuwait Ltd,* 112 Jermyn St, SW1Y 6LS (7925 0505); *Kuwait Oil Co,* Julco Ho, 26-28 Great Portland St W1N 5AD (7436 1990); *Kuwait Petroleum (GB) Ltd,* Burgen Ho, Staines TW18 3PA (01784 467788); *Kuwait Petroleum International Ltd,* 80 New Bond St, W1Y 9DA (7491 4000).

Other *Kuwait Investment Office,* St Vedast Ho, Cheapside EC2V 6LP (7606 8080).

EDUCATION *National Union of Kuwaiti Students,* 41 Porchester Terrace, W2 3TS (7706 2535).

GOVERNMENT *Embassy of the State of Kuwait,* 2 Albert Gate, SW1X 7JU (7590 3400) *and* 45-46 Queens Gate, SW7 5HR (7589 4533).

LEGAL *Stephenson Harwood,* 1 St Paul's Churchyard, EC4M 8SH (7329 4422).

MEDIA & INFORMATION *Kuwait Information Centre,* Hyde Park Ho, 60-60a Knightsbridge, SW1X 7JF (7235 1787); *Kuwait News Agency,* 6th fl, New Premier Ho, 150 Southampton Row, WC1B 5AL (7278 5445).

TRAVEL *Kuwait Airways,* 16-20 Baker St, W1M 2AD (7412 0006).

Kwa

The *Multilingual Capital* (2000) survey reported the presence of one **Kwa**-speaking pupil in the borough of Haringey. It is not possible to identify to which language this refers because there are four with this name: an Adamawic language of Nigeria, a Bantuic language of Cameroon, a **Bantuic** language of Nigeria, a Kruic language of the Ivory Coast, and an Aframic language of Ghana. There is also a **Kruic** language of Liberia called *Kwaa.* In addition, the families of languages which Dalby (1999-2000) terms Aframic and Benuic are called, respectively, 'Western Kwa" and "Eastern Kwa" by some linguists.

Kwangwa

Kwangwa is a Bantuic language of Zambia which has been mentioned in lists of languages spoken by some London pupils in recent years although none were reported at the time of the *Multilingual Capital* (2000) survey.

Kyrghyz (Kirghiz)

EDUCATION Courses in **Kyrghyz** are available at *SOAS Language Centre* (7898 4888).

GOVERNMENT *Kyrghyz Republic Embassy,* Ascot Ho, 119 Crawford St, W1 H 1AF (7935 1462).

LANGUAGE **Kyrghyz** is a language of the **Trans-Asia** geozone with official status in Kyrghyztan where it is the first language of the majority of the population. (Significant minorities speak Russian and Uzbek.) Although written in the Cyrillic script for several decades, the Roman alphabet has been used for **Kyrghyz** since 1992. The presence of two **Kyrghyz**-speaking pupils in Kingston was reported by the *Multilingual Capital* (2000) survey.

L

Lahnda

Lahnda is among the language names reported as spoken by some schoolchildren in London. It is a variety of *Panjabi* spoken in West Punjab (Pakistan), and was included in the figures for *Panjabi* in the *Multilingual Capital* (2000) survey.

Lam-nso

Lam-nso is a Benuic language spoken in Cameroon. The *Multilingual Capital* (2000) survey reporrted that there were three **Lam**-nso-speaking pupils in London.

Lango

Lango was reported as the language of just one London pupil in the *Multilingual Capital* (2000) survey. *Lango* is in fact the name of two Nilotic languages, one spoken in Uganda (and closely related to *Acholi*) and the other spoken in Sudan. It is uncertain which of this was spoken by the child in question.

Lao

EDUCATION Mother tongue education for young children in **Lao** is available at two places in London; visit <www.resourceunit.com> for details.

LANGUAGE **Lao** (sometimes called *Laotian*) is a **Daic** language with official status in Laos. It is written in its own semi-syllabic script which, like the language itself, is closely related to Thai. The *Multilingual Capital* (2000) survey identified noted the presence of 14 *Lao*-speaking schoolchildren in London, of whom 4 lived in Camden.

Laotian

Laotian is a variant name of the language also known as **Lao.** See under this name for details.

Lati

Lati is a Daic language of Vietnam. The presence of a few speakers of this in London has been reported within the past decade but none were noted at the time of the *Multilingual Capital* (2000) survey.

Latin

This heading refers exclusively to the Latin language of the former Roman Empire. The word *Latin* is also often used as an abbreviation of *Latin American*, for which see the next heading.

EDUCATION Several courses in Latin are available in London, see <www.floodlight.co.uk> for details.

French & Latin Private Tuition, 74 Manor Rd, Harrow HA1 2PE (8863 2582).

RELIGION *Latin Mass Society,* 11-13 Macklin St, WC2B 5NH (7404 7284). Latin mass is still sung at the church of *St Etheldredra,* 14 Ely Pl, EC1 (7405 1061).

Latin American

ACCOMMODATION *Latin American Housing Co-op Ltd,* 135 Stockwell Rd, Brixton, SW9 9TN (7207 1500).

ARTS & CULTURE *Latin American Entertainers,* 144 Sabine Rd, Battersea SW11 5LX (7585 1024); *Latin Touch Entertainment,* Fatima Community Centre, Commonwealth Ave, Shepherd's Bush W12 7QR (8740 9020).

ASSOCIATIONS *Bilongo Latin Club,* 642 High Rd, North Finchley, N12 ONL; *Elderly Project,* Bingfield Hall, Bingfield St, Islington, N1 OAG (7609 6660); *Elderly Project,* Kilburn, NW6 4TA (7328 50003); *Golden Years Club,* Cancell Rd, Brixton, SW9 6HN (7793 0469); *Latin Link International Office,* 55 Palmerston Rd, Harrow, HA3 7RR (8427 3188); *Latin Link,* 175 Tower Bridge Rd, Southwark, SE1 2AH (7939 9000); *Latin American House Association,* Latin American Ho, Kingsgate Pl, Kilburn, NW6 4TA (7372 5244); *Women's Rights Service,* Wesley Ho, Wild St, Holborn, WC2B 4AA (7831 4145); *Women's Rights Service Counselling & Advice,* Tindlemanor, 52-54 Featherstone St, Clerkenwell, EC1Y 8RT (7336 0888).

BARS & NIGHTCLUBS *Azteca Latin Lounge,* 315 Kings Rd, SW3 5EP (7352 8878); *Bilongo Latin Club Ltd,* 642 High Rd, North Finchley N12 0NL.

BUSINESS *G A B Robins Latin America Ltd* [chartered loss adjusters], 35 Great Saint Helens, EC3A 6AP (7200 3000); *Latin American Co-op Development Project Ltd,* 14 Marshalsea Rd, SE1 1HL (7357 9091); *Latin American Investment Partners Ltd,* 10 Dacre St, SW1H 0DJ (7222 8585); *Latin American Trade Advisory Group,* Canning Ho, 2 Belgrave Sq, SW1X 8PJ (7235 3651).

EDUCATION *Institute of Latin American Studies,* 31 Tavistock Sq, Bloomsbury, WC1H 9HA (7862 8870); *Masalda Latin American Community Nursery Ltd,* 29 Rhodesia Rd, Brixton SW9 9DT (7737 6494).

LEGAL *Latin American Association* [legal advice] Address: Kingsgate Pl, NW6 4TA (7624 6409).

MEDIA & INFORMATION *Latin American Newsletters,* 61 Old St, EC1V 9HX (7251 0012); *Latin Linkup Ltd* [information services], 2 Beaconsfield Rd, Ealing W5 5JE (7387 2001) and Argyle Ho, 29-31 Euston Rd, NW1 2SD (7833 4884); *Latin London Magazine,* 200 Earls Court Rd, SW5 9QF (7373 9611); *Latin London Magazine,* 44 Poland St, W1V 3DA (7734 5858); *Noticias Latin America Ltd,* 59 St.Martin's La, WC2N 4JS; *T & C Latin American Services,* Suite M 135 Stockwell Rd, Brixton SW9 9TN (7274 5947).

MOTORING *Latin Motors,* 61A Camden Mews, Camden, NW1 9BY (7284 2781).

RECREATION *Central London Dance* [Latin dance tuition], 13 Blandford St, W1H 3AA (7224 6004); *Hampstead School of Latin Dance,* Winchester Rd, Hampstead, NW3 3HB (7722 2288); *Latin Touch Entertainment,* Community Centre, Commonwealth Ave, Shepherd's Bush, W12 7QR (8740 9020).

RELIGION *Latin Link Places of Worship,* 186 Kennington Park Rd, Lambeth, SE11 4BT; *Latin Link Religious Organisations,* 325 Kennington Rd, Lambeth, SE11 4QE (7207 5877).

RESTAURANTS

West 1 *Latino,* 25 Frith St, W1V 5TR (7287 5676).

Hackney *Armadillo,* 41 Broadway Market, E8 (7249 3633).

SHOPS *EBL Music,* 5 Goodge Pl, West End, W1P 1FL (7636 8349); *Latin America Bureau* [bookshop], 1 Amwell St, EC1R 1UL (7278 2829); *Latin-Craft,* Kingsbridge Court, Castlehaven Rd, Camden, NW1 8QA (7485 4590); *Latin Village Shopping Centre,* 298 Camberwell Rd, SE5 0DL (7703 4000); *Tropic Melody Afro Latin Records & Travel Centre,* 409-17 Coldharbour La, SW9 8LH (7738 7278); *Tumi Latin American Crafts,* 23 Chalk Farm Rd, NW1 8AG (7485 4152).

SPECIAL *Latin America Language,* 96 Cotterill Rd, Surbiton KT6 7UL (8286 1817).

TRANSLATION *Latin Shield Ltd,* 61 Slagrove Pl, Lewisham, SE13 7HT (8690 7166);

TRAVEL *American & Latin Travel Ltd,* 198 Weir Rd, SW12 0NW (8673 8888); *Hayes & Jarvis Travel Ltd,* [Latin American reservations], W6 6QU (0870 898 9890); *Journey Latin America,* 12-13 Heathfield Terrace, Chiswick W4 4JE (8747 8315/3108); *Latin America Travel,* 7 Buckingham Gate, SW1E 6JX (7630 0070); *Latin America Travel,* 103 Gainsborough Rd, Richmond TW9 2ET (8948 4000); *Latin Horizons Enterprise Ltd,* Alfred Prior Ho, Grantham Rd, E12 5NA (8478 6040); *Latin Travel,* Phanet Ho, 19C Craven Rd, Bayswater, W2 3BS (7447 2750); *Scott Dunn Latin America Ltd,* 12a Noyna Rd, Tooting SW17 7PH (8767 8989); *Tropic Melody Afro Latin Records & Travel Centre,* 409-17 Coldharbour La, SW9 8LH (7738 7278).

WELFARE *Carila Latin American Welfare Group,* Manor Gardens Centre, 6-9 Manor Gdns, N7 6LA (7561 1931); *Friends of Latin American Expression,* 36 Tylney Ave, Upper Norwood SE19 1LN; *Latin American Disabled Peoples Project,* Unit 7, 42 Braganza St, Elephant and Castle SE17 3RJ (7793

8399); *Latin American Elderley Project,* Bingfield Hall, Bingfield St, Islington N1 0AG (7609 6660); *Latin American Elderley Project,* Kilburn NW6 4TA (7328 5003); *Latin American Elderly Project,* Ringcross Community Centre, Lough Rd, N7 8RH (7609 6660); *Latin American Golden Years Club Day Centre,* Cancell Rd, SW9 6HN (7793 0469); *Latin American House Association,* Latin America Ho, Kingsgate Pl, Kilburn NW6 4TA (7372 5244); *Latin American Women's Rights Service,* Tindlemanor, 52-54 Featherstone St, EC1Y 8RT (7336 0888); *Latin American Women's Rights Service,* Wesley Ho, Wild St, WC2B 4AA (7831 4145); *Latin Link,* 175 Tower Bridge Rd, SE1 2AH (7939 9000); *Latin Link International Office,* 55 Palmerston Rd, Harrow HA3 7RR (8427 3188).

Latvian

ACCOMMODATION *Latvian Welfare Fund* (hostel), 72 Queensborough Terrace, W2 3SH (7229 1652).

ASSOCIATIONS *Latvian Club,* 72 Queensborough Terrace, W2 3SH (7221 8252);

EDUCATION A course in Latvian is provided by *SSEES* (7862 8634).

GOVERNMENT *Embassy of Latvia,* 45 Nottingham Pl, W1U 5LR (7312 0040).

LANGUAGES *Latvian* is the main and official language of Latvia but there is also a substantial *Russian*-speaking minority. *Latvian* is a **Baltic** language which, at the time of the *Multilingual Capital* (2000) survey, was reportedly spoken by eight London schoolchildren.

RELIGION The church of *St Anne & St Agnes,* Gresham St, EC2 (7606 4986) holds occasional services in *Latvian.*

TRANSLATION *Tramont Translation Management,* 57 Upper Park Rd, NW3 2UL (7692 6319; fax 7504 8638).

Lebanese

ASSOCIATIONS *British Lebanese Association,* 7th fl, 111 Upper Richmond Rd, Putney, SW15 2TJ (7370 2752).

BUSINESS *Beirut Riyad Bank SAL,* 17a Curzon St, W1Y 7FE (7493 8342).

GOVERNMENT *Lebanese Embassy,* 15-21 Palace Gardens Mews, W8 4RB (7229 7265);

LANGUAGES *Arabic* is the official language of Lebanon but English and French are also spoken.

RELIGION More than half of the Lebanese population is Muslim, a large minority is Christian, and perhaps 7% is Druze.

Lebanese Maronite RC Church, 6 Dobson Close, NW6 5BB (7625 8584).

RESTAURANTS

West 1 *Abu Ali,* 136-138 George St, W1 (7724 6338); *Al Fawar,* 50 Baker St, W1U 7BR (7224 4777); *Al Hamra,* 31-33 Shepherd's Market, W1 (7493 1954); *Alicia,* 23 Warren St, W1 (7388 1414); *Al Sultan,* 51-52 Hertford St, W1Y 7HJ (7408 1155); *Fairuz,* 3 Blandford St, Marylebone W1 (7483 8108); *Fakhreldine,* 85 Piccadilly, W1J 7NE (7493 3424);

La Reash Cous-Cous House, 23-24 Greek St, W1 (7439 1063); *Maroush III*, 62 Seymour St, W1 (7724 5024); *Tarboush*, 11 Wardour St, W1 (7287 1220).

Camden *Le Mignon*, 9a Delancey St, Camden, NW1 (7387 0600).

Hammersmith & Fulham *Lebanese Tavern*, 38 Fulham Palace Rd, W6 9PH (8741 2277); **Hillingdon:** *El Nomad*, 132 Manor Way, HA4 8HR (01895 624700).

Kensington & Chelsea *Al-Dar*, 74 King's Rd, SW3 4TZ (7584 1873); *Al-Dar III*, 221 Kensington High St, W8 6SG (7938 1547); *Byblos*, 262 Kensington High St, W8 6ND (7603 4422); *Chez Marcelle*, 34 Blythe Rd, W14 0HA (7603 3241); *Maroush II*, 38 Beauchamp Pl, SW3 1NU (7581 5434); *Phoenicia*, 11-13 Abingdon Rd, W8 6AH (7937 0120).

Merton *Maison St Cassien* [Mediterranean / Lebanese], 71 High St, Wimbledon, SW19 (8944 1200).

Westminster *Ali Baba*, 32 Iver Pl, NW1 (7723 7474) [Egyptian/Lebanese]; *Al-Omaraa*, 27 Queensway, W2 4QJ (7221 8045); *Al Sultan*, 51-52 Hertford St, W1J 7ST (7408 1155); *Al-Waha*, 75 Westbourne Grove, W2 4UL (7229 0806); *Fatoush Juice Snack Bar*, 183 Edgware Rd, W2 1ET (7706 0725); *Lebanese*, 60 Edgware Rd, Marble Arch, W2 2EH (7723 9130); *Maroush I*, 21 Edgware Rd, W2 2JE (7723 0773); *Maroush Café*, 68 Edgware Rd, W2 (7224 9339); *Meshwar*, 128 Edgware Rd, W2 2DZ (7262 8304); *Tarboush 2*, 143 Edgware Rd, W2 2HR (7706 9793).

SHOPS

Bakeries *Lebanese Bakery 2000 Ltd*, Unit F01, Acton Business Centre, School Rd, NW10 6TD (8838 3729).

Butchers *Lebanese Butchery*, 348 Uxbridge Rd, W12 7LL (8743 9226).

Delicatessens *Lebanese Delicatessen*, 346 Uxbridge Rd, W12 7LL (7240 8300).

Supermarkets *Alarza Lebanese Food*, 134 Churchfield Rd, W3 6BS (8993 0471); *Archie Food Store*, 14 Moscow Rd, W2 (7229 2275); *Lebanese Food Centre*, 153 The Vale, W3 7RH (8740 7365).

WELFARE *Lebanese Welfare Community*, 8a Cambridge Ave, NW6 5BB (7625 8584).

Lesotho

GOVERNMENT *Lesotho High Commission*, 7 Chesham Pl, SW1X 8HN (7235 5686).

LANGUAGE See *Sesotho.*

Levantine

The word *Levantine* is applied collectively to the peoples and cultures of the eastern end of the Mediterranean, particularly those of Cyprus, Turkey, Syria, Lebanon, Israel and Palestine.

BUSINESS *Levant Consultants Ltd*, 21 Arlington St, SW1A 1RN (7491 8484).

FREIGHT *Levant Maritime Company Ltd*, 20 St Dunstan's Hill, EC3R 8HY (7626 0006); *Levant Shipping Co Ltd*, 16-22 Baltic St West, EC1Y 0UL (7250 0810); *Levant UK Ltd* [airfreight], Services, Caxton Ho, Printing House La, Hayes UB3 1AP (8813 5166).

RESTAURANTS

West 1 *Levant*, 76 Wigmore St, W1U 2SJ (7224 1111).

SPECIAL *Levant Serkan*, 117 Kingsland High St, E8 2PB (7241 1414).

Liberian

ASSOCIATION *Liberian Community Association*, 12 School Rd, Hounslow TW3 1QZ (8577 3226).

GOVERNMENT *Liberian Embassy*, 2 Pembridge Pl, Bayswater W2 4XB (7221 1036); *Liberian Permanent Mission*, Dean Bradley Ho, 52 Horseferry Rd, Westminster SW1P 2AF (7976 0725).

LANGUAGES Apart from about 5% who speak *Gola* – which is not among the languages reportedly spoken in London – roughly equal proportions of the population (40%+) speak either *Kru* languages (such as *Bassa*) or *Manding* languages (such as *Kpelle* or *Loma*).

Libyan

ASSOCIATIONS *Libyan Interest Society*, 119 Harley St, W1 (7486 8250).

EDUCATION *Society for Libyan Studies,* Institute of Archaeology, 31-34 Gordon Sq, WC1H 0PY (8467 2114).

GOVERNMENT *Libyan People's Bureau,* 61-62 Ennismore Gdns, SW7 1NH (7589 6120); *Libyan Interests Section,* 119 Harley St, W1N 1DH (7486 8387).

LANGUAGES **Arabic** is the first language of the vast majority of the Libyans but a small minority speak one of the **Berber** languages.

RELIGION Libyans are overwhelmingly Muslims.

TRAVEL *Libyan Arab Airlines,* Terminal 2, Heathrow Airport, TW6M 6AH (8897 2700).

Limba

Limba is an Atlantic language spoken in Sierra Leone. The presence of one **Limba**-speaking pupil in Greenwich was reported by the *Multilingual Capital* (2000) survey.

Lingala
====

ASSOCIATIONS *African Francophone Community Association,* c/o Mr J Nzau-Matomisa, 3rd fl, The Irish Centre, Pretoria Rd, Tottenham N17 8DX (8808 0999) [languages: **French** and **Lingala**].

EDUCATION Mother-tongue education for young children is available in **Lingala** in several locations in London; for full information visit <www.resourceunit.com>.

LANGUAGE **Lingala** (also known, without its prefix, as *Ngala)* is a **Bantuic** language spoken in both Congo (Brazzaville) and Congo (Kinshasa) where it is generally known as a second language rather than as a first language. In the *Multilingual Capital* (2000) survey, this was reported as the language of 980 London schoolchildren, of whom 270 were living in Haringey.

Lithuanian
====

ASSOCIATIONS *British-Lithuanian Society,* 85 Gloucester Pl, W1U 6HL (7486 6401),

EDUCATION A course in Lithuanian is provided by *SSEES* (7862 8632).

GOVERNMENT *Embassy of the Republic of Lithuania,* 84, Gloucester Pl, W1U 6HL (7486 6401/6402).

LANGUAGE **Lithuanian** is a **Baltic** language with official status in Lithuania. 178 **Lithuanian**-speaking schoolchildren in London were identified by the *Multilingual Capital* (2000) survey, of whom 34 lived in Ealing.

MEDIA & INFORMATION *Londono Zinios* [newspaper for Lithuanians in London], Channelsea Ho, Canning Rd, Abbey La, Stratford E15 3ND.

RECREATION *Lithuanian Sports & Social Club,* 345a Victoria Park Rd, E9 5DX (8985 4125).

RELIGION *Lithuanian Church,* 21 The Oval, E2 9DT (7739 8735).

RESTAURANTS
Newham *MaZoji Lietuva,* 59 Leytonstone Rd, Stratford E15 1JA (8534 6601).

SHOPS **Shops selling Lithuanian produce** *Baltic Food & Beverages Ltd,* Unit 3, 2a Knightsbridge Rd, Barking IG11 0BP (8591 9928); *Baltika,* 32 High St, Walthanstow E17 (8521 8669); *Continental Delicatessen,* 42-43 Food Hall, Wood Green Shopping Centre, N22; *DaCa,* 34 Aylmer Parade, East Finchley N2 (8241 2475); *Kalinka,* 23-25 Queensway, W2 (7243 6125); *KatiuSa Cash & Carry,* Ground fl, Oslo Ho, 63-67 Felstead St, Hackney Wick E9 (8985 8987); *M & J Continental Food,* 53a Goodmayes Rd, Ilford IG3 (8590 4804); *Russian Shop,* Unit 9, The Arches, Villiers St, WC2 (7930 3484); *Slieza Komsomolki,* 92 Lillie Rd, SW6 (7385 4426).

TRANSLATION *Tramont Translation Management,* 57 Upper Park Rd, NW3 2UL (7692 6319; fax 7504 8638);

WELFARE *Britu-Lietuviu pagalbos fondas "Lietuvos vaikams",* 21 The Oval, Hackney Rd, E2 9DT.

Logba

Logba is an Aframic language spoken in Ghana. At the time of the *Multilingual Capital* (2000) survey, it was also the language of two London schoolchildren living in Lewisham.

Logoli

Logoli (also known as *Maragoli)* is a **Bantuic** language of Kenya. Speakers of this in London schools have been reported within the past decade but none were noted at the time of the *Multilingual Capital* (2000) survey.

London(er)

ACCOMMODATION *Ealing Tourist Flats* [self catering], 94 Gordon Rd, West Ealing W13 8PT (8566 8187); *London Tourist Accommodation,* SW5 1AS (0870 588 7711); *London Tourist Flats* [self catering], 17 St. Marys Rd, Wimbledon SW19 7BZ (8947 0573); *London Tourist Hotel Reservation Service* (7233 8666); *Property for London,* Canary Wharf Tower, Canada Sq, E14 5DY (07010703694).

ARTS & CULTURE *Bank of England Museum,* Bartholomew La, EC2A 8HR (7601 5545); *Bramah Museum of Tea and Coffee,* 38 Southwark St, SE1 1UN (7403 5650); *Bethnal Green Museum of Childhood,* Cambridge Heath Rd, E2 9PA (8983 5200); *Charles Dickens House Museum,* 48 Doughty St, WC1N 2LX (7405 2127); *City of London Sinfonia,* 11 Drum St, E1 1LH *(7480 7743); Clink Prison Museum,* Winchester Wharf, Clink St, SE1 9DG (7403 6515); *Crystal Palace Museum,* Cottage Yard, Anerley Hill, SE19 2BA (8676 0700); *Cutty Sark* (Clipper Ship Museum), King William Walk, SE10 9HT (8858 3445); *Florence Nightingale Museum,* Gassiot Ho, 2 Lambeth Palace Rd, SE1 7EH (7620 0374); *Freud Museum,* 20 Maresfield Gdns, NW3 5SX (7435 2002); *Geffrye Museum,* Kingsland Rd, E2 8EA (7739 9893); *Grange Museum of Community History,* Neasden La, NW10 1QB (8208 3312); *Handel House Museum Ltd,* 25

Brook St, W1K 4HB (7495 1685); *HMS Belfast* (Museum Ship), Morgans La, SE1 2JH (7940 6300); *Horniman Museum and Gardens,* 100 London Rd, SE23 3PQ (8699 1872); *Keats House Museum,* 10 Keats Grove, NW3 2RR (7435 2062); *Livesey Museum,* 682 Old Kent Rd, SE15 1JF (7639 5604); *London Academy of Music & Dramatic Art,* 226 Cromwell Rd, SW5 0SR (7373 9883); *London Canal Museum,* 12 New Wharf Rd, N1 9RT (7713 0836); *London Fire Brigade Museum,* Southwark Bridge Rd, SE1 7SP (7587 2894); *London Transport Museum,* 39 Wellington St, WC2R 7BB (7379 6344); *Museum of Garden History,* Lambeth Palace Rd, SE1 7LB (7401 8865); *Museum of London,* London Wall, EC2Y 5HN (7600 3699).

BUSINESS *London Bullion Market Association,* 6 Fredericks Pl, EC2R 8AB (7796 3067); *London Chamber of Commerce and Industry,* 33 Queen St, EC4R 1AP (7248 4444); *London First Centre,* 1 Hobhouse Ct, Suffolk St, SW1 (7925 2000). *London Insurance & Reinsurance Market Association,* London Underwriting Centre, 3 Mincing La, EC3R 7DD (7617 4444); *London Investment Banking Association,* 6 Fredericks Pl, EC2R 8BT (7796 3606); *London Stock Exchange Ltd,* Old Broad St, EC2N 1HP (7797 1000).

EDUCATION

Universities *Birkbeck College* (University of London), Malet St, W1 (7631 6000); *City University,* Northampton Sq, EC1 (7040 5060); *Goldsmiths College* (University of London), Lewisham Way, New Cross Rd, SE14 6NW (7919 7537); *Heythrop College* (University of London), Kensington Sq, W8 (7795 6600); *Imperial College* (University of London), Exhibition Rd, SW7 (7589 5111); *Institute of Education* (University of London), 20 Bedford Way, WC1 (7612 6000); *King's College London* (University of London), Strand, WC2R 2LS (7836 5454); *London Guildhall University,* Old Castle St, E1 7NT (7320 1000); *London School of Economics & Political Science* (University of London), Houghton St, WC2A 2AE (7405 7686); *London School of Hygiene and Tropical Medicine* (University of London), Keppel St, WC1 (7636 8636); *Queen Mary College* (University of London), Mile End Rd, E1 4NS (7882 5555); *School of Oriental and African Studies* (University of London), Thornhaugh St, Russell Sq, WC1H (7580 0916); *University College London* (University of London), Gower St, WC1 (7679 2000); *University of East London,* RM8 2AS (8223 3000); *University of North London,* 166-220 Holloway Rd, N7 (7607 2789); *University of Westminster,* 309 Regent St, W1 (7911 5000).

GOVERNMENT Greater London comprises the City of London and 32 boroughs. The *Greater London Authority* is located at City Hall, the Queen's Walk, SE1 2AA (7983 4100). The *Corporation of London,* responsible only for the City, is located at Guildhall, EC2P 2EJ (7606 3030). Contact addresses for each of the 32 London boroughs are given under WELFARE below. The *Association of London Government,* on which all the boroughs are

represented, is at Southwark St, SE1 0AL (7934 9999).

City Hall (Greater London Authority)

HEALTH & BEAUTY *Medcall Ltd* [24 hr visiting doctor service for central London], SW12 (0800 136 106).

LEGAL (In addition to the law centres listed here, some legal advice may also be obtained from the Citizens Advice Bureaux listed under **WELFARE** below.) *Brent Community Law Centre,* 385 High Rd, NW10 (8451 1122); *Camden Community Law Centre,* 2 Prince of Wales Rd, NW5 (7485 6672); *Central London Community Law Centre Ltd,* 19 Whitcomb St, WC2H 7HA (7839 2998); *Eureka Law Centre,* 58a Allen Rd (7254 2222); *Family Law Practice,* Tower Hamlets Law Centre, Commercial Road, E1 (7791 0432); *Greenwich Community Law Centre,* 187 Trafalgar Rd, SE10 9EQ (8305 3350); *Hackney Law Centre,* 6 Lower Clapton Rd, E5 0PD (8985 8364); *Hammersmith & Fulham Law Centre Ltd,* 144 King St, W6 0QU (8741 4021); *North Kensington Neighbourhood Law Centre,* 74 Golborne Rd, W10 5PS (8969 7473); *Royal Courts of Justice Citizens Advice Bureau,* First Avenue Ho, 42-49 High Holborn (0845 120 3715); *Thamesmead Law Centre,* St Pauls Central, Bentham Rd, SE28 8AS (8311 055); *Tottenham Neighbourhood Law Centre,* 754 High Rd, N17 0AL (8808 5354); *Tower Hamlets Law Centre,* 214 Whitechapel Rd, E1 1BL (7247 8998); *Wandsworth & Merton Law Centre Ltd,* 101 Tooting High St, SW17 0SU (8767 2777).

MEDIA & INFORMATION *London Weekend Television,* London Television Centre, Upper Ground, SE1 9LT (7620 1620);

For information on a large number of London's tourist attractions, visit <www.londontown.com>.

Association of Professional Tourist Guides, 50 Southwark St, SE1 1UN (7717 4064); *Britannia Tourist Bureau* [tour guides, sightseeing], 194 Edgware Rd, W2 2DS (7224 9181); *Discover Islington,* 44 Duncan St, Islington N1 8BW (7278 8787); *[Greenwich] Tourist Information Centre,* 46 Greenwich Church St, SE10 9BL (8858 6376); *Greenwich Tourist Information Centre,* Pepys Ho, King William Walk, SE10 9NN (0870 608 2000); *Guild of Registered Tourist Guides,* Guild Ho, 52D

Borough High St, SE1 1XN (7403 1115); *[Harrow] Tourist Information Centre,* P O Box 57, Harrow HA1 2XF (8424 1102); *[Hillingdon] Tourist Information Centre,* Central Library, High St, Uxbridge UB8 1HD (01895 250706); *[Hounslow] Tourist Information Centre,* 24 Treaty Centre, High St, Hounslow TW3 1ES (8572 8279); *Lewisham Tourist Information Centre,* inside Lewisham Library, 199-201 Lewisham High St, SE13 6LG (8297 8317); *London Tourist Advice* (7370 7744); *London Tourist Board - London Line,* SW1E 5LT (09068 663344); *London Tourist Information,* 24-26 Earls Court Gdns, SW5 0TD (7259 2000); *London Tourism Information,* SW5 1AS (0870 588 7711); *London Tourist Network Ltd,* Southbank Ho, Black Prince Rd, SE1 7SJ (7840 2490); [Tower *Hamlets] Tourist Information* Centre, 18 Lamb St, E1 6EA (7364 4970).

RECREATION *City Cruises plc,* Cherry Garden Pier, Cherry Garden St, Rotherhithe SE16 4TU (7740 0400); *London Amateur Boxing Association,* 58 Comber Grove, SE5 0LD (7252 7008); *London Anglers Association,* Forest Road Hall, Harvey Park Rd, E17 6LJ (8520 7477); *London Community Cricket Association,* London Fruit & Wool Exchange, Brushfield St, E1 6EX (7247 4177); *London Eye (Millennium Wheel)* [advance ticket bookings] (0870 500 0600); *London Football Association,* 6 Aldworth Grove, SE13 6HY (8690 9626); *London Knights Icehockey Club,* 36 Harbour Exchange Sq, E14 9GE (7536 2600); *London Narrow Boat Association,* Battlebridge Basin, Wharfdale Rd, N1 9SB (7837 9256); *London Planetarium & Madame Tussaud's,* Marylebone Rd, NW1 5LN (0870 400 3000); *London Zoo,* Regent's Park, NW1 (7722 3333).

TRAVEL Information about all forms of public transport throughout the Greater London area is available 24 hours per day on 7222 1234.

WELFARE For information about welfare services provided by local authorities, initial enquiries should be addressed to the following, according to your location.

Within the City of London: *Corporation of London,* Guildhall, EC2 P 2EJ (7606 3030).

Elsewhere in Greater London: *Barking & Dagenham,* Civic Centre, Rainham Rd North, Dagenham RM10 7 BN (8592 4500); *Barnet,* Town Hall, The Burroughs, NW4 4BG (8359 2000); *Bexley,* Civic Offices, Broadway, Bexleyheath DA6 7LB (8303 7777); *Brent,* Town Hall, Forty La, Wembley HA9 9EZ (8937 1234); *Bromley,* Civic Centre, Stockwell Close, Bromley BR1 3UH (8464 3333); *Camden,* Town Hall, Judd St, WC1H 9JE (7278 4444); *Croydon,* Taberner Ho, Park La, Croydon CR9 3JS (8686 4433); *Ealing,* Perceval Ho, 14-16 Uxbridge Rd W5 2HL (8579 2424) *Enfield,* Civic Centre, Silver St, Enfield EN1 3XA (8366 6565); *Greenwich,* Town Hall, Wellington St, SE18 6PW (8854 8888); *Hackney,* Town Hall, Mare St, E8 1EA (8356 5000); *Hammersmith & Fulham,* Town Hall, King St, W6 9JU (8748 3020); *Haringey,* Civic Centre, High Rd, N22 4LE (8489 0000);

Harrow, Civic Centre, Station Rd, Harrow, HA1 2UW (8863 5611); *Havering,* Town Hall, Main Rd, Romford, RM1 3 RD (01708 434343); *Hillingdon,* Civic Centre, High St, Uxbridge UB8 1UW (01895 250 111); *Hounslow,* Civic Centre, Lampton Rd, Hounslow TW3 3DN (8583 2000); *Islington,* Town Hall, Upper St, N1 2UD (7527 2000); *Kensington & Chelsea,* Town Hall, Hornton St, W8 7NX (7937 5464); *Kingston,* Guildhall, Kingston upon Thames, KT1 1EU (8546 2121); *Lambeth,* Town Hall, Brixton Hill, SW2 1RW (7926 1000); *Lewisham,* Town Hall, Brixton, SE6 4RU (8314 6000); *Merton,* Civic Centre, London Rd, Merton SM4 5DX (8543 2222); *Newham,* Town Hall, East Ham, E6 2RP (8430 2000) Redbridge, Town Hall, High Rd, Ilford IG1 1DD (8478 3020); *Richmond,* Civic Centre, York St, Twickenham TW1 3AA (8891 1411); *Southwark,* Town Hall, Peckham Rd, SE5 8UB (7525 5000); *Sutton,* Civic Offices, St Nicholas Way, Sutton SM1 1EA (8770 5000); *Tower Hamlets,* Mulberry Pl, 5 Clove Crescent, E14 2BG (7364 5000); *Waltham Forest,* Town Hall, Forest Rd, E17 4JF (8527 5544); *Wandsworth,* Town Hall, Wandsworth High St, SW18 2PU (8871 6000); *Westminster,* Westminster City Hall, Victoria St, SW 1E 6QP (7641 6000).

Citizens Advice Bureaux *Barking,* 55 Ripple Rd, Barking IG11 7NT (8594 6715); *Beckenham & Penge,* 20 Snowdown Close, Avenue Rd, SE20 (8778 0921); *Bermondsey,* 8 Market Pl, SE16 (020 7231 1118); *Brent,* 270 High Rd, NW10 (8451 7817); *Catford,* 120 Rushey Green, SE6 4HQ (0870 126 4037); *Chelsea,* Old Town Hall, Kings Rd (opposite Sydney St), SW3 5EE (7351 2114, 0870 751 0930); *Chiswick,* Chiswick Town Hall, Heathfield Terrace, W4 (020 8994 4846); *City of London,* 32 Ludgate Hill, EC4M 7DR (020 7236 1156); *Croydon,* CR7 8RG (8684 2236); *Dagenham,* 339 Heathway, Dagenham RM9 5AF (8592 1084); *Dalston,* 491 Kingsland Rd, E2 (0870 126 4013); *Ealing,* 14-16 Uxbridge Rd, W5 2HL (8825 7711); *Edmonton,* Methodist Church, Lower Fore St, N18 (020 8807 1730); *Finchley,* Hertford Lodge Annexe, East End Rd, N3 (0870 128 8080); *Fulham,* 1 The Pavilion, Mund St, W14 (7385 6750); *Grahame Park,* The Concourse, Grahame Park NW9 5XA (0870 128 8080); *Greenwich,* Old Town Hall, Polytechnic St, SE18 (020 8317 0609); *Hackney,* 235-238 Mare St, E8 (0870 126 4013); *Hendon,* 40 Church End, NW4 (0870 128 8080); *Hornsey,* 7

Hatherley Gdns, N8 9JH (8374 3704); *Kensington & Chelsea,* Chelsea Old Town Hall, SW3 5EE (7351 2114); *Kentish Town,* 242 Kentish Town Rd, NW5 2AB (7485 7034); *Kilburn,* 200 Kilburn High Rd, NW6 (7372 6888); *Leytonstone,* Greater London Ho, 547-551 High Road (8988 9620); *Malden & Coombe,* Blagdon Rd, New Malden KT3 4AF (8255 6060); *Marylebone,* Council Ho, Marylebone Rd, NW1 5PT (7641 1157); *Merton,* Merton Civic Centre, London Rd, Morden SM4 5DX (8715 0707); *Merton Money Advice Centre,* 326 London Rd, Mitcham CR4 3ND (8640 3194); *Mitcham,* 326 London Rd, Mitcham CR4 3ND (8288 0450); *Morden,* 7 Crown Parade, Morden SM4 5DX (8715 0707); *New Barnet,* 30 Station Rd, EN5 (0870 128 8080); *North Cheam,* 320 Malden Rd, Sutton SM3 8EP (8770 4851); *Paddington,* 441 Harrow Rd, W10 4RE (0870 126 4040); *Peckham,* 97 Peckham High St, SE15 5RS (7639 4471); *Pimlico,* 140 Tachbrook St, SW1 (0870 126 4040); *Putney/Roehampton,* 228 Upper Richmond Rd, SW14 (8479 0049); *Richmond,* 26 Kew Rd, TW9 2NA (8940 2501); *Romford,* 7 Victoria Rd, Romford RM1 2JT (0870 120 4200); *Sheen,* Sheen Lane Centre, Sheen La, SW14 8LP (8876 1513); *Streatham,* Ilex Ho, 1 Barrhill Rd, SW2 4RJ (8674 8993); *Sydenham,* 299 Kirkdale, SE26 (0870 126 4037); *Tooting & Balham,* 215 Balham High Rd (8378 5892); *Tottenham,* Tottenham Town Hall, Town Hall Approach Rd, N15 4RY (8376 3700, 0870 126 4030); *Tower Hamlets East,* 86 Bow Rd, E3 (0870 126 4014); Turnpike Lane, 14a Willoughby Rd, N8 0JJ (8352 0202); *Upper Street (Islington),* 135 Upper St (7359 1043); *Walthamstow,* 167 Hoe St, E17 3AL (0870 126 4026); Wandsworth, Bedford Ho, Balham High Rd, SW17 7BQ (8682 3433) and 14 York Rd, SW11 3QA (7228 9462); *Whitechapel,* 32 Greatorex St, E1 (7247 4172).

Other London welfare organizations. *Action for Blind People* (London Association for the Blind), 14 Verney Rd, SE16 3DZ (7635 4800); *London Ethnic Minority Deaf Association,* 107 The Grove, E15 1HP (8522 1700); *Refugee Helpline Project,* Willoughby Rd, N8 0II (0800 413 848).

Losengo (Sengo)

Losengo (also known, without its prefix, as *Sengo*) is a **Bantuic** language of Congo/Kinshasa. Speakers of this have been reported in London schools within the past decade although none were noted at the time of the *Multilingual Capital* (2000) survey.

Lozi (Silozi)

Lozi (also known, with its prefix, as *Silozi*) is a Bantuic language spoken mainly in Zambia. A small number of *Lozi*-speaking London schoolchildren was identified by the *Multilingual Capital* (2000) survey.

Luba (Ciluba)

Luba (also known, with its prefix, as *Ciluba*) is a Bantuic language spoken in Congo/Kinshasa. Two *Luba*-speaking pupils were living in Lambeth at the time of the *Multilingual Capital* (2000) survey.

Luganda (Ganda)

EDUCATION Mother tongue education for young children in *Luganda* is available in Tower Hamlets; visit <www.resourceunit.com> for details.

LANGUAGE *Luganda* (also known, without its prefix, as *Ganda*) is a Bantuic language spoken in Uganda. It was also reported as the language of 816 London schoolchildren at the time of the *Multilingual Capital* (2000) survey, of whom the largest number lived in Haringey.

Lugbara

Lugbara is a Sudanic language of Uganda and Congo/Kinshasa. The *Multilingual Capital* (2000) survey reported that there was one *Lugbara*-speaking pupil in Hammersmith & Fulham.

Lugisu

Lugisu (also called *Gisu*) is a dialect of *Lumasaba* spoken in Uganda. See *Lumasaba.*

Lui

The *Multilingual Capital* (2000) survey reported the presence of a *Lui*-speaking pupil in Greenwich. However, it is not clear to which language this refers because there are three different African languages of this name – one **Sudanic** (spoken in Congo/Kinshasa), one **Nilotic** (spoken in Sudan), and one **Bantuic** (spoken in Zambia).

Lumasaba (Masaba)

Lumasaba (*M a s a b a*) is a Bantuic language, of which *Lugisu* (*Gisu*) is a dialect. Both of these are spoken in Uganda and the presence of speakers of these in London schools has been sporadically reported in recent years.

Lunda (Cilunda)

Lunda (also known, with its prefix, as *Cilunda*) is a Bantuic language spoken in Zambia. There was one *Lunda*-speaking pupil in Hammersmith & Fulham at the time of the *Multilingual Capital* (2000) survey.

Luo (Lwo)

EDUCATION Mother tongue education for young children in "Luo" – whether *Dhopalwo* or *Dholuo* is unclear – is available in three places in London; visit <www.resourceunit.com> for information.

LANGUAGES *Luo* and *Lwo* are both alternative spellings for two different **Nilotic** languages. Together, they were reported as the first languages of 137 schoolchildren in the *Multilingual Capital* (2000) survey. (It would be possible to distinguish between the two by determining the country of origin of the children (or their parents) or by using their full names *Dhopalwo* (or *Dhopaluo*; spoken in Uganda and closely related to **Acholi**) and *Dholuo* (or *Lwo*; spoken in Kenya and Tanzania and closely related to *Dhopadhola*), respectively.

Lusoga *(Soga)*

Lusoga (also known without its prefix as *Soga*) is a Bantuic language spoken in Uganda. The *Multilingual Capital* (2000) survey reported that there were then eight *Lusoga*-speaking pupils in London schools, of whom five lived in Greenwich.

Luvale

Luvale is a Bantuic language spoken in parts of Angola, Congo/Kinshasa and Zambia. Speakers of this have been noted among London schoolchildren within the past decade but none were reported in the *Multilingual Capital* (2000) survey.

Luxembourger

BUSINESS *Dexia Banque International à Luxembourg,* Shackleton Ho, 4 Battle Bridge La, SE1 2JB (7556 3000).

GOVERNMENT *Luxembourg Embassy,* 27 Wilton Crescent, SW1X 8SD (7235 6961).

LANGUAGES The national language is Luxembourgish, closely related to **German**. The latter has official status as does **French** (which is the main language of administration).

RELIGION Luxembourgers are overwhelmingly Roman Catholics.

TRAVEL *Luxair,* Room 2003, Terminal Two, Heathrow Airport, TW6 1HL (8745 4255); *Luxembourg Tourist Office,* 122 Regent St, W1R 5FE (7434 2800).

Luziba

Luziba is a Bantuic language of Tanzania which was reportly spoken by one pupil in Lewisham at the time of the *Multilingual Capital* (2000) survey.

Lwo

See under the alternative spelling, **Luo**.

M

Macanese

GOVERNMENT After more than 400 years as a Portuguese colony, Macau is now a special administrative area of China.

LANGUAGES The official language of Macau is now **Chinese** of which the officially approved spoken variety is **Mandarin**. However, the language most extensively spoken in Macau is **Cantonese.** A Portuguese-based Creole called **Macanese** was formerly spoken there but is now believed to survive only among a small community of exiles in Hong Kong.

TRAVEL *Macau Tourist Office,* 1 Battersea Church Rd, SW11 3LY (7771 7006).

Macedonian

BUSINESS *Macedonian Drinks Ltd,* Unit 8, City Forum, 250 City Rd, EC1V 2QZ; *Macedonia Steel Ltd,* 93-99 Upper Richmond Rd, SW15 2TG (8780 5577).

EDUCATION A course in Macedonian is available at *SSEES* (7862 8634).

GOVERNMENT *Embassy of the Republic of Macedonia,* 5th fl, 25 James St, W1U 1DU (7935 3842); *Macedonian Embassy,* Suite 10, Harcourt Ho, 19a Cavendish Sq, W1M 9AD (7499 5152).

LANGUAGES *Macedonian* is the first language of the majority of the population and Albanian is the most important of several minority languages.

Macedonian is a **Slavonic** language, closely related to **Bulgarian**. The *Multilingual Capital* (2000) survey identified 32 **Macedonian**-speaking pupils in London schools, half of whom lived in Ealing.

TRANSLATION *Tramont Translation Management*, 57 Upper Park Rd, NW3 2UL (7692 6319; fax 7504 8638).

TRAVEL *Macedonian Airways Ltd,* 15 Connaught St, W2 2AY (7723 9438).

Madagascan

GOVERNMENT *Republic of Madagascar Consulate,* 16 Lanark Mansions, Pennard Rd, Shepherd's Bush W12 8DT (8746 0133).

LANGUAGES Both **French** and **Malagasy** – see separate entries for these – have official status but **Malagasy**, of which there are several distinct, regional varieties, is the principal spoken language.

Madeiran

RESTAURANTS
Camden *Camacheira,* 43 Pratt St, NW1 (7485 7266).

Hounslow *Madeira Steak House,* 636 Bath Rd, Hounslow TW5 9TL (8759 0941).

Lambeth *Madeira Star,* 337 Kennington Rd, Lambeth SE11 4QE (7582 8778).

Waltham Forest *Cascais Madeira,* 337 High Road Leytonstone, Wanstead E11 4JT (8558 6210).

SHOPS *Madeira Patisserie,* 85 Glasshouse Walk, Lambeth SE11 5ES (7820 1117).

TRAVEL *Madeira Holidays,* 40 Rundell Tower, Portland Grove, SW8 1JB (7735 7055); *Travel (Madeira) International Ltd,* 84 Landor Rd, Brixton SW9 9PE (7737 4604).

Ma'di

Ma'di is a **Sudanic** language spoken in Sudan. In the *Multilingual Capital* (2000) survey, *Ma'di* was reported to be the language of four London schoolchildren living in Westminster.

Maghrebi

Maghrebi (also spelled *Maghribi*) refers to the people and cultures of northwest Africa, from Tunisia westwards. The word comes from Arabic *maghreb* meaning 'far west' or 'sunset'.

LANGUAGE The **Maghrebi** varieties of **Arabic** spoken in Tunisia, Algeria, and Morocco are sufficiently different from the **Mashriqi** (q.v.) varieties spoken from Egypt eastwards that the two may be regarded as separate but related languages. Nevertheless, in the vast majority of cases, schoolchildren speaking either of these varieties were reported simply as speakers of **Arabic** in the *Multilingual Capital* (2000) survey.

MEDIA & INFORMATION *Maghreb Arab Press,* 35 Westminster Bridge Rd, SE1 7JB (7401 8146).

SHOPS *Maghereb Halal Stores,* 51 Grand Parade, Green Lanes, N4 1AG (8809 2300); *Maghreb Bookshop,* 45 Burton St, WC1H 9AL (7388 1840); *Maghreb Stores,* 320 Holloway Rd, N7 (7700 3123).

Malagasy

Malagasy is a **Hesperonesic** language with official status in Madagascar. In the *Multilingual Capital* (2000) survey it was found to be the first language of one pupil living in Haringey.

Malawian

ASSOCIATIONS *Malawi Association,* 30 Swan Rd, Southall, UB1 2JC (8813 8035, 8368 0060).

GOVERNMENT *Malawi High Commission,* 33 Grosvenor St, W1K 4DE (7491 4172).

LANGUAGES Several **Bantuic** languages are spoken in Malawi. **Chewa** (full name, *Chichewa;* also known as *Nyanja*) has national status and is the first language of half the population. Ither important Bantuic languages spoken there are *Makua* (*Emakua*), *Yao* (*Ciyao*), and *Tumbuka* (*Citumbuka*) but no speakers of these in London were noted in the *Multilingual Capital* (2000) survey.

TRAVEL *Air Malawi,* 200 Buckingham Palace Rd, SW1W 9TA (7707 4573).

Malay

EDUCATION Courses in **Malay** are available at *SOAS Language Centre* (7898 4888).

LANGUAGE The word Malay is applied both to a large family of languages (all Hesperonesic languages in Dalby's (1999-2000) classification) as well as to just one of these which has official status in Malaysia, Brunei, and Singapore. The latter is very much the same language as **Indonesian** although there are some significant differences due to the differing colonial histories of the territories concerned. Considered as a single language, **Malay/Indonesian** is ranked ninth in the world with an estimated total of 160m speakers (of whom this is the first language of perhaps 50m). In the *Multilingual Capital* (2000) survey, the figures for Malay and Indonesian were also added together and found to be the first language of 345 London schoolchildren, of whom the largest number lived in Barnet.

RESTAURANTS Several restaurants were found which described themselves as **Malay** but, in the absence of any clear indication that the food they offer differs significantly from those described as **Malaysian**, they have all been tentatively included under the latter heading.

Malayalam

EDUCATION Mother tongue education for young children in Malayalam is available at three places in London; visit <www.resourceunit.com> for details.

LANGUAGE **Malayalam** is a Dravidic language with official status in the Indian state of Kerala. It is written in its own semi-syllabic script. The *Multilingual Capital* (2000) survey found this to be the first language if 313 London schoolchildren of whom the largest number lived in Ealing.

RELIGION The church of *St Andrew's by the Wardrobe,* Queen Victoria St, EC4 holds occasional services in Malayalam.

Malayan

The word *Malayan* is sometimes applied to the **Malay** people and/or their language. Such usage is becoming obsolete and is not recommended.

Malaysian

ACCOMMODATION *Malaysia Hall London* [hostel], 44 Bryanston Sq, W1H 2DH (7723 9484).

Association of Malaysian Community, 100 Cricketfield Rd, Clapton E5 8NS (8533 4765).

BUSINESS

Banking *Bank Bumiputra Malaysia Berhad,* 14 Cavendish Sq, W1M 0HA (7306 6050); *Bank Negara Malaysia,* Berkeley Square Ho, Berkeley Sq, W1X 5LA (7495 0222); *Malayan Banking Berhad,* 74 Coleman St, EC2R 5BN (7382 2266).

Other *Felda Marketing (Malaysia),* 17 Curzon St, W1Y 7FE (7409 0442); *Malaysian Industrial Development Authority* (London Office), 17 Curzon St, W1Y 7FE (7493 0616); *Malaysian International Shipping Corporation Agencies (UK) Ltd,* Town Quay Wharf, Abbey Rd, Barking IG11 7BZ (8591 3232); *Malaysian Trade Commission,* 17 Curzon St, W1Y 7FE (7499 7388).

GOVERNMENT *Office of the High Commissioner of Malaysia,* 45 Belgrave Sq, SW1X 8PH (7235 8033).

LANGUAGES *Malay* is the official language of Malaysia and the Malay people account for almost 60% of the population (*Whitaker's* 2002). More than a quarter of the population speak *Chinese* languages and there is a small *Tamil*-speaking minority. There is also a number of indigenous languages spoken in Sabah and Sarawak. *English* is widely known as a second language.

RELIGION Islam is the official language of Malaysia but adherence to other religions is in no way discouraged.

RESTAURANTS

East Central *Silks and Spice,* The Arcade, Liverpool St, EC2M 7PN (7626 1155); *Silks and Spice,* Temple Ct, Queen Victoria St, EC4N 4UJ (7248 7878).

South East 1 *Champor Champor,* 62 Weston St, SE1 3QJ (7403 4600); *Indonesian and Malaysian,* 98 Bermondsey St, Southwark SE1 3UB (7407 0329).

West 1 *Bahia* [Thai/Malaysian/Japanese], 28 Frith St, W1V 5TL (7434 3881); *New World* [Chinese / Malaysian], 1 Gerrard St, W1 (7734 0396); *Silks and Spice* [Thai/Malaysian], 23 Foley St, W1P 7LA (7636 2718).

Camden *Silks and Spice* [Thai/Malaysian], 28 Chalk Farm Rd, NW1 8AG (7267 5751).
Croydon *Kelong,* 1b Selsdon Rd, South Croydon CR2 6PU (8688 0726); *Malay House,* 60 Lower Addiscombe Rd, Croydon CR0 6AA (8666 0266); *Malay House Fusion,* 56 Lower Addiscombe Rd, Croydon CR0 6AA (8680 6042).

Enfield *A & M Malaysian T/A,* 208 Green Lanes, Palmers Green N13 5UE; *Kam Pung* [Thai/Malyasian/Szechuan], 879 Green Lanes, N21 2QS (8360 8998).

Greenwich *Jaya House* [Chinese/Malaysian], 754 Sidcup Rd, SE9 3NS (8857 2188); *Mandarin Palace T/A* [Chinese/Malaysian], 56 Charlton Church La, SE7 7AB (8853 1706).

Haringey *Penang Penang,* 45 Topsfield Parade, Tottenham La, London N8 8PT (8340 5247); *Penang Satay House,* 9 Turnpike La, N8 0EP (8340 8707); *Satay Malaysia,* 10 Crouch End Hill, N8 8AA (8340 3286).

Hounslow *Silks and Spice* [Thai/Malaysian], 95 Chiswick High Rd, W4 2EF (8994 7773).

Islington *May-Malay,* 326 Holloway Rd, N7 6NJ (7700 0271); **Lewisham** *Kaya House Malaysian Bistro,* 37 Deptford Broadway, SE8 4PQ (8692 1749).

Redbridge *Malaysian Satay Hut,* 765 High Rd, Ilford IG3 8RW (8597 8448); *Well Cooked T/A,* 35 Bagshot St, SE17 2QW (7703 9815).

Wandsworth *Yum Yum* [Chinese/Malaysian], 112 St Johns Hill, SW11 1SJ (7585 1802).

Westminster *Satay House Malay,* 13 Sale Pl, W2 1PX (7723 6763).

SHOPS *Lam's West Malaysian Food Co,* 100 High St, N8 7NT (8341 4754).

TRAVEL *Malaysia Airlines,* 247 Cromwell Rd, SW5 5TR (7373 2314); *Malaysian and Far Eastern Travel Ltd,* 18 Chiltern St, W1U 7QA (7486 8656); *Malaysian and Far Eastern Travel Ltd,* 57 George St, W1H 5PH (7487 5888); *Malaysia Experience,* 42-44 Station Rd, Harrow HA2 7SE (8424 9548); *Malaysia Tourism Promotion Board,* 57 Trafalgar Sq, WC2N 5DU (7930 7932).

Maldivian

GOVERNMENT *High Commission of the Republic of Maldives,* 22 Nottingham Pl, W1M 3FB (7224 2135).

LANGUAGE The language of the Maldivian people is *Dhivehi* – see this for details.

RELIGION The *Maldivian* people are Muslims.

TRAVEL *Maldive Travel Ltd,* 3 Esher Ho, 11 Edith Terrace, West Brompton, SW10 0TH (7352 2246).

Malinké

EDUCATION Mother tongue education for young children in *Malinké* is available in Newham; visit <www.resourceunit.com> for details.

LANGUAGE *Malinké* is the French name of one of the **Mandic** languages spoken mainly in Senegal and Guinea; see *Manding*. In the *Multilingual Capital* (2000) survey, the presence of seven *Malinké*-speaking London schoolchildren was reported.

Maltese

ASSOCIATIONS *British Association of the Sovereign Military Order of Malta,* 60 Grove End Rd, St John's Wood NW8 9NH (7586 7035); *Maltese Culture Movement,* 109 Cornwallis Rd, N19 4LQ (7272 9000).

BUSINESS *Malta Development Corporation,* Malta Ho, 36-38 Piccadilly, W1V 9PA (7292 4970).

GOVERNMENT *Malta High Commission*, Malta Ho, 36-38 Piccadilly W1J 0LE (7292 4800).

LANGUAGE *M a l t e s e* is a **Semitic** language, more specifically a variety of **Arabic** with considerable influence from *Italian* and *English*. It has official status in Malta and, unlike all other **Semitic** languages, is written in the Roman script. At the time of the *Multilingual Capital* (2000) survey, *Maltese* was reported as the language of 118 London schoolchildren of whom the largest number were living in Lambeth.

RELIGION *Franciscan Sisters of Malta,* 9 St.George's Drive, SW1V 4DJ (7834 4020).

SPECIAL *Sovereign Military Order of Malta,* 60 Grove End Rd, NW8 9NH (7586 3179).

TRAVEL *Air Malta,* Air Malta Ho, 314-316 Upper Richmond Rd, Putney SW15 6TU (8785 3199) and Malta Ho, 36-38, Piccadilly W1J 0DP (7292 4949); *Bellair Holidays & Malta Holidays,* 314-316 Upper Richmond Rd, Putney SW15 6TU (8785 3266); *Holiday Malta Co Ltd,* Air Malta Ho, 314-316 Upper Richmond Rd, Putney SW15 6TU (8785 3222); *Holiday Travel Club Ltd Malta,* 56 Coldharbour La, Hayes UB3 3ES (8561 9079); *Malta Air Transport,* 1st fl, 2 Conduit St, W1S 2XD (7491 7144); *Malta Direct Holidays,* 314 Upper Richmond Rd, SW15 6TU (8785 3233); *Malta Sun Holidays Ltd,* 467 Roman Rd, Bow E3 5LX (0800 091 2222); *Maltese Movement,* Air Malta Ho, 314-16, Upper Richmond Rd, SW15 6TU (8785 3233); *Malta Tourist Office,* Malta Ho, 36-38 Piccadilly, W1J 0LD (7292 4900).

Mampruli

Mampruli is a **Voltaic** language spoken in Ghana and Togo. The *Multilingual Capital* (2000) survey revealed that this was also the first language of one London pupil in Greenwich.

Mandarin

EDUCATION Mother tongue instruction in Mandarin is available for children in several places in London. Visit <www.resourceunit.com> for details.

More than 50 courses in *Mandarin* are available in London at a wide range of levels. For details, **visit** <www.floodlight.co.uk>.

LANGUAGE *Mandarin* is the usual name for the Chinese language which has official status in China. The Chinese government's preferred name for this is **Putonghua** (which means 'commonly understood language') but the latter shows no sign of replacing *M a n d a r i n* outside China. (Other Chinese languages such as **Cantonese** are officially considered to be non-standard dialects of *Mandarin*.) *Mandarin* is a **Sinitic** language and is the first language of some 800 million people – more than any other language in the world. (But **English** surpasses this figure when first- and second-language speakers are added together.)

RESTAURANTS

The word *Mandarin* occurs in the names of various restaurants but it is not clear that this has any special culinary significance so these are included under **Chinese** - RESTAURANTS.

TRANSLATION *Chinese & Mandarin Translation Services,* The Moorings, 164 Brindley Close, Wembley HA0 1BU (8991 6761).

Manding

Manding is the name of a subgroup of Mandic languages spoken in Gambia, Senegal, Guinea-Bissau, Guinea and Mali. These include **Kono, Malinké** and **Mandinka**.

Mandingo

EDUCATION Mother tongue education for young children in "Mandingo" is available in Newham; see <www.resourceunit.com> for further information. ("Mandingo" here probably means *Mandinka* – see entry for this.)

LANGUAGE *Mandingo* is used in English both as a general name for a group of Mandic languages (= *Manding*, see above) and also as an alternative name for **Mandinka**, see below).

Mandinka

Mandinka (also known as *Mandingo*) is a Mandic language spoken in Gambia, Senegal and Guinea-Bissau. The *Multilingual Capital* (2000) survey noted the presence of a few *Mandinka*-speaking schoolchildren in the boroughs of Southwark and Greenwich.

Mangbetu

Mangbetu is a Sudanic language of Congo /Kinshasa and Uganda. The *Multilingual Capital* (2000) survey reported that there was one *Mangbetu*-speaking schoolchild living in Brent.

Maori

Maori is a Trans-Pacific language with official status in New Zealand. Three *Maori*-speaking London pupils were identified in the *Multilingual Capital* (2000) survey.

Maragoli

See under the alternative name of *Logoli.*

Marathi

Marathi is an Indic language spoken mainly in the Indian state of Maharashtra. The *Multilingual Capital* (2000) survey showed that this was the first language of 49 London schoolchildren, of whom 19 lived in Barnet.

Maronite

A Christian sect named after its 4th century Syrian founder, Maron. Maronite Christians are today located mainly in the Lebanon – see *Lebanese*, RELIGION for details of Maronite facilities available in London.

Masaba

Masaba is a Bantuic language spoken in Uganda. Speakers of this have occasionally been noted in London schools but not were found at the time of the *Multilingual Capital* (2000) survey.

Mashriqi

Mashriqi refers to the people and cultures of the Arabic-speaking world from Egypt to Oman. The word means 'eastern' in Arabic.

LANGUAGE The *Mashriqi* varieties of *Arabic* spoken from Egypt eastwards (and also in Sudan) are sufficiently different from the *Maghrebi* varieties spoken in northwest Africa that the two may be regarded as separate but related languages. Nevertheless, in the vast majority of cases, schoolchildren speaking either of these varieties were reported simply as speakers of *Arabic* in the *Multilingual Capital* (2000) survey.

MEDIA & INFORMATION *Mashriq*, Unit 5, Linen Ho, 253 Kilburn Rd, W10 4BQ (8964 5834) [video filming service].

SHOPS *Mashreketab,* 157 North End Rd, W14 (7603 6936) [bookshop].

Mauritanian

GOVERNMENT *Mauritanian Honorary Consulate*, Bow Common La, E3 4BH (8980 4382).

LANGUAGES *Arabic* has official status and it the first language of about 80% of the population. Small minorities speak *Atlantic* or *Mandic* languages.

RELIGION Mauritanians are almost all Muslims.

Mauritian

This word is applied to people and things from the island of Mauritius, and to its principal language, Mauritian Creole.

ASSOCIATIONS *Anglo Mauritian Association,* 14 Red Lion Sq, WC1R 4QL (7404 0444); *Mauritius Association*, De Costa Ho, 44 Peckham Rd, SE5 (7703 1071/4071).

BARS & NIGHT-CLUBS *La Virginie Wine Bar*, 1 The Broadway, Gunnersbury La, Acton W3 8HR (8752 1716).

BOOKS A selection of recent books published in and/or about Mauritius is available by mail order at <www.mauritiusworld.com>.

FREIGHT *Access Couriers 7 Shipping (Worldwide) Ltd,* Unit 28, leyton Business Centre, Etloe Rd, E10 7BT (8539 0707); *Transway Red lines (UK) Ltd,* Hangar 2, North Weald Aerodrome, Merlin Way, near Epping, Essex CM16 6AA (01992 525700).

GOVERNMENT *Mauritius High Commission*, 32 Elvaston Pl, SW7 5NW (7581 0294).

LANGUAGES Mauritian Creole is the first language of at least 70% of Mauritians and the second language of almost all others. An *Indic* language known as Bhojpuri is the first language of well over 20% of the population while French is that of about 4%. Several other languages are spoken by small minorities. English is the official language but French is far more widely used in the media.

MEDIA & INFORMATION There are three newsletters or newspapers published in London for Mauritians: *Mauritius Association News*, 44 Peckham Rd, SE5 (7701 5600); *Mauritian International* (quarterly), P O Box 4100, SW20 0XN (8947 1912); and *Mauritius News* (monthly), 583 Wandsworth Rd., SW8 3JD 7498 3066). Selections from the leading daily newspapers published in Mauritius can be read on the internet: *L'Express* <www.lexpress-net.com> and *Le Mauricien* <lemauricien.com>

RELIGION The principal religions of Mauritius are Hinduism (51% of the population), Christianity (30%, mainly Roman Catholic), and Islam (17%). The church of *Notre Dame de Paris,* 5 Leicester Pl, WC2 (7437 9363) has a large Mauritian congregation and is where contact may be made with the *Association Chrétienne des Mauriciens à Londres.*

Mauritius Tamil Maha Sangham (8641 7452).

RESTAURANTS

Islington *Chez Liline,* 101 Stroud Green Rd, Finsbury Park, N4 (7263 6550) specializes in Indian Ocean fish dishes.

Kensington & Chelsea *Offshore*, 148 Holland Park Ave, W11 (7221 6090).

Westminster *Jason's Wharf,* opp. 60 Blomfield Rd, W9 (7286 6752)

SHOPS Fresh fish air-freighted from the Indian Ocean are available at *France Fresh Fish*, 99 Stroud Green Rd, N4 (7263 9767) which also sells chutnies and other culinary specialities imported from Mauritius. *Mauritius Quality Halal Meat,* 7 Hildreth St, Balham SW12 9RQ (8673 1629).

SPECIAL *Mauritius Chamber of Agriculture,* 35 Grosvenor Gdns, SW1 (7834 3381).

TRAVEL The national airline of Mauritius is *Air Mauritius*, 49 Conduit St, W1R 9FB (admin. 7437 7075). *Mauritian Forum,* 2 The Oaks, Woolwich, SE18 7JR; *Mauritius Tourism Promotion Authority,*

32, Elvaston Pl., SW7 5NW (7584 3666) is run by the Mauritian government. Agents specializing in travel to Mauritius include *A & M Travel,* 246 Fore St, Edmonton, N18 2QD (8807 6404) *and* 567 High St, Tottenham, N17 6SN (8808 2900); *Citibond Travel,* 1st fl, 20-22 Maddox St, W1S 1PN (0870 7552255); *Imbel Travel,* 22 West Green Rd, N15 5NN (8809 5522*);* *Mauritius-India Holidays*, 30 Trinity Rd, Tooting, SW17 7RE (8767 9911) and 22 West Green Rd, Tottenham N15 5NN (8800 2675); *Planet Mauritius,* 4 Marlborough Business Centre, 96 George La, South Woodford E18 1AD (8530 8296); *Sunset Travel Ltd,* 306 Clapham Rd, SW9 (7622 0777); and *Travel Centre* (Clapham) Ltd, 12 The Pavement, SW4 0HY (7720 8701).

WELFARE *Mauritian League of Friends,* Enterprise Ho, 8 Essex Rd, Dartford, DA1 2AU (01322 291450); *Overseas Mauritians Aid Trust,* 113 Ribblesdale Rd, SW16 6SP (8696 9897).

Mauritian Creole

EDUCATION Mother tongue education in **Mauritian Creole** is available in Waltham Forest; visit <www.resourceunit.com> for details.

LANGUAGE **Mauritian Creole** is a French-based Creole spoken by more than 1m people. There are many thousands of speakers of this in London but no reliable figure for the numbers of London schoolchildren who speak this can be given because many boroughs, including Wandsworth where the largest concentration of Mauritians is found, do not recognise this as a language and count those who report this as speakers of French.

Maya

Maya is a language spoken in Mexico and Belize. The existence of a few schoolchildren who speak this in Kensington & Chelsea has recently been reported but none were recorded at the time of the *Multilingual Capital* (2000) survey.

Mbum

Mbum is an Adamawic language of Cameroon which was recorded in the *Multilingual Capital* (2000) survey as the first language of two schoolchildren in Brent.

Mediterranean

BUSINESS *Eastern Mediterranean Maritime Ltd,* [shipping brokers], Fountain Ho, 130 Fenchurcg St, Monument, EC3M 5DJ (7283 9591); *Indo-Mediterranean Commodities Ltd,* Serendib Ho, 67A Boston Manor Rd, Brentford, TW8 9JQ (8568 6561); *Mediterranean Average Adjusting Co, The Friendly Societies,* King William Ho, 2A Eastcheap, Monument, EC3M 1AA (7929 0077);*Mediterranean Oil Plc Steel Stockholders,* HR Ho, 447 High Rd, North Finchley, N12 0AF; *Insurance & Reinsurance Co Ltd,* 20 St Dunstan Hill, Monument, EC3R 8HL (7480 5650); *Mediterranean Growers,* [export & import agents], Lawrence Ho, Goodwyn Av, Mill Hill,

NW7 3RH (8906 8787); *M M C Management Consulting Ltd,* 315 Oxford St, West End, W1R 1LA.

FREIGHT *Mediterranean Express Couriers & Messengers,* 521 Solent Rd, Heathrow Airport, Hounslow, TW6 3AZ (8759 7859).

RESTAURANTS

East Central *Futures Café Bar,* 2 Exchange Sq, EC2A 2EH (7638 6341); *The Eagle*, 159 Farringdon Rd, EC1 (7837 1353).

South West 1 *ICA Café,* The Mall, SW1 (7930 8619).

West 1 *Dover Street Restaurant & Bar* [French / Mediterranean], 8-10 Dover St, W1X 3PJ (7491 7509).

West Central *Faya,* Thistle Hotel, King's Cross Rd, WC1 (7278 2434).

Haringey *Mediterranean Café Restaurant,* 24 Blackstock Rd, Finsbury Pk, N4 2DW (7226 3913); *Mediterranean Fish Bar T/A,* 102 High Rd, N15 6JR (8800 7727).

Hillingdon *Taste of the Mediterranean,* 180 Field End Rd, HA5 1RF (8868 9621).

Hounslow *Tutto Mediterranean Brasserie,* 76-77 South Parade, Chiswick W4 5LF (8995 0737).

Islington *Arabisk,* 158 Fonthill Rd, N4 3HP (7272 5802); *Mediterranean Cafe,* 24 Blackstock Rd, N4 2DW (7226 3913); *The Furnace*, 1 Rufus St, Shoreditch, N1 (7613 0598).

Kensington & Chelsea *Mediterranean Greek Taverna,* 308 Earl's Court Rd, SW5 9BA (7373 5012); *Pasha,* 1 Gloucester Rd, SW7 4PP (7589 7969);

Lambeth *Peter Pepper's Mediterranean Cafe,* 60 Morrish Rd, Brixton, SW2 4EG (8671 5655).

Merton *Maison St Cassien* [Mediterranean / Lebanese] 71 High St, Wimbledon, SW19 (8944 1200); *Terraza Mediterranean Cafe Grill,* 33a High St, Wimbledon SW19 5BY (8946 1920).

Richmond *Red Peppers Mediterranean Cantina,* 53 Broad St, Teddington TW11 8QZ (8977 5452).

Westminster *Assaggi Mediterranean Cuisine,* 39 Chepstow Pl, Bayswater W2 4TS (7792 5501).

SHOPS *Carnevale* [Mediterranean vegetarian food], 135 Whitecross St, EC1Y 8JL (7250 3452); *George Skoulikas Ltd* [Mediterranean organic foods], Unit 5, 998 North Circular Rd, Coles Green Rd, NW2 7JR (8452 8465); *L'Algéroise,* 130 Cricklewood Broadway, NW2 (8452 3638). *Mediterranean Food Products,* 2 Central Parade, Western Ave, Greenford UB6 8TF (8991 5987).

TRAVEL *British Mediterranean Airways Ltd,* Cirrus Ho, Bedfont Rd, London Heathrow Airport, TW19 7NL (01784 266 300); *Mediterranean Connection,* 304 Old Brompton Rd, SW5 9JF (7373 4411); *Mediterranean Holidays,* 49 Great Cumberland Pl, W1H 7LH (7723 7234); *Mediterranean Shipping Cruises,* Walmar Ho, 296 Regent St, W1R 5HF (7637 2525); *Mediterranean Star Travel Ltd,* 41 Wadeson St, E2 9DP; *Trans Mediterranean Airways,* Building 560, Hounslow TW6 3QX (8759 2456).

"Memny"

See *"Memon"*

"Memon" ("Memny")

In the data collected for the *Multilingual Capital* (2000) survey, four schoolchildren in Ealing were listed as speakers of *Memon*. Our research has failed to find any language of this name. There is, however, a particular group of Muslim traders in India known as *Memon* and it thus seems likely that the children in question belonged to this group. Perhaps related to this, one child in Lambeth was said to speak *"Memny"*. Etymologically, this could derive from Memon + i (the final element in a great many language and dialect names in northern India).

Mende

EDUCATION Mother tongue education for young children in **Mende** is available in Lewisham; visit <www.resourceunit.com> for details.

LANGUAGE **Mende** is a **Mandic** language spoken in Sierra Leone. The *Multilingual Capital* (2000) survey recorded the presence of 107 **Mende**-speaking schoolchildren in London.

Mexican

BARS & NIGHT-CLUBS *Joe's Bar & Restaurant,* 99 High St, Hampton TW12 1NH (8941 7309); *La Perla del Pacifico Bar,* 28 Maiden La, WC2E 7JS (7240 7400); *Mickey Blue's Cafe & Wine Bar,* 63a Dartmouth Rd, Forest Hill SE23 3HN (8699 7104); *Tequila Rock Cafe,* 281 High St, Croydon CR0 1QH (8686 3223).

BUSINESS *Banco Nacional de Mexico,* 3 Creed Court, 5 Ludgate Hill, EC4M 7AA (7489 9260, 7827 6900); *Mexican Embassy Trade Commission,* 5th fl, 3 St James's Sq, SW1Y 4JU (7839 6586); *Nacional Financiera Mexican International Bank,* 19th fl, 1 Angel Ct, EC2R 7HJ (7417 0016).

GOVERNMENT *Mexican Consulate,* 8 Halkin St, SW1X 7DW (7235 6393); *Mexican Embassy,* 42 Hertford St, W1Y 7TE (7499 8586); *Mexican Embassy Trade Commission,* 5th fl, 3 St James's Sq, SW1Y 4JU (7839 6586); *Mexican Ministry of Tourism,* 60-61 Trafalgar Sq, WC2N 5DS (7734 1058); *Mexican Trade Commission,* 3 St. James's Sq, SW1Y 4JU (7839 6586).

LANGUAGES **Spanish** is the official language and the first language of the vast majority of Mexicans. Several Amerindian languages are also spoken of which only **Maya** has been reported in London.

MOTORING *Palace Garage* [Mexican Beetle agents], Palace Rd, Kingston KT1 2LG (8547 2022).

RESTAURANTS

South East 1 *Café El Paso,* 17-19 York Rd, SE1 7NJ (7633 9666); *El Turkisten,* 304 Old Kent Rd, SE1 5UE (7703 5172).

West 1 *Break for the Border,* 8 Argyll St, W1V 1AD (7734 5776); *Down Mexican Way,* 25 Swallow St, W1R 7HD (7437 9895); *El Pirata,* 5 Down St, W1Y 7DR (7491 3810); *L'Autre* [Polish / Mexican], 5b Shepherd St, W1 (7499 4680); *Si Señor,* 2 St Anne's Ct, 86 Dean St, W1V 3AX (7494 4632).

West Central *Break for the Border,* 5 Goslett Yard, Charing Cross Rd, WC2H 0EH (7437 8595); *Café Pacifico,* 5 Langley St, WC2H 9JA (7379 7728); *Chiquito,* 20-21 Leicester Sq, WC2H 7LE (7839 6925); *El Barco Latino,* Temple Pier, Victoria Embankment, WC2R 2PP (7379 5496); *La Perla del Pacifico,* 28 Maiden Lane, WC2E 7JS (7240 7400).

Barnet *Chiquito,* Unit 206 Staples Corner Retail Park, Geron Way, Edgware Rd, Cricklewood, NW2 6LW (8450 9326).

Bromley *Maya Mexican Cafe,* 238 High St, Bromley BR1 1PQ (8460 3798); *Mexican Dreams,* 237 High St, Bromley BR1 1NZ (8402 9517).

Camden *Acapulco Mexican Restaurant,* 291 Finchley Rd, Hampstead, NW3 6ND (7431 8277); *Arizona,* 2 Jamestown Rd, NW1 (7284 4730); *Cactus,* 83a Haverstock Hill, NW3 4RL (7722 4112); *Café Loco Tex-Mex Cantina,* 134 Fortress Rd, Kentish Town, NW5 2HP (7284 0200); *Camden Cantina,* 34 Chalk Farm Rd, NW1 8AJ (7267 2780); *El Parador,* 245 Eversholt St, NW1 1BA (7387 2789); *Mexican & Spanish T/A,* 102 Fleet Rd, NW3 2QX (7284 2619); *Nachos,* 79-81 Heath St, Hampstead, NW3 6UG (7431 0908); *Viva Zapata,* 7 Pond St, Hampstead, NW3 2PN (7431 9134).

Croydon *Mexican Renaissance,* 82 Links View Rd, Croydon CR0 8NX (8776 0020).

Ealing *Chiccanos,* 24 Broadway, West Ealing, W13 0SU (8840 1272); *Chiquito,* Royale Leisure Park, Kendal Av, Acton, W3 0PA (8896 3883).

Enfield *Chiquito,* 492 Gt Cambridge Rd, Enfield, EN1 3SA (8367 9991).

Greenwich *Cafe Sol,* 13 Nelson Rd, SE10 1XX (8853 4385).

Hackney *Pancho Villa,* 113 Lower Clapton Rd, Clapton, E5 0NP (8986 2950).

Hammersmith & Fulham *El Metro,* Fulham Broadway, SW6 1TB (7384 1264).

Harrow *Cheekos,* 360a Station Rd, Harrow, HA1 2DE (8933 2323).

Hounslow *Mexican Accent,* 43 Brainton Ave, Feltham TW14 0AZ (8890 8181); *Nachos,* 29 Chiswick High Rd, Chiswick W4 2ND (8995 0945).

Islington *El Molino,* 379 Holloway Rd, N7 0RN (7700 4312); *Nachos,* 57 Upper St, Islington, N1 0NY (7354 3340).

Kensington & Chelsea *El Blason,* 8-9 Blacklands Terrace, Chelsea, SW3 2SP (7823 7383); *El Cid 2,* 11 Beauchamp Pl, Chelsea, SW3 1NQ (7589 6361); *El Gaucho,* 125 Sydney St, Chelsea, SW3 6NR (7376 8514); *Footlights,* 1 Kensington High St, W8 5NP (7795 6533); *La Perla,* 803 Fulham Rd, SW3 6HR (7471 4895); *Nachos,* 212 Fulham Rd, SW10 9PJ (7351 7531); *Nachos,* 147-149 Notting Hill Gate, W11 3LF (7221 5250); *Salvadors El Bodegon,* 9 Park Walk, SW10 0AJ (7352 1330).

Lambeth *Café Sol Dos,* 56 Clapham High St, SW4 7UL (7498 9319); *El Rincon Latino,* 148 Clapham Manor St, SW4 6BX (7622 0599).

Lewisham *Cactus Pit,* 10-11 Royal Parade, Blackheath, SE3 (8852 0883); *El Pirta,* 15-16 Royal Parade Vale, Blackheath SE3 0BN (8297 1770); *Mickey Blue's Cafe & Wine Bar,* 63a Dartmouth Rd, Forest Hill SE23 3HN (8699 7104).

Merton *Nachos,* 36 High St, Wimbledon, SW19 5BY (8944 8875).

Redbridge *Joe's Bar & Restaurant,* 99 High St, Hampton TW12 1NH (8941 7309); *El Toro Loco,* 7 Cambridge Park, Wanstead, E11 2PU (8518 8111).

Richmond *El Torito,* 2 Hill St, Richmond TW9 1TN (8332 0055); *El Torito,* 22 York St, Twickenham TW1 3LD (8891 5200).

Sutton *El Torito,* 4 Ewell Rd, Cheam SM3 8BU (8661 2626).

Tower Hamlets *El Pirata,* Glengall Ho, Turnberry Quay, Poplar, E14 9RD (7537 1666);

Westminster *Chi-chi's,* Unit 212, Whiteleys Centre, W2 4YJ (7792 8462); *El Efes,* 94 Bishops Bridge Rd, W2 5AA (7229 3536).

SHOPS *House of Mexico* [furniture], 10 Aintree Rd, Greenford, UB6 7LA; *Mariposa Collection* [Mexican pottery], 1 Winkley St, E2 6PY (7739 9349); *Mexican Hammocks,* 81 Kirkton Rd, Seven Sisters, N15 5EY (8880 1090); *Tea & Coffee Plant* [Mexican organic coffee], 170 Portobello Rd, W11 2EB (7221 8137).

TRAVEL *Aeromar,* 200 Buckingham Palace Rd, SW1W 9TA (7707 4582); *Aero Mexico,* Cargo Service Centre, Sirius Ho, Bedfont Rd, Staines, TW19 7NL (01784 266210); *Cathy Matos Mexican Tours,* 215 Chalk Farm Rd, Camden NW1 8AB (7267 3787); *Cathy Matos Mexican Tours,* 75 St. Margarets Ave, N20 9LL (8492 0000); *Mexican Ministry of Tourism,* 60-61 Trafalgar Sq, WC2N 5DS

(7734 1058); *Mexican Tourism Board,* 41 Trinity Sq, EC3N 4AA (7488 9392); *Mexican Tourist Service,* 47 Causton St, SW1P 4AT (7976 5511); *Mexican Tours,* 215 Chalk Farm Rd, NW1 8AB (7284 2550); *Mexico Tourist Office,* 2nd fl, 60-61 Trafalgar Sq, WC2N 5DS (7839 3177).

Middle Eastern

ASSOCIATIONS *Jewish Philanthropic Association for Israel & Middle East,* 741 High Rd, N12 0BQ (8446 1477); *Middle East Association,* 33 Bury St, St James SW1Y 6AX (7839 2137).

BUSINESS *Bahrain Middle East Bank,* 40 Queen St, EC4R 1DD (7236 0413); *British Bank of the Middle East,* 27 Hill St, W1X 7FD (7355 6300); *Committee for Middle East Trade (COMET),* Bury Ho, 33 Bury St, SW1Y 6AU (7839 1170); *HSBC Bank Middle East,* 27 Hill St, W1X 7FB (7506 5600); *Middle East Business Consultants Ltd,* Unit 8 Progress Centre, Alexandra Rd, Enfield EN3 7AY (8443 3777); *Middle East Consultants Ltd,* 132 Sloane St, SW1X 9AX (7591 4816); *Middle East Markets Ltd,* 207-211 Eversholt St, NW1 1DE; *North Africa-Middle East Engineering Co,* Sophia Ho, 76-80 City Rd, EC1Y 2BJ (7250 1415); *Renwood Investments Middle East Ltd,* 7-11 Minerva Rd, NW10 6HJ.

EDUCATION *British Council, Middle East & North Africa Dept,* 10 Spring Gdns, SW1A 2BN (7930 8466); *Centre of Near and Middle Eastern Studies,* SOAS, Thornhaugh St, Russell Sq, WC1H 0XG (7898 4490).

FREIGHT *Mid Eastern Cargo,* Power Ho, 6 Power Rd, Chiswick W4 5PY (8995 2341).

LEGAL *A S Tayara Business Law,* c/o Millway Shippers Ltd, 6 York St, W1H 1AF (7935 5490); *Centre of Islamic & Middle Eastern Law,* SOAS, Thornhaugh St, Russell Sq, WC1H 0XG (7419 7632); *Dr Anis Al Qasem,* Flat 7, Chichester Rents, 5 Star Yard, Lincoln's Inn, WC2A 1EG (7831 9574); *Fairmays,* 10 Babmaes St, SW1Y 6HD (7959 0202); *Nader Middle East Law Ltd,* 31 Grendon Gdns, Wembley HA9 9NE (8904 6774); *N Saleh,* 6 Addison Pl, W11 (7602 6634); *Samir Saleh & Associates,* Flat 6, Bristol Ho, 80a Southampton Row, WC1 (7430 2102).

MEDIA & INFORMATION *Book Extra,* 140 Maida Vale, W9 1QB (7604 5508) [publishers and distributors]; *Contact Middle East,* 1 0 6 Hammersmith Grove, W6 7HB (8846 9255); *I B Tauris & Co Ltd,* 6 Salem Rd, W2 4BU (7243 1225); *Immel Publishing Ltd,* 14 Dover St, W1X 3PH (7491 1799); *Middle East and North Africa Information Services,* 13 St Georges Buildings, Bourdon St, W1K 3PY (7493 4656); *Middle East Broadcasting Centre,* 80 Silverthorne St, Battersea SW8 (7501 1111); *Middle East Economic Digest,* MEED Ho, 21 John St, WC1N 2BP (7404 5513); *Middle East International Advertising Co,* 163-169 Brompton Rd, SW3 1PY (7823 8553); *Middle East International (Publishers) Ltd* 21 Collingham Rd, SW5 0NU (7373

5228); *Middle East Publications Ltd,* 1 Watchfield Court, Sutton Court Rd, W4 4NA (8994 0515).

RESTAURANTS (See also the entries under the names of individual nationalities of the Middle East.)

South West 1 *Al Bustan,* 27 Motcombe St, SW1X 8JU (7235 8277).

West 1 *La Dauphine,* 136-138 George St, W1H 5LD (7724 2447).

Camden *Falafel House,* 95 Haverstock Hill, NW3 4RL (7722 6187).

Westminster *Islamic Halal,* 228 Edgware Rd, W2 (7724 1909).

SHOPS *Bestway,* 107 Edgware Rd, W2 (7732 6793); *Greenfields,* 25 Crawford St, W1 (7723 2510); *Green Valley,* 37 Upper Berkeley St, W1 (7402 7385); *Middle East Food Market,* 383-385 Uxbridge Rd, Acton W3 9SA (8752 0678); *Reza Patisserie,* 345 Kensington High St, W8 (7603 0924); *Riteway Supermarket,* 57 Edgware Rd, W2 (7402 5491); *Shazia Food Hall,* 124 Edgware Rd, W2 (7723 4511); *Super Bahar,* 349a Kensington High St, W8 (7603 5083).

SPECIAL *Middle East Navigation Aids Service,* 41 Tower Hill, EC3N 4DU (7702 2527); *Middle East Tobacco Assn,* Victoria Ho, 64 Paul St, EC2A 4NG.

TRANSLATION *Middle East Translation Services,* 4 Beaconsfield Terrace Rd, W14 0XF (7602 5942).

TRAVEL *Middle East Airlines,* 45 Albemarle St , W1S 4JL (7493 6321); *Middle East Cargo Services Ltd,* Unit 6, Gateway Industrial Estate, Hythe Rd, NW10 6RJ (8960 9642); *Middle East Travel and Tours Ltd,* 6 Conduit St, W1S 2XD (7409 3369); *Middle East Tours,* 25 Queensway, W2 (7727 8082); *Wind, Sand, & Stars,* 2 Arkwright Rd, NW3 6AD (7433 3684).

Mindanao

In the data collected for the *Multilingual Capital* (2000) survey, **Mindanao** was given as the language spoken by two schoolchildren in Brent. This is not the name of a language and probably merely records the fact that the children's parents came from the Philippines island of Mindanao.

Min-nan

Min-nan (which includes both *Hokkien* and *Teo-Chiu*) is a Sinitic language of China with some 55m speakers. In the *Multilingual Capital* (survey) *Min-nan* was found to be the language of 36 London schoolchildren of whom 27 lived in Ealing.

Mirpuri

Mirpuri is a distinctive variety of **Panjabi.** Although not reported among schoolchildren in the *Multilingual Capital* (2000) survey, it is one of the languages in which the new BBC Asian Network broadcasts

Moldavian

Since becoming independent in 1991, *Moldavia* has changed its name to *Moldova.* See **Moldovan.**

Moldovan

GOVERNMENT The **Moldovan** government is represented from its embassy in Belgium (Emile Maxlaan 175, B-1030 Brussels; +32 2 732 9659).

LANGUAGES **Moldovan**, formerly known as *Moldavian,* is generally regarded as a dialect of **Romanian**, but it has the status of official language in Moldova. **Moldovan** is the first language of about 2/3rds of the population but there are significant **Russian-** and **Ukrainian**-speaking minorities.

Moldovan was recorded as the language of two London schoolchildren in the *Multilingual Capital* (2000) survey.

Monégasque

BARS & NIGHT-CLUBS *Bar Monaco,* 18/20 Ganton St, W1F 7QU (7494 0705); *Bar Monaco,* 12 High St, Croydon CR0 1YA (8686 4875); *Bar Monaco,* 3 Panton St, SW1Y 4DL (7930 8583); *Bar Monaco,* 39 Shaftesbury Ave, W1V 7HB (7437 0847).

BUSINESS *Credit Commercial de Monaco plc,* 18 Randolph Ave, Maida Vale W9 1BL.

GOVERNMENT *Consulate General of Monaco,* 4 Cromwell Pl, South Kensington SW7 2JE (7225 2679).

LEGAL *Monaco & British (Legal) Ltd,* Flat 416, City View Ho, 463 Bethnal Green Rd, E2 9QY.

RESTAURANTS

West Central *Monaco Cafe,* 10-11 Great Russell St, WC1B 3NH (7636 0245).

SHOPS *Monaco,* 92 Old Oak Common La, Acton W3 7DA (8749 9083).

SPECIAL *Monaco Consultant Ltd* [public relations], P O Box 10261, Bayswater W2 1GW (7706 8737).

TRAVEL *Monaco Tourist & Convention Office,* The Chambers, Chelsea Harbour, SW10 0XF (7352 9962).

Mongolian

EDUCATION **Mongolian** is among the languages taught at *SOAS Language Centre* (7898 4888).

GOVERNMENT *Mongolian Embassy,* 7 Kensington Ct, W8 5DL (7937 5238).

LANGUAGE **Mongolian** is a language of the Trans-Asia geozone spoken in Mongolia, where it has official status, as well as in parts of Russia (Siberia) and China. It is currently written with the Cyrillic alphabet as well as in its own unique Vertical Mongolian script. The *Multilingual Capital* (2000) survey reported that this was the language of 45 London schoolchildren, half of whom lived in Kensington & Chelsea.

RELIGION Buddhism is the main religion of Mongolians.

RESTAURANTS

West Central *Mongolian Barbecue,* 12 Maiden La, WC2E 7NA (7379 7722).

Ealing *Mongolian Barbecue,* 38 Haven Green, Ealing W5 2NX (8998 2066).

Hammersmith & Fulham *Mongolian Barbecue T/A,* 31 Parsons Green La, Fulham SW6 4HH (7371 0433).

Hounslow *Mongolian Barbecue,* 1-3 Acton La, Chiswick W4 5NE (8995 0575).

Kensington & Chelsea *Mongolian Barbecue,* 61 Gloucester Rd, South Kensington SW7 4PE (7581 8747).

Merton *Mongolian Barbecue Ltd,* 68 Home Park Rd, Wimbledon SW19 7HN (8947 7500); *Mongolian Barbecue,* 162 The Broadway, Wimbledon SW19 1RX (8545 0021).

Montserratian

GOVERNMENT Montserrat is administered as an overseas territory of the UK.

WELFARE *Montserrat Community Support Trust,* 3 Bradbury St, Stoke Newington N16 8JN (7254 5766); *Montserrat Project,* 197-199 City Rd, EC1V 1JN (7336 8082); *Montserrat Volcano Fund,* 5 Westminster Bridge Rd, Southwark SE1 7XW (7928 6223).

Moroccan

ASSOCIATIONS *Al Hasaniya Moroccan Womens Project,* 4&5 Trellick Tower, Golborne Rd, W10 5PA (8969 2292); *British Moroccan Society,* 35 Westminster Bridge Rd, SE1 7JB (7401 8146); *Moroccan Widadia Community Association (Westminster),* 39 Chippenham Rd, W9 (7289 1324).

BUSINESS *BMCE Bank,* 26 Upper Brook St, W1Y 1PD (7518 8250); *BCP Bank of Morocco Representative,* 97 Praed St, W2 1NT (7724 0712); *CLM Morocco Ltd,* 69 Knightsbridge, SW1X 7RB (7235 0123); *Moroccan Bazaar,* Unit 10 Cumberland Business Park, 17 Cumberland Ave, Willesden, NW10 7RT (8961 7591).

EDUCATION *Society for Moroccan Studies,* Dr George Joffé, CNMES, SOAS, Thornhaugh St, Russell Sq, WC1H 0XG (7898 4330).

GOVERNMENT *Moroccan Consulate,* 97-99 Praed St, W2 1NT (7724 0719); *Moroccan Embassy,* 49 Queens Gate Gdns, SW7 5NE (7581 5001).

LANGUAGES *Arabic* is the official language of Morocco and the *Maghrebi* variety is the first language of perhaps 60% of the population. Up to 40% speak one of the *Berber* languages.

MEDIA & INFORMATION *Moroccan Information and Advice Centre,* 61 Golborne Rd, W10 (8960 6654); *Moroccan News Agency,* 35 Westminster Bridge Rd, SE1 7GB (7401 8146).

RELIGION Almost all Moroccans are Muslims and Islam is the state religion.

RESTAURANTS

West 1 *Mo Tea Room and Bazaar,* 23 Heddon St, W1 (7734 3999); *Momo Restaurant Familial,* 27 Heddon St, W1B 4AY (7434 4040).

Camden *Casablanca Delicatessen,* 73 Camden Rd, NW1 (7267 7212); *Le Petit Prince* [French/Moroccan], 5 Holmes Rd, NW5 (7267 3789); *Safir,* 116 Heath St, NW3 (7431 9888).

Hammersmith & Fulham *Adam's Café,* 77 Askew Rd, W12 (8743 0572) [Moroccan/Tunisian].

Haringey *Yamina,* 192 Stroud Green Rd, N4 3RN (7263 6161).

Kensington & Chelsea *Al Baraka,* 330 Portobello Rd, W10 (8960 8561); *Pasha,* 1 Gloucester Rd, SW7 4PP (7589 7969).

Lambeth *Nomades Moroccan Recipes,* 245 Coldharbour La, SW9 8RR (7733 3722).

Southwark *Casablanca,* 78 East Dulwich Grove SE22 (8299 6912).

Westminster *Agadir,* 84 Westbourne Grove W2 (7792 2207); *Couscous Café,* 7 Porchester Gdns, W2 (7727 6597); *Kyma,* 84 Westbourne Grove, W2 5RT (7792 2207); *Moroccan Comforts,* The Arches, Great Western Rd, W9 3NW (7221 0775).

SHOPS *El-Baraka Butchers,* 48 Blackstock Rd, N4 (7704 6122); *L'Étoile,* 79 Golborne Rd, W10 (8960 9769); *Le Maroc,* 94 Golborne Rd, W10 (8968 9783); *Maghreb Stores,* 320 Holloway Rd, N7 (7700 3123); *Morocco Made To Measure,* 69 Knightsbridge, SW1X 7RB (7235 0123); *Ryad Halalway Butchers & Deli,* 248 Wandsworth Rd, SW8 (7738 8811).

SPECIAL *Moroccan Enterprise & Training Centre,* Wornington Rd, W10 5QQ (8964 1698).

TRAVEL *Marrakesh Express Ltd,* 97 Praed St, W2 1NT (8100 2774) *Moroccan National Tourist Office,* 205 Regent St, W1R 7DE (7437 0073); *Moroccan Travel Bureau,* 304 Old Brompton Rd,

Earls Court, SW5 9JF (7244 8174); *Royal Air Maroc,* 205 Regent St, W1R 8PE (7439 4361).

WELFARE *Al Hasaniya Moroccan Women's Project,* 5 Golborne Rd, W10 5II (8960 9056); *Moroccan Information and Advice Centre,* 61 Golborne Rd, W10 (8960 6654)*; Westminster Moroccan Widadia,* 39 Chippenham Rd, Maida Vale, W9 2AH.

Motu

> *Motu* is a **Neoguinesic** languages spoken in Papua New Guinea. At the time of the *Multilingual Capital* (2000) survey, there were two Motu-speaking pupils living in London.

Mozambican

GOVERNMENT *Mozambique High Commission,* 21 Fitzroy Sq, W1T 6ER (7383 3800).

LANGUAGES At least 20 different Bantuic languages are spoken in Mozambique and, of these, Makua (38%) and Xitsonga (24%) have by far the greatest number of speakers. (No speakers of either of these were recorded in the *Multilingual Capital* (2000) survey.) *Portuguese* has official status.

SPECIAL *Mozambique-Angola Committee,* 25 Endymion Rd, N4 1EE, (8348 8463).

Mungaka

> *Mungaka* is a Bantuic language of Cameroon. It was also the language of three London schoolchildren living in Hammersmith & Fulham at the time of the *Multilingual Capital* (2000) survey.

Muslim

ASSOCIATIONS *Ahmadiyya Muslim Association,* Erskine Rd, E17 (8520 1247); *Ahmadiyya Muslim Association,* 16 Gressenhall Rd, Wandsworth SW18 5QL (8870 6134); *Ahmadiyya Muslim Association,* 10 Hardwicks Way, SW18 4AJ (8870 0919); *Ahmadiyya Muslim Association,* 53 Melrose Rd, SW18 (8870 1999); *Ahmadiyya Muslim Youth Association,* 10 Hardwicks Way, SW18 4AJ (8870 9955); *British Muslim Association,* BMA Ho, 58a Parkway, Raynes Park SW20 9HF (8542 8507); *Muslim Association of Britain,* 233 Seven Sisters Rd, N4 2DA (7272 2888); *Muslim Association of Nigeria,* 365 Old Kent Rd, SE1 5JH (7237 0009); *Muslimatt UK* [Muslim women's group], 169 Mile End Rd, E1 4AQ (7265 8886); *Muslim Cultural Society,* 715 High Rd Leyton, E10 5AB (8539 0769); *Muslim Families UK Charitable Trust,* 46 Goodge St, W1P 1FJ (7637 1971); *Muslim Institute,* 109 Fulham Palace Rd, W6 8JA (8563 1995); *Muslim World League,* 46 Goodge St, W1P 1FJ (7636 7568); *North London Muslim Housing Association,* 62 Cazenove Rd, Stoke Newington N16 6BJ (8806 9696); *S A Muslim Cultural Organisation,* 182a Brixton Rd, Brixton SW9 6AT (7735 9967); *Sisters in Islam* (**Muslim** Girls Club), c/o Mrs. Rahana Hassan, Ponders End Youth Centre, 129 South St, Ponders End EN3 4PX (8804 5908) [languages:

Bengali, Urdu, English]; *Southwark Muslim Women's Association,* Ballenden School, Ballenden Rd, Peckham SE15 2LD (7732 8053); *Union of Muslim Organisations of UK & Eire,* 109 Campden Hill Rd, Kensington W8 7TL ((7221 6608); *Young Muslim Organisation UK,* 52 Fieldgate St, Whitechapel E1 1ES (7247 7918); *Young Muslim Organisation UK,* 52 Fieldgate St, E1 1ES (7247 7918); *Young Muslim Organisation UK,* 169 Mile End Rd, Whitechapel E1 4AQ (07956230392); *Youth Muslim Organisation* [Bangladeshi], 74a High Street, Ponders End, Enfield EN3 4ER [Sundays 10.00 - 14.00; contact: Haji Abdul Sattar (8443 2140); languages: *Bengali,* English].

BUSINESS *Muslim Investment Corporation Ltd,* 127 Chalkhill Rd, Wembley HA9 9AL (8904 6699).

EDUCATION *Muslim College,* 20 Creffield Rd, W5 3RP (8992 6636); *Muslim Education & Literary Services,* 61 Alexandra Rd, NW4 2RX (8202 1799); *Muslim Educational Trust,* 130 Stroud Green Rd, Finsbury Park N4 3RZ (7272 8502).

GOVERNMENT *Muslim Parliament,* 109 Fulham Palace Rd, W6 8JA (8563 1995).

LEGAL *Muslim Law (Shariah) Council,* 20 Creffield Rd, W5 3RP (8992 6636).

MEDIA & INFORMATION *Impact International Independent Muslim News Magazine,* 233 Seven Sisters Rd, N4 2BL (7263 1417); *Institute of Muslim Minority Affairs,* 46 Goodge St, W1P 1FJ (7636 6740); *Muslim Directory,* 65a Grosvenor Rd, Hanwell W7 1HR (8840 0020); *Muslim Information Centre,* 233 Seven Sisters Rd, N4 2DA (7272 5170); *Muslim News,* 55 Banner St, Clerkenwell EC1Y 8PX (7608 2822); *Muslim News,* Room 17, 49 Wellington St, Holborn WC2E 7BN (7836 8988); *Muslim Pages,* 107 Olympic Way, Greenford UB6 8NJ (8813 1647); *Muslim Television Ahmadiyya,* 16 Gressenhall Rd, Wandsworth SW18 5QL (8870 0922); *Spectrum Radio,* International Radio Centre, 4 Ingate Pl, SW8 3NS (7627 4433) [*IQRA* (programme for Muslims in English 15.00 - 17.00 daily).

RELIGION *Charlton Mosque,* 32 Ransom Rd, Charlton SE7 8SR (8858 4479); *Haji Taslim* [Muslim funeral directors], 45 Fieldgate St, E1 1JU (7247 2625); *Indian Muslim Federation UK,* The Hall, Trinity Close, E11 4RP (8558 6399); *International Muslim Movement,* 1 St Mary Rd, Walthamstow E17 9RG (8520 4121); *London Muslim Centre,* 82 Whitechapel Rd, E1 1DU (7247 6090); *Muslim Association of Nigeria Mosque,* 365 Old Kent Rd, SE1 5JH (7237 0009); *Muslim Council of Britain,* 2 Empire Way, Wembley HA9 0EF (8903 9024); *Muslim Cultural Centre,* 225 High St North, E6 1JG (8472 3069); *Muslim Cultural Heritage Centre,* 244 Acklam Rd, W10 5YG (8964 1496); *Muslim World League,* 46 Goodge St, W1P 1FJ (7636 7568); *Union of Muslim Organizations of UK and Eire,* 109 Campden Hill Rd, W8 (7221 6608).

RESTAURANTS *Al Halal Fried Chicken T/A,* 142 Bethnal Green Rd, Bethnal Green E2 6DG (7613 5487); *Al Halal Fried Chicken T/A,* 63 Brick La,

Whitechapel E1 6QL (7377 0397); *Al Halal Fried Chicken T/A,* 38a Wightman Rd, Finsbury Park N4 1RU (8292 9282); *Halal Balti Express T/A,* 4a Grove Rd, Bow E3 5AX (8981 9771); *Halal Fried Chicken,* 200 Philip La, N15 4HH (8365 1299); *Halal Fried Chicken Cottage T/A,* 111 Turnpike La, N8 0DU (8374 0856); *Halal Kebab Hut,* 508 High Rd, Ilford IG1 1UE (8597 2222); *Halal of Marble Arch,* 118 Edgware Rd, W2 2DZ (7723 2248); *Halal of Marble Arch,* 98 Queensway, W2 3RR (7792 5888); *Halal Perfect Fried Chicken T/A,* 77 Roman Rd, Bethnal Green E2 0QN (8980 5240); *Halal Restaurant,* 2 St. Mark St, E1 8DJ (7481 1700); *Halal Tandoori,* 14 Conway Rd, SE18 1AH (0800 085 1831); *Karachi Tandoori Halal T/A,* 189 Leytonstone Rd, Stratford E15 1LH (8519 5015); *Shanti Tandoori Halal Balti Express* T/A, 206 Francis Rd, Leyton E10 6PR (8558 5727); *Shalimar Halal,* 70 Brick La, Whitechapel E1 6RL (7247 9846).

SHOPS

Bookshops: *Al Noor,* 82 Park Rd, NW1 4SH (7723 5414); *Dar Al Dawa,* 97 Westbourne Grove, W2 (7221 6256); *Dar Al-Taqwa,* 7a Melcombe St, NW1 6AE (7935 6385, fax 7224 3894); *Muslim Bookshop,* 233 Seven Sisters Rd, N4 2DA (7272 3214).

Halal produce :

West Central *Bloomsbury Halal Food Store,* 65 Marchmont St, WC1 (7713 0714),

Barnet *Ali Halal Butchers,* 92 Watling Ave, HA8 0LU (8952 0821); *Grahame Park Halal Butcher,* 3 The Concourse, Colindale NW9 5UR (8205 7066); *Halal Meat,* Finchley Food Store, Regents Park Rd, N3 1DP (8349 1922); *Hendon Halal Butchers,* 26 Vivian Ave, NW4 3XP (8202 9580); *Kiswa Halal Meats,* 8a Varley Parade, Colindale NW9 6RR (8205 7474).

Brent *A K Halal,* 62 Harrow Rd, Wembley HA9 6PL (89021563); *Ali's Halal Meats,* 787 Harrow Rd, Wembley HA0 2LP (8904 1650); *Brent Foodstore Halal Meat,* 20 Rockhall Rd, Cricklewood NW2 6DX (8452 3112); *Ferdow's Halal Food Processing Co,* 204-206 Church Rd, Willesden NW10 9NP (8451 5906); *Gama Halal Meat,* 286 Ealing Rd, Wembley HA0 4LL (8902 2588); *Halal Butchers,* 92 High St, Willesden NW10 4SL (8965 7111); *Halal Meat,* 232 Ealing Rd, Wembley HA0 4QL (8902 8282); *Halal Meat,* 92 High St, NW10 4SL (8965 7111); *Halal Meat Shop,* 214 High Rd, NW10 2NX (8459 1841); *Halal Meat Shop,* 43 Kilburn La, W10 4AE (8969 9710); *Insha Allah Halal Meat,* 4 Court Parade, Wembley HA0 3HY (8904 2226); *Iqbal Halal Butcher,* 89 Acton La, Willesden NW10 8UT (8838 3929); *Khan's Halal Butchers,* 1f Walm La, Willesden Green, Cricklewood NW2 5SJ (8459 1724); *Khyber Halal Meat,* 257 Neasden La, Willesden NW10 1QG (8450 2574); *Kingsbury Halal Butchers,* 650 Kingsbury Rd, NW9 9HN (8204 6890); *L'Algéroise,* 130 Cricklewood Broadway, NW2 (8452 3638). *London Halal Meat,* 102 High Rd, Willesden NW10 2PP (8459 7274); *Mustafa Halal Meat,* 646 Kingsbury Rd, Colindale NW9 9HN (8204 0201); *Pakeeza Halal Butchers,* 7 Sevenex Parade, London Rd, Wembley HA9 7HQ (8903 4555); *Preston Road Halal Meat,* 222 Preston Rd, Wembley HA9 8PB (8904 6602); *Raja Halal Meat,* 457 Kingsbury Rd, Colindale NW9 9DY (8206 1814); *Raza Halal Meat,* 1032 Harrow Rd, Willesden NW10 5NN (8964 2917); *Stonebridge Halal Meat,* Stonebridge Shopping Centre, Hillside, Willesden NW10 8LT (8838 0614);*Tariq Halal Butchers,* 3 Grand Parade, Forty Ave, Wembley HA9 9JS (8904 3141); *Tariq Halal Meat,* 213 Church Rd, Willesden NW10 9EP (84591938); *Tayyab Halal Meats,* 17 The Broadway, Wembley HA9 8JU (8908 3500); *United Halal Meats Ltd,* 256 High Rd, Willesden NW10 2EY (8459 1495); *Wembley Halal Meats,* 153c Harrow Rd, Wembley HA9 6DN ((8900 1552); *Willesden Best Halal Meat,* 175 High Rd, Willesden NW10 2SD (8459 3484); *Yakub's Halal Meat,* 618 Kingsbury Rd, Colindale NW9 9HN (8204 8081); *Zar Halal Meat,* 280 Church La, Colindale NW9 8LU (8205 6428).

Camden *Hampstead Halal Butchers,* 239 Finchley Rd, Hampstead NW3 6LS (74351661); *H R Halal Meats,* 2 Quex Rd Kilburn NW6 4PH (7372 2731); *Polok Halal International Foods,* 117 Hampstead Rd, Camden NW1 3EE (7388 8098).

Croydon *Al-Gohar Shahi Halal Meat,* 1423 London Rd, SW16 4AH (8679 9728).

Ealing *Acton Halal Meat,* 41 High St, Acton W3 6ND (8992 1311); *Baloch Halal Meat,* 72 King St, Southall UB2 4DD (8571 2458); *Food Store & Halal Meat,* 140 Churchfield Rd, Acton W3 6BS (8992 0297); *Greenford Halal,* 195 Greenford Rd UB6 8QY (8575 2262); *Greenford Halal Meat,* 48 Greenford Rd, UB6 9AT (8813 1728); *Hanwell Halal Meat,* 147 Uxbridge Rd, Hanwell W7 3ST (8567 8317); *Imran Halal Meat,* 227b Beaconsfield Rd,

Southall UB1 1DB (8574 1553); *Kaz Halal,* 105 The Broadway, Southall UB1 1LN (8574 1444); *Lady Margaret Halal Meat,* 197 Lady Margaret Rd, Southall UB1 2PT (8571 4434); *Pak Halal Poultry,* 227c Beaconsfield Rd, Southall UB1 1DB (8867 9165); *Perivale Halal,* 22 Bilton Rd, Greenford UB6 7BS (8997 8302); *Tariq Halal Butchers,*15 Liberty Shopping Centre, South Rd, Southall UB1 1RT (8574 9214); *Tariq Halal Meat Ltd,* 94-100 High St, Southall UB1 3DN.

Enfield *Bismla Halal Meat,* 217 Fore St, Upper Edmonton N18 2TZ (8807 8648).

Greenwich *Al-Madina Halal Meat,* 25 Anglesea Rd, Woolwich SE18 6EG (8316 2549).

Hackney *Eastern Halal Service,* 104 Lower Clapton Rd, Clapton E5 0QR (8985 0224); *Halal Meat,* 24 Ridley Rd, Hackney E8 2NR (7254 7320); *Kingsway Halal Butcher,* 7 Ridley Rd, Hackney E8 2NP (7923 0314); *Pak-Halal Butcher,* 101 Stoke Newington Rd, Stoke Newington N16 8BX (7254 2671); *Paradise Halal,* 110a Lower Clapton Rd, Clapton E5 0QR (8985 3395); *Punjab Halal Meats,* 84 Ridley Rd, Hackney E8 2NR (7254 0264); *Somali Halal,* 162 Stoke Newington High St, Stoke Newington N16 7JL (7241 3390).

Hammersmith & Fulham *Halal Food Authority,* 109 Fulham Palace Rd, W6 8JA (8563 1994); *Jamil Halal Meat,* Shepherds Bush Market, Shepherd's Bush W12 8DG (8743 7959); *Kenya Halal Meat and Poultry,* Unit S56-57, Shepherds Bush Market, W12 8DG (8932 2444); *Khyber Halal Meat,* 98 Goldhawk Rd, Shepherd's Bush W12 8HD (8743 3928); *Shaheer Halal Butcher,* 79 Uxbridge Rd, Shepherd's Bush W12 8NR (8740 0096).

Haringey *Maghereb Halal Stores,* 51 Grand Parade, Green Lanes, N4 1AG (8809 2300); *Medina Halal Meat,* 15a Turnpike La, N8 0EP (8340 2802); *Nurjahan Halal Meat,* 81 Turnpike La, N8 0DY (8340 6813); *Paradise Halal,* 31 Turnpike La, N8 0EP (8348 2210); *Paradise Halal,* 121 Turnpike La, N8 0DU (8347 9035); *Salam Halal Meat,* 25 Turnpike La, N8 0EP (8292 0506); *Stroud Halal Meat,* 49 Stroud Green Rd, Finsbury Park N4 3EF (7272 9799); *West Green Halal Meat & Groceries Ltd,* 29 West Green Rd, N15 5BX.

Harrow *Ahmad Halal Meat,* 387 Northolt Rd, Harrow HA2 8JD (8422 2419); *Faysal Halal Meat,* 188 Alexandra Ave, Harrow HA2 9BN (8422 6568); *Faysal Halal Meat,* 7a Broadway Parade, Pinner Rd, Harrow HA2 7SY (8427 3118); *Faysal Halal Meat,* 33 Station Rd, Harrow HA1 2UA (8427 6666); *Husseini Halal Meat,* 3 Lanson Ho, Whitchurch La, Edgware HA8 6NL (8381 2296); *Kenton Halal Butcher,* 176 Kenton Rd, Harrow HA3 8BL (8907 0380); *Madina Halal Meat & Grocers,* 61 Station Rd, Harrow HA1 2TY (8427 3767); *Shalimar Halal Butchers,* 9 Headstone Drive, Harrow HA3 5QX (8424 8345).

Hillingdon *Euro Halal Distribution Co.* [poultry], 652 Uxbridge Rd, Hayes UB4 0RY (8569 0108).

Hounslow *Zane Halal,* 60 Hibernia Rd, Hounslow TW3 3RP (8577 9746).

Kensington & Chelsea *Halal Butcher,* 218 Portobello Rd, Notting Hill W11 1LJ (7221 5409); *Halal Butcher,* 234 Portobello Rd, Notting Hill W11 1LJ (7229 0069).

Lambeth *A K Halal,* 21 Electric Ave, Brixton SW9 8JP (7738 6622).

Lewisham *Afro Muslim Butchers,* 16 Deptford High St, SE8 4AF (8692 8490); *Ali Brothers Halal Butchers,* 27 Deptford High St, SE8 (8691 3363); *Az Halal Butchers,* 83 Deptford High St, SE8 4AA (8692 1879); *Baboo Halal,* 24 Lewisham Model Market, Lewisham High St, SE13 6LS (8852 9342); *Halal Butchers,* 99 Deptford High St, SE8 4AA (8694 0041); *Halal Butchers,* 109 Deptford High St, SE8 4AA (8694 2350).

Merton *Halal Food Centre,* 524 Kingston Rd, SW20 8DT (8542 2811); *Surma Halal Foodstore,* 112 Merton High St, South Wimbledon SW19 1BD (8542 0200).

Newham *Bismillah Halal Meat,* 70 Upton La, Forest Gate E7 9LN (8548 0992); *Halal Meat & Poultry Wholesalers,* 168 Plashet Rd, Plaistow E13 0QT (8548 9666); *Iman Fresh Quality Halal Meat,* 319 Green St, Plaistow E13 9AR (8552 0045); *Islamabad Halal Butchers,* 134 Green St, Forest Gate E7 8JQ (8472 8125); *Islamabad Halal Meat Centre,* 389 Green St, Plaistow E13 9AU (8470 9093); *Islamia Halal Butchers,* 45 Plashet Rd, Plaistow E13 0QA (8472 0013); *Kashmir Halal,* 120-122 Katherine Rd, East Ham E6 1ER (8472 8669); *Kaz Halal Meat,* 397 Green St, Plaistow E13 9AU (8472 7267/7117); *Khyber Halal Meat,* 35 Queens Market, Plaistow E13 9BA (8472 6260); *Muslim Halal Meats,* 355 High St North, Manor Park E12 6PQ (8471 8871); *Nemo Halal Meat,* 17 Queens Market, Plaistow E13 9BA (8552 9324); *Noori Halal Butchers,* 328 High St North, Manor Park E12 6PH (8472 1655); *Saajan Halal Meat,* 344 Green St, Plaistow E13 9AP (8552 1350); *S & A Quality Halal Meat,* 133 Green St, Forest Row, Forest Gate E7 8JF (8552 2036); *S & A Quality Halal Meat,* 237 High St North, East Ham E6 1JG (8472 0350); *Subhan Halal Meats,* 184 Shrewsbury Rd, Forest Gate E7 8QJ (8470 8097); *Sylhet Grocers & Halal Meat,* 160 Green St, Forest Gate E7 8JT (85481793); *United Halal Meat & Groceries,* 3 Carlton Terrace Green St, Forest Gate E7 8LH (8586 0545); *United Halal Meats,* 255 Green St, Forest Gate E7 8LJ (8552 4813); *Upton Park Halal Meats,* 21 Queens Market, Plaistow E13 9BA (8472 1769).

Southwark *Kashmir Halal Butchers,* 153 Peckham Rye, Peckham SE15 3UL (7277 6287); *Peckham Halal,* 52 Rye La, Peckham SE15 5BY (7732 9144).

Tower Hamlets *Aslom Halal Meats,* 44d Settles St, Whitechapel E1 1JP (7375 2080); *East & West Halal Meat,* 274 Bethnal Green Rd, Bethnal Green E2 0AG (7739 6142); *Halal Meats,* 48 Fieldgate St, Whitechapel E1 1ES (7247 9776); *Lalbagh Halal Food Store,* 53 Ben Johnson Rd, Whitechapel E1 4SA (7702 7974); *Noor Halal Meat*

Ltd, 203 Mile End Rd, E1 4AA; *Oriental Halal Meat,* 63 Hanbury St, Whitechapel E1 5JP (7247 8799); *Shalamar Halal Meat,* 167 Cannon St Rd, Whitechapel E1 2LX (74811634); *Uddin Mazir* [Muslim butcher], 4 Hessel St, E1 2LP (7480 6186); *Woodcock Halal Meat,* 251b East India Dock Rd, Poplar E14 0EG (7538 9950).

Walthamstow *ASA Halal Foods,* 19 Walthamstow Business Centre, Clifford Rd, Walthamstow E17 4SX (8523 4952).

Wandsworth *ACA Halal Butchers,* 131 Balham High Rd, SW12 9AU (8675 3617); *Fair Price Halal Meat,* 225 Upper Tooting Rd, Tooting SW17 7TG (8672 6647); *JR's Quality Halal Meat,* 163 Upper Tooting Rd, Tooting SW17 7TJ (8682 3949); *JT Halal Meat,* 493 Garratt La, Wandsworth SW18 4SW (8875 0127); *Mauritius Quality Halal Meat,* 7 Hildreth St, Balham SW12 9RQ (8673 1629); *R B Halal Food Centre,* 34 Upper Tooting Rd, SW17 7PD (8672 5636); *Zahid Halal Food Centre,* 34 Upper Tooting Rd, Tooting SW17 7PD (8672 5647).

Westminster *Halal of Marble Arch,* 9 8 Queensway, W2 3RR (7243 5814); *Madina,* 399 Harrow Rd, W9 3NF (8960 2413); *Shaeer Halal Meat Market,* 77 Bishops Bridge Rd, W2 6BG (7229 4824).

WELFARE *Acton Muslim Welfare Association,* 2 Oldham Terrace, W3 6LS (8993 8073); *Canning Town Muslim Welfare Association,* 269 Barking Rd, Plaistow E13 8EQ (7511 7406); *Hackney Muslim Womens Council,* 101 Clapton Common, Clapton E5 9AB (8809 0993); *Indian Muslim Federation UK,* The Hall, Trinity Close, Wanstead E11 4RP (8558 6399); *Institute of Muslim Minority Affairs,* 46 Goodge St, W1P 1FJ (7636 6740); *Muslim Aid,* PO Box 3, Holloway N7 8LR (7609 4425); *Muslim Care,* 206-208 Brick La, E1 6SA (7613 0772); *Muslim Community Centre,* 177 Plashet Grove, East Ham E6 1BX (8552 6133); *Muslim Community & Welfare Centre,* 16-18 Hornsey Rd, N7 7BP (7609 4484); *Muslim Fostering Society UK,* 116 Stoke Newington High St, N16 7NY (7249 1444); *Muslim Welfare House,* 86 Stapleton Hall Rd, N4 4QA (8341 2893); *Muslim Welfare House & Information Services,* 233 Seven Sisters Rd, N4 2DA (7263 3071); *Muslim Women's Helpline,* 1st fl, Unit 3, GEC Estate, East La, Wembley HA9 7PY (8908 6715); *Muslim Womens Welfare Association Charity,* 96 Belgrave Rd, Ilford IG1 3AL (8554 7722); *North London Muslim Community Centre,* 68 Cazenove Rd, Stoke Newington N16 6AA (8806 1147); *North London Muslim Welfare Association,* c/o Mr. Qureshi, 51 Northfield Rd, Enfield EN3 4BT (8804 1762) [phone for time of monthly meeting; languages: **Gujarati, Punjabi, Urdu,** English]; *Pakistan Muslim Welfare,* Charlton Mosque, 32 Ransom Rd, Charlton SE7 8SR (8858 4479); *Union of Moslem Families (UK),* 55 Balfour Rd, N5 (7226 0934); *Union of Muslim Families Charitable Trust,* 46 Goodge St, W1P 4SD (7637 1971); *Waltham Forest Muslim Welfare Society,* 79 Queens Rd, Walthamstow, E17 8QR (8520 2658).

N

Namibian

ASSOCIATIONS *Namibia Society,* 6 Chandos St, W1M 0LQ (7636 6244).

GOVERNMENT *High Commission of the Republic of Namibia,* 6 Chandos St, W1G 9D (7636 6244).

LANGUAGES More than 30 different languages are spoken in Namibia. The three with the largest numbers of speakers are **Oshikwanyama** (46%), **Afrikaans** (14%), and Nama (13%; no speakers of this language in London were reported at the time of the *Multilingual Capital* (2000) survey).

MEDIA & INFORMATION *Namibian Advertising,* 7 Kensington High St, W8 (7411 3111).

TRAVEL *Namibia & Zimbabwe Fly-Drive & Safari,* 7-8 Upper Sq, Old Isleworth TW7 7BJ ((8232 9777).

Nauruan

GOVERNMENT *Nauru Government Office,* Romshed Courtyard, Sevenoaks TN15 0SD (01732 746061).

LANGUAGE *Nauruan* is a West-Pacific language spoken on the island of Nauru. The presence of one **Nauruan**-schoolchild in Barnet was recorded at the time of the *Multilingual Capital* (2000) survey.

Ndebele

EDUCATION Courses in **Ndebele** are available at *SOAS Language Centre* (7898 4888).

LANGUAGE **Ndebele** (full name, *Isindebele*) is a Bantuic language of South Africa and Zimbabwe. 13 speakers of this were recorded among London's school population at the time of the *Multilingual Capital* (2000) survey, of whom five lived in Haringey.

Near Eastern

ASSOCIATIONS *Association for the Study of Travel in Egypt and the Near East,* St Paul's Lodge, 97 Larkhall Rise, SW4 6HR (7622 9407).

EDUCATION *Centre of Near and Middle Eastern Studies,* SOAS, Thornhaugh St, Russell Sq, WC1H 0XG (7898 4490); *London Centre for the Ancient Near East, Centre of Near and Middle Eastern Studies,* SOAS, Thornhaugh St, Russell Sq, WC1H 0XG (7898 4335).

Nembe

Nembe (also known as *Brass*) is a Deltic language spoken in Nigeria. The *Multilingual Capital* (2000) survey recorded the presence of one **Nembe**-speaking child in Haringey.

Nepalese

See entry under **Nepali.**

Nepali *(Nepalese)*

EDUCATION **Nepali** is among the languages taught at *SOAS Language Centre* (7898 4888).

GOVERNMENT *Royal Nepalese Embassy,* 12a Kensington Palace Gdns, Kensington W8 4QU (7229 1594).

LANGUAGE **Nepali** is the most important of several languages spoken in Nepal. It is an Indic language, written in the semi-syllabic Devanagari script. The *Multilingual Capital* (2000) survey revealed that there were then 125 **Nepali**-speaking children attending schools in London.

RELIGION Most Nepalis are **Hindu** but there are Buddhist and Muslim minorities.

RESTAURANTS

West 1 *Gurkha Brasserie,* 23 Warren St, W1P 5DE (7383 4985).

Brent *Gurkha Village Nepalese T/A,* Empire Ho, Empire Way, Wembley HA9 0EW.

Camden *Great Nepalese,* 48 Eversholt St, NW1 1DA (7388 6737); *New Oriental Nepalese,* 43 Grafton Way, W1P 5LA (7387 6363); *Pink Rupee,* 38 Cricklewood Broadway, NW2 (8452 7665); *Vhujon,* 90 Fortune Green Rd, West Hampstead, NW6 1DS (7431 4802).

Ealing *Nepalese Enterprises T/A,* 86 South Ealing Rd, Ealing W5 4QB; *Palace of Nepal,* 31 High St, Acton W3 6ND (8992 3308).

Hammersmith & Fulham *Kathmandu Inn Tandoori,* 6-7 Seven Stars Corner, Goldhawk Rd, W12 8ET (8749 9802); *Light of Nepal,* 268 King St, W6 0SP (8748 3586); *Nepalese Tandoori,* 121 Uxbridge Rd, W12 8NL (8740 7551).

Harrow *Royal Nepal,* 439 Alexandra Ave, Harrow HA2 9SE (8866 5988); *Titash Indian & Nepalese Cuisine,* 52 Bridge St, Pinner, HA5 3JF (8866 1555).

Hillingdon *Royal Gurkha Tandoori,* 7 Park La, Uxbridge UB9 6BJ (01895 825154).

Hounslow *Gurkha Tandoori,* 78 Bedfont La, Feltham TW14 9BP (8890 0099).

Sutton *Munal,* 76 Central Rd, Worcester Park KT4 8HX (8330 3511).

Wandsworth *Kathmandu Valley,* 5 West Hill, SW18 1RB (8871 0240); *Light of Gurkha T/A,* 88 Balham High Rd, Balham SW12 9AG (8673 4160).

TRAVEL *Royal Nepal Airlines,* 13 New Burlington St, W1S 3BG (7494 0974).

WELFARE *Nepal Leprosy Trust,* 15 Duncan Rd, Richmond, TW9 2JD (8332 9023).

Nevisian

This word is applied to the inhabitants of the island of Nevis, part of the Federation of St Kitts & Nevis.

GOVERNMENT See under **Kittitian.**

TRAVEL *St Kitts & Nevis Tourism Office,*10 Kensington Ct, W8 5DL (7376 0881).

Newari

Newari is a Himalayic language of Nepal which is written in the Devanagari semi-syllabic script. One Newari-speaking London pupil in Brent was found in the *Multilingual Capital* (2000) survey.

New Zealander

ASSOCIATIONS *New Zealand Press Association,* 12 Norwich St, St Paul's, EC4A 1QP (7353 7040); *New Zealand & Australia Migration Bureau,* Hyde Park Ho, 5 Manfred Rd, Putney, SW15 2RS (8874 2844).

BUSINESS *Apple and Pear Marketing Board,* Bouverie Ho, 154 Fleet St, St Paul's, EC4A 2DQ (7583 5151); *Australia and New Zealand Banking Group,* Minerva Ho, Montague Cl, SE1 9DA (7378 2121); *Australia and New Zealand Chamber of Commerce UK,* 393 Strand, WC2R 0LT (7379 0720); *Enza Fruit,* Cheapside Ho, 138 Cheapside Ho, Moorgate, EC2V 6BJ (7505 3300); *Enza New Zealand (UK),* 119 London Wall, EC2Y 5ET (7588 5555); *Kiwi Contractors Ltd* [builders], 16 Cowley Rd, SW14Ê8QB (8876 4443); *Meat New Zealand Marketing* Board, 16-18 Hatton Grds, Clerkenwell, EC1N 8AT (7831 6315); *National Bank of New Zealand,* 71 Lombard St, Monument, EC3P 3BS (7356 1888); *Natural Food Co,* Unit 3, 55-57 Park Royal Rd, Willesden, NW10 7LP (8961 4410); *New Zealand Consultants Ltd,* 41 Thornton Ave, Chiswick, W4 1QF; *New Zealand Farmers Ltd,* Welken Ho, Charterhouse Sq, EC1M 6EH (7566 5000); *New Zealand Lamb Co.Ltd,* 2-5, Benjamin St, EC1M 5QL (7250 1811).

EMPLOYMENT *Kiwi Agency,* 28 South Molton St, W1KÊ5BP (7629 1666).

FREIGHT *Air New Zealand Freight Services,* Unit 8 Radius Pk, Faggs Rd, Feltham, TW14 ONG (8751 5000).

GOVERNMENT *New Zealand High Commission,* New Zealand Ho, Haymarket, SW1Y 4TQ (7930 8422).

LANGUAGES Both **English** and **Maori** have official status.

LEGAL *New Zealand, Australia & Canada Migration Bureau,* Hyde Park Ho, 5 Manfred Rd, SW15 2RS (8874 2844).

MEDIA *New Zealand Press Association,* 12 Norwich St, EC4A 1QP (7353 5430); *Telecom New Zealand Uk Ltd,*12-13 Plumtree Court, EC4A 4BY.

RESTAURANTS *Sugar Club,* 21 Warwisk St, W1 (7437 7776) [menu includes Asian influences].

SHOPS *Fine Wines of New Zealand,* 95 Camden Mews, NW1 9BU (7482 0093); *New Zealand Kiwi Fruits,* 7 Royal Opera Arcade, Pall Mall, SW1Y 4UY (7930 4587, fax 7839 0592) [gifts, souvenirs, books, magazines]; *New Zealand Wine Guild,* 8 0 Haymarket, Westminster, SW1Y 4TE (7973 8097).

TRAVEL *Air New Zealand Ltd,* Elsinore Ho, 77 Fulham Palace Rd, W6 8JA (8600 7600); *Air New Zealand Ltd,* Ground fl, New Zealand Ho, Haymarket, SW1Y 4TE (8741 2299); *Kirra Tours,* 1st fl, Beaumont Ho, Lambton Rd, London, SW20 0LW (8944 5423); *New Zealand Adventure,* 143 Windmill La, Greenford, UB6 9DP (8578 3155); *New Zealand Affair,* Hillgate Ho, 13 Hillgate St, W8 7SP (7616 9197); *New Zealand Tourism Board,* New Zealand Ho, Haymarket SW1Y 4TQ (7930 1662); *New Zealand Travel Advisory Information Services,* 3-4 Bentinck St, West End, W1M 5RN (7935 3144); HAO 2DH (8748 4455); *Mount Cook Line of New Zealand,* Elsinore Ho, 77 Fulham Palace Rd, Hammersmith W6 8JA (8741 5652).

Ngala

See under **Lingala**, the full name of this language.

Ngoni

The data obtained for the *Multilingual Capital* (2000) survey included three schoolchildren who were said to speak **Ngoni**. This is in fact the collective name for an important group of Bantuic languages which includes **Xhosa, Swazi, Zulu and Ndebele**, spoken in South Africa, Swaziland and Zimbabwe.

Ngwana

See under **Kingwana**, the full name of this language.

Nicaraguan

ASSOCIATIONS *Nicaragua Solidarity Campaign,* 129 Seven Sisters Rd, Holloway, N7 7QG (7272 9619).

GOVERNMENT *Embassy of Nicaragua,* 2nd floor, 36 Upper Brook St, W1Y 1PE (7409 2536); *Nicaraguan Consulate,* 58-60 Kensington Church St, W8 4DB (7938 2373).

LANGUAGES **Spanish** is the first language of perhaps 90% of the population but Amerindian languages or **Creole English** are the home languages of the remaining 10%.

Nigerian

ASSOCIATIONS *Britain Nigeria Association,* 2 Vincent St, SW1P 4LD (7828 5588); *Britain-Nigeria Association,* Hope Ho, 45 Great Peter St, SW1P 3LT (7222 1077); *Muslim Association of Nigeria,* 365 Old Kent Rd, SE1 5JH (7237 0009); *Nigeria Development Movement (NIDEMO),* 8 Underwood St, N1 7JQ (7477 6006); *Nigeria National Union,* Tooting, SW17 (8672 5055); *United Nigerians,* 23 Lawrence St, E16 (7474 5057).

BUSINESS *First Bank of Nigeria,* 29-30 King St, EC2V 8EH (7606 6411); *National Bank of Nigeria,* 62 Pymers Mead SE21 8NH (8761 5341); *Union Bank of Nigeria plc,* P O Box 148, 14-18 Copthall Ave, EC2R 7BN (7600 0751); *Nigerian National Petroleum Corporation,* 159 Hammersmith Rd, W6 8BS (8741 1131); *Nigerian Ports plc,* 2nd floor, Allenby Ho, 1a Temple Rd, Cricklewood NW2 6PJ (8450 3101); *Nigeria Re-insurance Corporation,* Plantation Ho, 31-35 Fenchurch St, EC3M 3DX (7623 2601); *Nigeria Re-Insurance Corporation,* Nicon Ho, 21 Worship St, EC2A 2BH (7628 4401); *Relugas Nigeria Ltd* [marine surveyors], 7 Jewry St, EC3N 2EX (7702 1228).

EDUCATION *Nigerian Universities Office,* 9 Northumberland Ave, WC2N 5BW (7930 8514);

FREIGHT *Yes Freight (Nigeria) Ltd,* 22 Desmond St, New Cross SE14 6JX (8692 0055);

GOVERNMENT *Nigeria High Commission,* Nigeria Ho, 9 Northumberland Ave, WC2N 5BX (7839 1244); *Consular Annexe of Nigerian High Commission,* 56-57 Fleet St, EC4Y 1JU (7353 3776).

LANGUAGES Some 400 different languages are spoken in Nigeria. Of these, the three with by far the greatest number of speakers are **Hausa** (21%), **Yoruba** (20%), and **Igbo** (17%).

MEDIA & INFORMATION *Concord Press of Nigeria Ltd,* 26-32 Whistler St, Highbury N5 1NH (7359 5335); *Isis Newsagents* [Nigerian newspapers], Wood Green Underground Station, N22 (8829 9638); *News Agency of Nigeria,* 44 Grays Inn Rd, WC1X 8LR (7242 5387); *Nigeria Link Magazine,* P O Box 6669, N5 2HH (7923 9161); *Nigerian News,*

171

23 Aberdeen Ct, W9 1AF (7266 4564); *Nigerian Trumpet*, P O Box 7246, E4 6YT (8523 8565).

RECREATION *London Nigerian Cricket Club* <www.londonnigerians.free-online.co.uk>, *London Nigerian Rugby and Football Club*, Linford Christie Stadium, Du Cane Rd, W12 0DF (8740 7379).

RELIGION *Muslim Association of Nigeria Mosque*, 365 Old Kent Rd, SE1 5JH (7237 0009).

RESTAURANTS

Hackney *Afrikico* (Nigeria and Ghana), 27A Dalston La, E8 (7254 0201); *Toksy B Suya Spot*, 199 Homerton High St, E9 6BB (8533 4028).

Haringey *Afri Carib Nigerian*, 1 Stroud Green Rd, N4 (7263 7440, 7263 5464).

Newham *Nigeria Palace / Taste of Nigeria*, 247 Plashet Rd, E13 (8552 8310).

Southwark *Jubilee Nigerian*, 1 Peckham High St, SE15 5EB (7252 4523); *Nigerian Kitchen*, 35 Peckham High St SE15 (7708 4764).

TRAVEL *Nigerian Airways*, 43 Davies St, W1K 4LT (7493 9726); *Nigerian Railway Corporation*, Suite C, Astra Ho, 23-24 Arklow Rd, SE14 6EB (8691 8755).

WELFARE *O"- Bay Charity Organisation for Nigerians*, 275 Scotland Green Rd North, Ponders End EN3 7UG (8443 3958 / 5752); *Women of Nigeria International*, 54 Camberwell Rd, Grovesnor Terrace, SE5 0EN (7252 4597).

Nordic

See also **Scandinavian.**

BARS & NIGHT-CLUBS *Nordic Bar Ltd*, 25 Newman St, W1T 1PN (7631 3174).

BUSINESS *Anglo Nordic Furnisher Manufacturer Agents*, 59 New Kings Rd, SW6 4SE (7736 2031); *Nordic Consultancy Services Ltd*, 37 Lombard St, EC3V 9BQ; *Nordic General Insurance Group*, 557 High Rd, Wembley, HAO 2DW (8903 3232); *Nordic Options Ltd*, 64 Queen St, EC4R 1AR (7246 8800); *Nordic Style Home & Office*, 109 Lots Rd, West Brompton, SW10 ORN (7351 1755); *Nordic Timber Council*, 33 Roseberry Rd, Muswell Hill, N10 2LE (8365 2700); *Nordic Touch*, 3 Sloane Court East, SW3 4TQ (7730 1007).

FREIGHT *Nordic Freight International Ltd*, 43 Axe St, Barking, IG11 7LX (8903 0511).

MEDIA & INFORMATION *JB Nordic Media Ltd*, 20-28 Dalling Rd, Hammersmith, W6 OJB (8742 6644).

MOTORING *Nordic Car Co*, 93 Stanley Rd, Teddington, TW11 8UB (8977 0302).

North African

See also entries for individual North African nationalities: **Algerian, Libyan, Moroccan, Tunisian**.

EDUCATION *British Council, Middle East & North Africa Dept*, 10 Spring Gdns, SW1A 2BN (7930 8466).

FREIGHT *North Africa Distribution Ltd*, Unit 5, Enterprise Way, Triangle Business Centre, Salter St, NW10 6UG (8968 1006).

MEDIA & INFORMATION *Middle East & North Africa Information Services*, 13 St Georges Bldgs, Bourdon St, W1K 3PY (7493 4656).

RESTAURANTS

East Central *Moro*, 34-36 Exmouth Market, EC1 (7833 8336) [Spanish/North African].

Barnet *Laurent*, 428 Finchley Rd, NW2 (7794 6854).

Hammersmith & Fulham *Adam's Café*, 7 7 Askew Rd, W12 (8743 0572) [Moroccan/Tunisian].

Islington *Royal Cous-Cous House*, 316 Holloway Rd, Islington, N7 (7700 2188).

SHOPS *La Belle Boucherie*, 3-5 Bell St, NW1; *North Africa Grocery*, 101 High St, NW10 4TS (8838 6261); *North Africa Store*, 101 High St, NW10 4TS (8963 1918).

Northern Irish

BUSINESS *Industrial Development Board for Northern Ireland*, 11 Berkeley St, W1J 8BU (7493 0601).

GOVERNMENT *I D B for Northern Ireland*, 11 Berkeley St, W1X 6BU (7493 0601).

TRAVEL *Northern Ireland Tourist Board*, 24 Haymarket, SW1Y 4DG (7766 9920).

WELFARE *Reach - All Northern Ireland*, 89 Albert Embankment, SE1 7TP (9086 4286); *Women Caring Trust for Children in Northern Ireland*, 38 Ebury St, SW1W 0LU (7730 8883).

Norwegian

ACCOMMODATION *Norwegian YWCA*, 52 Holland Park, W11 3RS (7727 9897).

ASSOCIATIONS *Norwegian Club*, Charles Ho, SW1Y 4LR ((7839 6242).

BUSINESS *Norwegian Chamber of Commerce London Incorporated*, Charles Ho, 5 Regent St,

SW1Y 4LR (7930 0181); *Norwegian Trade Council,* Charles Ho, 5 Regent St, SW1Y 4LR (7389 8800).

EDUCATION *Norwegian School in London Ltd,* 28 Arterberry Rd, SW20 8AH (8947 6627). Courses in Norwegian are provided by *Morley College* (7928 8501) and the *University of Westminster* (7911 5000).

GOVERNMENT *Norwegian Embassy,* 25 Belgrave Sq, SW1X 8QD (7591 5500).

LANGUAGE **Norwegian** is a Germanic language, closely related to **Danish** and other **Scandinavian** languages, which has official status in Norway. The *Multilingual Capital* (2000) survey identified 92 **Norwegian**-speaking pupils in London schools.

RELIGION *Norwegian Church & Seaman's Mission,* 1 St. Olavs Sq, Albion St, South Bermondsey, SE16 1JB (7237 5587).

SHOPS *Royal Norwegian Confectioney Company (UK) Ltd,* 108 Lower Ham Rd, Kingston Upon Thames KT2 5BD (8546 1235).

TRANSLATION *Norwegian Commercial & Technical Translations,* 585A Fulham Rd, SW6 5WA (7381 0967).

TRAVEL *Alvern Norway,* Airport Ho, Purley Way, Croydon CR0 0XZ (8781 1843); *Coast Air (Norway),* 200 Buckingham Palace Rd, SW1W 9TA (7707 4574); *Norwegian Coastal Voyage Ltd,* 3 Shortlands, W6 8ME (8846 2666); *Norwegian Tourist Board – Information,* 5 Regent St, SW1Y 4LR (09063 022003).

Nsenga

Nsenga is a Bantuic language spoken in Zambia, Mozambique and Zimbabwe. It was reported as the language of one pupil in Haringey in the *Multilingual Capital* (2000) survey.

Nubian

In the *Multilingual Capital* (2000) survey, one child was reported to be a speaker of **Nubian**. However, this is a collective name for a group of related languages of the East-Sahel geozone spoken in Sudan so the name of the particular language cannot be identified.

Nuer

EDUCATION Mother tongue education for young children in **Nuer** is available in Central London; visit <www.resourceunit.com> for details.

LANGUAGE **Nuer** is a Nilotic language spoken in Sudan. Speakers of **Nuer** have occasionally been reported among London's school population within the past decade but none were noted at the time of the *Multilingual Capital* (2000) survey.

Nupe

Nupe is a Benuic language of Nigeria. Speakers of **Nupe** have occasionally been reported among London's school population within the past decade but none were noted at the time of the *Multilingual Capital* (2000) survey.

Nwa

Nwa is a Mandic language spoken in the Ivory Coast. Speakers of **Nwa** have occasionally been reported among London's school population within the past decade but none were noted at the time of the *Multilingual Capital* (2000) survey.

Nyakyusa

Nyakyusa is a Bantuic language of Tanzania. The *Multilingual Capital* (2000) survey recorded the presence of two **Nyakyusa**-speaking pupils in Haringey.

Nyang

Nyang was reported to be the language of two schoolchildren in Lambeth in the *Multilingual Capital* (2000) survey. In this case, **Nyang** probably refers to the Bantuic language of this name spoken in Cameroon. However, **Nyang** is also the name of a Daic language spoken in China and Vietnam.

Nyanja

See under the alternative name, **Chewa.**

Nyankore

See under its full name, **Runyankore.**

Nyoro

Nyoro is a Bantuic language of Uganda. There were two **Nyoro**-speaking pupils Barnet at the time of the *Multilingual Capital* (2000) survey.

Nzema

Nzema is an **Aframic** language of Ghana and the Ivory Coast. The presence of five **Nzema**-speaking London schoolchildren was reported in the *Multilingual Capital* (2000) survey, of whom four lived in Islington.

Odual

Odual is a Benuic language of Nigeria. Speakers of Odual have occasionally been reported among London's school population within the past decade but none were noted at the time of the *Multilingual Capital* (2000) survey.

Ogori

Ogori is a Benuic language of Nigeria. The *Multilingual Capital* (2000) survey found this to be the language of three schoolchildren in Haringey.

Okrika

Okrika is a Deltic language of Nigeria. It was also found to be the language spoken by two London schoolchildren in the *Multilingual Capital* (2000) survey.

Olulumo

Olulumo is a Benuic language of Nigeria. The *Multilingual Capital* (2000) survey reported that there was one Olulumo-speaking schoolchild in Haringey.

Omani

BUSINESS Oman Professional Services Ltd, 15 Woodgate Crescent, Northwood HA6 3RB (01923 836100).

GOVERNMENT Embassy of the Sultanate of Oman, 167 Queens Gate, South Kensington SW7 5HE (7225 0001); Embassy of the Sultanate of Oman - Cultural Section, 64 Ennismore Gdns, Sw7 1NH (7589 0220).

LANGUAGE The official language of Oman is Arabic.

LEGAL Trowers & Hamlins, Sceptre Ct, 40 Tower Hill EC3N 4BN (7423 8000).

RELIGION Almost all Omanis are Muslims.

Ora

Ora is a Benuic language of Nigeria. It was also found to be the language of two London schoolchildren at the time of the *Multilingual Capital* (2000) survey.

Oriental

The word oriental is most often applied to people and things of Southeast Asia and the Far East, from Malaysia to Japan. Orient and oriental also have a wider sense, encompassing virtually the whole of Asia, particulary with reference to arts and cultural matters.

ACCOMMODATION London & Oriental Property Developers, 2 Mill St, W1R 9TE (7355 2888); London & Orient Property Ltd, 4 Portman Mews South, W1H 9AU (7629 5401).

BARS & NIGHT-CLUBS Sash Oriental Bar Brasserie, 32 Abbeville Rd, Clapham SW4 9NG (8673 9300); Sash Oriental Tapas Bar, 825 Fulham Rd, Fulham SW6 5HG (7736 9429); Zeta, Hertford St, W1 (7208 4067).

BUSINESS Banque Française de l'Orient, 50 Curzon St, W1Y 7PN (7312 7700); Oriental & African Strategic Investment Services Ltd, 3 Park Pl, SW1A 1LP (7629 7626).

EDUCATION Asian and Oriental School of Catering Ltd, Suite 111c, Business Design Centre, 52 Upper St, Islington N1 0QH; London College of Traditional Acupuncture & Oriental Medicines, 447 High Rd, North Finchley N12 0AZ (8371 0820); London Oriental Academy, Suite B, 1-3 Kempton Rd, East Ham E6 2LD; School of Oriental and African Studies, Thornhaugh St, Bloomsbury WC1H 0XG (7637 2388).

EMPLOYMENT Oriental Casting Agency, 60 Downton Ave, Brixton SW2 3TR (8678 7414) and 1 Wyatt Park Rd, Brixton SW2 3TN (8678 0171); Oriental Cleaners [domestic cleaning services], 47 Elmcourt Rd, Tulse Hill SE27 9BX (8670 4455).

HEALTH & BEAUTY London College of Traditional Acupuncture & Oriental Medicines, 447 High Rd, North Finchley N12 0AZ (8371 0820); Oriental Medical Centre, 2-4 Kenway Rd, Earl's Court SW5 0RR (7835 1163, 7296 0012).

MEDIA & INFORMATION Oriental Press UK Ltd, United Ho, North Rd, Holloway N7 9DP (7700 7891).

MOTORING Oriental Motor Repairs, Railway Arches, 203-204 Penrose Grove, SE17 3EZ (7252 7759).

RECREATION Oriental Martial Arts Centre, 69 Broadwick St, W1V 1FU (7734 9461).

RESTAURANTS

East Central East One, 175-179 St John St, EC1V 4LW (7566 0088); Suan-neo, 31 Broadgate Circle, EC2M 2QS (7256 5044); Tao, 11-11A Bow La, EC4 (7248 5833).

South West 1 Noodle Noodle, 312 Vauxhall Bridge Rd, SW1V 1AA (7828 8565).

West 1 *Gallery Rendezvous,* 53-55 Beak St, W1R 3LF (7734 0445); *Immortals,* 58-60 Shaftesbury Ave, W1V 7DE (7437 3119); *Melati,* 21 Great Windmill St, W1V 7PH (7437 2745); *Melati,* 30-31 Peter St, W1V 3RQ (7437 2011); *Spiga,* 84-86 Wardour St, W1 (7734 3444); *Wok Wok,* 10 Frith St, W1 (7437 7080).

West Central *Pu's Brasserie,* 10 Gate St, Holborn WC2A 3HP (7404 2132).

Barnet *Junction 88,* 2a Burroughs Parade, Hendon NW4 4BD (8203 3028); *Oriental Avenue,* 111-113 Golders Green Rd, NW11; *Oriental Classic T/A,* 270 Regents Park Rd, Finchley Central N3 3HN (8349 3270); *Oriental Hawker's Delight,* 20 Vivian Ave, Hendon NW4 3XP (8202 3889).

Brent *Imperial Gardens,* 56-58 Harrow Rd, Wembley HA9 6PL (8902 6007); *Oriental Chef,* 410 Ealing Rd, Wembley HA0 1JQ (8997 1138); *Oriental Express T/A,* 267 Edgware Rd, NW9 6NB (8201 3133); *Oriental Place,* 366 Neasden Lane North, Willesden NW10 0BT (8450 7026).

Camden *Lemongrass,* 243 Royal College St, Camden NW1 9LT (7284 1116); *Oriental Star,* 134 Finchley Rd, NW3 (7435 6127); Oriental *Taste,* 26 Fortess Rd, NW5 (7485 5992); *Street Hawker,* 237-239 West End La, NW6 1XN (7431 7808).

Ealing *Oki Tycoon,* 1261 Greenford Rd, UB6 0HY (8423 0909).

Greenwich *Oriental Garden,* 12 Well Hall Rd, Eltham SE9 6SF (8850 9889).

Hackney *Oriental Meals T/A,* 150 Homerton High St, Hackney E9 6JA (8985 7564).

Hammersmith & Fulham *Blue Elephant,* 4-6 Fulham Broadway, Fulham SW6 1AA (7385 6595); *New King Oriental,* 311 New Kings Rd, Fulham SW6 4RF (7736 8833); *Oriental Express T/A,* 5 Salisbury Pavement, Dawes Rd, Fulham SW6 7HT (7381 8188); *Oriental Garden,* 616 Fulham Rd, SW6 5RP (7736 9171); *Oriental T/A,* 2 Romney Ct, Shepherds Bush Green, W12 8PY (8749 1574).

Haringey *Oriental Cottage T/A,* 118 Alexandra Park Rd, Muswell Hill N10 2AE (8883 2919); *Tia*

Orient, 10 Turnpike La, Hornsey N8 0PT (8888 4488).

Harrow *Oriental Chef T/A,* 611 Kenton La, Harrow HA3 7HJ (8385 7636).

Hillingdon *Oriental Express Fish Bar,* 10 Marlborough Parade, Uxbridge Rd, UB10 0LR (01895 237521); *Zen Oriental,* Terminal Four, Heathrow Airport, Hounslow TW6 3AF (8564 9609).

Islington *Tiger Lil's,* 270 Upper St, Islington N1 2UH (7226 1118).

Kensington & Chelsea *Krungtap 9,* 227 Old Brompton Rd, Earl's Court SW5 0EA (7259 2314); *Nam Long Knightsbridge,* 136 Brompton Rd, SW3 1HY (7823 8019); *Nam Long Le Shaker,* 159 Old Brompton Rd, Earl's Court SW5 0LJ (7373 1926); *Saaghi,* 36 Gloucester Rd, SW7 4QT (7589 4060); *Soraya,* 36 Gloucester Rd, SW7 4QT (7589 4060).

Lambeth *Blue Bay,* 28 Brixton Water La, Brixton SW2 1PE (8244 3100); *Oriental Noodle Bars T/A,* 23 Blairderry Rd, Brixton SW2 4SD; *Tiger Lil's Wok & Steamboat,* 16a Clapham Common South Side, SW4 7AB (7720 5433).

Lewisham *Cafe Oriental,* 7 Lee High Rd, Lewisham SE13 5LD (8297 8838).

Newham *Oriental Kitchen,* 770 Barking Rd, Plaistow E13 9PJ (8472 2614).

Southwark *Oriental Noodle Hut T/A,* 18 Peckham High St, Peckham SE15 5DT (7639 1888); *Rainbow Oriental,* 33-37 Brunel Rd, Rotherhithe SE16 4LA (7231 0028).

Tower Hamlets *Sri Thong,* 1-3 Widegate St, Whitechapel E1 7ES (7375 0794).

Waltham Forest *Oriental House,* 156 Langthorne Rd, Wanstead E11 4HR (8556 6955).

Wandsworth *Sayur Mayur,* 87 Battersea Rise, SW11 1HW (7350 0900); *Udon Udon,* 12 Putney High St, SW15 1SL (8788 3199).

Westminster *New Yung's Noodle Restaurant,* 51 Queensway, Bayswater W2 4QH (7727 5753); *Southeast W9,* 239 Elgin Ave, W9 1NJ (7328 8883); *Sunset Bay,* 359 Harrow Rd, W9 3NA (8968 9053).

SHOPS *Oriental City* [shopping centre], 399 Edgware Rd, Colindale NW9 0JJ (8200 0009).

Antiques *Barry Davies Oriental Art Ltd,* 1 Davies St, W1Y 1LL (7408 0207); *Brandt Oriental Antiques,* 1st fl, 29 New Bond St, W1Y 9HD (7499 8835); *Christopher Sharp Oriental,* 103 Lots Rd, West Brompton SW10 0RN (7352 0012); *Continuum Antique Oriental & Tribal Art,* Stand 124 Grays Antique Market, 58 Davies St, W1Y 2LP (7493 4909); *Dragon Heritage London Oriental*

Antiques, 58 Davies St, W1Y 2LP; *Kevin Page Oriental Art,* 2, 4 & 6 Camden Passage, Islington N1 8ED (7226 8558); *Nicholas S Pitcher Oriental Art,* 1st fl, 29 New Bond St, W1Y 9HD (7499 6621); *Oriental Furniture & Arts,* 24 Devonshire Rd, Chiswick W4 2HD (8987 8571); *Orient Expressions Ltd,* London Research Station, 2 Michael Rd, Fulham SW6 2AD (7610 9311); *Paul Champkins Oriental Art,* Suite B2, 41 Dover St, W1X 3RB (7495 4600); *Phoenix Oriental Art,* 6 The Lower Mall, 359 Upper St, Islington N1 0PD (7226 4474); *Proud Orientals,* 5 Buckingham St, WC2N 6BP (7839 4942).

Bookshops *Arthur Probsthain* [Oriental and African bookshop], 41 Gt Russell St, WC1 3PL (7636 1096); *Fine Books Oriental Ltd,* 38 Museum St, Bloomsbury WC1A 1LP (7242 5288); *Luzac Oriental,* 38 Museum St, Bloomsbury WC1A 1LP (7242 5332); *Oriental Press UK Ltd,* Chancery Ho, 53-64 Chancery La, WC2A 1QS (7242 3085); *Oriental Trading Co,* 92 Saltram Crescent, Maida Vale W9 3JX (8960 3959).

Carpets *Alborz Oriental Carpets,* 2nd Floor Block F, 53-79 Highgate Rd, Kentish Town NW5 1TL (7485 5656); *Baluch Oriental Carpets,* 129 Wandsworth Bridge Rd, Fulham SW6 2TT (7731 7819); *Barin Oriental Carpet Repairs,* 57a New Kings Rd, Fulham SW6 4SE (7731 0546); *Frank Bolger Oriental Rugs,* 58 Maddox St, W1R 9PA (7629 7825); *Coats Antique Oriental Carpets,* 4 Kensington Church Walk, Kensington W8 4NB (7937 0983); *Covent Garden Oriental Carpets Ltd,* 20 Earlham St, WC2H 9LN (7240 3032); *David Black Oriental Carpets,* 96 Portland Rd, W11 4LN (7727 2566); *Haram Oriental Carpets,* 365 Northolt Rd, Harrow HA2 8JD (8423 2152); *Ibrahim Samad Oriental Carpets,* 161 Knightsbridge, SW1X 7PA (7584 6902); *I Nemetnejad Oriental Carpets,* 403-405 Edgware Rd, Cricklewood NW2 1RD (8830 5511); *Izash Oriental Carpets,* 131 Portobello Rd, Notting Hill W11 2DY (7229 7763); *Joss Graham Oriental Textiles,* 10 Eccleston St, SW1 9LT (7730 4370); *Latif Group Oriental Carpets & Rugs,* Latif

Ho, Wembley HA9 0JE (8795 3684); *London Oriental Carpets Ltd* [wholesale], 1053 Great West Rd, Brentford TW8 9AT (8560 2133); *Nassir Oriental Rug Gallery,* 28 Highgate Rd, Kentish Town NW5 1NS (7482 1200); *NGN Oriental Carpets,* 232 High St, Uxbridge UB8 1LD (01895 234590); *Oriental Bamyan Carpet & Rugs,* Magnet Rd, East Lane, Wembley HA9 7RG (8385 2323); *Oriental Carpet Centre,* 105 Eade Rd, Finsbury Park N4 1TJ (8800 8188); *Oriental Carpet Merchants,* 1 Page St, Mill Hill NW7 2EL (8202 0002); *Oriental Carpet Merchants,* 418 Watford Way, Mill Hill NW7 2QJ (8202 0002); *Oriental Carpets,* Unit 4, 53-79 Highgate Rd, Kentish Town NW5 1TL (7482 5712); *Orientalist Carpets,* 152 Walton St, SW3 2JJ (7581 2332); *Oriental Rugs Ltd,* 58 Maddox St, W1R 9PA (7493 3239); *Perez Antique Carpets & Textiles,* 199 Brompton Rd, SW3 (7589 2199); *Persian Cottage Oriental Carpets,* 9 Regency Parade, Finchley Rd, Hampstead NW3 5EG (7722 5188); *Resai Oriental Carpets Ltd,* 123 Portobello Rd, Notting Hill W11 2DY (7221 5012); *Robert Aigin Oriental Carpets,* Oriental Carpet Centre, 105 Eade Rd, Finsbury Park N4 1TJ (8880 1166); *Shaikh & Son (Oriental Rugs) Ltd,* 16 Brook St, W1Y 1AA (7629 3430).

Craftware *Dreams of Orient,* 49 Kensington High St, W8 5EG (7937 2250); *Exclusive Oriental Classics (UK) Ltd,* 1-6 Clay St, W1H 3FS; *Exclusive Oriental Classics,* Unit 1, Cannon Trading Estate, First Way, Wembley HA9 0JD (8903 8189); *Oriental Arts & Crafts,* 101 The Broadway, Wimbledon SW19 1QG (8544 0434); *Oriental Arts & Crafts,* 8 Walthamstow Business Centre, Clifford Rd, Walthamstow E17 4SX (8527 9091).

Food *Acton Oriental Stores,* 1 Central Parade, Gunnersbury La, Acton W3 8HL (8723 5654); *Al Manara Oriental Pastry Ltd,* Unit 7, 98 Victoria Rd, NW10 6NB (8838 3433); *Asian Oriental Supermarket,* 14 Selkirk Rd, Tooting SW17 0ES (8682 2155); *Chadha Oriental Foods,* 428 Long Drive, Greenford UB6 8UH (8575 8575); *Elichaoff Oriental,* 88 Hendon La, Finchley Central N3 3SL (8343 3487); *Gandhi Oriental Foods Ltd,* Stour Rd, Bow E3 2NT (8533 3446); *Golden Orient Ltd,* 17 Earlham St, WC2H 9LL (7836 5545); *Honey's Oriental & General Store,* 55 Station Rd, Willesden NW10 4UX (8453 0632); *KRS Oriental Stores,* 33 Lee High Rd, Lewisham SE13 5NS (8297 9432); *London Oriental Foods,* 122 Drummond St, NW1 2HN (7387 3740); *Oriental Delight,* Unit 2, Metro Trading Centre, Second Way, Wembley HA9 0YU (8795 3833); *Oriental Groceries,* 41 Exmouth Market, Clerkenwell EC1R 4QL (7833 2354); *Oriental Halal Meat,* 63 Hanbury St, Whitechapel E1 5JP (7247 8799); *Poplar Oriental Groceries,* 181 East India Dock Rd, Poplar E14 0EA (7515 0845); *St Anns Oriental Food Store,* 162 St Anns Rd, Seven Sisters N15 5RP (8800 5899); *Sunrise Oriental,* 41-43 Vivian Ave, Hendon NW4 3UX (8202 0321); *Taste of the Orient,* 56-58 Wood Green Shopping City, High Rd, Wood Green N22 6YD (8889 1643); *Tawana Oriental Supermarket,*

16-20 Chepstow Rd, Bayswater W2 5BD (7221 6316); *Tooting Oriental* [supermarket], 14 Selkirk Rd, SW17 0ES (8682 2155); *Vallo - the Oriental Shop,* Unit 18, Tooting Market, Tooting High St, SW17 0RH (8767 9250).

TRAVEL *Oriental Travel,* 107c Downs Rd, Clapton E5 8DS (8510 9577); *Orient Connections,* 70-72 The Green, Southall UB2 4BG (0870 241 0206); *Orient International Travel Ltd,* 91 Charlotte St, W1P 1LB (7637 1330); *Orient Lines Ltd,* 38 Park St, W1Y3PF (7409 7500); *Orient Travel Ltd,* 27 Noel St, W1V 3RD (7287 1020); *Orient Travel Service,* 100 Brick La, E1 6RL (7247 5932); *Western & Oriental Travel Ltd,* King Ho, 11 Westbourne Grove, Bayswater W2 4UA (7313 6600).

Oring

Oring is a **Benuic** language of Nigeria. Just one London schoolchild was reported as a speaker of this in the *Multilingual Capital* (2000) survey.

Oriya

Oriya is an **Indic** language spoken in the Indian state of Orissa. It is written in its own semi-syllabic script. Only one Oriya-speaking London schoolchild was identified at the time of the *Multilingual Capital* (2000) survey.

Oromo

EDUCATION Mother tongue education for young children in **Oromo** is available in Islington; visit <www.resourceunit.com> for details.

LANGUAGE *Oromo* (also known as *Galla*) is a **Nilotic** language spoken in Ethiopia and Kenya. In the *Multilingual Capital* (2000) survey, this was found to be spoken by two London schoolchildren.

Oron

Oron is a Benuic language of Nigeria. Speakers of **Oron** have occasionally been reported among London's school population within the past decade but none were noted at the time of the *Multilingual Capital* (2000) survey.

Oshikwanyama

Oshikwanyama (also known as *Oshiwambo* and *Ovambo*) is a Bantuic language spoken in Namibia. The *Multilingual Capital* (2000) survey found this to be the language of two London schoolchildren living in Barnet.

Oshiwambo

See under the alternative name, **Oshikwanyama**.

Ovambo

See under the alternative name, **Oshikwanyama**.

P

Pacific

BUSINESS *Pacific Islands Chamber of Commerce,* 314 Regent St, W1R 5AB (7487 5794); *Southern Pacific Securities plc,* 125 Kensington High St, W8 5PA (7590 1500); *UK Pacific Investments Ltd,* 2nd fl, 140 Brompton Rd, Chelsea SW3 1HY (7584 3333).

FREIGHT *Anglo Pacific International plc,* Units 1 & 2, Bush Industrial Estate, Standard Rd, North Acton NW10 6DF (8965 1234); *Asia Pacific Express Ltd,* London Heathrow Airport, TW6 3JJ (8754 8559).

MEDIA & INFORMATION *Pacific Media Group,* 162-170 Wardour St, W1V 3AT (7287 2233); *Pacific Telecom,* 174 Cannon Street Rd, Whitechapel E1 2LH (7363 4900).

RESTAURANTS
Kensington & Chelsea *The Collection,* 264 Brompton Rd, SW3 2AS (7225-1212).

TRAVEL *Anderson's The Pacific Way,* Shepperton Marina, Felix La, Shepperton TW17 8NJ (01932 222079); *Atlantic Pacific Travel Ltd,* 301 Triumph Ho, 189 Regent St, W1R 7WE (7439 8351); *Australian Pacific Touring,* 2nd fl, 14 Worple Rd, Wimbledon SW19 4DD (8879 7444); *Cathay Pacific Airways Ltd,* 7 Apple Tree Yard, SW1Y 6LD (7747 8888); *Pan Pacific Travel,* 4 Berners St, W1P 3AG (7580 3005); *South Pacific Tourism Organisation,* 48 Glentham Rd, Barnes SW13 9JJ (8741 6082).

Pakistani

ACCOMODATION *Pakistan Students Hostel,* 5 Barkston Gdns, SW5 0ER (7370 5859).

BUSINESS *Allied Bank of Pakistan,* 63 Mark La, EC3R 7QS (7481 0207); *National Bank of Pakistan,* 18 Finsbury Circus, EC2M 7BJ (7588 1511); *National Bank of Pakistan,* 30 Sloane St, SW1X 9NJ (7235 3608); *Pakistan British Chamber Of Commerce & Industry,* 1 Northumberland Ave, WC2N 5BW (7713 7860); *State Life Insurance Corporation of Pakistan,* 3 Golden Sq, W1R 3AD (7437 8221).

GOVERNMENT *High Commission for Pakistan,* 36 Lowndes Sq, SW1X 9JN (7664 9200).

LANGUAGES The most important languages of Pakistan are **Panjabi, Pashto, Sindhi** and **Urdu** (the national language).

LEGAL *Pakistan Law Centre,* 270a Belsize Rd, NW6 4BT (7604 3700); *Pakistani Law Consultant* [Advocate of High Courts & Supreme Court of Pakistan] (8552 0482); *Our Vision Ltd, Pakistan Islamic Law Chambers,* 1 Brady St, E1 5DG (7247 6560).

MEDIA & INFORMATION *Pakistan Centre,* Station Parade, NW2 4NU [information] (8452 4103); *Pakistani Channel,* 65 North Acton Rd, NW10 6PJ (8838 6300).

RELIGION 95% of the population is Muslim (*Whitaker's Almanack* 2002).

RESTAURANTS

Ealing *Lahore Karahi & Tandoori,* 162 The Broadway, Southall, UB1 1NN (8813 8669).

Newham *Karachi Tandoori Halal T/A,* 189 Leytonstone Rd, Stratford E15 1LH (8519 5015).

Tower Hamlets *New Tayyab,* 83 Fieldgate St, Whitechapel, E1 (7247 9543).

Wandsworth *Tabaq,* 47 Balham Hill, SW12 (8673 7820).

SHOPS *Ambala Sweet Centre* [Indian and Pakistani sweets], 112 Drummond St, NW1 2HN (7387 3521); *Islamabad Halal Butchers,* 134 Green St, Forest Gate E7 8JQ (8472 8125); *Islamabad Halal Meat Centre,* 389 Green St, Plaistow E13 9AU (8470 9093); *Khyber Halal Meat,* 98 Goldhawk Rd, Shepherd's Bush W12 8HD (8743 3928); *Khyber Halal Meat,* 257 Neasden La, Willesden NW10 1QG (8450 2574); *Khyber Halal Meat,* 35 Queens Market, Plaistow E13 9BA (8472 6260); *Pak-Halal Butcher,* 101 Stoke Newington Rd, Stoke Newington N16 8BX (7254 2671); *Pak Halal Poultry,* 227c Beaconsfield Rd, Southall UB1 1DB (8867 9165).

TRAVEL *Pakistan International Airlines,* 1-15 King St, W6 9HR (8741 8066) and 44 Dover St, W1S 4DB (7290 3600).

WELFARE *Indo Pakistan Cultural Centre,* 16-18 Hornsey Rd, N7 7BP (7609 4484); *Dr Z U Khan* [Chairman, Pakistan Welfare], 45 Streatham Common North, SW16 3II (8664 7001); *Pakistan Women's Welfare Association,* 225 Seven Sisters Rd, N4 2DA (7272 4030).

Palestinian

ASSOCIATIONS *Association of the Palestine Community,* 21 Collingham Rd, SW5 0NU (7370 3729).

EDUCATION *Friends of Birzeit University,* 21 Collingham Rd, SW5 0NU (7373 8414).

SPECIAL *European Palestine Israel Centre,* 4 Dollis Park, Finchley Central N3 1HG; *Palestine Exploration Fund,* 2 Hinde Mews, Marylebone La, W1M 5RR (7935 5379); *Palestine Liberation Organisation,* Unit 5, Galena Rd, Hammersmith, W6 0LT (8563 0008); *Trade Union Friends of Palestine,* Arab-British Centre, 21 Collingham Rd, SW5 0NU (7373 8414).

WELFARE *Medical Aid for Palestinians,* 33a Islington Park St, N1 1QB (7226 4114); *Palestine Return Centre,* 719 Crown Ho, North Circular Rd, NW10 7PN (8453 0919); *Palestine Solidarity Campaign,* 25 Horsell Rd, Highbury N5 1XL (7700 6192).

Pampangan

Pampangan is a Hesperonesic language of the Philippines (Luzon). The presence of seven **Pampangan**-speaking London schoolchildren was noted in the *Multilingual Capital* (2000) survey.

Panamanian

GOVERNMENT *Consulate General of Panama,* 40 Hertford St, W1Y 7TG (7409 2255); *Embassy of Republic of Panama,* 48 Park St, W1Y 3PD (7493 4646); *Panama's Permanent Mission to I M O,* 40 Hertford St, W1J 7SE (7493 1371).

LANGUAGE The official language of Panama is **Spanish.**

LEGAL *Morgan & Morgan* [Panamanian attorneys], 20 Queen St, W1X 7AG (7493 1978); *Quijano Associates & Partners* [Panamanian solicitors], 41 South Audley St, W1Y 5DH (7499 4654).

Pangasinan

Pangasinan is a Hesperonesic language spoken in the Philippines. Speakers of this have occasionally been reported among London's schoolchildren over the past decade although none were found at the time of the *Multilingual Capital* (2000) survey.

Panjabi (Punjabi)

Panjabi is the logical spelling of the name of this language and people when written in the Roman alphabet. This spelling is particularly favoured where reference is made to the language itself. However, in most other circumstances, the traditional English spelling **Punjabi** continues to be used and will be found in many of the entries below*.*

ASSOCIATIONS *"Deep" Indian 50+ Club* [Enfield] (contact: Mrs G Merchant 8245 0724) [languages: **Gujarati, Hindi, Punjabi;** activities include reflexology, yoga and swimming]; *Redbridge Panjabi Sabhia Charik (Cultural) Sabha,* 293-297, Ley St, Ilford IG1 4BN (8478 4962).

BARS & NIGHT-CLUBS *Glassy Junction,* 97 South Rd, Southall, UB1 (8574 1626).

BUSINESS *Punjab Catering Service,* Unit 3, Leyton Business Centre, Etloe Rd E10 7BT (8532 8300); *Punjab Enterprises,* 16 Western Rd, Southall UB2 5DS (8574 0471); *Punjab Textiles Ltd,* 13 Barrett Industrial Park, Park Ave, Southall UB1 3AF (8571 7670).

EDUCATION Mother-tongue education for young children in **Panjabi** is available in a dozen locations in London; for full information visit <www.resourceunit.com>. Courses in **Panjabi** for adults are available in several London boroughs (see <www.floodlight.co.uk>) and at *SOAS Language Centre* (7898 4888).

HEALTH & BEAUTY Leaflets on Caring for Dementia are available in Panjabi from the *Alzheimer's Disease Society,* Gordon Ho, 10 Greencoat Pl, SW1P 1PH (7306 0606).

Quitline [in Panjabi; for help with stopping smoking] (0800 002 277).

Enfield Saheli, Community House, 311 Fore Street, Edmonton N9 0PZ [advice on mental health] (8373 6220).

LANGUAGE *Panjabi* (including *Lahnda*) is ranked 13th among the world's languages with some 85m speakers. It is an Indic language spoken in the Panjab (also written Punjab) which straddles the Pakistan-India border. *Panjabi* is written in two different scripts – an adaptation of the Arabic script resembling that of Urdu (used mainly in Pakistan) and the Gurmukhi semi-syllabic script (used in India and illustrated on the Southall station sign).

The *Multilingual Capital* (2000) survey found that there were 29 802 *Panjabi*-speaking school-children in London, making this the capital's third most important language (after English and Bengali). One quarter of these live in Ealing. Map 22, showing the areas of London where the greatest proportion of *Panjabi*-speakers live, can be viewed at <www.global-london.com/gallery>.

LEGAL *Enfield Saheli,* Community House, 311 Fore Street, Edmonton N9 0PZ [advice for Asian women on legal matters] (8373 6218).

MEDIA & INFORMATION *Desi Radio* [music and talk for the Punjabi community in Southall on 1602]; *Panjab FM,* The Panjabi Centre, 30 Sussex Road, Southall UB2 5EG <panjabfm@hotmail.com>); *Punjab Monitor,* 2 Chignell Pl, W13 0TJ (8840 3222); *Punjabi Press,* 50 Hammond Rd, Southall, UB2 4EQ (8843 2288); *Panjab Radio Ltd,* Hayes Metro Centre, Springfield Rd, Hayes UB4 0LE (8848 8877); *Spectrum Radio,* International Radio Centre, 4 Ingate Pl, SW8 3NS (7627 4433) [*Soul of Punjab* broadcast Sundays 00.00-4.00 a.m.]; *Sunrise Radio Ltd,* Sunrise Ho,Sunrise Rd,Southall, UB2-4AU (8574-6666) [broadcasts in Panjabi 21.00-22.00 weekdays].

RELIGION Pakistani Panjabis are Muslims while, in India, Panjabi Sikhs outnumber Panjabi Hindus by about 2 : 1. The proportions of Muslims, Sikhs, and Hindus among *Panjabi*-speakers in London remains to be established.

Krishna Yoga Mandir, c/o Pandit K C Krishnatreya, 61 Churchbury Rd, Enfield EN1 3HP (8363 9187) [*Hindi, Punjabi*, Sanskrit, English].

RESTAURANTS

West Central *Punjab,* 80/82 Neal St, WC2H 9PA (7836 9787).

Barnet *Punjab Kebab,* 1017 Finchley Rd, NW11 7ES (8201 8345).

Ealing *Great Punjab,* 102 Uxbridge Rd, W7 3SU (8840 9444); *Punjab Karahi Ltd,* 175 The Broadway, Southall UB1 1LX (8574 1112); *Shahanshah* [vegetarian], 60 North Rd, Southall UB1 2JB (8574 1493).

Greenwich *Taste of Punjab T/A,* 2 Plumstead High St, Woolwich SE18 1SN (8855 8725).

Hounslow *Punjabi Karahi,* 89 Kingsley Rd, Hounslow TW3 4AH (8569 5511).

Islington *Sitara Punjabi Cuisine,* 784 Holloway Rd, Archway N19 3JH (7281 0649).

Kensington & Chelsea *Taste of Punjab,* 316b Ladbroke Grove, W10 5NQ (8960 9925).

Redbridge *Abshar Punjabi Cuisine,* 43 High St, Barkingside, IG6 2AD (8550 6213); *Pakwaan Punjabi Cuisine,* 307-309 High Rd, Ilford IG1 (8553 2004); *Punjabi Dhaba,* 108 Goodmayes Rd, Ilford IG3 9UZ (8220 7171).

Wandsworth *Punjab House,* 37 Balham High Rd, Balham SW12 9AL (8673 8251).

SHOPS *Punjab Halal Meats,* 84 Ridley Rd, Hackney E8 2NR (7254 0264); *Punjab Jewelers,* 138 Palmerston Rd, E17 6PY (8520 6020); *Punjab Meat Market,* 20 Cameron Rd, Ilford IG3 8LB (8590 2078); *Punjab Meat Market,* 63 King St, Southall UB2 4DQ (8574 1532); *Punjab Sweet House,* 20 Dudley Rd, Southall UB2 5AR (8574 2019); *Punjab Sweets,* 172 Upper Tooting Rd, SW17 7ER (8767 3535); *Punjab Textile Ltd,* 1-3 Featherstone Rd, Southall UB2 5AA (8574 2059); *Punjab Textiles Ltd,* 8 The Broadway, Southall UB1 1PS (8571 3833).

TRANSLATION *Urdu & Punjabi Translators & Interpreters,* 89 Southampton Way, SE5 7SX (7564 9113).

TRAVEL *New Punjab Coaches Ltd,* 16 Western Rd, Southall UB2 5DS (8843 1000); *New Punjab Tours Ltd,* 15 Endsleigh Rd, Southall UB2 5QL.

WELFARE *Enfield Asian Welfare Association,* 129-139 South St, Ponders End EN3 4RJ (8443 1197) [languages: *Bengali, Gujarati, Hindi, Panjabi, Urdu,* English]; *Enfield Saheli,* Community House, 311 Fore Street, Edmonton N9 0PZ (8373 6219) [languages: *Gujarati, Hindi, Punjabi, Urdu,* English]; *North London Muslim Welfare Association,* c/o Mr. Qureshi, 51 Northfield Rd, Enfield EN3 4BT (8804 1762) [phone for time of monthly meeting; languages: *Gujarati, Punjabi, Urdu,* English]; *Punjab Community Centre,* 293 Ley St, Ilford IG1 4BN (8478 4962); *Panjabi Sabhiacharik Centre,* 293-297 Ley St, Ilford IG1 4BN (8478 4962);

Sangam Indian Elderly Ladies Group, c/o Kamaljit Patti, Ruth Winston Activities and Resource Centre for Over 55s, 190 Green Lanes, Palmers Green N13 5UE (8886 5346) [Fridays 12.45 - 16.00; languages: *Gujarati, Hindi, Punjabi*].

Papua New Guinean

GOVERNMENT *Papua New Guinea High Commission*, 14 Waterloo Pl, SW1Y 4AR (7930 0922);

LANGUAGES More than 800 languages are spoken in Papua New Guinea, many of them by fewer than 1 000 people. *English* has official status but an English-based Creole called *Tok Pisin* is by far the most widely spoken language of this country.

RELIGION *Papua New Guinea Church Partnership*, St Mary Abbots Hall, Vicarage Gate, W8 4HN (7937 5794) and 157 Waterloo Rd, SE1 8XA (7928 8681).

TRAVEL *Air Niugini*, 200 Buckingham Palace Rd, SW1W 9TA (7707 4146).

Paraguayan

GOVERNMENT *Embassy of Paraguay*, Braemar Lodge, Cornwall Gdns, SW7 4AQ (7937 1253).

LANGUAGES Both *Spanish* and *Guarani* have official status.

Parji

Parji is a *Dravidic* language spoken in India (Madhya Pradesh and Orissa). The presence of Parji-speaking schoolchildren in London has occcasionally been reported within the past decade although none were recorded at the time of the *Multilingual Capital* (2000) survey.

Pashto

EDUCATION Mother-tongue education for young children in *Pashto* is available in several locations in London; for full information visit <www.resourceunit.com>. Courses in *Pashto* for adults are available at *SOAS Language Centre* (7898 4888).

LANGUAGE *Pashto* is an *Iranic* language with official status in Afghanistan which is also spoken in Pakistan. It is written in an adaptation of the Arabic consonantal script. In the *Multilingual Capital* (2000) survey, *Pashto* was recorded as the language of 444 pupils in London, of whom a quarter lived in Ealing.

Patwa

Patwa (also written *Patois* and *Patua*) regularly appears in lists of languages other than English spoken by London schoolchildren. Unfortunately, this term is used ambiguously to refer to various Creole languages of the Caribbean area, some based in English and others based on French. See *English Creoles* and *French Creoles* for further information.

Pekingese

The words *Peking* or *Pekingese* is used by Chinese restaurants to indicate that they offer Beijing-(Peking-) style food (as opposed to Cantonese, Szechuan, or other regional cuisines).

RESTAURANTS
Barnet *The Wing Ki* [Peking/Szechuan], 29 Burnt Oak Broadway, HA8 5LD (8205 0904).
Islington *Beijing* [Cantonese / Peking / Szechuan], 205 Holloway Rd, N7 8DL (7609 1312).

Persian

Other entries which relate to *Persian* can be found under *Iranian.*

EDUCATION For courses in the Persian language, see under *Farsi.*
British Institute of Persian Studies, British Academy, 10 Carlton House Terrace, SW1Y 5AH (7969 5203).
LANGUAGE See under the alternative name of *Farsi.*
RESTAURANTS
Brent *Javad's,* 45 Cricklewood Broadway, NW2 (8452 9226); *Persia Kebab,* 1088 Harrow Rd, NW10 (8962 2733).

Camden *Hafez,* 559 Finchley Rd, NW3 7BJ (7431 4546); *Persian Cottage,* 9 Regency Parade, Finchley Rd, NW3 5EG (7722 5188); *Vanak,* 289 Finchley Rd, NW3 (7435 5054).
Ealing *Hatam,* 193 Uxbridge Rd, W13 9AA (8567 6800).
Hammersmith & Fulham *Yas,* 7 Hammersmith Rd, W14 8XJ (7603 9148); *Rumi,* 13 Hammersmith Rd, W14 8XJ (7371 2000).
Kensington & Chelsea *Soraya,* 36 Gloucester Rd, SW7 4QT (7589 5745).
Merton *Masoud's Persian Cuisine,* 319 Haydons Rd, SW19 8LA (8540 6233).
SHOPS
Carpets: *Alex Zadah Persian Carpets,* 35 Bruton Pl, W1J 6NQ (7493 2622); *Anglo Persian Carpet Co. (London) Ltd*, 6 South Kensington Station Arcade, SW7 2NA (7589 5457); *M & S Persian Carpets,* 53 Highgate Rd, NW5 1TL (7284 2882).

Peruvian

ASSOCIATIONS *Peru Support Group*, 37-39 Great Guildford St, SE1 0ES (7620 1103).

GOVERNMENT *Peruvian Consulate,* 52 Sloane St, SW1X 9SP (7235 6867).

RESTAURANTS *Fina Estampa,* 150 Tooley St, SE1 2TU (7403 1342).

LANGUAGES Both **Spanish and Quechua** have official status in Peru.

RESTAURANTS

South East 1 *Fina Estampa,* 150 Tooley St, London Bridge, SE1 (7403 1342).

SHOPS *Inca* [clothing, gifts, etc.], 45 Elizabeth St, SW1 (7259 9018).

TRAVEL *Aero Peru,* Cargo Service Centre, Sirius Ho, Bedfont Rd, Staines, TW19 7NL (01784 266210).

Philippino

See under *Filipino.*

Pidgin English

In the *Multilingual Capital* (2000) survey, one child in Barnet was reported as a speaker of *"Pidgin".* This probably refers to the Pidgin English spoken in Nigeria and Cameroon (in most cases, as a second language).

Pilipino

See under the alternative name of *Tagalog.*

Polish
====

ACCOMMODATION *Ognisko Polskie (Polish Hearth) Ltd,* 9a Station Parade, Uxbridge Rd, Ealing W5 3LD; *Polish St Anthony's Home* (sheltered housing), 47-49 Foxbourne Rd, Tooting SW17 8EN (8672 5106); *Polish YMCA,* 20 Gunnersbury Ave, Ealing, W5 3QL (8992 5699).

ARTS & CULTURE *Polish Historical Commission,* 19 Woodville Gdns, Ealing W5 2LL (8997 7965); *Polish Institute & Sikorski Museum,* 20 Princes Gate, South Kensington SW7 1PT (7589 9249).

ASSOCIATIONS *Association of Polish Merchant Navy Officers and Seamen,* 238 King St, Hammersmith W6 0RF (8741 3129); *Association of Polish Students In Great Britain,* 238-246 King St, Hammersmith W6 0QX (8741 2779); *Polish Air Force Association,* 14 Collingham Gdns, Earl's Court SW5 0HT (7373 1085); *Polish Cultural Institute,* 34 Portland Pl, W1N 4HQ (7636 6033); *Polish Hearth Club,* 55 Princes Gate, South Kensington SW7 2PG (7589 4635); *Polish Parish Committee,* 6 Oliver Grove, South Norwood SE25 6EJ (8771 2295); *Polish Parish Council* and *Polish Ex-combatants Association,* c/o Mrs Zofia Pelc, 1644 Great Cambridge Rd, Enfield EN1 4SZ (01992 767445); *Polish Scouting Association Ltd,* 23-31

Beaver La, Hammersmith W6 9AP (8748 8006); *Polish Social & Cultural Association Ltd,* 238-246 King St, Hammersmith W6 0RF (8741 1940); *Polish White Eagle Club,* 211 Balham High Rd, Tooting SW17 7BQ (8672 1723).

BARS *Na Zbrowie Polish Bar,* 11 Little Turnstile, Bloomsbury WC1V 7DX (7831 9679).

BUSINESS *British-Polish Chamber of Commerce,* 55 Princes Gate, Exhibition Rd, South Kensington SW7 2PN (7591 0057); *Polish Business Centre,* 1 London Wall Buildings, Moorgate EC2M 5PP (7282 0281); *Polish Shipping Mission,* 238 City Rd, Clerkenwell EC1V 2QL (7253 8998).

EDUCATION *Association of Polish Students In Great Britain,* 238-246 King St, Hammersmith W6 0QX (8741 2779); *Polish Educational Society,* 238 King St, Hammersmith W6 0RF (8741 1993); *Polish University Abroad,* 240 King St, Hammersmith W6 0RF (8846 9305); *Polish University In London,* 238-246 King St, Hammersmith W6 0RF (8846 9305).

Mother-tongue education for young children is available in *Polish* in more than a dozen locations in London; for full details visit <www.resourceunit.com>. Courses for adults in Polish are provided by several universities and local education authorities – see *Floodlight* or visit <www.floodlight.co.uk> for details.

GOVERNMENT *Polish Embassy,* 47 Portland Pl, W1N 4JH (7580 4324).

LANGUAGE *Polish* is a *Slavonic* language with official status in Poland. In the *Multilingual Capital* (2000) survey, *Polish* was reported to be the first language of 1 547 London schoolchildren of whom 339 lived in Ealing.

MEDIA & INFORMATION *Polish Daily Ltd,* 63 Jeddo Rd, Shepherd's Bush W12 9ED (8740 1991); *Polish Information Centre,* 238 King St, Hammersmith W6 0RF (8748 1203); *Polish Library,* 238-246 King St, Hammersmith W6 0RF (8741 0474).

RELIGION *Polish Catholic Centre and Church,* St Johns Hall, Ravenna Rd, Putney SW15 6AW (8788 3933); *Polish Parish Committee Croydon,* 8 Oliver Grove, South Norwood SE25 6EJ (8653 8701); *Polish R C Church,* 2 Windsor Rd, Ealing W5 5PD (8567 1746); *St Andrews Polish Church,* 1 Leysfield Rd, Shepherd's Bush W12 9JF (8740 5862).

RESTAURANTS

West 1 *L'Autre* [Polish/Mexican], 5b Shepherd St, W1 (7499 4680).

Hammersmith & Fulham *Lowiczanka Polish Centre Restaurant*, 238-246 King St, Hammersmith W6 0RF (8741 3225).

Kensington & Chelsea *Daquise*, 20 Thurloe St, SW7 (7589 6117); *Ognisko Polish Club* [restaurant], 55 Princes Gate, Exhibition Rd, South Kensington SW7 2PN (7589 4635); *Wodka* [Polish/Eastern European], 12 St Alban's Gr, W8 (7937 6513).

SHOPS

Bookshops *Orbis Books,* 66 Kenway Rd, Earl's Court, SW5 0RD (7370 2210, fax 7742 7686); *PMS Bookshop,* 240 King St, W6 0RF (8748 5522);.

Groceries *Korona,* 30 Streatham High Rd, SW16 (8769 6647); *Parade Delicatessen,* 8 Central Bldgs, The Broadway, W5 (8567 9066); *Prima,* 192 North End Rd, W14 (7385 2070).

SPECIAL *Polish Trustee Association Ltd,* 238 King St, Hammersmith W6 0RF (8748 1120) [will-writing services].

TRANSLATION *Polish and Eastern European Translators & Interpreters,* 14 Blenheim Terrace, St John's Wood NW8 0EB (7372 4852); *Polish Language Services,* 52 Caversham Rd, Kentish Town NW5 2DS (7284 3543); *Polish Language Services,* 19 Hollywood Rd, West Brompton SW10 9HT (7352 7147); *Polish Translating and Interpreting,* 156 Archway Rd, Highgate N6 5BH (8341 4007); *Polish Translation Services,* 44 Bletchley Ct, Wenlock St, Islington N1 7NX (7251 5437); *Tramont Translation Management,* 57 Upper Park Rd, NW3 2UL (7692 6319; fax 7504 8638).

TRAVEL *LOT Polish Airlines,* 313 Regent St, W1R 7PE (7580 5037) and Room 124, Terminal Two, London Heathrow Airport, Hounslow TW6 1DX (8745 7270); *Polish Air Tours,* 87 Regent St, W1R 7LF (7287 6334); *Polish National Tourist Office,* 310-312 Regent St, W1B 3AX (7580 8811).

WELFARE *Abbeyfield Polish Society*, 104 Balham Park Rd, Balham SW12 8EA (8682 1864); *Association of the Friends of Polish Children,* 50 Nightingale La, Balham SW12 8TE (8673 4177); *Fifth Polish Kresowa Infantry Division Fund,* 238-246 King St, Hammersmith, W6 0RF (8741 1974); *Polish Benevolent Fund,* 2 Devonia Rd, Islington N1 8JJ (7359 8863) and 55 Foxbourne Rd, Tooting SW17 8EN (8672 6810); *Polish Centre,* 1 Courtfield Gdns, West Ealing W13 0EY (8998 1982); *Polish Citizens' Committee for the Refugees,* 55 Princes Gate, South Kensington SW7 2PG (7584 6992);

Polish Ex-combatants' Association, 238-246 King St, Hammersmith W6 0RF (87411911); *Polish Naval Association Welfare Fund,* 14 Collingham Gdns, Earl's Court SW5 0HT (7370 2659); *Polish Underground Movement Study Trust,* 11 Leopold Rd, Ealing W5 3PB (8992 6057); *Polish Womens Association,* 16 Warwick Rd, Earl's Court SW5 9UD (7373 9936); *Romany Support Group* [mainly Polish], PO Box 23610, London E7 0XB (8514 7820) [meetings Tuesdays 14.00 - 18.00; also organizes advice sessions in White City and an English language class]; *Union of Polish War Disabled Ex-Servicemen,* 244 King St, Hammersmith W6 0RF (8563 2528).

Portuguese

ARTS & CULTURE *Portuguese Arts Trust,* 14 Hanover Sq, W1R 0BE.

ASSOCIATIONS *Anglo Portuguese Society,* 2 Belgrave Sq, SW1X 8PJ (7245 9738).

BARS & NIGHT-CLUBS *Bar Estrela,* 111-115 South Lambeth Rd, Stockwell SW8 (7793 1051).

BUSINESS *Banco Comercial Português,* 107 Cheapside, EC2V 6DT (7600 8380); *Banco Espírito Santo,* 33, Queen St, EC4R 1ES (7332 4300); *Portuguese Caterers,* 247-249 Gray's Inn Rd, WC1X 8QZ; *Portuguese UK Chamber of Commerce,* 4th fl, 22-25a Sackville St, W1X 1DE (7494 1844).

EDUCATION *Portuguese Language School,* 235 Upper Richmond Rd, SW15 6SN (8877 1738).

Mother-tongue education for young children is available in **Portuguese** in some 20 locations in London; for details visit <www.resourceunit.com>. There are many courses in Portuguese for adults in London provided by universities and local authorities and a few of these are specifically for Brazilian Portuguese. For details, see *Floodlight* or visit <www.floodlight.co.uk>.

FREIGHT *Trans-**Portugal** European Ltd,* 59 St Thomas St, Southwark SE1 3QX (7403 1440).

GOVERNMENT *Portuguese Consulate General,* 62 Brompton Rd, SW3 1BJ (7581 8722); *Portuguese Embassy,* 11 Belgrave Sq, SW1X 8PP (7235 5331); *Portuguese Trade & Tourism Office,* 4th floor, 22-25a Sackville St, W1X 1DE (7494 1517).

LANGUAGE **Portuguese** is a Romanic language ranked 8th in the world. It is estimated to be the first language of some 180m people and to have a total of 200m competent speakers. The *Multilingual Capital* (2000) survey found that there were 6 051 **Portuguese**-speaking school-children in London, and that almost half of these were resident in the three adjoining boroughs of Kensington & Chelsea, Lambeth, and Westminster. Map 23, showing the areas of London where the largest numbers of Portuguese-speakers live, can be viewed at <www.global-london.com/gallery>. (Although there are marked differences between Portuguese as spoken in Brazil and Portugal, the above figures do not distinguish between these varieties.)

RECREATION *Centro Desportivo Cultural Portugues,* 7 Lansdowne Way, South Lambeth SW8 1HL (7820 9145).

RELIGION *Portuguese Catholic Church,* 165 Arlington Rd, NW1 7EX (7267 9612); *Spanish & Portuguese Synagogue,* 2 Ashworth Rd, W9 1JY (7289 2573), *Spanish & Portuguese Synagogue,* 8 St James Gdns, W11 4RB (7603 7961).

RESTAURANTS

Camden *Camacheira,* 43 Pratt St, NW1 0BJ (7485 7266); *Pescador,* 33 Pratt St, NW1 (7482 0777).

Kensington & Chelsea *Caravela,* 39 Beauchamp Pl, SW3 1NX (7581 2366); *Lisboa Patisserie,* 57 Golborne Rd, W10 (8968 5242); *O Fado,* 49-50 Beauchamp Pl, SW3 (7589 3002); .

Lambeth *Gallery,* 256a Brixton Hill, SW9 (7326 5001); *O Cantinho,* 137 Stockwell Rd, SW9 (7924 0218).

Wandsworth *Café Portugal,* 5a-6a Victoria Ho, South Lambeth Rd, SW8 (7587 1962).

SHOPS *Almonda,* 119 South Lambeth Rd, SW8 (7642 8238); *Ferreira Delicatessen,* 40 Delancey St, NW1 (7485 2351); *Funchal Bakery,* 141 Stockwell Rd, SW9 (77733 3134); *Lisboa,* 54 Golborne Rd, W10 (8969 1052); *Lisboa Patisserie,* 57 Golborne Rd, W10 (8968 5242); *Lisboa Delicatessen,* 4 Plender St, NW1 (7387 1782); *Lusitana* [delicatessen], 328 Kennington Park Rd, SE11 4PP (7735 2900); *Madeira Patisserie,* 46a&b Albert Embankment, SE1 (7820 1117); *O Talho* [butchers], 13 Atlantic Rd, Brixton (7501 9540); *Plender Continental,* 7 Plender St, NW1 (7380 0602); *Sintra Delicatessen & Tapas,* 146, 146a & 148 Stockwell Rd, SW9 (7733 9402); *Vila Franca,* 3 Plender St, NW1 (7387 8230).

SPECIAL *Hispanic & Luso Brazilian Council,* 2 Belgrave Sq, SW1X 8PJ (7235 2303);

TRANSLATION *JC Portuguese Community,* 135 Stockwell Rd, SW9 9TN (7737 6260); *Portuguese & Spanish Translations & Interpreting,* 94 Inverness Terrace, W2 3LD (7727 1884); *Portuguese Technical Translation Service,* 28 Helena Rd, NW10 1JA (8452 7326).

TRAVEL *Portuguese Affair Ltd,* 5-7 Humbolt Rd, W6 8QH (7385 4775); *Portuguese National Tourist Office,* 22 Sackville St, W1X 1DE (7494 1441).

WELFARE *Aliança Portuguese Community Centre,* 56 Clapham Park Rd, SW4 7BG (7498 9951); *Spanish & Portuguese Sheltered Housing,* Edinburgh Ho, 36-44 Forty Ave, Wembley HA9 8JP (8908 1440).

Portuguese Creole

Portuguese Creole languages are spoken in Cape Verde islands, Guinea-Bissau, São Tomé & Príncipe, and by small minorities in Hong Kong, India, Malaysia and Singapore. The *Multilingual Capital* (2000) survey noted the presence of three **Portuguese-Creole**-speaking schoolchildren in Westminster but did not establish the particular variety spoken.

Provençal

====

ACCOMMODATION *Provence Alpes Cote D'Azur* [properties in France], 61 Holmewood Gdns, SW2 3NB (8671 9293).

RESTAURANTS

Camden *Provence Cafe,* 53 Fortune Green Rd, NW6 1DR (7794 8178).

Ealing *Café Provence,* 187 South Ealing Rd, W5 4RH (8569 8933).

Southwark *Café Provençal,* 4 Half Moon La, SE24 9HU (7978 9228).

SHOPS *Couleurs et Provence* [glassware], 226 Fulham Rd, SW10 9NB (7349 9923).

Puerto Rican

====

TRAVEL *Puerto Rico Villas Ltd,* 162 Heath Rd, Twickenham TW1 4BN (8891 6530).

Punjabi

Punjabi is the traditional English spelling for the language and people of the Punjab, an area divided between Pakistan and India since these countries became independent. The spelling **Panjabi** better reflects the sound system of this language and is increasingly used in London, particularly in reference to the language. For that reason, all entries relating to the people and language of the Punjab will be found under **Panjabi.**

Putonghua

Putonghua, meaning 'commonly understood language', is the Chinese government's currently preferred name for the Sinitic language which has official status in that country and which has traditionally been called *Mandarin* in English. However, since the Chinese living in London appear to prefer to term the language **Mandarin**, the entry will be found under that name.

Q

Quaker

See under **Christian.**

Qatari

BUSINESS *Qatar National Bank S A Q,* 135-141 Cannon St, EC4N 5AH (7647 2600); *Qatar National Bank S A Q,* 36 Curzon St, W1Y 7AF (7493 7411); *Qatar National Bank S A Q,* 1 Mount St, Mayfair W1Y 6HQ (7647 2600).

GOVERNMENT *Qatar Embassy,* 1 South Audley St, W1K 1HF (7493 2200); *Qatar Embassy Medical Office,* 30 Collingham Gdns, Earl's Court SW5 0HN (7370 6871).

TRAVEL *Qatar Airways,* 10 Conduit St, W1R 0QR (7896 3636).

Quechua

LANGUAGE *Quechua* is a Quechuic language spoken in Peru and parts of Bolivia and Argentina. In the *Multilingual Capital* (2000) survey, one *Quechua*-speaking schoolchild was located in Westminster.

R

Rajasthani

LANGUAGE *Rajasthani* is an Indic language spoken in the Indian state of Rajasthan, written in a semi-syllabic script. In the *Multilingual Capital* (2000) survey, the presence of eight *Rajasthani*-speaking schoolchildren was recorded, of whom seven lived in Ealing.

RESTAURANTS
East Central *Rajastan 2,* 8 India St, EC3N 2HS (7488 9777); *Rajasthan,* 49 Monument St, EC3R 8BU (7626 4796).

Rastafarian

ASSOCIATIONS *Rastafarian Society,* 290-296 Tottenham High Rd, N15 4AJ.

MEDIA & INFORMATION *Rastafari Universal Zion* [printers], 290 High Rd, N15 4AJ (8808 2185).

RESTAURANTS
Lambeth *Zionly Manna Vegan Restaurant,* Granville Arcade, Coldharbour La, SW9 8PS (7738 7831).

SHOPS *B B Ras Music Ltd,* 186a Goldhawk Rd, W12 9NS; *Beta Rastafari Enterprises Ltd,* 69 Mayes Rd, Wood Green N22 6TN.

Romani

ARTS *Boros Gypsy Ensemble,* 357 Kenton Rd, Harrow HA3 0XS (8907 7953); *Romany Rad* [musical group], c/o Romany Support Group, PO Box 23610, London E7 0XB (8514 7820).

ASSOCIATIONS *Association of Gypsy Organisations / Romani Institute,* c/o D Kenrick, 61 Blenheim Crescent, W11 2EG (7727 2916); *National Association of Teachers of Travellers,* c/o Essex Traveller Education Service, Alec Hunter High School, Stubbs La, Braintree, Essex CM7 3NT (01376 340360).

EDUCATION Greenwich is the only British university offering **Romani** studies – contact *Dr T A Acton,* Professor of Romani Studies, University of Greenwich, Avery Hill Rd, Eltham, SE9 2UG (8331 8923/8900).

Organizations concerned with Romani education: *Advisory Council for the Education of Romanies and Other Travellers,* Moot Ho, The Stow, Harlow, Essex CM20 3AG (01279 418666); *Greenwich Traveller Education Service,* Boxgrove Primary School, Boxgrove Rd, Abbey Wood SE2 9JP (8310 9209); *Gypsy Council for Education, Culture, Welfare and Civil Rights,* c/o C Smith, 8 Hall Rd, Aveley, Essex, RM15 4HD (01708 868986); *Traveller Education Project,* London Borough of Hackney, Queensbridge Bldg Annexe, Albion Drive, E8 4ET (7241 7433).

LANGUAGE **Romani** is the name of a group of Indic languages, varieties of which are spoken in many parts of Europe. In the *Multilingual Capital* (2000) survey, 75 London schoolchildren were reported to be **Romani**-speakers.

LEGAL *Labour Campaign for Travellers' Rights*, c/o Andrew Ryder, Flat A, 25 Clarence Rd, N22 8PG [political pressure group];

SPECIAL *Romanestan Publications* [mail order book service], 22 Northend, Warley, Brentwood, Essex CM14 5LA; *Romany and Traveller Family History Society* , Membership Secretary, 27 Conyers Close, Hersham, Surrey KT12 4NG.

WELFARE *BIAS Irish Travellers Project,* 90 High St, Harrow on the Hill, HA1 3LP (8422 3541); *Ealing Travellers Project,* 241 King St, Hammersmith W6 9LP (8741 9094); *Europe-Roma* [refugee organization, currently mainly Czech. Open meetings Thursdays 19.00 in North London (phone 8802 7496 for address). Advice available at Chestnuts Community Centre, 280 St Anns Rd, N15 (Mon - Fri 11.00 - 14.30)]; *Gypsy Council for Education, Culture, Welfare and Civil Rights,* c/o C Smith, 8 Hall Rd, Aveley, Essex, RM15 4HD (01708 868986); *London Gypsy & Traveller Unit,* 6 Westgate St, E8 3RN (8533 2002); *National Association of Gypsy Women,* c/o S Dunn, Meadowview, Goldsmith Drive, Lower Holbridge Rd., Rayleigh, Essex (01268 782792); *Romany Support Group* [mainly Polish], PO Box 23610, London E7 0XB (8514 7820) [meetings Tuesdays 14.00 - 18.00; also organizes advice sessions in White City and an English language class].

Romanian

BUSINESS *Anglo-Romanian Bank,* 3 Finsbury Sq, EC2A 1AE (7826 4200); *British Romanian Chamber of Commerce,* 509 Footscray Rd, Eltham SE9 3UG.

EDUCATION Courses in Romanian are provided by the *University of Westminster* (7911 5000).

GOVERNMENT *Embassy of Romania,* 4 Palace Green, W8 4QD (7937 9666).

LANGUAGE **Romanian** is a **Romanic** language which has official status in Romania. 40 London schoolchildren were recorded as speakers of **Romanian** in the *Multilingual Capital* (2000) survey, of whom nine lived in Ealing.

RELIGION *St Dunstan's-in-the-west,* Fleet St, EC4 (7242 6027) [occasional services in Romanian].

SHOPS **Charity shops** *Relief Fund for Romania,* 54-62 Regent St, W1B 5RE (7437 6978); *Relief Fund For Romania,* 22 Notting Hill Gate W11 3JE (7792 0047).

TRANSLATION *Romanian, French and English Translation Bureau,* 14 Laurel View, N12 7DT (8445 8080); *Romanian Interpreting & Translating Services,* 4 Garthorne Rd, Forest Hill SE23 1EW (8291 9508); *Romanian Language Services,* 31 Woodstock Rd NW11 8ES (8458 4463); *Romanian*

Translations & Interpreting, 4 King Henry's Yard, Barretts Grove N16 8XB (7254 0482).

TRAVEL *Romanian National Tourist Office,* 22 New Cavendish St, W1G 8TS (7224 3692); *Tarom Romanian Air Transport,* 27 New Cavendish St, W1G 9UE (7224 3693).

WELFARE *Relief Fund for Romania,* PO Box 2122, W1A 2XX (01969 663667); *Stirling Work For Children In Russia & Romania,* 1-4 Crawford Mews, W1H 1PT (7724 3595).

Romany

See under **Romani.**

Rundi

Rundi is the element common to the name of the country, **Burundi**, and its principal language, **Kirundi** – see these names for further details.

Runyankore

Runyankore (also known as *Nyankore*) is a Bantuic language spoken in Uganda. 17 speakers of this were recorded among London's school population in the *Multilingual Capital* (2000) survey.

Russian

ARTS *Iconastas Russian Works of Art,* 5 Piccadilly Arcade, SW1Y 6NH (7629 1433); *Pushkin Club,* 46 Ladbroke Grove, W11 2PA (7221 1981); *Russian Arts Gallery,* 257 High St, Acton W3 9BY (8993 9096); *Russian Art Studio* [ballet school], Trinity Church, 71 Hodford Rd, Golders Green NW11 (8248 0116); *Russian Music Services,* 21 Broad St, Teddington TW11 8QZ (01932 711906); *Russian Music Services,* 21 Broad St, Teddington TW11 8QZ (8977 5487).

ASSOCIATIONS *Britain-Russia Centre,* 14 Grosvenor Pl, SW1X 7HW (7235 2116); *Russian European Trust,* 5 Tavistock Pl, WC1H 9SN (7813 0244); *Society for Co-operation in Russian & Soviet Studies,* 320 Brixton Rd, SW9 6AB (7274 2282).

BARS & NIGHT-CLUBS *Potemkin,* 144 Clerkenwell Rd, EC1R 5DP (7278 6661).

BUSINESS *Moscow Consulting Group,* 68 South Lambeth Rd, SW8 1RL (7582 3086); *Moscow Narodny Bank Ltd,* 81 King William St, EC4P 4JS (7623 2066); *Promstroybank of Russia,* 78 Cannon St, EC4P 4LN (7626 8016); *Russian Connections* [corporate hospitality], 47 Elms Rd, SW4 9EU (7498 0596); *Russian Engineering Consultancy,* 2 1 Hazeldene Drive, Pinner HA5 3NJ (8866 1267); *Russian Input* [horticultural consultants], 197 Tolcarne Drive, HA5 2DN (8868 6816); *Russian Investment and Metal Co Ltd,* 15 St Helens Pl, EC3A 6DE (7628 2681); *Russian Investment Fund Ltd,* 312 Long La, East Finchley N2 8JP (8343 4088); *Russian Trade Delegation in the UK,* 32-33 Highgate West Hill, N6 6NL (8340 4492); *Russo-British Chamber of Commerce,* 42 Southwark St, Southwark SE1 1UN (7403 1706).

EDUCATION Courses in Russian at a wide range of levels are provided by several universities and many local education authorities in London. See *Floodlight* or visit its website at <www.floodlight.co.uk>.

Russian Art Studio [ballet school], Trinity Church, 71 Hodford Rd, Golders Green NW11 (8248 0116); *Russian for All,* 48 Kingfield Rd, Ealing W5 1LB (8991 1296); *Russian Hungarian Language School,* 7 St Kildas Rd, Harrow HA1 1QD (8930 9090); *Russian Language Centre,* 11 Coldbath Sq., EC1R 5HL (7689 5400); *Russian Language Experience,* 4th fl, 53-56 Great Sutton St, Clerkenwell EC1V 0DE (7608 3794); *Russian Language in London,* 1a Marylebone High St, W1M 3PA; *Russian Language in London,* 4 St James Gdns, Notting Hill W11 4RB (7603 0256); *Society for Cooperation in Russian & Soviet Studies,* 320 Brixton Rd, SW9 6AB (7274 2282).

GOVERNMENT *Permanent Mission of The Russian Federation,* 37 Harrington Gdns, South Kensington SW7 4JU (7370 6764); *Russian Federation Embassy,* 5 Kensington Palace Gdns, W8 4QS (7229 3628), [commercial enquiries] (09065 200171).

LANGUAGES *Russian* is the dominant language of Russia but a great many other languages are spoken by minorities within that country.

Russian is a Slavonic language ranked fifth in the world with 170m primary speakers and a total, including second-language speakers, of 320m speakers worldwide. It is written with the Cyrillic alphabet. The *Multilingual Capital* (2000) survey reported that there were 679 **Russian**-speaking pupils in London's schools. The two boroughs with by far the highest proportion of **Russian**-speakers were Westminster and Kensington & Chelsea.

LEGAL *Visa to Russia,* 12 Chepstow Rd, Bayswater W2 5BD (7229 1412).

MEDIA & INFORMATION *Interfax Russian Newsagency,* 1st fl, 50 Hans Crescent, SW1X 0NA (7222 3443); *London Courier* [Russian newspaper], Berkley Ho, High St, Edgware HA8 2PQ (8952 3131); *Russian Information Agency,* 3 Rosary Gdns, South Kensington SW7 4NW (7370 1162); *Russian London,* 12 Ilkley Court,4 Garsdale Cl, N11 3EF (8361 9680); *Russian Magazines Ltd,* 52 Brixton Rd, SW9 6BS; *Russian Research Ltd* [media & market research], 9 Cursitor St, EC4A 1LL (7242 3223); *Spectrum Radio,* International Radio Centre, 4 Ingate Pl, SW8 3NS (7627 4433) [broadcasts in Russian 13.00-14.00 Sun.-Fri.]; *Zone Broadcasting (Romantica) Russia Ltd,* Bridge Ho, 181 Queen Victoria St, EC4V 4DZ.

MOTORING *Speedway Motorcycles* [Russian motorcyle specialists], 12 Rushey Green, SE6 4JF (8690 8609).

RELIGION *Russian Church,* 3 Brookwood Ave, SW13 0LR (8876 7993); *Russian Church, 99* Kenilworth Ave, SW19 7LP (8879 1461); *Russian Church,* 20 Rothschild Rd, W4 5HS (8995 2769); *Russian Convent of Annunciation,* 26 Brondesbury

Park, NW6 7DL (8459 0263); *Russian Orthodox Cathedral,* 67 Ennismore Gdns, SW7 1NH; *Russian Orthodox Church,* 3 Brookwood Ave, Barnes SW13 0LR (8876 7993); *Russian Orthodox Church Abroad,* 57 Harvard Rd, W4 4ED (8995 9503); *Word of Eternity Church Russian Fellowship,* Carlton Centre, Granville Rd, NW6 5QY (7328 7770).

RESTAURANTS
East Central *Potemkin,* 144 Clerkenwell Rd, EC1R 5DP (7278 6661);

West 1 *Firebird Tsarist Russian Restaurant,* 23 Conduit St, W1S 2XR (7493 7000);

Camden *The Birch* [Russian/East European], Finchley Rd, NW6; *Trojka* [Russian/Eastern European], 101 Regent's Park Rd, NW1 (7483 3765).

Hackney *Little Georgia* [Russian/Georgian], 2 Broadway Market, Haggerston, E8 (7249 9070).

Hammersmith & Fulham *Stravinsky's Russian Tea House,* 6 Fulham High St, Fulham SW6 3LQ (7371 0001).

Islington *Luba's Place,* 164 Essex Rd, Islington N1 8LY (7704 2775).

Kensington & Chelsea *Borshtch'n Tears,* 46 Beauchamps Pl, SW3 (7589 5003); *Nikita's,* 65 Ifield Rd, SW10 9AU (7352 6326).

Richmond *Kozachok* [Russian/Ukrainian], 10 Red Lion St, Richmond TW9 1RW (8948 2366).

SHOPS *Caviar House,* 161 Piccadilly, W1 (7409 0445); *Caviar Kaspia,* 18-18a Bruton Pl, W1 (7493 2612); *Russian Orthodox Cathedral Bookshop,* 67 Ennismore Gdns, South Kensington SW7 1NH (7722 2879); *Russian Shop,* Unit 9, The Arches, Villiers St, WC2 (7930 3484).

SPECIAL *Russian European Trust,* 5 Tavistock Pl, W14 0LH (7813 0244).

TRANSLATION *German Russian Language Services,* 14 West End La, Pinner HA5 1BT (8429 2943); *RTTS Russian & French,* 12 Elers Rd, W13 9QD (8579 4925); *Russian & East European Translation & Interpreting,* 32 Paget Rise, SE18 3QQ (8854 5521); *Russian & French Translations,* 27 South Drive, Ruislip HA4 8EU (01895 637597); *Russian Bureau,* 74 Pond Ho, Pond Pl, Chelsea SW3 6QT (7225 0008); *Russian Commercial & Technical Translation & Interpreters,* 166 Munster Rd, Fulham SW6 6AT (7731 3230); *Russian Interpreter & Translations,* 9b Adelaide Rd, Richmond TW9 1XW (8940 4106); *Russian Language Services Ltd,* 165 Princes Gdns, Acton W3 0LS (8993 3404); *Russian Service L G Z,* 22 Fitzjohns Ave, Hampstead NW3 5NB (7916 9699);

Russian Services, 10 Corinne Rd, Archway N19 5EY (7609 8268); *Russian Technical Translation & Interpreting Service,* 31 Parke Rd, SW13 9NJ (8748 8822); *Russian Translation and Typesetting,* Berkeley Square Ho, Berkeley Sq, W1X 5LE (7409 0953); *Russian Translation Interpreting & Research,* 32 Paget Rise, Woolwich SE18 3QQ (8854 8642); *Russian Translations,* 125 Ossulton Way, East Finchley N2 0JS (8883 0588); *Russian Translations & Typesetting,* 132 Cleveland St W1P 6AB (7692 7700).

TRAVEL *Aeroflot Russian International Airlines,* 70 Piccadilly, W1V 9HH (7355 2233) *and* Room 128, New Office Block, Terminal 2, Heathrow Airport, TW6 1HE (8897 0579); *Anglo Russian Cultural Tours,* 27 Cecil Ct, WC2N 4EZ; *Inntel-Moscow Travel Co Ltd,* 70 Piccadilly W1J 8HP (7495 7555); *Russia Experience Ltd,* Research Ho, Fraser Rd, Greenford UB6 7AQ (8566 8846); *Russia House Ltd,* 37 Kingly Ct, Kingly St, W1R 5LE (7439 1271); *Russian National Tourist Office,* Orchard Ho, 167-169 Kensington High St, W8 6SH (7937 7217); *Russian Tourist Office,* 70 Piccadilly, W1J 8HP (7495 7570); *Russian Tour Operator,* 219 Marsh Wall, E14 9FJ (7538 8600); *Travel Russia Ltd,* 21 The Bakehouse, Bakery Pl, 119 Altenburg Gdns, Battersea SW11 1JQ (7223 1060).

WELFARE *Friends of Russian Children,* Chichester Ho, 278 High Holborn WC1V 7ER (7404 7766); *Friends of Russian Children,* 47 Elms Rd, Clapham SW4 9EP (7720 9219); (8994 2599); *Russia House Ltd,* 55 Southwark St, Southwark SE1 1RU (7450 3262); **Russian** *European Trust,* 5 Tavistock Pl, Bloomsbury WC1H 9SN (7813 0244); *Russian Immigrant Aid Fund,* 97 Stamford Hill, N16 5DN (8800 6688); *Russian Refugees Aid Society,* 27 Blenheim Rd, Chiswick W4 1ET *and* 57 Harvard Rd, W4 4ED (8994 2599); *Stirling Work For Children In Russia & Romania,* 1-4 Crawford Mews, W1H 1PT (7724 3595).

Rutoro

Rutoro is a Bantuic language spoken in Uganda and also, at the time of the *Multilingual Capital* (2000) survey, by three London schoolchildren.

Rwanda

GOVERNMENT *Embassy of the Republic of Rwanda,* 58-59 Trafalgar Sq, WC2N 5DS (7930 2570) and 42 Aylmer Rd, East Finchley N2 0BX (7347 6967).

LANGUAGE **Rwanda** is a **Bantuic** language with official status in Rwanda. At the time of the *Multilingual Capital* (2000) survey there were 47 speakers of this among London's school population, of whom 15 lived in Barnet.

S

Saho

Saho is a Cushitic language of Ethiopia. In the *Multilingual Capital* (2000) survey there were a few **Saho**-speaking schoolchildren in Southwark and Tower Hamlets.

Saint Christopher & Nevis

See entries for **Kittitian** and **Nevisian**.

Saint Helenan

GOVERNMENT *St Helena Representative,* 30b Wimpole St, W1G 8YD (7224 5025).

Saint Kitts–Nevis

See entries for **Kittitian** and **Nevisian**.

Saint Lucian

GOVERNMENT *High Commission for St Lucia,* 1 Collingham Gdns, SW5 0HW (7370 7123).

LANGUAGES Both **Creole French** and **Creole English** are spoken. **English** has official status.

TRAVEL *St Lucia Tourist Board,* 421a Finchley Rd, NW3 6HJ (7431 3675).

Saint Vincent and the Grenadines

See under **Vincentian**.

Samoan

GOVERNMENT Samoa is represented in London from Brussels – *High Commission for Samoa,* Franklin D Rooseveltlaan 123, B-1050 Brussels, Belgium (+32 2 660 8454).

LANGUAGE **Samoan** is a Transpacific language.

Sanmarinese

GOVERNMENT *San Marino Consulate,* Flat 51, 162 Sloane St, SW1X 9BS (7823 4768).

LANGUAGE The official language is **Italian.**

RELIGION The people of San Marino are Roman Catholics.

RESTAURANTS

Waltham Forest *San Marino Coffee Co. Cafe,* 668 High Road Leytonstone E11 3AA (8532 8048).

Sanskrit

EDUCATION Courses in **Sanskrit** are available at *SOAS Language Centre* (7898 4888).

LANGUAGE *Sanskrit* is the classical Indic language associated with the Hindu religion.

Sardinian

LANGUAGE *Sardinian* is distinct Romanic language rather than a dialect of *Italian.*

RESTAURANTS

West 1 *Sardo,* 45 Grafton Eay, W1 (7387 2521).

SHOPS *Sardinian Food & Wine Co,* Units 10-17, Northfield Industrial Estate, Beresford Ave, Wembley HA0 1GJ (8902 4206); *Sardinia Organic,* Acton Business Centre, School Rd, NW10 6TD (8963 0007);

TRAVEL *Sardinia Accommodation,* 1 Early Mews NW1 7HG (07050377457); *Simply Sardinia,* Kings Ho, Wood St, Kingston KT1 1UG (8541 2213).

Saudi Arabian

ASSOCIATIONS *Saudi British Society,* 21 Collingham Rd, SW5 0NU (7373 8414).

BUSINESS *National Commercial Bank of Saudi Arabia,* 78 Cornhill, EC3V 3QQ (7283 4233); *Riyad Bank Europe,* 17b Curzon St, W1Y 8LS (7830 4000); *Saudi British Bank,* 18c Curzon St, W1Y 8AA (7409 2567).

FREIGHT *National Shipping Company of Saudi Arabia,* Exchange Tower, Harbour Exchange Sq, E14 9GE (7536 2800).

GOVERNMENT *Royal Embassy of Saudi Arabian,* 30 Charles St, W1X 7PN (7917 3441); *Royal Embassy of Saudi Arabia – Health Office,* 60 Queen Anne St, W1M 9LA (7935 9931); *Saudi Arabian Cultural Office,* 29 Belgrave Sq, SW1X 8QB (7245 9944).

LANGUAGE *Arabic* is the national language.

LEGAL *Bryan Cave,* 29 Queen Anne's Gate, SW1H 9BU (7896 1900) [office in Riyadh]; *Clifford Chance,* 200 Aldersgate St, E1A 4JJ (7600 1000) [offices in Jeddah & Riyadh]; *Howard Kennedy,* 19 Cavendish Sq, W1A 2AW (7499 8921) [office in Saudi Arabia]; *Leboeuf, Lamb, Greene, & Macrae,* 6th fl, 1 Mincing Ct, Mincing La, EC3R 7AA (7459 5000) [office in Riyadh].

MEDIA & INFORMATION *Saudi Arabian Information Centre,* Cavendish Ho, 18 Cavendish Sq, W1G 0AQ (7629 8803); *Saudi Press Agency,* 18 Cavendish Sq, W1M 1AQ (7495 0418).

RELIGION Islam is the state religion.

SPECIAL *King Fahd Academy,* Bromyard Ave, W3 7HD (8743 0131).

TRAVEL *Saudi Arabian Airlines,* Atlas Ho, 173 Victoria St, SW1E 5NE (7798 9898).

Scandinavian

BUSINESS *Anglo-Scandinavian Investments,* 33 Davies St, W1K 4LR (7355 4414); *Anglo-Scandinavian Developments Ltd,* 196a Cromwell Rd, SW5 0SN (7259 2519); *Royal Scandinavia UK Ltd,* Kingsway Business Park, Oldfield Rd, Hampton TW12 2HD (8979 2929); *Scandinavian Investments plc,* 2nd fl, Lynton Ho, 7-12 Tavistock Sq, Bloomsbury WC1H 9BQ; *Scandinavian Finance (UK) Ltd,* Independent Ho, 178 Brompton Rd, SW3 1HQ (7225 2220); *Scandinavian Financial Management Ltd,* 29 Abingdon Rd, Kensington W8 6AH (7376 0528); *Scandinavian Re-Insurance Company (Representative Office) Ltd,* Marlon Ho, Mark La, EC3R 7HS (7265 1651); *Scandinavian Underwriters Agency,* 1 Knightrider Ct, EC4V 5JP (7489 8008); *Scanmeridian,* 15 Daleham Mews, NW3 5DB ((7431 5393); *Skandinaviska Enskilda Banken/Scandinavian Bank Ltd,* Scandinavian Ho, Cannon St, EC4M 6XX (7236 6090);

FREIGHT *Scandinavian Timber & Marine Services Ltd,* 3 Duke of York St, SW1Y 6JP (7839 6541);

HEALTH & BEAUTY *Scandinavian Medical Clinic Ltd,* 15 Harley St, W1N1DA (7636 7780);

MEDIA *Scandinavian Broadcasting System,* 36 St. Ives St, SW3 2ND (7590 3600).

RESTAURANTS

South West 1 *Scandinavian Restaurant,* 14 Little Chester St, SW1X 7AP (7245 1224);

SPECIAL *Red Green Scandinavia UK Ltd,* 189 Munster Rd, SW6 6AW (7381 9761); *Scandinavia Connection,* 26 Woodsford Sq, W14 8DP (7602 0657);

TRAVEL *S A S-Scandinavian Airlines,* S A S Ho, 52 Conduit St, W1R 0AY (7437 7086); *Scandinavian Airlines System,* World Business Centre, Newall Rd, Hounslow TW6 2RE (8990 7000); *Scandinavian Leisure Group,* 1 Spring St, Bayswater W2 3RA (7706 0338); *Scandinavian Seaways,* 28a Queensway, W2 3RX (7616 1400); *Scandinavian Travel Service Ltd,* 3 Bergham Mews, Blythe Rd, W12 0HN (7559 6688); *Specialised Travel Ltd* [Scandinavian holidays], W5 3EL (8799 8350);

Scottish

ACCOMMODATION *Highland Lettings,* 67 Tottenham La, Hornsey N8 9BE (8374 3030).

ARTS *Highland Piper* [entertainer], 9 Grove Pl, Hampstead NW3 1JP (7431 8972); *Royal Scottish Country Dance Society,* 71d Sutherland Ave, W9 2HF (7286 1923); *Scottish & Irish Bagpiper* [musicians], 9 Grove Pl, NW3 1JP.

BUSINESS

East Central *Bank of Scotland,* 37-38 Threadneedle St, EC2R 8AU (7601 6666); *Royal Bank of Scotland plc,* Waterhouse Sq, EC1N 2TH (7427 8000); *Royal Bank of Scotland plc,* 32-34

Cheapside, EC2V 6DJ (7236 2615); *Royal Bank of Scotland plc*, 36-37 New Bridge St, EC4V 6BJ (7489 8078); *Royal Bank of Scotland plc*, 1 Fleet St, EC4Y 1BD (7353 4080); *Scottish Life Assurance Co*, 55 King William St, EC4R 9HH (7200 4848); *Scottish Lion Insurance Co. Ltd*, 69-70, Mark Lane, EC3R 7HS (7702 9995); *Scottish Widows Investment*, 10, Fleet Place, EC4M 7RB (7203 3000).

South West 1 *Institute of Chartered Accountants of Scotland*, 17 Cockspur St, SW1Y 5BL (7839 4777); *Royal Bank of Scotland plc*, 48 Haymarket, SW1Y 4SE (7930 1396); *Royal Bank of Scotland plc*, 49 Charing Cross, SW1A 2DX (7839 1200); *Royal Bank of Scotland plc*, 24 Grosvenor Pl, SW1X 7HN (7235 1882); *Royal Bank of Scotland plc*, 119 Victoria St, SW1E 6RA (7630 1500).

West 1 *Highland Mills Ltd*, House of Hanover, 13-14 Hanover St, W1S 1YH (7629 1103); *Royal Bank of Scotland plc*, 28 Cavendish Sq, W1G 0DB (7499 3601); *Royal Bank of Scotland plc*, 60 Conduit St, W1S 2YY (7437 7744); *Royal Bank of Scotland plc*, 43 Curzon St, W1J 7UG (7408 1888); *Royal Bank of Scotland plc*, 171 Tottenham Court Rd, W1T 7DL (7387 6564); *Scottish Amicable*, 7 Curzon St, W1J 5HF (7493 3484); *Scottish Life International*, 45, Clarges St, W1J 7ES (7560 2951).

West Central *Scottish Equitable plc*, 90, Long Acre, WC2E 9RA (7497 3300); *Scottish Equitable plc*, 40 Strand, WC2N 5HZ (7484 6100);

Brent *Royal Bank of Scotland plc*, 86 Craven Park Rd, NW10 4AE (8965 7123).

Camden *Royal Bank of Scotland plc*, 189-191 Camden High St, NW1 7BP (7482 3939);

Ealing *Royal Bank of Scotland plc*, 14 High St, W5 5EB (8840 7171); *Scottish Fisheries*, 117 Northfield Ave West, Ealing W13 9QR (8567 3280).

Islington *Royal Bank of Scotland plc*, 42 Islington High St, N1 8XL (7833 2121).

Kensington & Chelsea *Royal Bank of Scotland plc*, 175-177 Kensington High St, W8 6SH (7937 3210); *Royal Bank of Scotland plc*, 29 Old Brompton Rd, SW7 3JE (7581 7955).

Lambeth *Royal Bank of Scotland plc*, 59 Streatham High Rd, SW16 1PN (8677 9641).

Westminster *Royal Bank of Scotland plc*, 2 Elgin Ave, W9 3QR (7289 2525); *Royal Bank of Scotland plc*, Northwest Ho, 119 Marylebone Rd, NW1 5PY (7402 7251).

EMPLOYMENT *The Highland Bureau*, Chesham Ho, 150 Regent St, W1BÊ5SJ (7432 0322).

GOVERNMENT *Scottish National Party*, Whips Office, House of Commons, Westminster SW1A 0AA (7219 0074).

MEDIA & INFORMATION *Scottish & Irish Radio Sales* [advertising], Market Tower 1, Nine Elms La, SW8 5NQ (7819 4200); *Scottish Media Newspapers Ltd*, 20 Lincolns Inn Fields, WC2AÊ3ER (7446 7040); *Scottish Television Ltd*, 20 Lincoln's Inn Fields, WC2A 3ED (7446 7000).

RECREATION *London Scottish Golf Club*, Windmill Enclosure, Windmill Rd, Wimbledon Common, SW19 5NQ (8789 7517);

RELIGION *Church of Scotland Crown Court (Presbyterian)*, Russell St, WC2B 5EZ (7836 5643); *St Columba's Church of Scotland*, Pont St, SW1X 0BD (7584 2321).

RESTAURANTS
South West 1 *Boisdale Scottish Restaurant*, 13-15, Eccleston St, SW1W 9LX (7730 6922).

Brent *Highland Glen Cafe*, 238 North Circular Rd, Willesden NW10 0JU (8459 3823).

Islington *Highland Steakhouse*, 262 Pentonville Rd, N1 9JY (7837 8502).

Wandsworth *Buchan's*, 62-64 Battersea Bridge Rd, Battersea, SW11 (7228 0888).

SHOPS *Albion Highland All Tartan Kilts & All Ltd*, 2 Old Brompton Rd, SW7 3DQ (7735 2255); *Scottish Wear*, 209 Regent St, W1B 4NE (7287 3810); *Highlander Organic Butchers*, 14 Bittacy Hill, Mill Hill NW7 1LB (8346 1055); *Highland Gathering* [music, musical instruments], 135, Colchester Rd, E10 6HD (8556 8914); *Highland Organics* [organic food], 4 Bittacy Hill, NW7 1LB; *Highland Store*, Marchmont St. WC1; *House of Scotland*, 467 Oxford St, W1C 2PZ (7499 2404); *House of Scotland*, 241 Regent St, W1B 2EH (7734 1521);

Lochcarron of Scotland [clothing], Suite 401-402,Golden Ho, 29 Great Pulteney St, W1F 9NN (7434 4334); *Pringle of Scotland Ltd*, 9-10 Grafton St, W1S 4EH (7647 8500); *Scottish Wear*, 209 Regent St, W1B 4NE (7287 3810).

SPECIAL *Scottish Scenic Trust* [conservation], Cinnamon Wharf, 24 Shad Thames, SE1 2YJ (7403 7061).

TRAVEL *Highlander Travel,* Eurolink Business Centre, 49 Effra Rd, SW2 1BZ (7978 8444).

WELFARE *Reach,* 89 Albert Embankment, SE1 7TP (*North of Scotland* 01888 568855, *West of Scotland* 01360 661110); *Royal Scottish Corporation,* Flat 13a St Ninian's Ct, Bawtry Rd, N20Ê0SX (8368 0932).

Scottish Gaelic

See entry under *Gaelic*

Senegalese

GOVERNMENT *Embassy of the Republic of Senegal,* 39 Marloes Rd, W8 6LA (7938 4048).

LANGUAGES Some 30 languages are spoken in Senegal, of which the following have "national" status (with approximate percentage of speakers in brackets): *Wolof* (44%), *Fula* (21%), *Serer* (16%), *Mandinka* (6%), *Jola* (6%), and *Soninke* (2%). *French* has official status.

RELIGION The great majority of the Senegalese population is Muslim. A small minority is Christian.

SHOPS *Senegal Design,* Rye Lane Indoor Market, Rye La, SE15 5BY (7732 8457);

Senga

Senga is a Bantuic language of Zambia, spoken by one schoolchild in Hammersmith & Fulham at the time of the *Multilingual Capital* (2000) survey.

Serbian

ACCOMMODATION *Serbian Club & Hotel,* 29 Holland Park Ave, W11 3RW (7221 4282).

ASSOCIATIONS *Serbian Club & Hotel,* 29 Holland Park Ave, W11 3RW (7221 4282).

EDUCATION See "Serbo-Croat".

GOVERNMENT See *Yugoslav.*

LANGUAGE *Serbian* is a *Slavonic* language which has official status in Serbia and which is written with the Cyrillic alphabet. For further information, see *"Serbo-Croat".*

MEDIA & INFORMATION *Serbian Information Centre,* 89 Lancaster Rd, W11 1QQ (7792 9711);

RELIGION *Serbian Orthodox Church,* 89/91, Lancaster Rd, W11 1QQ (7727 8367).

WELFARE *Serbian Community Centre,* 89 Lancaster Rd, W11 1QQ (7727 9718).

"Serbo-Croat"

EDUCATION Mother-tongue education for young children in *"Serbo-Croat"* is available in several locations in London; for full information visit <www.resourceunit.com>. Courses for adults in Serbo-Croat (*Serbian / Croatian*) are provided by SSEES (7862 8634) and the *Univerity of Westminster* (7911 5000).

LANGUAGE *"Serbo-Croat"* is the cover name which has traditionally been used in English for the two near-identical Slavonic languages, *Serbian* and *Croatian,* which have official status in Serbia and Croatia, respectively. The most striking difference is that *Serbian* is written in the Cyrillic alphabet while *Croatian* uses the Roman alphabet. Since the break up of Yugoslavia, there has been the feeling that "Serbo-Croat" is no longer an appropriate name to use but no alternative name has yet won general acceptance.

In the *Multilingual Capital* (2000) survey, some boroughs listed *"Serbo-Croat"* as one language while others gave separate figures for *Serbian* and *Croatian.* Adding all these together, there were found to be 659 speakers among London's school population, of whom one fifth lived in Ealing.

Sesotho

Sesotho is a Bantuic language with official status in *Lesotho* where it is almost everyone's first language. *Sesotho* is also spoken by about 7% of the population of South Africa (where the abbreviated form of the name, *Sotho,* is generally preferred). In the *Multilingual Capital* (2000) survey, this was found to be the first language of ten London schoolchildren, five of whom lived in Barnet.

Setswana

EDUCATION Courses in *Setswana* are available at *SOAS Language Centre* (7898 4888).

LANGUAGE *Setswana* is a Bantuic language which has offical status in Botswana and which is also spoken by about 8% of the population of South Africa (where it is generally known, without its prefix, as *Tswana*) *Setswana* was recorded as the language of three London schoolchildren in the *Multilingual Capital* (2000) survey.

Seychellois

BUSINESS *Seychelles Interior Designs Ltd,* 343 Uxbridge Rd, Pinner HA5 4JN (8421 3212);

GOVERNMENT *Seychelles High Commission,* 2nd fl, Eros Ho, 111 Baker St, W1U 6RR (7224 1660).

LANGUAGES *Seychellois* (a French Creole) is the first language of most of the population. *English* and *French* are the first languages of small minorities but these are known as second or additional languages by many other islanders.

TRAVEL *Air Seychelles,* The Mill, Horton Rd, Staines TW19 6BJ (01753680203); *Just Seychelles,* 74 New Oxford St, WC1A 1EU (7462 5690); *Seychelles Tourist Office,* 2nd fl, 111 Baker St, W1M 1FE (7224 1670); *Seychelles Tourist Office,* 48 Glentham Rd, SW13 9JJ (8741 6262).

Shelta

Shelta is basically a cant, i.e. a "secret", restricted language for use in special circumstances, which has a substantial *Gaelic*-derived vocabulary. As such, it is rarely anyone's first language. It was nevertheless reported to be the first language of 18 schoolchildren in Ealing in the data collected for the *Multilingual Capital* (2000) survey.

Shilluk

Shilluk is a Nilotic language of Sudan. One speaker of this was found among London's school population at the time of the *Multilingual Capital* (2000) survey.

Shona

====

EDUCATION Courses in **Shona** are available at *SOAS Language Centre* (7898 4888).

LANGUAGE **Shona** is a Bantuic language spoken by the majority of the population of Zimbabwe. The *Multilingual Capital* (2000) survey found that this was the language of 257 London schoolchildren, of whom 40 lived in Haringey.

Shqipe

See under **Albanian.**

Siberian

====

BUSINESS *Anglo Siberian Oil Services Ltd,* Brookfield Ho, 44 Davies St, W1K 5JA (7569 1100).

Sicilian

====

BUSINESS *Banco di Sicilia,* 25 Old Broad St, EC2N 1HT (7638 0201).

RESTAURANTS

West 1 *Cafe Bar Sicilia,* 32 Great Windmill St, W1V 7PE (7734 3015); *Il Siciliano,* 33 Dean St, W1D 4PR (7437 6024).

Hillingdon *Pizzeria Sicilia,* 134 Ryefield Ave, Uxbridge UB10 9DA (01895 254555).**Kingston** *Il Siciliano,* 129 Kingston Rd, New Malden, KT3 3NX (8336 0665).

SHOPS *La Bella Sicilia* [delicatessen], 23 Warwick Way, SW1V 1QT (7630 5914); *Sicily in your mouth,* St Martin's La, WC2.

TRAVEL *Air Sicilia,* 6 Lower Grosvenor Pl, SW1W 0EN (7592 9333).

Sidamo

Sidamo is a Cushitic language of Ethiopia. The presence of one **Sidamo**-speaking schoolchild in Ealing was recorded in the *Multilingual Capital* (2000) survey.

Sierra Leonean

====

ASSOCIATIONS *Sierra Leone Association,* 70 Elthorne Rd, Kingsbury, NW9 8BI.

GOVERNMENT *Sierra Leone High Commission,* 1st & 3rd fl, Oxford Circus Ho, 245 Oxford St, W1D 2LX (7287 9884) *and* 33 Portland Pl, W1N 3AG (7636 6483).

LANGUAGES The two main indigenous languages are **Mende** and **Temne** which together account for more than 60% of the population. Of a dozen other languages spoken natively by small minorities, only **Krio** is extensively known as a second language. **English** has official status.

Sikh

====

ASSOCIATIONS *Brent Sikh Centre,* 241 Stag La, NW9 0EF (8206 1231); *Greenwich Sikh Association,* Woolwich Temple, Calderwood St, SE18 6QW (8854 4233); *Network of Sikh Organisations,* 192 The Broadway, SW19 1RY (8540 3974); *Ramgarhia Sikh Association Community Centre (Wilmount St),* Masons Hill, SE18 6EJ (8854 4694); *13th Southall (Sikh) Scout Group,* Trojan Hall 140, Allenby Rd, Southall UB1 2HL (8578 1355); *World Sikh Council,* Unit 5 20/22, Highbury Grove, N5 2EA (7226 7070).

EDUCATION *Guru Nanak Sikh College,* Springfield Rd, Hayes UB4 0LT (8573 6085); *International School of Sikh Studies,* 26 St Thomas Drive, Pinner HA5 4SS; *Sikh University London,* 10 College Rd, Harrow HA1 1BE (8427 4880).

MEDIA & INFORMATION *Spectrum Radio,* International Radio Centre, 4 Ingate Pl, SW8 3NS (7627 4433) [Sikh religious programme broadcast 4.00-5.00 a.m. daily].

RECREATION *Sikh Sports Club,* 52 The Green, Southall UB2 4BQ (8843 9101).

RELIGION *Dashmesh Darbar* [Sikh temple], 99 Rosebery Ave, E12 6PT (8471 2204); *G N N S Jatha Sikh Temple,* 134 Martindale Rd, Hounslow TW4 7HQ (8570 0580); *Gurdwara Sikh Sangat,* 71 Francis Rd, Leyton E10 6PL (8556 4732); *North London Sikh Temple,* 136 High Rd, N11 1PG (8368 7104); *Ramgarhia Sabha Southall Sikh Temple Community Centre,* 90 St. Josephs Drive, Southall UB1 1RW (8843 1167); *Ramgarhia Sikh Association,* Masons Hill, Woolwich SE18 6EJ (8854 1786); *Ramgarhia Sikh Association,* The Sikh Temple, Golden Crescent, Hayes UB3 1AQ (8561 4084); *Ramgarhia Sikh Gurdwara Temple,* 10-16 Neville Rd, E7 9QX (8472 3738); *Sikh Gurdwara South London,* 142 Merton Rd, SW18 5SP (8874 3518); *Sikh Missionary Society UK,* 10 Featherstone Rd, Southall UB2 5AA (8574 1902); *Sikh Temple,* 27 Hibernia Rd, Hounslow TW3 3RU (8577 2793); *Woolwich Sikh Temple,* Calderwood St, SE18 6QW (8854 4233); *Singh Sabha London East,* North St, Barking IG11 8JD (8594 3940).

WELFARE *Sikh Community Care Project,* 100b, Francis Rd, E10 6PP; *Sikh Welfare and Research Trust,* 2 Chignell Pl, W13 0TJ (8579 8898).

Sindhi

====

ASSOCIATIONS *Sindhi Association of UK,* 230a Kenton Rd, Harrow HA3 8BY (8909 2151).

191

LANGUAGE *Sindhi* is an **Indic** language spoken in Sindh (Pakistan) and written in the ***Arabic*** script. The *Multilingual Capital* (2000) survey reported that there were 52 *Sindhi*-speaking schoolchildren in London, most of whom lived in Lambeth or Merton.

Singaporean

BUSINESS *Development Bank of Singapore,* 12-15 Finsbury Circus, EC2M 7BT (7628 3288).

GOVERNMENT *Monetary Authority of Singapore,* 2nd fl, 1 Minster Ct, EC3R 7AA (7256 3940); *Singapore Economic Development Board,* 30 Charles II St, SW1Y 4AE (7839 6688); *Singapore High Commission,* 9 Wilton Crescent, SW1X 8RN (7235 8315).

LANGUAGES ***Chinese, English, Malay,*** and ***Tamil*** all have official status. Several varieties of *Chinese* are spoken.

MEDIA & INFORMATION *Contact Singapore,* Charles Ho, 5-11 Regent St, SW1Y 4LR (7321 5600); *Singapore Press Holdings (Overseas) Ltd,* 102 Temple Chambers, Temple Ave, EC4Y 0DA (7353 0895); ***Singapore*** *Telecom Europe Ltd,* 5th fl, Halton Ho, 20-23 Holborn, EC1N 2JD (7404 8877).

RESTAURANTS
East Central *Singapura,* 78-79 Leadenhall St, EC3A 3DH (7929 0089); *Singapura,* 1-2 Limeburner La, EC4M 7HY (7329 1133).

South West 1 *Singapore Sam,* 1 Victoria Place Shopping Centre, Buckingham Palace Rd, SW1W 9SJ (7931 8721).

West 1 *Straits,* 5 White Horse St, W1Y 7LA (7493 3986).

Camden *Singapore Garden,* 83 Fairfax Rd, NW6 4DY (7328 5314); *Singapore Garden 2,* 154 Gloucester Pl, Camden NW1 6DT (7723 8233); *Singapore Orchard,* 279c Finchley Rd, NW3 6ND (7435 2188); *Singapore Sling,* 16 Inverness St, Camden Town, NW1 (7424 9527).

Croydon *Kelong,* 1b Selsdon Rd, South Croydon CR2 6PU (8688 0726).

Hounslow *Singapore Garden T/A,* 474 Chiswick High Rd, W4 5TT (8994 2222).

Kensington & Chelsea *Singapore Chinese,* 120-122 Holland Park Ave, W11 4UA (7727 6341); *Singapore Mandarin,* 120 Holland Park Ave, W11 4UA (7727 6341).

SPECIAL *Contact Singapore,* Charles Ho, 5-11 Regent St, SW1Y 4LR (7321 5600);

TRAVEL *Singapore Airlines,* 143 Regent St, W1B 4JB (0870 6088886); *Singapore Tourist Board,* Carrington Ho, 126-130 Regent St, W1B 5SA (7437 0033).

Sinhala (Sinhalese)

While there is a good deal of variation in the use of these two terms, ***Sinhala*** is generally preferred for the language and ***Sinhalese*** for the people who speak ***Sinhala.***

EDUCATION Courses in ***Sinhala*** are available at *SOAS Language Centre* (7898 4888).

LANGUAGE ***Sinhala*** is an **Indic** language spoken in Sri Lanka which is written in its own semi-syllabic script. Of 408 ***Sinhalese*** pupils in London schools reported in the *Multilingual Capital* (2000) survey, 96 lived in Ealing.

MEDIA & INFORMATION *Sunrise Radio Ltd,* Sunrise Ho, Sunrise Rd, Southall, UB2 4AU (8574 6666) [broadcasts in Sinhala on Thursdays 22.00-23.00].

RELIGION Most of the ***Sinhalese*** people are ***Buddhist.***

Slav

ASSOCIATIONS *British Southern Slav Society,* 24 Weymouth St, W1N 3FA (7637 0650).

Slavic

RESTAURANTS
Camden *Zamoyski Slavic Restaurant,* 85 Fleet Rd, Hampstead NW3 (7794 4792).

Slavonic

EDUCATION *School of Slavonic & East European Studies,* Senate Ho, Malet St, WC1E 7HU (7862 8575).

LANGUAGES The **Slavonic** languages, which include Croatian, Czech, Polish, Russian and Serbian among several others, have a generally similar distribution across London and are mapped collectively on Map 24 which can be viewed at <www.global-london.com/gallery>. The three boroughs with the greatest proportion of speakers of Slavonic languages are Kensington & Chelsea, Westminster, and Hammersmith & Fulham.

Slovak

EDUCATION A course in Slovak is provided by *SSEES* (7862 8634).

GOVERNMENT *Embassy of the Slovak Republic,* 25 Kensington Palace Gdns, W8 4QY (7243 0803).

LANGUAGE ***Slovak*** is a Slavonic language with official status in Slovakia. The presence of 57 ***Slovak***-speaking pupils in London was recorded in the *Multilingual Capital* (2000) survey and, of these, 13 lived in Bexley.

RELIGION Roman Catholicism is the predominant religion.

RESTAURANTS
Camden *Czech and Slovak House,* 74 West End La, NW6 (7372 5251).

SHOPS *Orbis Books,* 66 Kenway Rd, Earl's Court, SW5 0RD (7370 2210, fax 7742 7686).

TRANSLATION *Tramont Translation Management,* 57 Upper Park Rd, NW3 2UL (7692 6319; fax 7504 8638).

WELFARE *Anglo-Czechoslovak Trust,* 23 Stonefield St, Islington, N1 0HW (7278 8459);

Slovene

See under ***Slovenian.***

Slovenian (Slovene)

While there is some variation in usage, **Slovene** is generally preferred for the language and **Slovenian** for the people and other aspects of their culture.

EDUCATION A course in Slovene is provided by *SSEES* (7862 8634).

GOVERNMENT *Embassy of the Republic of Slovenia,* Suite 1, Cavendish Ct, 11-15 Wigmore St, W1U 1PJ (7495 7775).

LANGUAGE *Slovene* is a *Slavonic* language with official status in Slovenia. The *Multilingual Capital* (2000) survey found that there were 29 **Slovene**-speaking pupils in London's schools.

TRAVEL *Slovenia Tourist Board,* 49 Conduit St, W1S 2YJ (7287 7133).

Solomon Islander

GOVERNMENT *Solomon Islands Consulate,* 17-19 Springfield Rd, Wimbledon SW19 7AL (8296 0232).

TRAVEL *Solomon Airlines,* 200 Buckingham Palace Rd, SW1W 9TA (7707 4587).

Somali

ASSOCIATIONS *Anglo-Somalia Society,* Praxis, Pott St, E2 0EF (7729 7985); *Barnet Somali Community Group,* Barnet Multicultural Centre, Algernon Rd, NW4 3TA (8202 3957); *British Somali Community,* 43 Carol St, NW1 0HT (7916 9527); *Croydon Somali Community Association,* Cornerstone Ho, Willis Rd, Croydon CR0 2XX (8665 0921); *Ealing Somali Welfare & Cultural Association,* 20 Merrick Rd, Southall UB2 4AU (8843 0439); *East London Somali Association,* 728 Romford Rd, E12 6BT (8553 0615); *East London Somali Association,* 2a Streatfield Ave, East Ham E6 2LA (8470 6484); *Edmonton Somali Social Club,* 1 Angel Corner Parade, Fore St, N18 2QH (8807 6444); *Puntland Society,* Somali Community Association, 365 Brixton Rd, SW9 7DA (7737 0985); *Somali Association,* 12 School Rd, Hounslow TW3 1QZ (8577 3226); *Somalia Woman Association,* Community Centre, Greenleaf Rd, E17 6QQ (8503 7121); *Somali Community and Cultural Association,* Selby Centre, Selby Rd, Tottenham N17 8JL (8885 1307); *Somali Cultural Revival & Employment Training Association,* 84 Mile End Rd, E1 4UN (7423 9619); *Somali Enfield Community and Cultural Association,* Community Ho, 311 Fore St, Edmonton, N9 0PZ (8373 6207); *Somaliland Lewisham Community,* 1 Kingfisher Sq, SE8 5TW (8692 5640); *Somali Luncheon Club,* 3 Beresford Sq, SE18 6BB (8855 7900); *Somali Community Cultural Association,* 12 Wickford St, E1 5QN (7790 1171); *Somali Parents' & Children's Association,* 2 Thorpe Close, Ladbroke Grove, W10 5XL (8960 5879); *Somali Speakers' Association,* 12 Barnsbury Rd, N1 0HB (7833 3757); *Somali Women's Association,* 51 Hugon Rd, SW6 3ER (7610 6741); *Waltham Forest Somali Women Association,*

William Morris Community Centre, Greenleaf Rd, Walthamstow E17 6QQ (8503 7121).

EDUCATION Mother tongue education in **Somali** is available for young children in many places in London; visit <www.resourceunit.com> for full details. Courses in **Somali** for adults are provided by *SOAS Language Centre* (7898 4888) and several local authorities – visit <www.floodlight.co.uk> for details.

Somalia Teaching Group, Training Centre, Walpole Pl, SE18 6TP (8854 0697); *Somali Caring & Education Association,* Palingswick Ho, King St, W6 9LP (8563 0320); *Somali Cultural Revival & Employment Training Association,* 84 Mile End Rd, E1 4UN (7423 9619); *Somali Educational & Cultural Projects,* Bow House Business Centre, Bow Rd, E3 2SE (8980 5948); *Somali Educational & Cultural Projects,* Community Centre, Hadleigh St, E2 0LD (8981 4486); *Somali Education Development Centre,* Deptford Family Resource Centre, Deptford Strand, SE8 3BA (8692 4448); *Somali Woman Training & Development,* 32 Ryan Close, SE3 9II (8319 8957); *Somali Woman Training & Development Organisation,* 36 Walpole Pl, SE18 6II (8316 7266).

GOVERNMENT There is currently no **Somali** diplomatic representation in London.

LANGUAGES Somali is the first language of the overwhelming majority of the population of Somalia. Both **Arabic** and **Somali** have official status. A small minority (less than 1%, but well represented in London) speak a **Bantuic** language, **Barawan**.

Somali is a *Cushitic* language spoken in Somalia (and also in parts of Kenya, Ethiopia and Djibouti). According to the *Multilingual Capital* (2000) survey, there were then 8,203 Somali-speaking London schoolchildren. Map 25, showing the distribution of Somali-speaking schoolchildren across London can be viewed at <www.global-london.com/gallery>.

MEDIA & INFORMATION *Somali Community Information Centre,* 1 Chippenham Mews, W9 2AN (7286 9144); *Somali Community Information Centre,* 453a Harrow Rd, W10 4RG (8964 4540).

MOTORING *Somali Motor Insurance,* 61 Brick La, E1 6QL (7247 0366).

RESTAURANTS

Greenwich *Kah Somali Cafe,* 21 Anglesea Rd, SE18 6EG (8316 4440).

Wandsworth *Mooge Somali Coffee,* 8 Amen Corner, Mitcham Rd, SW17 (8682 3117).

SHOPS *Alkheyr Cash & Carry,* 2 Broadway, W7 (8567 6700); *Somali Halal,* 162 Stoke Newington High St, Stoke Newington N16 7JL (7241 3390).

SPECIAL *Somali Consortium,* Cardinal Heenan Centre, High Rd, IG1 1QP (8262 2988);

WELFARE *Barnet Somali Community Group,* 156 Golders Green Rd, NW11 8HE (8731 7588); *British Somali Southwark Refugee Council,* 24 Mayward Ho, 94 Benhill Rd, Camberwell SE5 7QX (7277 1800); *Consortium of Somali Refugee Associations,* 27 Northolt Rd, Harrow HA2 0LH (8864 9677); *Craig Park Youth Centre (Black Youth Projects),* Asha Urhobo, Lawrence Rd, Edmonton N18 2HN (8803 8292) [languages: **French, Somali,** English]; *Ealing Somali Welfare & Cultural Association,* 20 Merrick Rd, Southall UB2 4AU (8843 0439); *Ealing Somali Welfare & Cultural Association,* 71 Northcroft Rd, W13 9SS (8840 7413); *East London Somali Youth & Welfare Centre,* Oxford Ho, Derbyshire St, E2 6HG (7729 9892); *International Somali Community Trust,* 85a Upper Clapton Rd, Clapton E5 9BU (8806 8757); *Iskawaran Somali Mental Health Trust,* Park Parade, NW10 4HT (8838 6163); *Islington Somali Community Association,* 65 Halliford St, Islington N1 3HF (7354 9895); *Lambeth Somali Community Association,* 13 Stockwell Rd, SW9 9AU (7738 6372); *Lewisham Somali Community Centre,* Etta Community Hall, Gosterwood St, SE8 5PB (8694 6065); *Lewisham Somali Community Organisation,* Parker Ho, 144 Evelyn St, Deptford SE8 5DD (8694 6065); *Princess Royal Trust Carers Centre Tower Hamlets (Somali),* 21 Brayford Sq, E1 0SG (7791 3464); *Somali Action Forum,* St Johns Church Centre, Albert Rd, North Woolwich E16 2JB (7473 0961); *Somali Advice & Guidance,* 117 Mansford St, Bethnal Green E2 6LX (7729 8188); *Somali Advisory Bureau,* Main Capital Ho, Craven Rd, W2 3XP (7262 9845); *Somali Bajuni Welfare Association,* 270 Ley St, Ilford IG1 4BP (8478 4608); *Somali Bravanese Action Group,* 340 High Road Leyton, E10 5PW (8558 2204); *Somali Care & Cultural Society,* 513a High Rd, Wembley HA0 4AG (8795 0657); *Somali Carers Project,* 3 Wellington St, SE18 6NZ (8854 8665); *Somali Caring & Education Association,* Palingswick Ho, King St, W6 9LP (8563 0320); *Somali Community Centre,* Dalby St, Kentish Town NW5 3NQ (7482 2211); *Somali Community of North West London,* 2 Empire Way, Wembley HA9 0TL (8900 0607); *Somali Community of North West London,* 373 Greenrigg Walk, Wembley HA9 9UL (8908 6274); *Somali Cultural Centre Camden,* 107 Kingsgate Rd, NW6 2JH (7372 6101); *Somali Cultural Revival & Employment Training Association,* 84 Mile End Rd, E1 4UN (7423 9619); *Somali Mental Health Council Project,* 5 Westminster Bridge Rd, SE1 7XW (7633 0729); *Somali Refugee Action Group,* Macbean Centre, Macbean St, Woolwich SE18 6LW (8317 3447); *Somali Welfare and Development Centre,* 16 Solomon Ave, Edmonton N9 0SQ; *Somali Welfare Association,* Canalside Ho, 383 Ladbroke Grove, W10 5AA (8968 1195); *Somali Welfare*

Organisation, 12 Donovan Ct, Exton Crescent, Willesden NW10 8DB (8961 4694); *Somali Woman's Refugee Centre,* Priory Centre, Acton La, Chiswick W4 5NA (8752 1787); *Somali Woman Training & Development,* 32 Ryan Close, SE3 9II (8319 8957); *Somali Woman Training & Development Organisation,* 36 Walpole Pl, SE18 6II (8316 7266); *Somali Women Association,* 326 High Rd, Ilford IG1 1QP (8491 8091); *Somali Womens Support Group,* 1-4 Beresford Sq, Woolwich SE18 6BB (8855 0512); *Southwark Somali Refugee Council,* 24 Mayward Ho, Benhill Rd, Camberwell SE5 7NA (7277 1770).

Sotho

> **Sotho** is the root found in the names of the country, **Lesotho**, and the language, **Sesotho**. See these entries for more information.
>
> The **Sotho** people live in South Africa as well as **Lesotho**. In **South African** usage, a distinction is made between Northern Sotho (= Sepedi) and Southern Sotho (= **Sesotho**). Since no speakers of Sepedi were found in London, it is omitted from this listing.

South African

BARS & NIGHT-CLUBS *Springbok Bar*, 20 Bedford Street WC2 (7379 1734).

BUSINESS *Real Estate Corporation of South Africa Ltd,* Royal Exchange, EC3P 3DN (7283 7101); *Anglo American Corporation of South Africa Ltd,* 19 Charterhouse St, Clerkenwell EC1N 6QP (7404 1944).

GOVERNMENT *High Commission for the Republic of South Africa,* South Africa Ho, Trafalgar Sq, WC2N 5DP (7451 7299).

LANGUAGES The most important first languages of the population are given by *Whitaker's Almanack 2002* as: **Zulu** 22.9%, **Xhosa** 17.9%, **Afrikaans** 14.4%, Sepedi 9.2%, **English** 8.6%, **Setswana** 8.2%, and **Sesotho** 7.7%.

MEDIA & INFORMATION *New South Africa*, South Africa Ho, Trafalgar Sq, WC2N 5DP (7930 4488); *South African Morning Newspapers*, 32 Hatton Gdns, EC1N 8DL (7405 3742); *South African National Magazine*, 7 Bury Pl, WC1 (7404 3216); *South African Times*, 16 Baldwin Gdns, EC1 (7405 6148).

RELIGION Most of the population is **Christian** but there are **Hindu, Jewish,** and **Muslim** minorities.

RESTAURANTS
Hounslow *Dumela* (formerly *Springbok Café*), 43 Devonshire Rd, W4 (8742 3149).

SHOPS *Cape Province Wine,* 77 Laleham Rd, Staines TW18 2EA (01784 451860); *St Marcus Fine Foods,* 1 Rockingham Close, Priory Lane, SW15 (8878 1898); *Wines of South Africa Ltd,* 5 Alt Grove, SW19 4DZ (8947 7171).

TRAVEL *Inter Air (South Africa),* 200 Buckingham Palace Rd, SW1W 9TA (7707 4581); *South Africa Fly Drives & Tours,* Sunvil Ho, Upper Sq, Isleworth TW7 7BJ (8232 9777); *South African Airways,* St Georges Ho, 61 Conduit St, W1B 4JE (7312 5005).

South American

BUSINESS *South American Trading,* 15 West Park, Eltham SE9 4RZ (8851 8487).

RESTAURANTS See also the names of individual South American nationalities and under **Latin American.**

Islington *La Piragua,* 175 Upper St, Islington N1 (7354 2843).

TRAVEL *South America Aviation,* Old Manor Yard, 240 Earls Court Rd, SW5 9AA (7370 3203); *South America with Austral Tours,* 20 Upper Tachbrook St, SW1V 1SH (7233 5384); *South American Experience Ltd,* 47 Causton St, SW1P 4AT (7976 5511).

Southern African

BUSINESS *Southern Africa Business Association,* Queensland Ho, 393 Strand, WC2R 0LT (7836 9980).

EDUCATION *Canon Collins Educational Trust for Southern Africa,* Unit 22, The Ivories, 6 Northampton St, N1 2HY (7354 1462).

RELIGION *Southern Africa Church Development Trust,* 51 Heathside, Esher KT10 9TD (8398 9638).

TRAVEL *Cedarberg Southern African Travel,* 16A High St, Hampton TW12 2SJ (8941 1717);

WELFARE *Action for Southern Africa,* 28 Penton St, Islington N1 9SA (7833 3133); *Community HEART (for Southern Africa),* 88 Hornsey Rd, N7 7NN (7700 3886); *Southern Africa Church Development Trust,* 51 Heathside, Esher KT10 9TD (8398 9638).

South Indian

LANGUAGES The principal South Indian languages are **Kannada, Malayalam, Tamil** and **Telugu.**

RELIGION While Hinduism is the main religion, there are substantial Christian (especially in Kerala and Tamil Nadu) and Muslim minorities.

RESTAURANTS See also **Keralite** and **Tamil.**

South West 1 *Quilon,* Crowne Plaza Hotel, 41 Buckingham Gate, SW1 (7821 1899); *Woodlands* [vegetarian], 37 Panton St, SW1 (7839 7258).

West 1 *Ragam,* 57 Cleveland St, W1 (7636 9098); *Rasa Samudra,* 5 Charlotte St, W1 (7637 0222).

West Central *Madras T/A,* 17 Earlham St, WC2H 9LL; *Malabar Junction,* 107 Great Russell St, WC1B 3NA (7580 5230).

Brent: *Gana Cafe and Restaurant,* 24 Ealing Rd, Wembley HA0 4TL (8903 7004); *Kovalam,* 12 Willesden La, NW6 7SR (7625 4761); *Palm Beach,* 17 Ealing Rd, Wembley (8900 8664).

Camden: *Diwana Bhelpoori House* [vegetarian], 121-123 Drummond St, NW1 2HL (7387 5556); *Madras Valley T/A,* 123 Castlehaven Rd, Kentish Town NW1 8SJ; *Ravi Shankar,* 133-135 Drummond St, Euston, NW1 2HL (7388 6458).

Kensington & Chelsea *Malabar,* 27 Uxbridge St, W8 7TQ (7727 8800);

Newham: *Madras,* 305 High St North, Manor Park E12 6SL; *Ronak* [vegetarian], 317 Romford Rd, Forest Gate E7 9HA (8534 2944);

Richmond: *Pallavi,* Unit 3, Cross Deep Ct, Heath Rd, Twickenham, TW1 4QJ (8892 2345).

Tower Hamlets *Cafe Spice Namaste,* 16 Prescot St, Tower Hill, E1 (7488 9242).

Wandsworth: *Cafe Spice Namaste,* 247 Lavender Hill, SW11 (7738 1717); *Radha Krishna,* 86 Tooting High St, SW17 0RN (8767 3462).

Spanish

The word *Spanish* is applied to all citizens of Spain, and to almost everything and anything associated with that country. It is also the usual word in English for the Castillian language (*Castellano*) which has by far the largest number of speakers in Spain but which also has official status in all the following territories: Argentina, Bolivia, Chile, Colombia, Costa Rica, Cuba, Dominican Republic, Ecuador, El Salvador, Guatemala, Honduras, Mexico, Nicaragua, Panama, Paraguay, Peru, Puerto Rico, Uruguay, Venezuela. Each of these Latin American countries has its own distinct culture and cuisine – see the corresponding nationality names.

ACCOMMODATION *Cubits Spanish Properties,* 26 York St, W1H 1FE (7935 7970); *Propertunities,* 249 Cranbrook Rd, Ilford, IG1 4TG (8518 1155); *Spanish Homes Magazine,* 116 Greenwich South St, SE10 8UN (8469 4381).

ARTS *Music Theatre in Spanish Ltd,* 16th Floor, 125 London Wall, EC2Y 5AE; *Spanish Guitar Centre,* 36 Cranbourn St, WC2H 7AD (7240 0754).

ASSOCIATIONS *Anglo-Spanish Society,* Woodsyre, Sydenham Hill, SE26 6SS (8761 0955);

Hispanic and Luso Brazilian Council, Canning Ho, 2 Belgrave Sq, SW1X 8PJ (7235 2303).

BARS & NIGHTCLUBS *Barcelona Tapas Bar & Restaurant,* 481 Lordship Lane, SE22 8JY (8693 5111); *Barcelona Tapas Bar & Restaurant,* 15 St. Botolph St, EC3A 7DT (7377 5111); *Barcelona Tapas Bar & Restaurant,* 1a Bell Lane, E1 7LA (7247 7014); *Bar Gansa,* 2 Inverness St, NW1 7HJ (7267 8909); *Bar Lorca,* 175 Stoke Newington High St, Stoke Newington, N16 (7275 8659); *Bar Madrid,* 4 Winsley St, W1N (7436 4649); *Bradley's Spanish Bar,* 42 Hanway St, W1T 1UP (7636 0359); *Finca,* 96 Pentonville Rd, N1 9JB (7837 5387) [tapas and salsa classes]; *Las Fuentes,* 36 High St, Purley, CR8 2AA (8763 1983).

BUSINESS *Banco Bilbao Vizcaya Argentaria (BBVA),* 100 Cannon St, EC4N 6EH (7623 3060); *Banco Bilbao Vizcaya Argentaria (BBVA),* 142 Brompton Rd, SW3 1HY (7225 2415); *Banco Bilbao Vizcaya Argentaria (BBVA),* Market Towers, 1 Nine Elms La, SW8 5NU (7720 6751); *Banco Español de Crédito,* 33 King St, EC2V 8EH (7606 4883); *Banco Pastor,* Clutha Ho, 10 Storeys Gate, SW1P 3AY (7233 3043); *Banco Popular Español,* 19b Craven Rd, W2 3BP (7402 7393); *Banco Rural Europa SA,* 1st floor, 127 Cheapside, EC2V 6LJ (7600 6660); *Banco Sabadell,* Sabadell Ho, 120 Pall Mall, SW1Y 5EA (7321 0020); *Banco Santander Central Hispano,* 100 Ludgate Hill, EC4M 7RE (7332 6900); *Caja Bilbao Bizkaia,* Warnford Ct, 29 Throgmorton St, EC2N 2AT (7628 0441); *Spanish Chamber of Commerce,* 5 Cavendish Sq, W1M 0DP (7637 9061); *Spanish Chamber of Commerce,* 1-7 Harley St, W1N 1DA (7291 4542); *Spanish Economic & Commercial Office,* International Ho, 66 Chiltern St, W1U 4LS (7486 0101); *Spanish Promotion Centre,* 23 Manchester Sq, W1U 3PY (7935 6140).

EDUCATION *Anglo-Spanish Nursery School,* 152 Clapham Manor St, SW4 6BX (7622 5599); *Colegio Español Cañada Blanch* (Spanish Day Nursery), 317 Portobello Rd, W10 5SZ (8969 2664) provides bilingual Spanish/English education at both primary and secondary level. Mother-tongue education for young children in *Spanish* is available in several other locations in London; for details visit <www.resourceunit.com>. A huge range of Spanish courses for adults is provided by universities and local education authorities in London. See *Floodlight* and its website at <www.floodlight.co.uk> for details.

The *Education and Science Office of the Spanish Embassy* is located at 20 Peel St, W8 7PD (7727 2462).

The *Instituto Cervantes,* 102 Eaton Sq, SW1W 9AN (7201 0753) is a centre for teaching, and for training teachers of, the Spanish language. It also organises such things as academic events, theatrical performances and the visual arts, <www.cervantes.es>.

English & Spanish Studies, Macmillan Ho, 96 Kensington High St, W8 4SG (7937 3110); *French and Spanish à la Carte,* 97 Revelstoke Rd, SW18 5NL (8946 4777); *French and Spanish Language Holidays,* 13 Crouch Hall Rd, N8 8HT (8348 2400); *Anglo-Spanish Nursery School,* 152 Clapham Manor St, SW4 6BX (7622 5599); *Living Spanish,* 10 Barley Mow Passage, W4 4PH (8747 2018); *Peques Spanish Nursery School,* Tasso Baptist Church, 138 Greyhound Rd, W6 8NS (7385 0055); *Spanish Education Office,* Spanish Embassy, 20 Peel St, W8 7PD (7727 2462); *Spanish for Life,* 47 Runnymede, SW19 2PG (8543 4303); *Spanish Institute,* 317a Portobello Rd, W10 5SY (8969 2664); *Spanish Tuition,* 85 Royal Cres, Ruislip, HA4 0PL (8841 1017); *Spanish University,* 317 Portobello Rd, W10 5SZ (8969 8926).

EMPLOYMENT *Spanish Angels,* 31 Bushfield Crescent, Edgware, HA8 8XQ (8958 7003); *Spanish Labour Office,* 20 Peel St, W8 7PD (7221 0098).

FREIGHT *Spanish Couriers,* Building 209, Epsom Sq, Hounslow, TW6 2BU (8564 9977); *Spanish Express,* Unit 5a, Ascot Rd, Feltham, TW14 8QH (01784 240997).

GOVERNMENT *Cultural Office of the Embassy of Spain,* 39 Chesham Pl, SW1X 8SB (7201 5522); *Spanish Commercial Office,* International Ho, 66 Chiltern St, W1M 2LS (7486 0101); *Spanish Consulate,* 20 Draycott Pl, SW3 2RZ (7589 8989); *Spanish Embassy,* 24 Belgrave Sq, SW1X 8QA (7235 5555); *Spanish Embassy Naval Attaché,* Flat 4, 3 Hans Crescent, SW1X 0LN (7589 5731).

LANGUAGE *Spanish* (Castillian, *Castellano*) is the principal language of Spain and also has official status in about 20 other countries (see the introduction to this section for the full list). *Spanish* ranks as the 4th most extensively spoken language in the world with some 450m speakers (of whom it is the first language of about 400m). It is a Romance language. The London boroughs with the highest proportion of *Spanish*-speakers are Kensington & Chelsea, Westminster, and Lambeth. Other languages of Spain are *Basque, Catalan,* and *Galician* - see separate entries for these.

LEGAL *Hispanic Services,* 81a Praed St, W2 1NS (7706 0398).

MEDIA & INFORMATION Spanish newspapers are widely available in newsagents and at newsstands in central London. The website <www.cec-spain.org.uk> provides links to other websites, newspapers, directories, universities with a Spanish department, etc.

Spanish National Radio, 46 Clifton Gardens, W9 1AU (7286 8137); *Spanish News Agency,* 5 Cavendish Sq, W1M 0DP (7636 5226); *Spanish Television,* 16 Berners St, W1T 3LN (7631 3706).

MOTORING *Spanish Inter-Motors*, 25 Bolton Rd, N18 1HN (8884 3585).

RECREATION There is a growing number of Latin/*Salsa* type bars and clubs all over London, both of independent and chain status. Quite a few of these clubs hold salsa dance classes.

RELIGION *Hispanic Church,* 39 Brendon St, W1H 5HD (7723 9224); *Spanish & Portuguese Jews Congregation,* 9 Lauderdale Rd, W9 1LT (7286 2153); *Spanish & Portuguese Synagogue,* 2 Ashworth Rd, W9 1JY (7289 2573); *Spanish & Portuguese Synagogue,* 8 St. James Gdns, W11 4RB (7603 7961); *Spanish & Portuguese Synagogue Communal Hall,* 8 St James Gdns, W11 4RB (7603 7961); *Spanish Catholic Chaplaincy,* 47 Palace Ct, W2 (7229 8815); *Spanish Evangelical Church,* 116 Bramley Rd, W10 6SU (8964 1520).

RESTAURANTS

East Central *Barcelona Tapas Bar,* Unit 1, 15 St Botolph Street, EC3A 7DT (7377 5111); *Barcelona Tapas Bar, Well Court,* 13 Well Court, EC4M 9DN (7329 5111); *Fuego,* 1a Pudding Lane, EC3R 8LB (7929 3366); *Fuego @ City Circle,* 10 Basinghall St, EC2B 5BQ (7600 1633); *Gaudi Restaurante,* 63 Clerkenwell Rd, EC1M 5RR (7608 3220); *Las Brasas,* 63a Clerkenwell Rd, EC1R 5DH (7250 3401); *Leadenhall Wine & Tapas Bar,* 27 Leadenhall Market, EC3V 1LR (7623 1818); *Moro,* 34 Exmouth Market, EC1R 4QE (7833 8336) [Spanish / North African]; *Pintxos,* 1 Shakespeare Tower, Barbican, EC2Y 8DR (7256 2900).

South East 1 *Mesón Don Felipe,* 53 The Cut, SE1 8LF (7928 3237).

South West 1 *Flamenco,* 54 Pimlico Rd, SW1 8LP (7730 4484); *Goya Pimlico,* 34 Lupis Street, SW1 (7976 5309).

West 1 *Cafe España,* 63 Old Compton St, W1 (7494 1271); *Café Med,* Paramount Ho, 162-170 Wardour St, W1 3AT (7434 3287); *Costa Dorada,* 47 Hanway St, W1 (7631 5117); *El Pirata,* 5 Down St, W1 7DR (7491 3810); *La Rueda,* Wigmore St, W1H 9DR (7486 1718); *Navarro's,* 67 Charlotte St, W1P 1LA (7637 7713); *Six International Tapas Bar Restaurant,* 6 Upper James St, W1 3HF (7434 2294); *Spanish Club,* 5 Cavendish Sq, W10DP (7436 2553).

West Central *Arts Theatre Tapas Bar,* 6/7 Great Newport St, WC2H7JA (7240 8855); *Cigala,* 54 Lamb's Conduit St, WC1N 3LW (7405 1717); *El Barco Latino,* Temple Pier, Victoria Embankment, WC2 2PP (7379 5496); *Salsa,* 96 Charing Cross Rd, WC2 0JG (7379 3277).

Brent *Mesón Bilbao,* 33 Malvern Rd, NW6 5PS (7328 1744).

Bromley *El Molino,* 251 Beckenham Rd, Beckenham, BR3 4RP (8659 2622).

Camden *Andurina,* 298 Kentish Town Rd, NW5 (7482 3616); *El Parador,* 245 Eversholt St, NW1 (7387 2789); *Gansa,* 2 Inverness St, NW1 (7267 8909); *Mexican & Spanish T/A,* 102 Fleet Rd, NW3 2QX (7284 2619).

Croydon *Capricho,* 64-66 London Rd, Croydon, CR0 (8667 1788); *Flamingo,* 7 South Norwood Hill, SE25 6AA (8653 3759); *Picasso,* 910 London Rd, Thornton Heath, CR7 (8684 0049); *Las Fuentes,* 36 High St, Purley CR8 (8763 1983).

Greenwich *El Pirata Tapas Bar,* 58-62 Tranquil Vale, Blackheath, SE3 0BN (8297 1770).

Hammersmith & Fulham *El Metro,* 10 Metropolitan Station Arcade, Beadon Rd, W6 (748 3132); *Iberica Tapas Bar,* 295 New Kings Rd, SW6 4RE (7371 5939); *La Terraza Restaurant & Tapas Bar,* 53 Fulham Broadway, SW6 (7385 9272); *Los Reyes,* 217 King St, W6 (8563 7007).

Haringey *La Bota,* 31 Broadway Parade, Crouch End, London N8 9DB (8340 3082).

Islington *Finca,* 96-98 Pentonville Rd, N1 9JB (7837 5387) [tapas and salsa classes]; *La Primavera,* 82 Highbury Park, N5 2XE (7704 9187).

Kensington & Chelsea *Albero Grana,* 89 Sloane Ave, SW3 3DX (7225 1049); *Café Madrid Tehran Restaurant,* 3 Hammersmith Rd, W14 8XJ (7602 3247); *Café Med,* 2 Hollywood Rd, SW10 9HY (7823 3355); *Cambio de Tercio,* 163 Old Brompton Rd, SW5 (7244 8970); *El Blasón,* 89 Blacklands Terrace, SW3 2SP (7823 7383); *El Cid 2,* 11 Beauchamp Pl, SW3 1NQ (7589 6361); *El Gaucho,* 125 Sydney St, SW3 6NR (7376 8514); *La Rueda,* 642 Kings Road, SW6 (7384 2684); *Lomo,* 222 Fulham Rd, SW10 9NB (7349 8848).

Lambeth *Carmen,* 6 Clapham Common South Side, SW9 (7622 6848); *El Rincón Latino,* 148 Clapham Manor St, SW4 6BX (7622 0599); *Finca Tapas Bar,* 185 Kennington Lane, SE114EZ (7735 1061); *La Paella,* 96 Streatham Hill, SW2 4RD (8674 1519); *La Rueda, Clapham,* 66-68 Clapham High St, SW4 7UL (7627 2173); *Manjualda,* 176a Wandsworth Rd, SW8 (7622 7526); *Rebato's,* 169 South Lambeth Rd, SW8 1XW (7735 6388).

Southwark *Barcelona Tapas Bar, Lordship Lane,* 481 Lordship Lane, SE22 8JY (8693 5111); *Café El Paso,* 127 Lordship Lane, SE22 (8693 7034); *Mesón Don Felipe,* 53 The Cut, SE1 8LF (7928 3237); *Viva España,* 29-33 Camberwell Church St, SE5 8TR (7252 6055).

Sutton *El Nido,* 79 Manor Rd, Wallington, SM6 (8647 0940).

Tower Hamlets *Baradero Restaurant & Tapas Bar,* Turnberry Quay, off Pepper Street, Crossharbour, E14 9RD (7537 1666); *Barcelona Tapas Bar, Bell Lane,* 1 Bell Lane, E1 7LA (7247 7014); *Mesón Los Barriles,* 8a Lamb Street, E1 (7375 3136); *Mesón Los Barriles Take Away,* 15 New Rd, E1 1HE.

Wandsworth *Castilla Bar,* 74 Battersea Rise, SW11 (7738 9597); *La Concha,* 31 Balham High Rd, SW12 (8675 3072); *La Mancha,* 32 Putney High St, SW15 1SQ (8780 1022); *San Miguel's,* Molasses Ho, Plantation Wharf, SW11 3TN (7801 9696).

Westminster *Don Pepe,* 99 Frampton St, NW8 (7262 3834); *El Efes,* 94 Bishops Bridge Rd, W2 5AA (7229 3536); *Hyde Park Tapas Restaurant,* 28 Sussex Pl, W2 2TH (706 8083); *Los Remos,* 38A Southwick St, W2 (7723 5056); *San Miguel's,* 256 Edgware Rd, W2 1DS (7262 1709).

SHOPS Spanish food and ingredients are now widely available in large supermarkets. Specific ingredients such as *colorante* (colouring for paella), Spanish short grained rice and Christmas sweets/cakes are obtainable in Spanish supermarkets or Mediterranean delicatessens.

Brindisa, Central Line Stand, Borough Market, SE1 (8772 1600); *Casa Pepe,* 89 High Rd, N2 (8444 9098); *Continental Touch,* 10 Hornsey Rd, N7 (7609 6878); *De la Fuente,* 288 Portobello Rd, W10 (8960 5687); *Products from Spain Ltd,* 89 Charlotte St, W1P 1LB (7580 2905); *Products from Spain Ltd,* Unit 18, Cumberland Ave, NW10 7RT (8965 7274); *R Garcia & Son,* 250 Portobello Rd, W11 (7221 6119); *Spanish Food Imports,* 66 Station Rd, E7 0AD (8503 1977); *Spanish Pots,* 265 Mitcham La, Streatham, SW16 6QB (8664 6602).

SPECIAL *Hispanic & Luso Brazilian Council,* 2 Belgrave Sq, SW1X 8PJ (7235 2303).

TRANSLATION *Alvárez Spanish and French Translations,* 3 The Crest, 21 Ellington Rd, Muswell Hill, N10 3DE (8352 9785); *Lourdes Reece (Spanish),* 8 High Rd, South Woodford, E18 2QL (8989 6825); *Portuguese & Spanish Translations & Interpreting,* 94 Inverness Terrace, W2 3LD (7727 1884); *S de Domingo Spanish Translations,* 70 Ewell Rd, Surbiton, KT6 6JA (8399 3556); *Spanish & French Interpreter Services,* 53 Dale St, W4 2BY (8995 7647); *Spanish and French Solutions,* 14 St Augustines Ct, Mornington Rd, E11 3BQ (8539 4457); *Spanish & Italian Translation & Interpreting Services,* Flat 1, 109 Kings Ave, SW4 8EN (8671 0447); *Spanish & Portuguese Translation,* 32 Longmoore St, SW1V 1JF (7834 8262); *Spanish Interpreting & Translation,* 54c Camden St, NW1 0DX (7383 3971); *Spanish Interpreting & Translation,* 34 Parr Court, New North Rd, N1 7JD (7608 3039); *Spanish Language Services,* 12 Bridge Wharf, 156 Caledonian Rd, N1 9UU (7713 8013); *Spanish Speaking Services Ltd,* 138 Eversholt St, NW1 (7388 1732); *Spanish Technical Translations,* 73 Queens Gate, SW7 5JT (7244 8906); *Spanish Translation Bureau,* 15 Bridge Wharf, 156 Caledonian Rd, N1 9UU (7713 8013); *Spanish Translations,* Flat 8, 3 The Mansions, Earls Court Rd, SW5 9BW (7259 2968); *Spanish Translations,* 59 Bute Gdns, W6 7DX (7603 6931); *Spanish Translations,* 18 Colet Gdns, Hammersmith W14 9DH (8563 7110); *Spanish Translation Service,* 19 Compton Terrace, N1 2UN (7704 6969); *Spanish Translation Services,* 32a Sunset Rd, Denmark Hill, SE5 8EA (7733 4028).

TRAVEL *Hidden Spain,* 63 Grays Inn Rd, WC1X 8TL; *Iberia International Airlines of Spain,* 11 Haymarket, SW1Y 4BP (7921 3054); *Spanish Affair,* 5-7 Humbolt Rd, W6 8QH (7385 8127); *Spanish Aviation Services Ltd,* 72 Lupus St, SW1V 3EJ (7821 5801); *Spanish Rail Service,* Berkeley Square Ho, Berkeley Sq, W1J 6BS (7629 4543); *Spanish Tourist Office,* 22-23 Manchester Sq, W1U 3PY (7486 8077); *Spanish Travel Service,* 138 Eversholt St, NW1 1BL (7387 5337).

WELFARE *Hogar Español,* 47 Palace Ct, W2 4LS (7229 8815); *Spanish Youth Service,* 116 Bramley Rd, W10 6SU (8968 5152); *Spanish & Portuguese Jews Home for the Aged,* Edinburgh Ho, 36-44 Forty Av, Wembley, HA9 8JP (8908 4151); *Spanish Day Nursery,* 45 St Georges Drive, SW1V 4DG (7828 1417).

Sri Lankan

ASSOCIATIONS *Sri Lanka Islamic Association,* Broadway Bldg, Boston Rd, W7 3TT (8840 3270).

BUSINESS *Bank of Ceylon,* 1 Devonshire Sq, EC2M 4UJ (7377 1888).

FREIGHT *Ceylon Shipping Corporation,* Clairville House, 27 Oxendon St, SW1Y 4EL (7839 7555).

GOVERNMENT *Sri Lanka High Commission,* 13 Hyde Park Gdns, W2 2LU (7262 1841).

LANGUAGES The national languages are **Sinhala** and **Tamil**. First-language speakers of **Sinhala** outnumber those of **Tamil** by about 3 : 1.

MEDIA & INFORMATION See under **Sinhala**.

RELIGION More than two-thirds of Sri Lankans are **Buddhist**; the remaining 31% are **Hindu**, **Muslim**, or **Christian**.

Redbridge Buddhist Cultural Centre [Theravada (Sri Lanka)], 9 Balfour Rd, Ilford, IG1 4HP (8478 8286); *Sri Lanka Islamic Association*, 7 Broadway Bldg, Boston Rd, W7 3TT (8840 3270).

RESTAURANTS
Barnet: *Prince of Ceylon*, 39 Watford Way, Hendon NW4 3JH (8202 5967).

Brent: *Cinnamon Gardens*, 42-44 Ealing Rd, Wembley HA0 4TL (8902 0660), *Gana*, 24 Ealing Rd, Wembley HA0 4TL (8903 7004); *Palm Beach*, 17 Ealing Rd, Wembley (8900 8664).

Ealing: *Sigiri Sri Lankan Cuisine*, 161 Northfield Avenue W13 9QT (8579 8000).

Tower Hamlets: *Laxeiro*, 95 Columbia Rd, E2. (7729 1147).

SHOPS *Bismillah Butchers*, 141 Ealing Rd, Wembley (8903 4922); *Lihiniya*, 70 Cricklewood Broadway, NW2 3EP (8208 2658) [arrack and other Sri Lankan specialities].

SPECIAL [not yet categorized] *Forum on Sri Lanka*, 33 Islington High St, N1 9LH (7278 1665) [development organization]; *Lanka 2000 (UK) Ltd*, 41 Springrice Rd, SE13 6HS (8852 5450); *Uni Lanka*, 1412 London Rd, SW16 4BZ (8764 1664).

TRAVEL *Sri Lanka (Ceylon) Tourist Board*, Clareville Ho, 26-27 Oxendon St, SW1Y 4EL (7930 2627); *Sri Lanka Holidays*, 4 Kingly St, W1B 5PE (7439 0944); *Sri Lanka Tours*, 2nd floor, 4 Kingly St, W1B 5PE (7434 3921).

Sudanese

ASSOCIATIONS *South Sudanese Community Association*, 73 Hornsey Rd, Holloway, N7 6DJ (7607 4292); *Sudan Archaeological Society*, c/o Department of Egyptian Antiquities, British Museum, Great Russell St, WC1B 3DG (7323 8306); *Sudanese Community & Information Centre*, 1 Thorpe Clo, Ladbroke Grove, W10 5XL (8964 0973). *Sudanese Community Association and Information Centre*, 1 Thorpe Place, W10 5XL (8964 0973); *Sudan People Support Association*, 15a Churton St, SW1V 2LY (7834 9578);

BUSINESS *Sudanese Tractor Co UK Ltd*, Unit 5 Calico Ho, Clove Hitch Quay, Battersea, SW11 3TN (7924 6001).

GOVERNMENT *Sudan Embassy*, 3 Cleveland Row, SW1A 1DD (7839 8080).

LANGUAGES **Arabic** is the official language and the first language of about half the population. The remaining population speak between them more than 100 different languages.

MEDIA & INFORMATION *Sudan Democratic Gazette*, P O Box 2295, W14 0ND; *Sudan Focus*, P O Box 3751, N12 8TE (7263 8005); *Sudan Human Rights Voice*, BM Box 8238, WC1N 3XX (fax 75871298).

RELIGION Islam is the state religion but there are many Christians in the south of the country.

RESTAURANTS
Kensington & Chelsea *Mandola Sudanese Cafe*, 139-141 Westbourne Grove, W11 2RS (7229 4734).

TRAVEL *Sudan Airways*, 31-32 Rutland Gate, South Kensington SW7 1PG (7584 2400).

WELFARE *South Sudan Women's Concern*, 51 Sheepcote Rd, Harrow HA1 2JL (8427 1832); *Sudanese Victims of Torture Group*, Park Business Centre, Kilburn Park Rd, NW6 5LF (7625 8055); *Sudan Relief & Rehabilitation*, Interchange Studios, Dalby St, Kentish Town NW5 3NQ (7209 5859).

Sufi

ARTS & CULTURE *Khayaal Theatre Co*, 39 Northview Rd, Luton LU2 7LF (01582 535840).

RELIGION *London Sufi Centre*, Beauchamp Lodge, 2 Warwick Crescent, W2 6NE (7266 3099).

Swahili

ASSOCIATIONS *Darji Mitra Mandal of the UK*, The Darji Pavilion, Oakthorpe Road, Palmers Green N13 5HY (contact: Mr Raman V Tailor 8361 5981) [languages: **Gujarati, Hindi, Swahili**, English].

EDUCATION Mother-tongue education for young children in **Swahili** is available in several locations in London; for full information visit <www.resourceunit.com>. Courses for adults in **Swahili** are provided by *SOAS Language Centre* and a few local education authorities in London – see <www.floodlight.co.uk> for details.

LANGUAGE **Swahili** (full name, *Kiswahili*) is a Bantuic language with about 55m speakers but it is the first language of only about 6m of these (Dalby 1999). It has official status in Kenya, Tanzania and Uganda, and is widely known as a second or additional language in territories adjoining these and in the Comoro islands.

The *Multilingual Capital* (2000) survey recorded **Swahili** as the language of 1,042 pupils in London schools, of whom 191 were in Redbridge. However, these figures included those for **Barawan**, spoken in the extreme south of Somalia, which is closely related to **Swahili** but is perhaps better treated as a separate language.

RELIGION The church of *St Anne & St Agnes*, Gresham St, EC2 (7606 4986) holds occasional services in **Swahili**.

WELFARE *Afro - Care Umbrella*, c/o Andy Hammond, 45 North Sq, Edmonton Green N9 0HY (8372 5528) [languages: **French, Igbo, Swahili**, English].

Swati

See under **Swazi.**

Swazi (Swati)

GOVERNMENT *High Commission of the Kingdom of Swaziland*, 20 Buckingham Gate, SW1E 6LB (7630 6611).

LANGUAGE *Swazi* (also frequently called *Swati*) is a Bantuic language with official status in Swaziland which is also spoken in adjoining areas of South Africa. It is closely related to **Zulu.** In the *Multilingual Capital* (2000) survey, the presence of eight **Swazi**-speaking schoolchildren was noted, three of whom lived in Barnet.

MEDIA & INFORMATION *Focus on Swaziland*, 14B Westbourne Grove, W2 (7727 1755).

TRAVEL *Royal Swazi Airlines*, 200 Buckingham Palace Rd, SW1W 9TA (7707 4067).

Swedish

ACCOMMODATION *London & Stockholm Properties Ltd*, 691, High Rd North, Finchley N12 0DA (8446 0453).

BUSINESS *Invest in Sweden Agency*, 11 Montagu Pl, W1H 2AL (7723 2000); *Svedberg of Sweden Ltd*, 717 Fulham Rd, SW6 5UL (7371 9214); *Swedish Chamber of Commerce for the UK*, 5 Upper Montagu St, W1H 2AL (7224 8001); *Swedish Conservatory Co*, Suite 8, Skillion Business Centre, Harbet Rd, Lea Valley Trading Estate, N18 (8345 5224); *Swedish Farmers*, Shakespeare House Business Centre, 168 Lavender Hill, SW11 5TG (7801 6215); *Swedish Trade Council*, 73 Welbeck St, W1G 0AL (7935 9601).

EDUCATION *Swedish School Society*, 82 Lonsdale Rd, Barnes SW13 9JS (8741 1751).

Courses in Swedish are provided by *Morley College* (7928 8501), the *University of Westminster* (7911 5000), and a few local education authorities in London. See *Floodlight* or visit its website at <www.floodlight.co.uk> for details.

GOVERNMENT *Embassy of Sweden*, 11 Montagu Pl, W1H 2AL (7917 6400).

HEALTH & BEAUTY **Dental care** *Dr Lundquist (Bernhardson)*, 77 Harley St, W1G 8QZ (7486 0237); *Swedish Implant Centre*, 2 Harley St, W1G 9PB (7580 9286).

LANGUAGE **Swedish** is a Germanic language with official status in Sweden and Finland (although the first language of only a minority of the population of the latter). 181 **Swedish**-speaking schoolchildren in London were identified in the *Multilingual Capital* (2000) survey and, of these, 37 were in Richmond.

MOTORING *German & Swedish Car Centre Ltd*, 284-286 Wightman Rd, N8 0LT (8341 7570); *German & Swedish Car Parts Ltd*, 843 Harrow Rd, NW10 5NW (8960 8182); *German & Swedish Car Parts Ltd*, 69-75 Robin Hood Way, SW15 3PW (8547 3101); *Swedish Car Centre*, 193-199 Northfield Ave, W13 9QU (8567 4432, 8579 2969);

Swedish Motor Services, 77 Sutherland Rd, E17 6BH (8503 3559).

RELIGION *Swedish Church*, 6-11 Harcourt St, W1H 4AG (7723 5681); *Swedish Seaman's Church*, 120 Lower Rd, SE16 2UB (7237 1956).

RESTAURANTS

West 1 *Garbo's*, 42 Crawford St, W1 (7262 6582).

Islington *Anna's Place*, 90 Mildmay Park, Highbury, N1 (7249 9379).

SHOPS *Holmes Place Health Clinic* [Swedish massage], Plaza Shopping Centre, 120 Oxford St, W1N 9DP (7436 6165); *Ikea*, 255 North Circular Rd, NW10 (8208 5600) [furniture, but also Swedish foods such as crispbreads and meatballs];

Original Swedish Wheat Heat Co [wheat-filled cushion for the relief of pain], Heddon Ho, 149 Regent St, W1R 8BA (7437 3332); *Swedish Affair Ltd* [delicatessen], 32 Crawford St, W1H 1PL (7224 9300).

TRAVEL *Swedish Travel & Tourism Council*, 11 Montagu Pl, W1H 2AL (7870 5600).

Swiss

ASSOCIATIONS *Swiss Benevolent Society*, 83 Marylebone High St, W1U 4QW (7935 1303).

BUSINESS *Swiss Connection Co. Ltd*, 88-90 North Hill, N6 4RL; *Swiss Exchange Swx*, 34th floor, 1 Canada Sq, E14 5AA (7864 4300); *Swiss Re-Insurance Company U.K Ltd*, 71-77 Leadenhall St, EC3A 2PQ (7623 3456); *Swiss Re Life & Health*, Moorfields Ho, Moorfields, EC2Y 9AL (7628 7070).

BUSINESS *Gerner Swiss Co Ltd* [**clock & watch repairs & parts**], 123 Clerkenwell Rd, EC1R 5DB (7405 3992); *Pernet's Swiss Patisseries*, 94 Streatham Hill, SW2 4RD (8674 6086); *Swiss Japan Marketing Ltd* [accessories-fashion], 64 Middlesex St, E1 7EZ (7247 3549); *Swiss Watch Centre*, 153 Grays Antique Market, 58 Davies St, W1K 5JF (7495 7404); *Swiss Watch Co.*, 15 Devonshire St, W4 2EU (8994 4567); *Swiss Wine Exporters Association*, Swiss Centre, 10 Wardour St, W1D 6QF (7851 1731).

FREIGHT *Anglo-Swiss Maritime Co. Ltd*, 12 Well Ct, EC4M 9DW (7329 4897).

GOVERNMENT *Embassy of Switzerland*, 16-18 Montagu Pl, W1H 2BQ (7616 6000).

LANGUAGES Four languages have official status (with percentage of first language speakers in brackets): **German** (63.7%), **French** (19.2%), **Italian** (7.6%), and Romansch (0.6%). Note that **Swiss German** is a distinctive Germanic language, very different from the standard variety of German.

RELIGION *Swiss Church in London (Eglise suisse de Londres)*, 79 Endell St, WC2H 9AJ (7836 1418).

TRAVEL *Swiss Ski Company Ltd*, 10 Barb Mews, W6 7PA (7371 1555).

Sylheti

ACCOMMODATION *Sylhet Housing Co-operative Ltd,* 46 Myrdle St, Whitechapel E1 1HL.

BUSINESS *New Sylhet Holdings plc*, 5 3 Mayow Rd, Forest Hill SE23 2XH; *Sylhet & Company,* 6 Commercial St, E1 6LP (7247 7331); *Sylhet Tea Co Ltd,* 91 Salford Rd, Brixton SW2 4BE.

EDUCATION A course in spoken Sylheti is available in Tower Hamlets (8983 1047).

LANGUAGE *Sylheti* is an Indic language, related to *Bengali,* which is spoken in the Sylhet region of Bangladesh. See *Bengali* for further information.

RESTAURANTS
Brent *Sylhet Tandoori Express,* 314 Preston Rd, HA3 0QH (8385 1001).

Tower Hamlets *Sylhet Select Tandoori Indian T/A,* 46 Tiddworth Rd, Bow E3 4XH (8983 3500).

SHOPS *Sylhet Bazar*, 99 Kingsley Rd, Hounslow TW3 4AH (8572 1414); *Sylhet Cash & Carry,* 58 Fieldgate St, E1 1ES (7247 2367); *Sylhet Grocers & Halal Meat*, 160 Green St, Forest Gate E7 8JT (85481793); *Sylhet Sweet Shop,* 109 Hanbury St, Whitechapel E1 5JQ (7247 0563);

SPECIAL *Greater Sylhet Council UK,* 100 Mile End Rd, Whitechapel E1 4UN (7702 8120).

TRAVEL **Local** *New Sylhet Cars,* 127 Brick La, E1 6SB (7739 6060); *Sylhet Mini Cab,* 1 4 6 Church Rd, Manor Park E12 6HL (8514 6666).

WELFARE *Greater Sylhet Development & Welfare Council UK,* 100 Mile End Rd, E1 4UN (7702 8120).

Syrian

ASSOCIATION *Syrian Arab Association,* 8 Comeragh Rd, W14 9HP (7381 9788).

GOVERNMENT *Syrian Embassy,* 8 Belgrave Sq, SW1X 8PH (7245 9012).

RELIGION Islam is the religion of the majority of the population,

TRAVEL *Syrian Arab Airlines,* Birkett Ho, 27 Albemarle St, W1S 4BJ (7493 2851).

Szechuan

RESTAURANTS
Barnet *The Wing Ki* [Peking/Szechuan], 29 Burnt Oak Broadway, HA8 5LD (8205 0904).

Camden *Cheng-Du,* 9 Parkway, NW1 7PG (7485 8058); *Gung-Ho Szechuan,* 332 West End La, NW6 1LN (7794 1444).

Enfield *Kam Pung* [Thai / Malyasian / Szechuan], 879 Green Lanes, N21 2QS (8360 8998).

Hounslow *Szechuan City,* 4 Douglas Rd, Hounslow TW3 1DA (8569 4322).

Islington *Beijing* [Cantonese / Peking / Szechuan], 205 Holloway Rd, N7 8DL (7609 1312).

T

Tagalog

Tagalog (also called **Pilipino**) is a Hesperonesic language ranked 31st in the world with 40m speakers. 1,649 **Tagalog**-speaking pupils in London were identified in the *Multilingual Capital* (2000) survey, of whom 272 were in Kensington & Chelsea.

Taiwanese

ACCOMMODATION *British Taiwan Cultural Institute,* Mortimer Mansion, 73 Mortimer St, W1N 7TB (7436 2610).

BUSINESS *Bank of Taiwan,* Evergreen Ho, Euston Rd, NW1 2BN (7388 3800); *Taiwan Trade Centre Ltd,* 29 Wilson St, EC2M 2SJ (7638 4676).

GOVERNMENT *Taipei Representative Office in the UK – Consular Services,* 50 Grosvenor Gdns, SW1W 0EB (7396 9152); *Taipei Representative Office – Cultural Division,* Clarebell Ho, Cork St, W1X 1PB (7494 2500). *Cultural Division Taipei Representive Office in the UK,* Suite 3, Mortimer Mansion, 73-75 Mortimer St W1W 7SQ (7436 5888).

HEALTH & BEAUTY *Formosa Centre,* 26 Wigmore St, W1H 9DF (7224 2884).

LANGUAGES **Mandarin Chinese** has official status but a variety of **Min-nan** Chinese often termed "Taiwanese" is the first language of most of the population.

RESTAURANTS
Hammersmith & Fulham *Formosa Chinese Cuisine,* 1 Walham Green Ct, Fulham Rd, SW6 2DH (7381 0735).

Tajiki

GOVERNMENT *Honorary Consulate of Tajikistan,* 33 Ovington Sq, SW3 1LJ.

LANGUAGE **Tajiki** is an **Iranic** language, closely related to **Farsi,** spoken in Tajikistan, Uzbekistan and Kirghizstan. This language has occasionally been reported among London schoolchildren in recent years but none were reported at the time of the *Multilingual Capital* (2000) survey.

TRAVEL *Tajikistan International Airlines,* 154 Horn La, Acton W3 6PG (8993 8885).

Tamil

ACCOMMODATION *Tamil Community Housing Association Ltd,* 10 Hatherley Mews, Walthamstow E17 4QP (8520 2042).

ASSOCIATIONS *Downham Tamil Association,* Goldsmith Community Centre, Castillon Rd, SE6 1QD (8695 9118); *London Tamil Sangam,* 369 High St North, E12 6PG (8471 7672); *Waltham Forest Thamil Sangam,* 364 Forest Rd, Walthamstow E17 5JF (8925 2969).

EDUCATION *Tamil Refugee Centre - Enfield Education & Training Centre,* 65 North Sq, Lower Edmonton N9 0HY (8345 6301); *Tamil Refugee Training and Education Centre,* 221 Forest Rd, Walthamstow E17 6HE (8527 4471).

Mother-tongue education for young children is available in **Tamil** in more than a dozen locations in London; for full information visit <www.resourceunit.com>. *SOAS Language Centre* provides a course in **Tamil** for adults (7898 4888).

LANGUAGE **Tamil** is a Dravidian language, written in its own semi-syllabic script, with some 70m speakers, mainly in India (Tamil Nadu), Sri Lanka, Malaysia and Singapore. In the *Multilingual Capital* (2000) survey, this was found to be the language of 3,641 London schoolchildren, of whom 629 lived in Brent. Map 27, showing the areas of London where the largest numbers of **Tamil**-speakers live, can be viewed at <www.global-london.com/gallery>.

MEDIA & INFORMATION *IBC Tamil Media Ltd,* 10 Wyvil Rd, SW8 2TG (7787 8000); *Tamil Broadcasting Corporation,* 168 Greenford Rd, Harrow HA1 3QS (8864 0909); *Spectrum Radio,* International Radio Centre, 4 Ingate Pl, SW8 3NS (7627 4433) [broadcasts in Tamil 19.00-21.00 daily]; *Sunrise Radio Ltd,* Sunrise Ho, Sunrise Rd, Southall, UB2 4AU (8574 6666) [broadcasts in Tamil 22.00-23.00 Mon.-Wed.]; *Tamil Information Centre,* 720 Romford Rd, Manor Park E12 6BT (8514 6390).

RELIGION *Edmonton Tamil Church of God,* 34 Dickens La, Upper Edmonton N18 1PH (8245 8584); *Southall Tamil Church of God,* 3 North Rd, Southall UB1 2JQ (8571 2156).

RESTAURANTS See also **South Indian.**
Camden *Madras Valley T/A,* 123 Castlehaven Rd, NW1 8SJ (7482 6460);
Newham *Madras,* 305 High St, E12 6SL (8503 5255).

SHOPS *Guru Books,* 106 Drummond St, NW1 2HN; *Rathy* [jewellers], 28 Ealing Rd, Wembley.

WELFARE *International Tamil Foundation,* 816 Garratt La, Tooting SW17 0LZ (8672 7222); *Tamil Refugee Action Group,* 111 High Holborn, WC1V 6JS (7405 4152); *Tamil Refugee Action Group,* 449-451 High Rd, NW10 2JJ (8459 9070); *Tamil Refugee Centre,* Community Ho, 311 Fore St, Lower Edmonton N9 0PZ (8373 6249); *Tamil Rehabilitation Organisation,* 1079 Garratt La, SW17 0LN (8682 3567); *Tamil Rehabilitation Organisation,* 79 Hoe St,

Walthamstow E17 4SA (8520 5876); *Tamil Relief Centre*, Community House, 311 Fore St, Edmonton, N9 0PZ (8373 6249).

Tangale

Tangale is a Bauchic language spoken in Nigeria. At the time of the *Multilingual Capital* (2000) survey, there were seven *Tangale*-speaking London schoolchildren, all living in Ealing.

Tanzanian

ASSOCIATIONS *Britain-Tanzania Society*, 14b Westbourne Grove Terrace, W2 5SD (7727 1755).

BUSINESS *Tanzania Trade Centre*, 80 Borough High St, Southwark SE1 1LL (7407 0566).

GOVERNMENT *Tanzania High Commission*, 43 Hertford St, W1Y 8DB (7499 8951).

LANGUAGES About 100, for the most part Bantuic, languages are spoken in Tanzania but only two of these - *Kigwe* and *Swahili* - are the first languages of as much as 10% of the population. However, *Swahili* is known as a second language by most of the rest of the population and has joint official status with *English.*

MEDIA & INFORMATION *Bulletin of Tanzania Affairs*, 14B Westbourne Grove Terrace, W2 5SD (7727 1755).

TRAVEL *Tanzania Experience*, Linburn Ho, 342 Kilburn High Rd, NW6 2QJ (7624 5128).

WELFARE *Tanzanian Affairs*, 14b Westbourne Grove Terrace, Bayswater W2 5SD (7727 1755).

Taoist

ACCOMMODATION *Buddhist And Taoist Housing Association Ltd*, 41 King St, Plaistow E13 8DB.

ASSOCIATIONS *Buddhist and Taoist International Association*, Flat 1, 21-22 Gerrard St, W1V 7LA; *Tien Yi Confucius & Mencius Tao De Association*, 63 Wolvercote Rd, Abbey Wood SE2 9TG.

HEALTH & BEAUTY *Zen School of Shiatsu & Healing Tao Centre*, 188 Old St, EC1V 9BP (7490 4740); *Zen Shiatsu & Healing Tao*, 19 Phipp St, EC2A 4NP (7739 9916).

Telugu

Telugu is a Dravidic language of South India (Andhra Pradesh) with some 70m speakers which is written in its own semi-syllabic script. 13 London schoolchildren were recorded as *Telugu*-speaking at the time of the *Multilingual Capital* (2000) survey.

Temne

Temne is a Melic language spoken in Sierra Leone. At the time of the *Multilingual Capital* (2000) survey, there were reported to be 62 *Temne*-speaking London schoolchildren.

Teo-Chiu

See under **Min-nan.**

Teso

See under its full name, **A-Teso.**

Texan

BUSINESS *Texaco group of companies*, Westferry Circus, Canary Wharf, E14 (7719 3000), *Texas Pacific Group (Europe) Ltd*, Stratton Ho, Stratton St, W1 (7544 6500).

RESTAURANTS
South West 1 *Texas Embassy Cantina*, 1 Cockspur St, W1 (7925 0077).
Hounslow *Texas Lone Star Saloon*, 50 Turnham Green Terrace, W4 (8747 0001).
Kensington & Chelsea *Texas Lone Star Saloon*, 154 Gloucester Rd, SW7 (7370 5625).

Thai

BARS & NIGHT-CLUBS *Vow Thai Wine Bar & Restaurant*, 53 Cleveland St, W1T 4JH (7580 7608).

BUSINESS *Bangkok Bank Public Co Ltd*, 61 St Mary Axe, EC3A 8BY (7929 4422); *Bank of Thailand*, London Representative Office, 8th fl, 1 Angel Ct, Moorgate EC2R 7HJ (7606 2703); *Sinn Thai Import/Export Ltd*, 75 The Broadway, SW19 1QE (8540 2099); *Thai Commercial Office*, 11 Hertford St, W1Y 7DX (7493 5749); *Thai Farmers Bank Public Co Ltd*, 80 Cannon St, EC4N 6HL (7623 4975).

EDUCATION Mother-tongue education for young children is available in *Thai* in at least one location in London; for full information visit <www.resourceunit.com>. Courses in *Thai* for adults are provided by SOAS Language Centre (7898 4888).

GOVERNMENT *Royal Thai Embassy*, 29-30 Queens Gate, SW7 5JB (7589 2944); *Royal Thai Embassy*, 11 Hertford St, W1Y 7DX (7493 5749).

HEALTH & BEAUTY *Muay Haircut*, 237 Old Brompton Rd, Earl's Ct 7373 7862); *Thai Rose Medicines & Therapies*, 58 Paddington St, W1U 4JA (7935 2117); *Thai Sauna*, 262 Langham Rd, N15 3NP (8888 7667).

LANGUAGE *Thai* is a Daic language with some 45m speakers. It has official status in Thailand and is also spoken in adjacent parts of Laos. It is written in its own semi-syllabic script. The presence of 346 *Thai*-speaking London schoolchildren was recorded at the time of the *Multilingual Capital* (2000) survey.

MEDIA & INFORMATION *New York London Bangkok News Publisher Ltd*, 80 Great Eastern St, EC2A 3JL.

K O Kick-boxing & Thai Boxing, 41 Broadley Terrace, NW1 6LQ (7289 5849); *Lateef Thai Boxing Club,* 30 Eastcote La, Harrow, HA2 8BP (8621 0991); *LMTC Thai Kickboxing Club,* Victoria Rd, Ruislip, HA4 0JE (8845 6010); *Vipers Clubs Thai boxing tuition* (07765471073): *Vipers Central London,* The 52 Club, 52 Gower St, WC1; *Vipers East London,* Kelmscott Leisure Centre, Markhouse Rd, E17; *Vipers South London,* Haxman Sports Centre, Carew St, SE5 9DF.

RELIGION The great majority of **Thai** people is **Buddhist** but there are small **Christian** and **Muslim** minorities.

RESTAURANTS

East Central *City Thaicoon,* 61 Carter La, EC4V 5DY (7236 2634); *Lakorn,* 197 Rosebery Ave, EC1R 4TJ (7837 5048); *Rising Sun,* 61 Carter La, EC4V 5DY (7236 2634); *Silks and Spice,* The Arcade, Liverpool St, EC2M 7PN (7626 1155); *Silks and Spice,* Temple Ct, Queen Victoria St, EC4N 4UJ (7248 7878); *Sri Siam,* 85 London Wall, EC2M 7AD (7628 5772); *Sri Thai,* Bucklersbury Ho, 3 Queen Victoria St, EC4N 4TQ (7827 0202); *Thonburi,* 9-10 The Arcade, Liverpool St, EC2M 7PN (7623 5750); *Yamo,* 9-11 Cursitor St, EC4A 1LL (7405 3729).

South East 1 *Kwan,* Unit 1, Hays Galleria, Tooley St, SE1 2HD (7403 7373); *Orchid,* 101 Westminster Bridge Rd, SE1 7HR (7620 2384); *Sino Thai,* 127 Lower Marsh, SE1 7AE (7401 9702); *Suchard,* 102 Tooley St, SE1 2TH (7357 6381); *Thai Silk,* 103-107 Waterloo Rd, SE1 8UL (7633 9886).

South West 1 *Bangkok Brasserie,* 48-49 St James's St, SW1A 1JT (7629 7565); *Blue Jade,* 44 Hugh St, SW1V 4EP (7828 0321); *Muang Thai Cafe & Restaurant,* 22 Charlwood St, SW1V 2DY (7592 9584); *Pad Thai Restaurant,* 4 Panton St, SW1Y 4DL (7930 4474); *Thai Square,* 21-24 Cockspur St., Trafalgar Square, SW1Y 5BN (7839 4000); *Victoria Thai Restaurant,* 322 Vauxhall Bridge Rd, SW1V 1AA (7931 0935); *Vong* [Thai/French] Wilton Pl, SW1 (7235 1010).

West 1 *Bahia* [Thai/Malaysian/Japanese], 28 Frith St, W1V 5TL (7434 3881); *Bahn,* 21a Frith St, W1V 5TS (7437 8504); *Bangkok Brasserie,* 48-49 St. James's St, SW1A 1JT (7629 7565); *Lotus,* 80 Cleveland St, W1T 6NE (7580 7213).

Pun Kum, 31 Windwill Street, W1 (7636 0810); *Sawasdee,* 26-28 Whitfield St, W1P 5RB

(7631 0289); *Silks and Spice* [Thai/Malaysian], 23 Foley St, W1P 7LA (7636 2718); *Sing Thong,* 64 George St, W1U 7EF (7224 0165); *Soho Thai,* 27 St. Anne's Ct, W1V 3AW (7287 2000); *Sri Siam,* 16 Old Compton St, W1V 5PE (7434 3544); *Straits,* 5 Whitehorse St, W1J 7LQ (7493 3986); *Thai Cottage,* 34 D'Arblay St, W1F 8EU (7439 7099); *Thai Pavilion,* 42 Rupert St, Piccadilly W1D 6DN (7287 6333); *Thai Pot,* 5 Princes St, W1B 2LB (7499 3333); *Thai Terrace T/A,* 24 Old Bond St, W1X 3DA: *Thai West,* 10-12 Crawford St, W1H 1PE (7224 1367); *Vow Thai Wine Bar & Restaurant,* 53 Cleveland St, W1T 4JH (7580 7608).

West Central *Athitaya,* 71 Red Lion St, WC1R 4NA (7242 5251); *Bangkok (London) Ltd T/A,* 4th fl, 46-47 Chancery La, WC2A 1BA; *Ben's Thai Restaurant,* 48 Red Lion St. WC1R 4PF (7404 9991); *City Thai Cuisine,* 17 New North St., WC1N 3PJ (7404 0758); *Manorom Thai T/A,* 16 Maiden La, WC2E 7NA (7240 4139); *Neal's,* 16a Shorts Gdns, WC2H 9AU (7240 1083); *Paolina Thai restaurant,* 181 King's Cross Rd, WC1 (7278 8176); *Thai Express,* 302 Regent St, W1R 5AL (7636 1145); *Thai Garden Café,* 32 Museum St, WC1A 1LH (7323 1494); *Thai Metro,* 14 Charlotte St, W1T 2LX (7436 4201); *Thai Pin,* 7 Maiden La, WC2E 7NA (7497 0999); *Thai Pot,* 1 Bedfordbury, WC2N 4BP (7379 4580); *Thai Pot Express,* 148 Strand, WC2R 1JA (7497 0904).

Barnet *Ben's Thai Restaurant,* Elephant Inn, 283 Ballards La, N12 8NR (8492 0201); *Go Thai,* 3 Vivian Ave, NW4 3UT (8202 7215); *Lemon & Lime,* 634 Finchley Rd, Golders Green, NW11 7RR (8458 2012); *Manora,* 757 Finchley Rd, NW11 8DL (8455 9497); *Sapphire,* 59 Station Rd, HA8 7HX (8905 6487); *Thai Concept,* Western Parade, Great North Rd, New Barnet, EN5 1AD (8441 4003); *Thai Cuisine (Five Stars) T/A,* 634 Finchley Rd, Golders Green NW11 7RR.

Bexley *Thai Dynasty,* 75 Bellegrove Rd, Welling, DA16 3QA (8303 9552).

Brent: *Flying Elephant,* 37 Chamberlayne Rd, NW10 3NB (8960 9044); *Lanna,* 273 Neasden La, NW10 1QJ (8450 7900); *Ploy,* 7 Craven Park Rd, NW10 8SE (8965 3260); *Sino Thai,* 9 High Rd, NW10 2TE (8459 1622); *Taste of Thai,* 273 Neasden La., NW10 1QJ (8208 2000); *Tong Kanomtha,* 833 Harrow Rd, NW10 5NH (8964 5373).

Bromley *Spices,* 226 High St, BR1 1PQ (8464 8932).

Camden *Bangkok Thai Café*, 17-18 New College Parade, NW3 5EP (7722 9605); *Galangal Thai Canteen,* 29 Parkway, NW1 7PN (7485 9933); *Jasmine Café*, 4 Castlehaven Rd, NW1 8QU (7482 3785); *Lumpini*, 96 West End La, NW6 2LU (7624 8897); *Silks and Spice* [Thai/Malaysian], 28 Chalk Farm Rd, NW1 8AG (7267 5751); *Thai Pepper*, 115 Finchley Rd, NW3 6HY (7722 8470); *Thai café T/A,* 53 Fortess Rd, NW5 1AD (7485 3262); *Tip Top*, 77 Heath St, NW3 6TP (7433 3455).

Croydon *Mantanah*, 2 Orton Buildings, SE25 4UD (8771 1148); *Sweet Basil/Burapa,* 69 Westow Hill, SE19 1TX (8766 7424); *Tamnag Thai*, 50-52 Westow Hill, SE19 1RX (8761 5959).

Ealing *Alisa Thai Cafe & Restaurant*, 2 The Broadway, Gunnersbury La, W3 8HR (8992 3160); *Bangkok Broadway*, 157 Uxbridge Rd, West Ealing W13 9AU (8567 9474); *Butlers Thai Cuisine*, 14 St. Marys Rd, W5 5ES (8840 7893); *Sala-Thai,* 182 South Ealing Rd W5 4RJ (8758 2239); *Thai Beach,* 88 Old Oak La, Acton W3 7DA (8749 9414); *Thai Café*, 134, Uxbridge Rd, W7 3SL (8566 1252); *Thai Garden*, Mandeville Rd, UB5 5HG (8841 8400); *Thai Restaurant,* 57 New Broadway, W5 5AH (8567 5577); *Thai Spice House*, 125 Uxbridge Rd, West Ealing, W13 9AU (8840 2475).

Enfield *Jim Thompson's at The Green Dragon*, 889 Green Lanes, N21 2QP (8360 0005); *Kam Pung*, 879 Green Lanes, N21 2QS (8360 8998); *Thai Phimarn*, 64 Aldermans Hill, N13 4PP (8447 8213).

Greenwich *Kum Luang*, 326-328 Creek Rd, SE10 9SW (8293 4011); *Laicram*, 1 Blackheath Grove, SE3 0AT (8852 4710); *Thai Chung*, 8 Nelson Rd, Greenwich SE10 9JB (8858 8588); *21st Century Chinese & Thai Cuisine*, 556 Westhorne Ave, SE9 6DR (8850 6888).

Hackney *Yum Yum*, 30 Stoke Newington Church St, N16 0LU (7254 6751).

Hammersmith & Fulham *Blue Elephant*, 4-6 Fulham Broadway, SW6 (7385 6595); *Esarn Kheaw*, 314 Uxbridge Rd, W12 7LJ (8743 8930); *Jasmine*, 16 Goldhawk Rd, W12 8DH (8743 7920); *Jim Thompson's Flaming Wok,* 243 Goldhawk Rd, W12 8EU (8748 0229); *Jim Thompson's Oriental Bar Restaurant & Bazaar*, 617 Kings Rd, Fulham, SW6 2ES (7731 0999); *Latymers Thai Café*, 157 Hammersmith Rd, W6 8BS (8741 2507); *Mae Nam*, 35 Fulham High St, SW6 3JH (7610 6977); *Pataloong*, 95 Fulham Palace Rd, W6 8JA (8741 7453); *Reunthai*, 100 Fulham Palace Rd, W6 9PL (8748 4881); *Sabai*, 270-272, King St, Hammersmith W6 9HW (8748 7363); *Somtam,* 131 Askew Rd, W12 9AU (8749 9030); *Ta-Khai*, 100 North End Rd, W14 9EX (7386 5375); *Tasty Thai*, 355a Lillie Rd, SW6 7PA (7381 8085); *Thai City*, 130 King St, W6 0QU (8846 9010); *Thai Elephant*, 311 New Kings Rd, SW6 4RF (7736 8833); *Thai Magic Touch*, 139a

King St. W6 9JG (8748 9482); *Typhoon Taverns*, 243 Goldhawk Rd, W12 8EU (8748 0229).

Haringey *Cats*, 79 Stroud Green Rd, N4 3EG (7281 5557); *J D Thai Café*, 510a High Rd, N17 9JF (8808 7083); *O's Thai Café*, 10 Topsfield Parade, N8 8PR (8348 6898); *Thai Café*, 3 Muswell Hill, N10 3TH (8883 0035); *Thai Café*, 10 Toxfield Pde, N8 8PR (8348 6898); *Thai Garden,* 6 Topsfield Parade, Middle La, Crouch End, N8 8PR (8340 8124); *Thai Orient,* 10 Turnpike La, N8 0PT (8888 4488).

Harrow *Bangkok*, 498 Kenton La, HA3 8RD (8909 2488); *Panom*, 262 High Rd, HA3 7BB (8863 1144); *Thai Castle*, 28 Broadwalk, HA2 6ED (8427 4732).

Hounslow *Bridge Inn -Thai Restaurant*, 457 London Rd, TW7 5AA (8568 0088); *Kala*, 313 Chiswick High Rd, W4 4HH (8995 0546); *Silks and Spice* [Thai/Malaysian], 95 Chiswick High Rd, W4 2EF (8994 7773); *Thai Bistro*, 99 Chiswick High Rd, W4 2ED (8995 5774); *Thai Villa*, 9 York Parade, TW8 9AA (8569 7223); *Turnham Green Café*, 57 Turnham Green Terrace, W4 1RP (8994 3839).

Islington *Black Cobra*, 10 Brecknock Rd, N7 0DD (7700 1292); *Tuk Tuk*, 330 Upper St, Islington N1 2XQ (7226 0837); *Pin-Petch*, 39 Newington Green Rd, N1 4QT (7354 8545); *Rabieng*, 143 Upper St, N1 1QY (7226 2014); *Siamese Twins*, 110 Junction Rd, N19 5LB (7281 4926); *Thai Jen*, 10-11, Clerkenwell Green, EC1R 0DP (7490 4041); *Tuk Tuk*, 330 Upper St, N1 2XQ (7226 0837).

Kensington & Chelsea *Addie's Thai Café*, 121 Earls Court Rd, SW5 9RL (7259 2620); *Bangkok*, 9 Bute St, SW7 3EY (7584 8529); *Blue Lagoon*, 284 Kensington High St, W14 8NZ (7603 1231); *Busabong*, 1a Langton St, SW10 0JL (7352 7517); *Busabong Tree,* 112 Cheyne Walk, SW10 (7352 7534); *Churchill Arms*, 119 Kensington Church St, W8 (7792 1246); *Khun Akorn*, 136 Brompton Rd, SW3 1HY (7225 2688); *Churchill Thai Kitchen*, 119 Kensington Church St, W8 7LN (7792 1246); *Market Thai*, 240 Portobello Rd, W11 1LL (7460 8320); *Noi's*, 343 Kensington High St, W8 6NW (7603 3613); *Orchid*, 1 De Vere Gdns, W8 5AR (7823 8793); *Papaya Tree*, 209, Kensington High St, W8 6BD (7937 2260); *Patara Thai Cuisine*, 9 Beauchamp Pl, SW3 1NQ (7581 8820); *Patara,* 181 Fulham Rd, SW3 6JN (7351 5692); *Pin-Petch*, 4-12 Barkston Gdns, SW5 0EN (7370 1371); *Siam Garden*, 5a Hogarth Pl, SW5 0QT (7370 4371); *S.P Patara*, 9 Beauchamp Pl, SW3 1NQ (7581 8820); *Sugar Hut*, 374 North End Rd, SW10 (7386 8950); *Thai bar & restaurant*, 93 Pelham St, SW3 (7584 4788); *Thai Break*, 30 Uxbridge St, W8 7TA (7229 4332); *Thai Break T/A*, 35 Abingdon Rd, W8 6AH; *Thai on the River*, Chelsea Wharf 15, Lots Rd, SW10 0QJ (7351 1151); *Thai Silk*, 112 Cheyne Walk, SW10 0DJ (7351 5232); *Thai Taste*, 130 Cromwell Rd, SW7 4ET (7373 1647); *Thai Terrace*, 14 Wrights La, W8 6TF (7938 2227); *Tonghai*, 206 Fulham Rd, SW10 9PJ (7352 8664); *209 Thai Restaurant*, 209 Kensington High St, W8 6BD (7937 2260).

Lambeth *Blue Bay*, 28 Brixton Water La, SW2 1PE (8244 3100); *Oriental Cottage*, 401 Coldharbour La, SW9 8LQ (7274 2020); *Pepper Tree*, 19 Clapham Common South Side, SW4 7AB (7622 1758); *Sopar*, 105 Southampton Way, SE5 7SX (7703 8983); *Southeast*, 26 Westow Hill, SE19 1RX (8670 6222); *Thai Orchard*, 76 Clapham High St, SW4 7UL (7627 1588); *Thai Silk*, 1-5 Windmill Row, SE11 5DW (7735 9338); *Thai Thani*, 6 Gleneagle Rd, SW16 6AB (8769 7529).

Lewisham *Mathurose*, 92 Kirkdale, SE26 4BG (8699 1184); *Overland Thai Café*, 106 Foxberry Rd, SE4 2SH (8469 0953); *Sweet Chilli*, 47 London Rd, SE23 3TY (8699 9959); *Thai House*, 81 Rushey Green, SE6 4AF (8695 9995); *Thailand*, 15 Lewisham Way, SE14 6PP (8691 4040).

Merton *Jim Thompson's Flaming Wok*, 141 The Broadway, SW19 1QJ (8540 5540); *Larn Ya Mo*, 21 Leopold Rd, SW19 7BB (8947 1070); *Mai Thai Restaurant*, 75 The Broadway, SW19 1QE (8542 8834); *North & South*, 147 Arthur Rd, SW19 8AB (8947 8885); *Siam Classic*, 21 Leopold Rd, SW19 7BB (8944 8648); *Thai Paradise*, Merton Abbey Mills, Watermill Way, SW19 2RD (8540 0216); *Thai Tho*, 20 High St, SW19 5DX (8946 1542).

Newham *Tepa*, 118 High Rd Leyton, E15 2BX (8539 2311).

Richmond *Bangkok Garden*, 8 Rocks La, SW13 0DB (8392 9158); *Khamwan*, 5 White Hart La, SW13 0NT (8876 3335); *Lemon Grass*, 40 Sheen La, SW14 8LW (8876 7571); *Manee*, 273 Upper Richmond Rd, SW15 6SP (8788 2588); *Siam Court*, 40 Sheen La, SW14 8LW (8876 7571); *Thai Garden*, 431 Richmond Rd, TW1 2EF (8891 4707); *Thai Pin*, 147 St Margarets Rd, TW1 1RG (8891 6592).

Southwark *Delicious Thai*, 117a Grove La, SE5 8BG (7733 0000); *Sema*, 57 Lordship La, SE22 8EP (8693 3213); *Thai Corner Café*, 44 North Cross Rd, SE22 9EU (8299 4041); *Thai House*, 49 Camberwell Church St., SE5 8TR (7771 6366); *Thai Pavilion*, 11-15 Melbourne Grove, SE22 8RG (8299 3973); *Tumnan*, 55 Denmark Hill, SE5 8RS.

Tower Hamlets *Elephant Royale*, Locke's Wharf, West Ferry Rd, E14 (7987 7999); *New Thai Garden*, 562 Commercial Rd, E14 7JD (7791 2283); *Pearl of Siam*, 107 Roman Rd, E2 (8980 1676); *Ploy Pilin*, London Fruit Exchange, Brushfield St, E1 6EP (7377 9725); *Sri Thong Thai Restaurant*, 1 Widegate St. E1 7HP (7375 0794); *Sweet Chilli*, 63 Mile End Rd, E1 4TT (7702 7977); *Thai Fast Food Restaurant*, 218

Bethnal Green Rd, E2 0AA (7729 3180); *Thai Garden*, 562 Commercial Rd, E14 7JD (7791 2283); *Thai Gardens*, 249 Globe Rd, E2 0JD (8981 5748).

Waltham Forest *Patpong*, 146 Station Rd, E4 6AN (8524 7065); *Shoelaces Pub*, 777 High Rd Leyton, E10 5AB (8556 1297); *Tepa*, 118 High Rd Leyton, E15 2BX (8539 2311).

Wandsworth *Bangkok Symphonie*, 141 Upper Richmond Rd, SW15 2TX (8789 4304); *Chada Thai Cuisine*, 208-210 Battersea Park Rd, SW11 4ND (7622 2209); *Gratom*, 36 Lavender Hill, SW11 5RL (7924 5893); *Manee*, 273 Upper Richmond Rd, SW15 6SP (8788 2588); *O & S Thai Restaurant*, 246 Battersea Park Rd, SW11 3BP; *Oh Boy*, 843 Garratt La, SW17 0PG (8947 9760); *Old School Thai*, 147 Lavender Hill, SW11 5QJ (7228 2345); *Options Thai*, Waterside Food Court Centre, Arndale Centre, SW18 4TD (8871 2243); *Phuket*, 246 Battersea Park Rd, SW11 3BP (7223 5924); *P S Thai House*, 159 Lavender Hill, SW11 5QH (7978 5403); *Talad*, 320 Upper Richmond Rd SW15 6TL (8789 8084); *Thai Buffalo*, 561 Garratt La, SW18 4SR (8944 7617); *Thai Café & Noodle Bar*, 346 Garratt La, SW18 4ES (8874 9036); *Thai Garden*, 58 Battersea Rise, SW11 1EG (7738 0380); *Thonburi Superwok*, 26 Upper Richmond Rd, SW15 2RX (8875 0269); *Tumnan Thai Restaurant*, 163 Lavender Hill, SW11 5QH (7223 1046).

Westminster *Ben's Thai Restaurant*, 93 Warrington Cres, W9 1EH (7266 3134); *Bhan*, 103 Boundary Rd, NW8 0RG (7624 1485); *Blue Jade*, 44 Hugh St, SW1V 4EP (7828 0321); *I Thai Restaurant*, 31 Craven Hill Gdns, W2 3EA (7298 9001); *Jewel of Siam*, 39 Hereford Rd, W2 4AB (7229 4363); *Star*, 91-93 Frampton St, NW8 8NA (7724 6770); *Tawana*, 3 Westbourne Grove. W2 4UA (7229 3785); *Taxin*, 79 Castellain Rd, W9 1EU (7286 3912); *Thai Kitchen*, 108 Chepstow Rd, Bayswater W2 5QS (7221 9984).

SHOPS *Sri Thai*, 56 Shepherds Bush Rd, W6 7PH (7602 0621); *Talad Thai*, 320 Upper Richmond Rd, SW15 6TL (8789 8084); *Tawana Oriental Supermarket*, 16-20 Chepstow Rd, W2 (7221 6316); *Thai Dang*, 166 Old Brompton Rd, SW5 0BA (7373 1927); *Thai Design Distributors Ltd* [jewellery], Lilia Ho, 14 Beresford Ave, Wembley HA0 1YP (8903 0233).

TRANSLATION *Thai Translations*, 67 Brookwood Rd, Wandsworth SW18 5BG (8874 9578).

TRAVEL *Thai Airways International Airlines*, 41 Albemarle St, W1X 4LE (7499 9113); *Tourism Authority of Thailand*, 49 Albemarle St, W1X 3FE (7499 7679).

WELFARE *Anglo-Thai Foundation*, 3 Malcolm Rd, SW19 4AS (8541 1712).

Tibetan

ASSOCIATIONS *Tibet Foundation*, 1 St James's Market, London SW1Y 4SB (7930 6001) [a non-political organisation promoting Tibetan culture and welfare].

GOVERNMENT There has been a Chinese military presence in Tibet since the early 1950s and the country has been administered as an autonomous region of China since 1965.

The Government of Tibet in Exile is represented in London at the *Office of Tibet,* Tibet Ho, 1 Culworth St, London NW8 7AF (7722 5378).

EDUCATION *Tibetan* is taught at *SOAS Language Centre* (7898 4888).

LANGUAGES *Tibetan* was the official language of Tibet prior to the Chinese occupation and is spoken by perhaps 2m people there and in adjoining areas to the south and east. It is written in its own semi-syllabic script. The presence of six Tibetan-speaking schoolchildren in London was recorded at the time of the *Multilingual Capital* (2000) survey. Three of these lived in Islington.

MEDIA & INFORMATION *Tibet Images,* 5 Torrens St, EC1V 1NQ (7278 2377); *Tibet Information Network,* City Cloisters, 188-196 Old St, EC1V 9FR (7814 9011).

RELIGION *Drukpa London (Drukpa Kargyud Trust)* [Tibetan, Kagyu, Drikung], 114 Harvist Rd, NW6 6HJ (8964 2337); *Jamyang Buddhist Centre* [Mahayana tradition], The Old Courthouse, 43 Renfrew Rd, Kennington, SE11 4NA (7820 8787) [Monday -Thursday from 2 pm.]; *Kagyu Samye Dzong Tibetan Buddhist Centre* [Karma Kunchab Choling], Carlisle La, SE1 7LG (7928 5447); *RIGPA Buddhist Centre* [Tibetan Nyingmapa], 330 Caledonian Rd, N1 1BB (7700 0185); *ROKPA - London* [Tibetan Kagyu], c/o Ramos-Gonzales, 67 Parkholme Rd, Dalston E8 3AQ (8254 5004).

RESTAURANTS

West Central *Tibetan Restaurant,* 17 Irving St, WC2H 7AU (7839 2090).

Lambeth *Courtyard Café* [vegetarian, Monday-Friday 9 a.m. – 3.30 p.m.], Jamyang Buddhist Centre, The Old Courthouse, 4 3 Renfrew Rd, Kennington, SE11 4NA.

SHOPS *Su Su Ma Ma World Wear* [Tibetan knitwear for children], 243 Holcroft Ct, Clipstone St, W1P 7DZ (7436 6768); *Tibet Shop* [a subsidiary of the Tibet Foundation], 1A St James's Market, SW1Y 4SB (7930 6005) [11.30-18.30, Tue - Sat] ; *Zam Tibetan Buddhist Shop,* 330 Caledonian Rd, Islington N1 1BB (7700 0334).

SPECIAL *Appropriate Technology For Tibetans,* 117 Cricklewood Broadway, NW2 3JG (8450 8090).

TRAVEL *Trekking Tibet Ltd,* Flat 1, 68a Westbourne Grove, Bayswater W2 5SH.

WELFARE *Free Tibet Campaign,* 1 Rosoman Pl, EC1R 0JY (7833 9958); *Tibet Foundation,* 1 St James's Market, London SW1Y 4SB (7930 6001) [a non-political organisation promoting Tibetan culture and welfare]; *Tibet House Trust,* 1 Culworth St, St John's Wood NW8 7AF (7722 5378); *Tibet Society & Tibet Relief Fund of the UK,* 114-115 Tottenham Court Rd, W1P 9HL (7383 7533).

Tigray

See under *Tigrinya.*

Tigre

Tigre is a Semitic language spoken in Ethiopia, Eritrea and Sudan which is written in the Ethiopic semi-syllabic script. 83 London schoolchildren were recorded as being *Tigre*-speaking in the *Multilingual Capital* (2000) survey, of whom 34 lived in Southwark. [The name *Tigre* should not be confused with *Tigray* (*Tigrinya*)].

Tigrinya

Tigrinya is in fact the **Amharic** name for the language called *Tigre.* Unusually, however, even speakers of this language appear happy for it to be called *Tigrinya,* perhaps in part because this is less likely to be confused with **Tigre.**

ASSOCIATIONS *Tigray Development Association,* TDA Ho, 211 Clapham Rd, Brixton SW9 0QH (7924 0191).

EDUCATION Mother-tongue education for young children in *Tigrinya* is available in about 10 locations in London; for full information visit <www.resourceunit.com>. Courses for adults are provided by *SOAS Language Centre* (7898 4888). Other courses in *Tigrinya* are occasionally available elsewhere in London – check with *Floodlight,* <www.floodlight.co.uk>.

LANGUAGE *Tigrinya (Tigray)* is a Semitic language spoken in Eritrea and Ethiopia which is usually written in the Ethiopic semi-syllabic script. The *Multilingual Capital* (2000) survey recorded the presence of 805 *Tigrinya*-speaking London schoolchildren and found that these were located predominantly in three boroughs: Kensington & Chelsea, Hammersmith & Fulham, and Islington. Map 28, showing the distribution of *Tigrinya* speakers across London, can be viewed at <www.global-london.com/gallery>.

WELFARE *Eritrean Community in Haringey,* c/o Tesfay Gebremichael, Selby Centre, Selby Rd, London N17 8JN (8365 0819) [language: Tigrinya].

Tiv

LANGUAGE *Tiv* is a Bantuic language of Nigeria and adjoining parts of Cameroon. The presence of a few *Tiv*-speaking pupils in Southwark was noted by the *Multilingual Capital* **(2000) survey**.

Tok Pisin

Tok Pisin is an English-based Pidgin which is the lingua franca of Papua New Guinea. It has also become the first language of a steadily growing minority of the population, making it technically a Creole language. *Tok Pisin* was given as the first language of one pupil in Barnet in the *Multilingual Capital* **(2000) survey**.

Tonga

Tonga was reported as the language of seven London schoolchildren in the *Multilingual Capital* (2000) survey, of whom five lived in Lambeth. There are, in fact, several Bantuic languages called **Tonga**, and this is also an alternative name for **Tongan**. It is thus impossible to know which and how many of these languages are represented among the reported speakers of this.

Tongan

GOVERNMENT *Tonga High Commission,* 36 Molyneux St, W1H 6AB (7724 5828).

LANGUAGE *T o n g a n* is a Trans-Pacific language spoken on the Tonga islands. The *Multilingual Capital* (2000) survey reported that this was the first language of 30 London schoolchildren but this figure is suspect because of possible confusion with *Tonga.*

Traveller

See under **Romani.**

Trinidadian

ASSOCIATIONS *Trinidad & Tobago Association,* 380 Green Lanes, N4 1DW (8800 5857).

BUSINESS *Trinidad Asphalt Ltd,* 2 Mercury Way, SE14 5RR (7732 3366).

GOVERNMENT *Trinidad & Tobago High Commissioner,* 42 Belgrave Sq, SW1X 8NT (7245 9351).

LANGUAGES **English** has official status. Both **English Creole** and **French Creole** are spoken there (although few speakers of the latter now survive). In addition, an overseas variety of the **Indic** language, **Bhojpuri,** is spoken.

RESTAURANTS *Trini's Trinidadian Roti Shop T/A,* 245 Balham High Rd, Tooting SW17 7BE (8767 0843).

TRAVEL *Trinidad & Tobago Tourist Office,* 66 Abbey Rd, Enfield EN1 2RQ (8350 1015).

Tswana

Tswana is the root found in both the country name, **Botswana,** and in the language name, **Setswana.** See entries for these. In South Africa where many **Setswana**-speakers also live, *Tswana* is applied to both the people and their language. (Within **Botswana,** the people are called *Batswana* (plural) and *Motswana* (singular).)

Tumbuka

Tumbuka is a Bantuic language spoken in Malawi and Zambia. The *Multilingual Capital* (2000) survey reported the presence of four **Tumbuka**-speaking pupils in London, two of them in Haringey.

Tunisian

ASSOCIATIONS *British-Tunisian Society,* c/o The Tunisian Embassy, 29 Prince's Gate, SW7 1QG (7584 8177).

BUSINESS *Tunisian Date Centre,* Cooper Ho, Unit Gh 2, Michael Rd, Fulham, SW6 2AD (7371 5555); *Tunisian Investment Office,* 301-304 Sardinia Ho, 52 Lincoln's Inn Fields, WC2A 3LZ (7430 1315).

GOVERNMENT *Tunisian Embassy,* 29 Prince's Gate, SW7 1QG (7584 8177).

LANGUAGES **Arabic** is the official language and **Maghrebi Arabic** is the first language of the vast majority of the population. The remainder speak **Berber** languages or **French.**

MEDIA & INFORMATION *Focus on Tunisia/ Tunisian Information Bureau,* 9 Young St, W8 5EH (7937 2226); *Tunisia Information and Documentation Centre,* PO Box 14593, W5 3FR (fax: 8864 3563).

RELIGION Most Tunisians are Muslims.

RESTAURANTS

Hammersmith & Fulham *Adam's Café* [Tunisian couscous restaurant], 77 Askew Rd, Shepherd's Bush, W12 9AH (8743 0572).

TRAVEL *Tunis Air,* 6 Vigo St, W1S 3HF (7437 6236) and 24 Sackville St, W1S 3DS (7734 7644); *Tunisian National Tourist Office,* 77a Wigmore St, W1H 9LJ (7224 5561).

Turkish

ASSOCIATIONS *Anglo-Turkish Society,* 43 Montrose Pl, SW1X 7DT (7235 8148); *Anglo Turkish Housing Association,* 86 Stoke Newington Church St, N16 OAP; *Association of Turkish People in the UK,* 76b Fore St, N18 2SL (8803 0208); *Enfield UK Turkish Islamic Cultural Centre,* 10 Caxton Rd, N22 6TB (8352 1435); *London Islamic Turkish Association,* 16 Green Lanes, N16 9ND (7249 5417); *Turkish Association Club,* 547 High Rd, N17 6SB (8801 3141); *Turkish Community Project,* Suite 3, 203 Lewisham High St, Se13 6LY (8318 2864); *Turkish and Greek Social Club,* 130 Clarence Rd, E5 8DY (8986 4341); *Turkish Association Club,* 547 High Rd, N17 6SB (8801 3141); *Turkish Social Club,* 115 High St, SE20 7DT (8776 6473); *Turkish Social Club,* 13b Stoke Newington Rd, N16 8BH (7249 3951); *Turkish Social Club,* 294 Walworth Rd, SE17 2TE (7701 1975); *Turkish Social Club,* 263 Well St, E9 6RG (8985 4580); *Turkish Speaking People Cultural Centre,* 84 Balls Pond Rd, Islington N1 4AJ (7923 1202); *Turkish Women's Philanthropic Association,* 4 Willoughby Rd, N8 0HR (8348 6613); *Turkish Youth Association,* 628 Green Lanes, Hornsey N8 0DS (8888 3080); *UK Turkish Islamic Association,* 117-119 Stoke Newington Rd, N16 8BU (7254 0046); *Waltham Forest Turkish Association,* 34 Station Rd, E17 8AA (8520 2480).

BUSINESS *Central Bank of the Republic of Turkey,* Centric Ho, 391 Strand, WC2R 0LT (7379 0548); *Garanti Bankasi Turkiye,* 50 Knightsbridge, SW1X 7LY (7626 3803); *Turkish Bank (UK) Ltd,* 84-86 Borough High St, SE1 1LN (7403 5656); *Turkish Bank (UK) Ltd,* 577-579 Green Lanes, Harringay N8 0RG

(8348 9600); *Turkish Bank (UK) Ltd,* 121 Kingsland High St, E8 2PB (7923 3339); *Turkish-British Chamber of Commerce,* 89 Goswell Rd, Clerkenwell EC1V 7ER (7336 0686); *Turkish-British Chamber of Commerce and Industry,* Bury Ho, 33 Bury St, SW1Y 6AX (7321 0999); *Istanbul Ship Management,* 39 Oakleigh Crescent, N20 0BT (8362 0901); *Turkish-British Chamber of Commerce,* 89 Goswell Rd, Clerkenwell EC1V 7ER (7336 0686).

EDUCATION Turkish mother-tongue education for young children is available in more than 20 locations in London; for details visit <www.resourceunit.com>. Courses in **Turkish** for adults are provided by *SOAS Language Centre* (7898 4888), the *University of Westminster* (7911 5000), and many other places – see *Floodlight* or visit <www.floodlight.co.uk> for details.

British Institute of Archaeology at Ankara, British Academy, 10 Carlton House Terrace, SW1Y 5AH (7969 5204); *Happy Nest Turkish Nursery,* Fellows Court Family Centre, Weymouth Terrace, E2 8LR (7739 3193); *Southwark Turkish Education Group,* 43a Missenden Roland Way, SE17 2HS (7708 2047); *Southwark Turkish Education Group,* Thomas Calton School, Alpha St, SE15 4NX (7277 6829); *Turkish Community Library,* 86 Balla Pond Rd, Islington, N1 4AJ (7923 2095); *Turkish Education Group,* 2 Newington Green Rd, N1 4RX (7226 8647); *Turkish Education Group Haringey Women's Project,* Earlham Grove, N22 5HJ (8881 6687).

GOVERNMENT *Turkish Consulate General,* Rutland Lodge, Rutland Ct, SW7 1BW (7589 0949); *Turkish Embassy,* 43 Belgrave Sq, SW1X 8PA (7393 0202); *Turkish Republic of Northern Cyprus,* 29 Bedford Sq, WC1B 3EG (7631 1920).

HEALTH & BEAUTY An information leaflet on *breast cancer* is available in Turkish from the Women's Nationwide Cancer Control Campaign, 1st fl, Charity Ho, 14-15 Perseverence Works, EC2 8BD (7729 4688, fax 7613 0771).

Docklands Turkish Steam Baths Ltd, 30a Stephenson St, E16 4SA (7473 1454); *Porchester Spa Turkish Baths,* Queensway, W2 5HS (7792 3980); *Turkish-Kurdish Health, Advocacy, and Counselling Services,* The Lawson Practice, St Leonards, Nuttall St, Islington N1 5LZ (7613 5944).

LANGUAGE *Turkish* is the principal language of Turkey but *Kurdish* is spoken in the southeast of the country. *Turkish* is a language of the Trans-Asia geozone which has 60m speakers

worldwide, mainly in Turkey and neighbouring countries. The *Multilingual Capital* (2000) survey recorded 15,659 *Turkish*-speaking London schoolchildren of whom 3,207 lived in Haringey.

Two maps showing the distribution of speakers of **Turkish** in London can be viewed at <www.global-london.com/gallery>. Map 29 shows how the percentage of *Turkish*-speakers varies across the whole of London while Map 30 illustrates how their proportion varies within Haringey.

LEGAL *Kaya Turkish Law Consultant,* 2 Priority Ct, Pilgrim St, EC4V 6DE (7248 3828); *Turkish-Kurdish Health, Advocacy, and Counselling Services,* The Lawson Practice, St Leonards, Nuttall St, Islington N1 5LZ (7613 5944).

MEDIA *Anatolian News Agency,* 314 Regent St, W1B 3LN (); *British Turkey Information Service,* Bury Ho, 126-128 Cromwell Rd, South Kensington SW7 4ET (7244 7701); *Hurriyet Turkish Newspaper,* 35 D'Arbly St, West End, W1V 3FE (7439 2587); *London Turkish Radio / Londra Turk Radyosu* [North London 1584]; 185b High Rd, Wood Green, N22 6BA (8881 0606/2020); *Milet Ltd,* P O Box 9916, London W14 0GS (7603 5477) [distributor of Turkish books]; *Turkish Community Library,* 86 Balls Pond Rd, N1 4AJ (7923 2095); *Turkey Briefing,* 87 Glebe St, W4 2BB (8994 4632); *Turkish International News Agency,* 18-22 Ashwin St, E8 3DL (7923 0066); *Turkish Radio (UK) Ltd,* 185b High Rd, N22 6BA (8881 5566/0606); *Turkish Text Centre,* Unit B8, Chadwell Heath Industrial Park, Dagenham RM8 1SL (8597 4141).

MOTORING *Ottoman Motors,* 171 Hertford Rd, N9 7EP (8245 7883); *Soför Okulu Driving School,* West Green Rd, Tottenham.

RECREATION *Bingöl Karakoçan Kigi Social Club,* 54 Green Lanes, N13 (8889 7848); *Istanbul Social Club,* 286 Kingsland High St, Hackney.

RELIGION Almost all Turks are Muslims.
Aziziye Mosque, UK Turkish Islamic Association, 117-119 Stoke Newington Rd, N16 8BU (7254 0046);

London Islamic Turkish Association, 16 Green Lanes, N16 9ND (7249 5417); UK Turkish Islamic Cultural Centre, 10 Caxton Rd N22 6TB (8352 1435); UK Turkish Islamic Cultural Centre, 1 Clissold Rd, N16 9EX (7275 9001); UK Turkish Islamic Funeral Service, Sheikh Mazim Mosque, 9-15 Shacklewell La, Hackney E8 2DA (7690 6213). UK Turkish Islamic Funeral Services, 203 Green Lanes, N16 9DJ (7359 1170).

RESTAURANTS

East Central Harput Kebab, 6 Spafield St, EC1R 4QB (7833 5566).

South East 1 Capital, 63 The Cut, Waterloo, SE1 8LL (7207 2274); Tas, 33 The Cut, Waterloo, SE1 (7928 1444); Turkish Touch, 189-191 New Kent Rd, SE1 4AG (7357 0110).

South West 1 Marmaris, 45 Warwick Way, SW1V 1QS (7828 5940).

West 1 Efes I, 80-82 Great Titchfield St, W1 (7636 1953); Efes 2, 175 Great Portland St, W1W 5PA (7436 0600); Gigs Fish & Kebab House, 12 Tottenham St, W1P 9PB (7636 1424); Istanbul Meze Bar & Grill, 100 Cleveland St, W1T 6NU (7387 0785); Safa, 22 Nutford Pl, W1H 5YH (7723 8331); Topkapi, 25 Marylebone High St, W1M 3PE (7486 1872).

West Central Sarastro, 126 Drury La, WC2B 5QG (7836 0101); Sofra, 26 Tavistock St, WC2 (7240 3773).

Barking & Dagenham Best Turkish Kebab, 153a Broad St, Dagenham RM10 9HX (8595 6730).

Barnet Anatolia, 185 Edgware Rd, Colindale, NW9 6LP (8200 6576); Anatolia, 1031 Finchley Rd, NW11 7ES (8455 4884); Antalya, 14 North End Rd, NW11 7PH (8209 0079); Baran, 748 Finchley Rd, NW11 7TH (8458 0515); Diamond Kebab, 1289 High Rd, N20 9HS (8446 9916); Istanbul Express T/A, 3 Silkstream Parade, Watling Ave, Edgware HA8 0EJ (8959 1633); Leyla Turkish Cuisine, 48 The Broadway, Mill Hill, NW7 3LH (8906 4755); Tülay's Ottoman Cuisine, 628 Finchley Rd, Golder's Green (8731 6866); Turkish Delight, 119 East Barnet Rd, Barnet EN4 8RF (8440 1414).

Bexley Turkish Delight, 165 Long La, Bexleyheath DA7 5AE (8306 0600).

Brent Chorum Kebab House, 367 High Rd, NW10 2JR (8451 6272); Istanbul Exprcss T/A, 3 Silkstream Pde, Watling Av, HA8 OEJ (8959 1633); Nadia Kebab House, 244 Neasden La, NW10 0AA (8830 5655).

Bromley Istanbul Kebab House, 14 Green La, Chislehurst, BR7 6AG (8402 0240/0242); Lezzetli Ocakbasi, 132 High St, Beckenham BR3 1EB (8658 4440).

Camden Golden Horn, 194 Kentish Town Rd, NW5 2AE (7485 6797); Marathon Kebab House, 87 Chalk Farm Rd, NW1 8AR (7485 3814); Rhodes Kebab House, 139 Queens Crescent, NW5 4ED (7267 7715); Vanak, 289 Finchley Rd, NW3 6ND (7435 5054).

Croydon Palace Kebab, 86 Westow Hill, SE19 1SB (8766 7887); Turkish Barbecue Pit, 3 Russell Hill Parade, Purley CR8 2LE (8660 6424).

Enfield Anatolia, 1031 Finchley Rd, NW11 7ES (8455 4884); Kimiz, 361 Fore St, Edmonton N9 0NR (8803 6060); Mezopotamya, 47 Green Lanes, N13 4TD (8881 6852).

Greenwich Eltham Kebab House, 16 Tudor Parade, Well Hall Rd, SE9 6SX (8850 6902).

Hackney Anadolu Lokantasi, 117 Kingsland High St, Dalston, E8 (7275 0403); Anglo Anatolian 1, 123 Stoke Newington Church St, N16 0UH (7923 4349); Anatolya Kebab Shop, 263a Mare St, E8 3NS (8986 2223); Aziziue, 117-119 Stoke Newington Rd, N16 8BU (7254 7475); Gaziantep, 115 Stoke Newington Rd, N16 8BX (7275 7924); Golden Fish, Chips & Kebab, 170 Stoke Newington Rd, N16 7UY (7254 4291); Highbury, 163 Blackstock Rd, N4 2JS (7354 3899); Istanbul Iskembecisi, 9 Stoke Newington Rd, N16 8BH (7254 7291); Mangal, 10 Arcola St, Hackney E8 2DJ (7275 8981); Mangal Pide & Lahmacun Salonu Ltd, 27 Stoke Newington Rd, N16 8BJ (7254 6999); Ozlem Turkish Pizza, 85 Stoke Newington Rd, N16 8AB (7275 9974); Ozlem Turkish Pizza, Unit 1, Prince George Rd, N16 8DL (7275 9974); Shen Kebab House, 299 Mare St, E8 1EJ (8985 0636).

Hammersmith & Fulham Best Mangal, 104 North End Rd, W14 9EX (7610 1050); Charcoal Grill, 30 Hammersmith Broadway, W6 7AB (8748 0590); Oz Best Mangal Barbecue Restaurant, 647 Fulham Rd, Fulham, SW6 5PU (7736 1032); Pasha, 18 Goldhawk Rd, W12 8DH (8743 1541).

Haringey Asma Alti, 602 Seven Sisters Rd, N15 6HT (8442 8869); Best Turkish Kebab T/A, 125 Stoke Newington Rd, N16 8BT (7254 7642); Crystal, 10 White Hart La, N17 8DP (8801 2524); Diyarbakir, 69 Grand Parade, Green Lanes, N4 1DU (8809 2777); Dolphin, 172-174 Muswell Hill Broadway, N10 3SA (8883 1111); Ezgi, 783 High Rd, N17 8AH (8801 5101); Gaziantep, 52 Grand Parade, Green Lanes, N4 1AG (8802 5498); Gokyuzu, 27 Grand Parade, Green Lanes, N4 1LG (8211 8406); Istanbul Kebab House T/A, 13 Hallam Rd, Seven Sisters N15 3RE (8888 5619); Kebab Palace, 39 Turnpike La, N8 0EP (8341 1527); Mazgal, 19 Topsfield Parade, Tottenham La, N8 8PT (8340 3194); Selale, Salisbury Promenade, Green Lanes, N8 0RX (8800 1636); Turkish Cafe, 454 West Green Rd, Seven Sisters N15 3PT (8889 3291); Yayla, 429 Green Lanes, N4 1HA (8348 9515).

Islington *Angel Mangal,* 139 Upper St, N1 1QP (7359 7777); *Gallipoli Again,* 120 Upper St, N1 1QP (7359 1578); *Hodja Nasreddin,* 53 Newington Green Rd, N1 4QU (7226 7757); *Iznik,* 19 Highbury Park, N5 1QJ (7354 5697); *Lezzet Lokanta,* 330 Essex Rd, N1 3PB (7226 7418); *Night Star Steak House,* 149 Holloway Rd, N7 8LX (7607 9622); *Pasha,* 301 Upper St, N1 2TU (7224 1454); *Sparks,* 278 St. Pauls Rd, N1 2LH (7226 2851); *Sultan Ahmet,* 326 Essex Rd, N1 (7226 1986).

Lambeth *Bogazici,* 111 Streatham Hill, SW2 4UG (8674 5640); *Orient Express,* 62 Streatham High Rd, SW16 1DA (8677 5100); *Orient Express Kebab T/A,* 12 Leigham Hall Parade, Streatham High Rd, SW16 1DR (8677 6808); *Palace Kebab,* 86 Westow Hill, SE19 1SB (8766 7887).

Lewisham *Anatolia T/A,* 305 Southend La, SE6 3ND (8697 4664); *Best Kebab in Town,* 360 Baring Rd, SE12 0DU (8851 0790); *Kafe Kebab,* 7 The Facade, Devonshire Rd, SE23 3HA (8699 7080); *That Turkish Place,* 29-31 Lewisham Way, New Cross SE14 6PP (8692 6357).

Merton *Kebab Delight,* 25 Leopold Rd, SW19 7BB (8947 4291).

Newham *Anatolia Kebab House T/A,* 21-23 Broadway, E15 4BQ (8519 4859); *F Kaygusuz Kebab Steak House,* 227 Barking Rd, E6 1LB (8472 7381); *Kebab,* 105 Romford Rd, E15 4LY (8555 1673); *Kings Yard Cafe,* 9a Kings Yard, Carpenters Rd, E15 2HD (8525 5394); *Mevlana,* 20A Leytonstone Rd, E15 1SE (8519 1103).

Southwark: *Anatolia,* 36 Forest Hill Rd, SE22 0RR (8693 1852); *Anatolian Cafe,* 25 Bartholomew St, SE1 4AL (7407 7608); *Istanbul,* 83 Camberwell Rd, SE5 0EZ (7703 5029); *Istanbul Kebabs House,* 19 Upper Tooting Rd, SW17 7TS (8767 7500); *Lale Kebab & Hamburger Bar,* 163 Bellenden Rd, SE15 4DH (7635 8528); *The Turkish Touch,* 189 New Kent Rd, SE1 4AG (7357 0110).

Tower Hamlets *Paradise Cottage Kebabs*, 477 Bethnal Green Rd, E2 9QH (7729 6119).

Waltham Forest *Best Kebab & Fried Chicken,* 68 Omnibus Way, E17 4QF (8531 9825); *Yaser Doner Kebab Ho,* 8 Blackhorse La, E17 6HJ (8527 4081).

Wandsworth *Artemis Kebab T/A,* 731 Garratt La, SW17 0PD (8944 6728); *Barbecue Pit,* 127A Lavender Hill, SW11 5QJ (7223 6664); *Istanbul Kebab,* 83 Battersea Rise, SW11 1HW (7223 3062); *Oriental Turkish Cuisine,* 41 St.

John's Hill, SW11 1TT (7228 8056); *Istanbul Kebab,* 83 Battersea Rise, SW11 1HW (7223 3062); *Istanbul Kebab House T/A,* 19 Upper Tooting Rd, SW17 7TS (8767 7500); *Turkish Barbecue Pit,* 127a Lavender Hill, SW11 5QJ (7223 6664).

Westminster *Efes 2,* 175 Great Portland St, W1W 5PA (7436 0600); *K-Bab,* 26 London St, W2 1HH (7262 1111); *Marmaris,* 45 Warwick Way, SW1V 1QS (7828 5940); *Safa,* 22 Nutford Pl, W1H 5YH (7723 8331).

SHOPS *Istanbul Showroom,* 405 Mare St, Hackney E8 1HY (8525 0106); *Turkish Food Centre,* 363 Fore St, Edmonton N9 0NR (8807 6766); *Ottoman Wine Co Ltd* [convenience store], 132-134 Essex Rd, N1 8LX (7226 6602); *Ottoman Wine Co Ltd,* 217 Reede Rd, Dagenham RM10 8EH (8593 6608); *Turkish Food Centre,* 89 Ridley Rd, Dalston, E8 2NH (7254 6754); **Haringey:** *Anatolia's Supermarket,* 264 High Rd, N22 8JX (8888 3666); *Turkish Food Centre,* 105 Brantwood Rd, N17 0DX (8365 1930); *Turkish Food Centre,* 363 Fore St, N9 0NR (8807 6766); *Turkish Food Centre,* 385 Green Lanes, Haringey N4 1EU (8340 4547); *Turkish Food Centre,* 589-591 Green Lanes, Haringey N8 0RG (8347 9950); *Turkish Food Centre,* 542 Lordship La, N22 5BY (8365 8846); **Waltham Forest:** *Turkish Food Centre,* 647-661, High Rd, Leytonstone E11 4RD (8558 8149/3289); *Turkish Food Centre,* 89 Ridley Rd, Dalston E8 2NH (7254 6754).

SPECIAL *Docklands Turkish Steam Baths Ltd,* 30a Stephenson St, E16 4SA (7473 1454); *Porchester Spa Turkish Baths,* Queensway, W2 5HS (7792 3980); *Turkish Bath Showroom,* 95 The Broadway, NW7 3TG (8201 1250); *Turkish Community Library,* 86 Balls Pond Rd, Islington N1 4AJ (7923 2095); *Turkish Food Hygiene Centre,* Falklands Ho, Green Lanes, N8 0QY (8341 7371/6343); *Turkish Food Centre,* 89 Ridley Rd, E8 2NH (7254 6754); *Turkish Food Centre,* 363 Fore St, N9 0NR (8807 6766); *Turkish Food* Centre, 542 Lordship La, N22 5BY (8635 8846); *Turkish Food Centre,* 661 High Rd, E11 4RD (8558 8149); *Turkish Food Centre,* 105 Brantwood Rd, SE24 ODJ (8365 1930); Turkish *Solution Ltd,* Unit 15 Tudor Grove, Well St, E9 7QL (8986 4674).

TRANSLATION *Aradco VSI Ltd,* 132 Cleveland St, W1P 6AB (7692 7000); *Associated Translators,* 96 Kensington High St, W8 4SG (7937 7733); *G Greenslade Turkish Translators,* 28 Hinksey Path, Abbey Wood, SE2 9TB (8310 2072)); *Kern (UK) Ltd,* Romms 45-46 New Ho, 67-68 Hatton Gdn, EC1N 8JY (7831 5600); *Turkish Bureau of Interpreters,* 69 Flaxman Ct, Flaxman Terrace, Bloomsbury WC1H (7387 0937); *Turkish Commercial & Technical*

Translations, 585A Fulham Rd, SW6 5WA (7381 0967); *Turkish Cinnection,* 31a Chalton St, NW1 1JD (7388 3240); *Turkish Translation & Interpreting Service,* 9 Denmark St, WC2H 8LS (7240 3827); *Turkish Translations & Interpreting Service,* 96 Exeter Rd, Southgate N14 5JS (8368 6906); *Turkish Translations,* 64 Queen St, EC4R 1AD (7248 8707); *Turkish Translation,* 11 The Byeway, Eastsheen, SW14 7NN (8876 1176).

TRAVEL *Daydream Travel,* 30 Bedford Pl, Bloomsbury, WC1H 5JH (7631 4426); *Istanbul Airlines,* 17b Riding House St, W1P 7PB (7637 3031) and 92 Park La, Croydon CR0 1JF (8688 7555); *Ride the World (Turkey) Ltd,* 276 Chase Rd, Southgate N14 6HA; *Seriously Turkey,* 41 Salmon La, Poplar E14 7NA (7790 0202); *Simply Turkey,* 598-608 Chiswick High Rd, W4 5RT (8747 1011); *Treasures of Turkey,* 145 Oxford St, W1R 1TB (7494 2292); *Turkish Airlines,* 125 Pall Mall, SW1Y 5EA (7766 9300); *Turkish and Tours,* 487a Green Lanes, Finsbury Park N4 1AJ (8348 3616); *Turkish Leisure & Tours,* 52 Great Cambridge Rd, N17 7BU (8885 2100); *Turkish Leisure & Tours,* 122 St. Pancras Way, NW1 9NB ; *Turkish Tourist & Information Office,* 170 Piccadilly, W1V 9DD (7629 7771); *Turkish Tourist Office,* 1st fl, Egyptian Ho, 170-173, Piccadilly W1J 9EH (7629 7771); *Turkish Travel Centre (UK) Ltd,* 2 Crossway, N16 8HX (7249 9677); *Turkish Travel Centre (UK) Ltd,* 20-22 Maddox St W1S 1PN (7408 0094); *Turkish Travel Centre (UK) Ltd,* 9 Grand Parade, Green Lanes, N4 1JX (8211 7779).

WELFARE *Ottoman Community & Heritage Foundation,* 277 St. Anns Rd, N15 5RG (8880 1423); *Turkish & Kurdish Community Centre,* 92-100 Stoke Newington Rd, N16 7XB (7249 6980); *Turkish Community Project (Lewisham),* Suite 2, 203 Lewisham High St, SE13 6LY (8318 2864); *Turkish-Kurdish Health, Advocacy, and Counselling Services,* The Lawson Practice, St Leonards, Nuttall St, Islington N1 5LZ (7613 5944); *Turkish-speaking People's Cultural Centre,* 84 Balls Pond Rd, Islington N1 4AJ (7923 1202); *Turkish Woman's Support Group,* 42 North Sq, N9 0HY (8807 2289); *Turkish Womens Philanthropic Association,* 4 Willoughby Rd, N8 0HR (8348 6613); *Turkish Women's Support Group,* 42 North Sq, N9 0HY (8807 4525); *Waltham Forest Turkish Association,* 34 Station Rd, E17 8AA [advice] (8521 5072).

Turkish Cypriot

ASSOCIATIONS *Akincilar Turkish Cypriot Association,* 83 Kingsland High St, Hackney, E8 2PB; *Cyprus-Turkish Association / Kibris Turk Cemiyeti,* 34 D'Arblay St, W1A 4YL (7437 4940); *Cyprus Turkish Women's Association,* c/o Mrs Pervin Ulug, 109 The Grove, Palmers Green N13 5JS (8886 9286); *Enfield Turkish Cypriot Association,* Community Ho, 311 Fore St, Edmonton N9 0PZ (8373 6300); *Enfield Turkish*

Cypriot Association, 7 Plevna Rd, N9 0BU (8807 4141); *Turkish Cypriot Community Association,* 117 Green Lanes, N16 9DA (7359 5231); *Turkish Cypriot Association (ETCA),* 7 Plevna Rd, N9 0BU (8807 4141); *Turkish Cypriot Cultural Association,* 14a Graham Rd, E8 1DA (7249 7410).

BUSINESS *Cyprus Turkish Co-operative Central Bank Ltd,* Avondale, Bressey Grove, South Woodford E18 2HP.

EDUCATION *Cypriot Community Centre/Turkish Education Group Haringey Woman's Project,* Earlham Gr, N22 5HJ (8881 6687); *Turkish Cypriot Research Group,* 18 Ashwin St, E5 (7241 3645).

GOVERNMENT *Turkish Republic of Northern Cyprus,* 29 Bedford Sq, WC1B 3EG (7631 1920).

RESTAURANTS

Hackney *Cyprus Fish & Chips & Kebabs Ltd,* 92 Northwold Rd, Clapton E5 8RL; *Turkish Cypriot,* 6 Hampden Rd, N8 0HT (8967 7066).

TRANSLATION *Turkish Cypriot Research Group,* 18 Ashwin St, E8 3DL (7241 3645).

TRAVEL *Cyprus Turkish Airlines,* 88 Green Lanes, N16 9EJ (7241 5523); *Cyprus Turkish Airlines,* Ground fl, 11-12 Pall Mall, SW1Y 5LU (7930 4851); *North Cyprus Tourist Office,* 29 Bedford Sq, Bloomsbury WC1B 3EG (7631 1930).

WELFARE *Turkish Cypriot Cultural Association,* 14A Graham Rd, E8 1DA (7249 7410); *Turkish Cypriot Counselling Service,* 6 Hampden Rd, Hornsey N8 0HX (8348 9070); *Turkish Cypriot Women's Project,* 140a Falkland Rd, Hornsey N8 0NP (8340 3300, 8341 7240)); *Turkish Cypriot Women's Project,* 320 High Rd, Wood Green N22 8JR.

Turkmen

GOVERNMENT *Embassy of Turkmenistan,* 2nd fl, 14 Wells St, W1T 3PG (7255 1071).

LANGUAGES *Turkmen* is the first language of 72% of the population while *Russian* and *Uzbek* account for about 9% each (*Whitaker's Almanack* 2002). *Turkmen* is a Turkic language of the Trans-Asia geozone spoken in Uzbekistan, Turkmenistan, Iran, and Afghanistan. It is written in the Cyrillic alphabet in Turkmenistan. In the *Multilingual Capital* (2000) survey, just one *Turkmen*-speaking pupil was recorded in Hammersmith & Fulham.

Turks & Caicos Islander

GOVERNMENT The Turks & Caicos islands are administered as a UK overseas territory.

TRAVEL *Turks & Caicos Tourist Information Office,* Mitre Ho, 66 Abbey Rd, Enfield EN1 2QE (8350 1017).

Twi

EDUCATION Mother-tongue education for young children in *Twi* is available in several locations in London; for full information visit <www.resourceunit.com>. *Twi* is among the languages taught at *SOAS Language Centre* (7898 4888).

LANGUAGE See under *Akan.*

U

Ugandan

GOVERNMENT *Uganda High Commission,* Uganda House, 58-59 Trafalgar Sq, WC2N 5DX (7839 5783).

LANGUAGES About 50 different languages are spoken in Uganda. *Luganda* is the first language of 16% of the population. Others which are each the first language of at least 5% are *A-Teso, Luo,* and several Bantuic languages. *Luganda, Swahili,* and *English* are widely known as second languages.

MEDIA & INFORMATION *Uganda Newsletter,* Uganda High Commission, 58-59 Trafalgar Square, WC2N 5DX; *Uganda Review,* Selum Publications, P.O. Box 9140, W3 6NG.

WELFARE *Uganda Community Relief Associations (UCRA),* Selby Centre, Selby Rd, N17 8JL (8808 6221); *Uganda Welfare Action Group,* Harrow Rd Centre, Harrow Rd, W13 0SE (8470 5541).

Ukaan

Ukaan is a **Benuic** language spoken in Nigeria which was reported to be the language of two London schoolchildren in the *Multilingual Capital* (2000) survey.

Ukrainian

ASSOCIATIONS *Association of Ukrainians in Great Britain,* 49 Linden Gdns, Notting Hill Gate W2 4HG (7229 8392); *Ukrainian Association in Great Britain,* W2 4II (7229 8392); *Ukrainian Society,* 15 Godolphin Rd, W12 8JE (8743 6756).

BUSINESS *First Ukrainian International Bank,* 100 Pall Mall, SY1Y 5HP (7321 3900).

EDUCATION Mother-tongue education for young children is available in *Ukrainian* in at least one location in London; for full information visit <www.resourceunit.com>. A course in *Ukrainian* for adults is provided by *SSEES* (7862 8635).

GOVERNMENT *Embassy of Ukraine,* 60 Holland Park, W11 3SJ (7727 6312); *Ukraine Consulate,* 78 Kensington Park Rd, W11 3BY (7243 8923).

LANGUAGE *Ukrainian* is a Slavonic language with official status in the Ukraine which is written with the Cyrillic alphabet. It was reported as the language of 74 London schoolchildren in the *Multilingual Capital* (2000) survey.

LEGAL *Visa to Russia (Ukraine) Direct,* 12 Chepstow Rd, W2 5BD (7229 1412).

MEDIA & INFORMATION *Ukrainian Information Services Ltd,* 200 Liverpool Rd, N1 1LF (7607 6266).

RECREATION *Ukrainian Social Club,* 154 Holland Park Ave, W11 4UH (7603 9482).

RELIGION *Bond St Ukrainian Cathedral (RC),* Duke St, W1Y 1YN (7629 1534); *Ukrainian Catholic Cathedral,* 21 Binney St, W1Y 1YN (7629 1534); *Ukrainian Orthodox Church,* 1a Newton Ave, Acton W3 8AJ (8992 4689); *Ukrainian Religious Society of St. Sophia,* 79 Holland Park, W11 3SH (7221 1890).

RESTAURANTS

Richmond *Kozachok* [Russian and Ukrainian], 10 Red Lion St, Richmond TW9 1RW (8948 2366).

SHOPS *Ukrainian Booksellers & Publishers "Ukrainian Thought",* 49 Linden Gdns, W2 4HQ (7229 0140).

United Arab Emirates

BUSINESS *Emirates Bank International PJSC,* 19 Motcomb St, SW1X 8XE (7259 6262); *Emirates Trading Agency Ltd,* Langham Ho, 302-308 Regent St, W1R 5AL (7580 8310).

GOVERNMENT *Embassy of United Arab Emirates,* 30 Princes Gate, South Kensington SW7 1PT (7581 1281); *Consular and Cultural Section of the Embassy of United Arab Emirates,* 48 Prince's Gate, SW7 1PT (7589 3434).

TRAVEL *Emirates Airlines,* Gloucester Park, 95 Cromwell Rd, South Kensington SW7 4DL (7808 0033).

Urdu

EDUCATION Mother-tongue education in *Urdu* is available for young children in many places in London; visit <www.resourceunit.com> for full details. Courses in *Urdu* are available at a variety of levels are provided by *SOAS Language Centre* (7898 4888) and several other locations – see *Floodlight* or visit <www.floodlight.co.uk> for details.

HEALTH & BEAUTY General information on cancer is available at *Asian Cancer Information Line* in Bengali, Gujerati, Hindi/Urdu - freephone (08088 080000). An information leaflet on *breast cancer* is available in Cantonese from the Women's Nationwide Cancer Control Campaign, 1st fl, Charity Ho, 14-15 Perseverence Works, EC2 8BD (7729 4688, fax 7613 0771).

Leaflets on Caring for Dementia are available in Urdu from the *Alzheimer's Disease Society,* Gordon Ho, 10 Greencoat Pl, SW1P 1PH (7306 0606).

LANGUAGE *Urdu* is one variety, written in an adaptation of the Arabic script, of the language known as *Hindi* when written in the Devanagari script. It is an Indic language widely spoken in Pakistan and India.

MEDIA & INFORMATION *Spectrum Radio,* International Radio Centre, 4 Ingate Pl, SW8 3NS

(7627 4433) [broadcasting mainly in Hindi/Urdu 04.00 - 13.00 Mon-Fri, 07.00- - 12.00 Sat-Sun]; *Sunrise Radio Ltd*, Sunrise Ho,Sunrise Rd,Southall, UB2-4AU (8574-6666) [broadcasting mainly in Hindi/Urdu from 01.00 - 21.00 daily].

SHOPS *Sub Rung Centre,* 117 Green St, E13 [bookshop].

TRANSLATION *Urdu & Punjabi Translators & Interpreters,* 89 Southampton Way, SE5 7SX (7564 9113); *Urdu Services,* 26 Farnborough Ave, Walthamstow E17 6HX (8531 3020).

WELFARE *Community Aid (Asian Project),* c/o Rina Choudhury, Ponders End Area Housing Office, Curlew Ho, 4 Napier Rd, Enfield EN3 4QW (8443 4361) [languages: Bengali, Hindi, **Urdu**, English]; *Enfield Asian Welfare Association,* 129-139 South St, Ponders End EN3 4RJ (8443 1197) [languages: Bengali, Gujarati, Hindi, Punjabi, **Urdu**, English]; *Enfield Saheli,* Community House, 311 Fore Street, Edmonton N9 0PZ [advice for Asian women on legal matters (8373 6218), mental health (8373 6220), general (8373 6219); languages: Gujarati, Hindi, Punjabi, **Urdu**, English]; *North London Muslim Welfare Association,* c/o Mr. Qureshi, 51 Northfield Rd, Enfield EN3 4BT (8804 1762) [phone for time of monthly meeting; languages: Gujarati, Punjabi, **Urdu**, English]; *Sisters in Islam* (Muslim Girls Club), c/o Mrs. Rahana Hassan, Ponders End Youth Centre, 129 South St, Ponders End EN3 4PX (8804 5908) [languages: Bengali, **Urdu**, English].

Urhobo
====

EDUCATION Mother-tongue education for young children is available in **Urhobo** in at least one location in London; for information visit <www.resourceunit.com>.

LANGUAGE *Urhobo* is a **Benuic** language of Nigeria. [93 pupils (Southwark; 24 Lambeth)].

Uruguayan
====

GOVERNMENT *Uruguayan Consulate,* 140 Brompton Rd, SW3 1HY (7589 8735, 7584 8192).

LANGUAGES The official and majority language is **Spanish** but a substantial minority of the population is of **Italian** descent.

Uzbek
====

GOVERNMENT *Embassy of the Republic of Uzbekistan,* 72 Wigmore St, W1H 9DL (7935 1899);

Uzbekistan Embassy, 41 Holland Park, W11 3RP (7229 7679).

EDUCATION Course in **Uzbek** are available at SOAS Language Centre (7898 4888).

LANGUAGE *Uzbek* is a Turkic language of the Trans-Asia geozone spoken in Uzbekistan, Tajikistan, Afghanistan and Kirghizstan which has some 18m speakers. It is generally written with the Cyrillic alphabet. The presence of ten **Uzbek**-speaking London schoolchildren was reported by the *Multilingual Capital* (2000) survey, of whom five lived in Hammersmith & Fulham.

TRAVEL *Uzbekistan Airways,* 70 Marylebone La, W1M5FF (7935 1899) *and* 69 Wigmore St, W1H 9LG (7935 4775).

V

Venezuelan

GOVERNMENT *Venezuelan Embassy,* 1 Cromwell Rd, SW7 2HR (7584 4206); *Venezuelan Embassy Consulate Section,* 56 Grafton Way, W1P 5LB (7387 6727).

LANGUAGES *Spanish* is the first language are the vast majority of Venezuelans.

TRAVEL *Venezuela Tourist Office,* 56 Grafton Way, W1P 5LB (7387 6727).

Vietnamese

ASSOCIATIONS *Southwark Vietnamese Youth,* Bellenden Old School, Bellenden Rd, SE15 5BB (7732 6114); *Vietnamese Community Association of South West London,* 44 Church Rd, Teddington TW11 8PB (8943 4842).

BARS & NIGHTCLUBS *Le Shaker Cocktail Bar* [Vietnamese Cuisine], 159 Old Brompton Rd, SW5 0LF (7373 1926).

EDUCATION Mother-tongue education in *Vietnamese* is available for young children in more than a dozen places in London; visit <www.resourceunit.com> for full details. Courses in *Vietnamese* for adults are provided by *SOAS Language Centre* (7898 4888).

GOVERNMENT *Vietnam Embassy,* 12 Victoria Rd. W8 5RD (7937 1912).

HEALTH & BEAUTY An information leaflet on *breast cancer* is available in Vietnamese from the Women's Nationwide Cancer Control Campaign, 1st fl, Charity Ho, 14-15 Perseverence Works, EC2 8BD (7729 4688, fax 7613 0771).

Community Health South London NHS Trust – Vietnamese Advice Centre, Lind Clinic, Grove St, SE8 3QF (8692 8830); *Vietnamese Mental Health Services,* Thomas Carlton Centre, Alpha St, SE15 4NX (7639 2288).

LANGUAGE *Vietnamese* is a language of the South-Asia geozone with some 75m speakers located mainly in Vietnam. The *Multilingual Capital* (2000) survey reported that there were 2,448 *Vietnamese*-speaking schoolchildren in London, of whom 424 lived in Greenwich. Map 31, showing the areas of London where the largest numbers of Vietnamese-speakers live, can be viewed at <www.global-london.com/gallery>.

RELIGION *Buddhist Interhelp* [Vietnamese Zen], 12 Shell Rd, SE13 7TW (8692 1737); *Central London/St James Sangha* [Vietnamese Mahayana], 34 Kennington La, SE11 4LS (7820 9703); *Chua Linh Son,* 89 Bromley Rd, Catford SE 6 (8461 1887); *Linh Sonh Phat Duong Temple* [Vietnamese Mahayana], 11 Ermine Rd, Tottenham N15 (8809 1566); *Linh Son Tu Temple* [Vietnamese Mahayana], 76 Beulah Hill, Upper Norwood SE19 3EW (8771 5933/5484); *Quan Am Ni Tu Temple* [Vietnamese Mahayana], 8 Fenn St, Hackney E9 6JN (8985 1122); *Saint James's Church Sangha* [Vietnamese Zen], 7 Sundorne Rd, SE7 7PR (8293 1775); *Thich Ca Temple* [Vietnamese], 185a Victoria Rise, Clapham (8627 0393); *Vietnamese Chaplancy,* 117 Bow Common La, E3 4AU (7987 3477).

RESTAURANTS

South East 1 *Little Saigon,* 139 Westminster Bridge Rd, SE1 7HR (7928 5415).

South West 1 *Mekong,* 46 Churton St, SW1 2LP (7630 9568).

West 1 *BamBou* [French/Vietnamese], 1 Percy St, W1P (7323 9140); *Cam Phant* [Chinese / Vietnamese], 12 Macclesfield St, W1D 5BP (7437 5598); *Saigon,* 45 Frith St, W1V 5TE (7437 7109); *Vietnamese Restaurant,* 34 Wardour St, W1A 3BX (7494 2592).

Barnet *Saigon Vietnam & Chinese Restaurant,* 340 Regents Park Rd. N3 2LN (8343 4149).

Camden *Bluu Grass,* 6 Plender St, NW1 (7380 1196); *Thanh Binh,* 14 Chalk Farm Rd, NW1 8AG (7267 9820).

Greenwich *Saigon,* 16 Nelson Rd, SE10 9JB (8853 0414); *Vietnam Restaurant,* 17 King William Walk SE10 9JH (8858 0871).

Hackney *East* [Chinese/Vietnamese], 54-64 Kingsland Rd, E2 8DP (7729 5544); *Green Papaya,* 191 Mare St, E8 (8985 5486); *Loong Kee,* 134g Kingsland Rd, E2 (7729 8344); *Red River,* 28 Stamford Rd, N1 4JL (7241 2228); *Thang Long,* 9 Chatsworth Rd, E5 0LH (8533 9566); *Viet Hoa,* 70-72 Kingsland Rd, E2 (7729 8293); *Vietnamese Canteen,* An Viet Ho, 12-14 Englefield Rd, N1 4LN (7249 0877).

Hammersmith & Fulham *Bonjour Vietnam* 593-599 Fulham Rd SW6 5UA (7385 7603).

Haringey *My Nhi,* 493 High Rd, N17 6QA (8808 7799).

Islington *Aulac,* 82 Highbury Park, N5 2XE (7704 9187); *Nam Bistro,* 326 Upper St, N1 2XQ (7354 0851).

Tower Hamlets *Duccung,* 507 Hackney Rd, E2 9ED (7739 7222); *Sinh Le,* 41 Mile End Rd, E1 4TP (7790 0773).

Wandsworth *Good Morning Vietnam,* St John's Hill, SW11; *Saigon Thuy,* 189 Garratt La, SW18 (8871 9464).

SHOPS Hackney: *Huong-Nam Supermarket,* 185-87 Mare St, E8 (8985 8050); *Vietnam Supermarket,* 193a Mare St, E8 3QE (8525 1655).

TRAVEL *Vietnam Airlines,* 295 King St. W6 9NH (8741 7129); *Visit Vietnam,* 30-32, Fulham High St. SW6 3LQ (7736 4347).

WELFARE *Community of Refugees from Vietnam,* West Library, Bridgman Rd. N1 1BD (7607 6271); *Greenwich Vietnam Community,* 3-4 Beresford St. SE18 6BE (8854 9907); *Lambeth Community of Refugees from Vietnam,* 56b Courland Grove SW8 2PX (7622 2119); *Southwark Vietnamese/Chinese Refugee Community,* Thomas Carlton Centre, Alpha St, SE15 4II (7635 0022); *Tower Hamlets Community of Refugees from Vietnam,* Poplar Methodist Mission, Annabel Close, E14 6DE (7538 4986); *Vietnamese Carers' Support Project,* 1 Kingfisher Sq, SE8 5TW (8469 0364); *Vietnamese Refugee Community,* 9 Granville Ct, Nynehead St, SE14 6II (8469 0307); *Vietnamese Refugee Community,* 12 Walkford Way, SE12 6II (7701 0031); *Vietnamese Refugee Community in Croydon,* Cornerstone Ho, Willis Rd, Croydon CR0 2II (8665 0713); *Vietnamese Women's Group Southwark,* Bellenden Primary School, Bellenden Rd, SE15 4DG (7277 8642); *West & North West London Vietnamese Elderly Project,* 58 Bulwer St, W12 8AP (8742 9745).

Vincentian

GOVERNMENT *High Commission for St Vincent and the Grenadines*, 10 Kensington Ct, W8 5DL (7565 2874).

TRAVEL *St Vincent & the Grenadines Tourist Office,* 10 Kensington Ct, W8 5DL (7937 6570).

Visayan

See under **Bisayan.**

Wa

Wa (also known as *Kawa*) is a language of the South-Asia geozone spoken in Burma and China (Yunnan). The *Multilingual Capital* (2000) survey located in **Wa**-speaking pupil in Greenwich.

Wali

Wali is listed in the *Multilingual Capital* (2000) as the name of a language spoken by a pupil in Haringey. Unfortunately there are three unrelated languages of this name, spoken, respectively, in Ghana, Indonesia, and Sudan. Thus, the language concerned cannot be established without knowing the country of origin of the child's parents.

Welsh

ARTS *London Welsh Chorale,* 157-163 Grays Inn Rd, WC1X 8UE (7278 7525); *Welsh Visual Artists & Design,* Flat 19, Barwell House, Chester St, E2 6HZ (7613 1722).

ASSOCIATIONS *London Welsh Association,* 157 Grays Inn Rd, WC1X 8UE (7837 3722).

BUSINESS *Welsh Slate,* Business Design Centre,Unit 205, 52 Upper St, N1 0QH (7354 0306).

EDUCATION *London Welsh School, 265 Willesden La, Cricklewood NW2 5JG (8459 2690); Welsh School in London within Stonebridge Primary School,* Shakespeare Ave, NW10 8NG (8965 3585).

Courses in **Welsh** for adults are available at several locations in London – see *Floodlight* or visit <www.floodlight.co.uk>.

FREIGHT *Parcelforce Worldwide - Welsh-speaking enquiries,* N1 1XX (0800 731 3428).

GOVERNMENT *Plaid Cymru,* Palace of Westminster, SW1A 2PW; *Welsh Development Agency,* 2 Queen Anne's Gate Bldgs, SW1H 9BP (7222 2822); *Welsh Office,* Gwydyr Ho, Whitehall, SW1 (7270 3000).

LANGUAGE **Welsh** is a Celtic language with official status in Wales. The number of Welsh-speaking pupils in London reported at the time of the *Multilingual Capital* (2000) survey was only 66 but, as suggested in that book, this appears to be the result of serious under-recording.

MEDIA & INFORMATION *South Wales Evening Post,* 31 John St, WC1N 2QB (7400 1100); *Wales Information Bureau, British Columbia Ho, 1 Regent St, SW1Y 4NS (7409 0969).*

RECREATION *England & Wales Cricket Board, Lords Cricket Ground, St Johns Wood Rd, NW8 8QZ (7432 1200); London Welsh Rugby Football Club* [administration], 187 Kew Rd, Richmond TW9 2AZ (8940 2368).

RELIGION *Jewin Welsh Presbyterian Church*, 70 Fann St, EC1Y 0SA (7628 8370); *St Benet's Metropolitian Welsh Church,* Queen Victoria St, EC4V 4ER (7489 8754); *St David's Welsh Church,* St Marys Terrace, Bayswater W2 1SJ (7723 3104); *Welsh Baptist Church,* 30 Eastcastle St, W1W 8DJ; *Welsh Congregational Church,* Lower Rd, Harrow HA2 0DE (8427 7074); *Welsh Presbyterian Church,* Ealing Green, W5 5EN (8579 3723); *Yr Eglwys Fethodistaidd*, 82a Chiltern St, W1 (7272 2496).

TRAVEL *Wales Tourist Board, 1 Regent St, SW1Y 4XT (7808 3838); Welsh International Travel,* Friendly Ho, Tabernacle St, EC2A 4PL (7895 8080).

West African

MEDIA & INFORMATION *West Africa Magazine,* Allenby Ho, Temple Rd, NW2 6PJ (8450 4848); *West Africa Magazine,* 43-45 Coldharbour Lane, SE5 9NR (7737 2946); *West Africa Magazines,* 321 City Rd, EC1V 1LJ (7837 4116).

SPECIAL *West Africa Committee,* 2 Vincent St, SW1P 4LD (7828 5544).

WELFARE *West African Senior Citizens Centre*, Community Hall, White Hart Lane, N17 (8808 9213); *West African Welfare Association*, 98 Craven Park, NW10 8QE (7586 1080).

West Indian

ASSOCIATIONS *West Indian Ex-Servicemen Association (UK)*, 161-167 Clapham Manor St, SW4 6DB (7627 0702); *West Indian Women's Association,* William Morris Community Centre, Greenleaf Rd, E17 6QQ (8521 4456).

BUSINESS *Electro West Indian Management,* 45a Loughborough Rd, SW9 7TB (7738 5515); *West Indian Concern Ltd,* Caribbean Ho, Bridport Pl, N1 5DS (7739 0840).

HEALTH & BEAUTY *Cheers West Indian Ladies' Hairdressers,* 105 Bruce Grove, N17 6UR (8885 2324).

RESTAURANTS
Brent *West Indian T/A,* 271 Neasden La, NW10 1QJ (8208 2006).

Greenwich *Guyanese and West Indian T/A,* 148 Plumstead Rd, SE18 7DY (8854 5115).

Hackney *Casablanca West Indian Restaurant,* 170 Sandringham Rd, E8 2HS (7249 4448); *Joe's Oasis T/A,* 4 Chatsworth Rd, E5 0LP (8985 3276).

Haringey *Flava,* 110 High Rd, N15 6JR (8800 9332); *Ipal Vipal T/A,* 134 High Rd, N15 6JN (8211 7358).

Kensington & Chelsea *Coconut Grove,* 23 All Saints Rd, W11 1HE (7229 7961).

Lambeth *Nyam Food T/A,* 423 Coldharbour La, Brixton (7738 4030); *Stop Gap T/A,* 500 Brixton Rd, SW9 8EQ (7737 0148).

Lewisham *Cool Breeze T/A,* 266 Hither Green La, SE13 6TT (8697 4050); *Jade West Indian T/A,* 127 New Cross Rd, SE14 5DJ (7207 2723).

Westminster *Sania's West Indian Snackette,* 8 Fernhead Rd, W9 3ET (8964 8734).

SHOPS *Finch's Stores,* 6 Lewisham Model Market, Lewisham High St, SE13 6LS (8318 6521); *Heman's West Indian Bakery,* 523 Seven Sisters Rd, Tottenham N15 6EP (8809 3468).

TRAVEL *B W I A International Airways,* Room 272a, North Wing, Terminal Three, Hounslow TW6 1PD (8759 0923).

WELFARE *Haringey West Indian Centre,* Clarenden Rd, N8 0DD (8881 5881); *West Indian Standing Conference*, 5 Westminster Bridge Rd, SE1 7XW (7928 7861).

Wolof

Wolof is an Atlantic language spoken in Senegal, the Gambia, and Mauritania. 130 London schoolchildren were reported to be **Wolof** speakers at the time of the *Multilingual Capital* (2000) survey.

X

Xhosa

EDUCATION Courses in **Xhosa** are available at *SOAS Language Centre* (7898 4888).

LANGUAGE **Xhosa** is a Bantuic language of South Africa. At the time of the *Multilingual Capital* (2000) survey, this was recorded as the language of 11 pupils attending London schools.

Xiang

See **Hunanese.**

Y

Yaunde

See under the alternative name, **Ewondo.**

Yemeni

ASSOCIATIONS *British-Yemeni Society,* c/o 23 The Green, Richmond TW9 1LX (8940 6101); *Friends of Hadhramaut,* c/o 48 Richmond Park Rd, SW14 8JT (8392 9823); *Yemeni Community Association,* Capital Ho, Craven Rd, W2 3PX (7262 9806).

FREIGHT *Yemen Gulf Line Ltd,* Prince Albert Ho, Kingsmill Terrace, NW8 6AA (7586 9571).

GOVERNMENT *Republic of Yemen Embassy,* 57 Cromwell Rd, SW7 2ED (7584 6607).

LANGUAGE The population is **Arabic**-speaking.

MEDIA & INFORMATION *Yemen Observer,* 153 Regent St, W1R 7RD (7287 7338).

TRAVEL *Yemen Airways,* 52 Stratton St, W1X 5FF (7491 7186).

Yiddish

EDUCATION **Yiddish**-medium education is provided in at least two London schools: *Talmud Torah (Beis Schlomo),* 122 Bethune Rd, N16 5DU, and *Talmud Torah Yelev Lev,* 111 Cazenove Rd, N16 6AX (8806 3834).

LANGUAGE **Yiddish** is a Germanic language insofar as it is based on medieval German but it is heavily influenced by Hebrew and is written in the consonantal Hebrew script. The *Multilingual Capital* (2000) survey reported only 16 Yiddish-speaking pupils in London schools but this excluded private schools such as the two listed under **EDUCATION** above which between them have more than 500 **Yiddish**-speaking pupils.

SHOPS

Bookshops (publications in Yiddish): *Jewish Memorial Council Bookshop,* 25-26 Enford St, W1H 2DD (7724 7778, fax 7706 1710); *Manor House Books,* 80 East End Rd, Finchley N3 2SY (8349 9484, fax 8346 7430); *Mesoiroh Seforim Bookshop,* 61 Oldhill St, N16 6LU (8809 4310).

Yoruba

EDUCATION Mother-tongue education in **Yoruba** is available for young children in more than a dozen locations in London; for details visit <www.resourceunit.com>. Courses in **Yoruba** are provided by *SOAS Language Centre* (7898 4888).

LANGUAGE **Yoruba** is a Benuic language of Nigeria and Benin with some 26m speakers. The *Multilingual Capital* (2000) survey recorded the presence of 10,363 **Yoruba**-speaking pupils of whom almost one quarter lived in Southwark.

Yue

See *Cantonese*

Yugoslav

GOVERNMENT *Yugoslav Embassy*, 5 Lexham Gdns, Kensington W8 5JJ (7370 6105).

LANGUAGES The principal language of Yugoslavia is **Serbian.**

TRAVEL *Yugoslav Airlines,* 37 Maddox St, W1R 0AQ (7409 1319).

Z

Zambian

ASSOCIATIONS *Zambia Society*, Memaco Ho, 215 Marsh Wall, E14 9FJ (7293 8000).

BUSINESS *Zambia National Commercial Bank Ltd,* 9 King St, EC2V 8EA (7726 6364).

GOVERNMENT *Zambian High Commission*, 2 Palace Gate, W8 5NG (7589 6655).

LANGUAGES Some 50 languages are spoken in Zambia of which the three with the largest number of speakers are **Bemba, Nyanja,** and **Tonga. English** has official status.

TRAVEL *Zambia National Tourist Board,* 2 Palace Gate, Kensington W8 5NG (7589 6343).

Zande

Zande is an Ubangic language spoken in parts of Congo-Kinshasa, Sudan, and the Central African Republic.

Zimbabwean

BUSINESS *Zimbabwe Trade & Investment Consultants,* 10 Adam St, WC2N 6AA (7497 5454).

GOVERNMENT *Zimbabwe High Commission*, 429 Strand, WC2R 0QE (7836 7755).

LANGUAGES 67% of the population speak varieties of **Shona** as their first language while 15% are speakers of **Ndebele.**

MEDIA & INFORMATION *Zimbabwe Daily & Financial Gazette*, 7 Kensington High St, W8 (7711 3111).

TRAVEL *Air Zimbabwe,* 52-55 Piccadilly, W1V 9AA (7491 0009); *Namibia & Zimbabwe Fly-Drive & Safari,* 7-8 Upper Sq, Old Isleworth TW7 7BJ ((8232 9777); *Zimbabwe Express* [airline], 200 Buckingham Palace Rd, SW1W 9TA (7707 4572); *Zimbabwe Tourist Office,* 429 Strand, WC2R 0QE (7240 6169); *Zimbabwe Tours & Travel,* 3 The Broadway, Southgate N14 6PJ (8882 0141).

WELFARE *Zimbabwe Welfare Society,* 1 8 Ashwin St, Hackney E8 3DL (7254 7004); *Zimbabwe Welfare Society*, 15 Marson Ho, Murray Grove, N1 7QY (7272 6035); *Zimbabwe Welfare Society*, 1A Waterloo Rd, N19 5NJ.

Zoroastrian

RELIGION *World Zoroastrian Organisation,* 135 Tennison Rd, South Norwood, SE25 5NF.

SPECIAL *Zoroastrian Trust Funds of Europe,* Zoroastrian Ho, 88 Compayne Gdns, West Hampstead NW6 3RU.

Zulu

EDUCATION A course in **Zulu** is available at *SOAS Language Centre* (7898 4888).

LANGUAGE **Zulu** is a Bantuic language of South Africa. The *Multilingual Capital* (2000) survey reported that this was spoken by 47 pupils in London.

Tower Bridge and the City of London

St Paul's Cathedral and the City from the South Bank

The Linguasphere classification of the world's languages[†]

Ten Sectors each comprising Ten Zones

Five Geosectors	*Languages represented in London*	Five Phylosectors	*Languages represented in London*
50 Zones[††]		50 Zones	

0 AFRICA

00	MANDIC	Dyula, Kono, Kpelle, Malinke, Mandingo, Mandinka, Mende, Nwa
01	SONGHAIC	
02	SAHARIC	
03	SUDANIC	Lugbara, Ma'di, Mangbetu
04	NILOTIC	Acholi, Alur, A-Teso, Bari, Dhopadhola, Dinka, Kakwa, Kalenjin, Lango, Luo, Nuer, Oromo Shilluk
05	*EAST-SAHEL*	Nubian
06	*KORDOFANIC*	
07	*RIFT-VALLEY*	
08	KHOISANIC	Damara
09	*KALAHARI*	

2 AUSTRALASIA

20	*ARAFURA*	
21	*MAMBERAMO*	
22	MADANGIC	
23	OWALAMIC	
24	TRANSIRIANIC	Itigo
25	*CENDRAWASIH*	
26	*SEPIK-VALLEY*	
27	BISMARCK-SEA	Baining
28	*NORTH-AUSTRALIA*	
29	*TRANSAUSTRALIA*	

4 EURASIA

40	EUSKARIC	Basque
41	URALIC	Estonian, Finnish, Hungarian
42	*CAUCASUS*	Abkhaz, Georgian
43	*SIBERIA*	
44	TRANS-ASIA	Azeri, Kazakh, Kyrghyz, Mongolian, Turkish, Turkmen, Uzbek
45	EAST-ASIA	Japanese, Korean
46	SOUTH-ASIA	Burushaski, Khasi, Korku, Vietnamese, Wa
47	DAIC	Lao, Lati, Thai
48	MON-KHMERIC	Khmer
49	DRAVIDIC	Kannada, Malayalam, Parji, Tamil, Telugu

6 NORTH-AMERICA

60	ARCTIC	
61	IROQUOIC	
62	ALGIC	
63	*SAINT-LAWRENCE*	
64	*MISSISSIPPI*	
65	AZTECIC	
66	*WEST-COAST*	
67	*PUEBLO-DESERT*	
68	*EAST-COAST*	
69	MESOAMERICA	Maya

8 SOUTH-AMERICA

80	CARIBIC	Carib
81	*CHIBCHANIC*	
82	ARAWAKIC	
83	*PRE-ANDES*	
84	*ANDES*	
85	QUECHUIC	Quechua
86	*CHACO-MATO*	
87	*AMAZON*	
88	TUPIC	Guarani
89	*BAHIA*	

1 AFROASIAN

10	TAMAZIC	Berber
11	COPTIC	
12	SEMITIC	Amharic, Arabic, Aramaic, Harari, Hebrew, Maghrebi, Maltese, Mashriqi, Tigre, Tigrinya
13	BEJIC	Beja
14	CUSHITIC	Afar, Saho, Sidamo, Somali
15	EYASIC	
16	OMOTIC	
17	CHARIC	
18	MANDARIC	Bata
19	BAUCHIC	Hausa, Tangale

3 AUSTRONESIAN

30	FORMOSIC	
31	HESPERONESIC	Bisayan, Cebuano, Hiligaynon, Ilocano, Indonesian, Malagasy, Malay, Pampangan, Pangasinan, Tagalog
32	MESONESIC	
33	HALMAYAPENIC	
34	NEOGUINEIC	Motu
35	MANUSIC	
36	SOLOMONIC	Hahon
37	NEOCALEDONIC	
38	WEST-PACIFIC	Kusaie, Nauruan
39	TRANSPACIFIC	Fijian, Hawaiian, Maori, Samoan, Tongan

5 INDO-EUROPEAN

50	CELTIC	Irish Gaelic, Scottish Gaelic, Shelta, Welsh
51	ROMANIC	Catalan, French, French Creole, Galician, Italian, Latin, Mauritian Creole, Moldovan, Portuguese, Portuguese Creole, Romanian, Sardinian, Spanish
52	GERMANIC	Afrikaans, Aku, Danish, Dutch, English, English Creole, Flemish, German, Icelandic, Krio, Norwegian, Pidgin English, Swedish, Swiss German, Tok Pisin, Yiddish
53	SLAVONIC	Belarusian, Bulgarian, Czech, Macedonian, Polish, Russian, Serbo-Croat, Slovak, Slovene, Ukrainian
54	BALTIC	Latvian, Lithuanian
55	ALBANIC	Albanian, Kosovan
56	HELLENIC	Greek
57	ARMENIC	Armenian
58	IRANIC	Balochi, Dari, Farsi, Kurdish, Kirmanji, Pashto, Tajiki
59	INDIC	Assamese, Bengali, Bihari, Dhivehi, Gujarati, Hindi Kashmiri, Katchi, Konkani, Marathi, Nepali, Oriya, Panjabi, Rajasthani, Romani, Sanskrit, Sindhi, Sinhala, Sylheti, Urdu

7 SINO-INDIAN

70	TIBETIC	Jonkha, Tibetan
71	HIMALAYIC	Newari
72	GARIC	
73	KUKIC	
74	MIRIC	
75	KACHINIC	Jingpho
76	RINGIC	
77	IRRIWADIC	Burmese
78	KARENIC	Karen
79	SINITIC	Cantonese, Hakka, Hokkien, Hunanese, Mandarin, Min-nan

9 TRANSAFRICAN

90	ATLANTIC	Fula, Limba, Wolof
91	VOLTAIC	Bariba, Bimoba, Dagari, Dagbane, Gurenge, Gurma, Mampruli
92	ADAMAWIC	Mbum
93	UBANGIC	Zande
94	MELIC	Gola, Kisi, Temne
95	KRUIC	Bassa, Kru
96	AFRAMIC	Abe, Adangme, Akan, Akpafu, Anyi, Ashanti, Efutu, Ewe, Fante, Fon, Gã, Gonja, Kposo, Krobo, Logba, Nzema, Twi
97	DELTIC	Calabari,, Ijo, Nembe, Okrika
98	BENUIC	Abua, Anaang, Che, Ebira, Edo, Efik, Eggon, Ekpeye, Igede, Ikwere, Isoko, Itsekiri, Kaje, Katab, Khana, Ki, Lam-nso, Nupe, Nzema, Odual, Ogori, Olulumo, Ora, Oring, Oron, Ukaan, Urhobo, Yoruba
99	BANTUIC	Ambo, Bemba, Bende, Bravanese, Bukusu, Chewa, Chiga, Chokwe, Comoran, Ewondo, Fang, Gikuyu, Gogo, Herero, Kahe, Kamba, Kimbundu, Kimeru, Kingwana, Kirundi, Kongo, Kwangwa, Lingala, Logoli, Losengo, Lozi, Luba, Luganda, Lumasaba, Lunda, Lusoga, Luvale, Luziba, Masaba, Mungaka, Ndebele, Nsenga, Nyakyusa, Nyang, Nyoro, Oshikwanyama, Runyankore, Rutoro, Rwanda, Senga, Sesotho, Setswana, Shona, Swahili, Swazi, Tiv, Tonga, Tumbuka, Xhosa, Zulu

† For full details of this referential classification, see Dalby (1999-2000). †† Geographic zones (Geozones) are written in upper-case italics, *e.g. BAHIA*